PEARSON

ALWAYS LEARNING

Marvin L. Bittinger • David J. Ellenbogen • Scott A. Surgent

Calculus
And Its Applications

Fourth Custom Edition for Mississippi State University

Taken from:
Calculus: And Its Applications, Eleventh Edition
by Marvin L. Bittinger, David J. Ellenbogen, and Scott A. Surgent

Cover Art: Courtesy of Eric Tamlin.

Taken from:

Calculus: And Its Applications, Eleventh Edition
by Marvin L. Bittinger, David J. Ellenbogen, and Scott A. Surgent
Copyright © 2016, 2012, 2008 by Pearson Education, Inc.
New York, New York 10013

This special edition published in cooperation with Pearson Learning Solutions.

Pearson Learning Solutions, 330 Hudson Street, New York, New York 10013
A Pearson Education Company
www.pearsoned.com

Printed in the United States of America

4   16

000200010271992315

KM

ISBN 10: 1-323-25203-7
ISBN 13: 978-1-323-25203-1

To Elaine, Victoria, and Beth

Contents

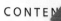

An alternative, expanded version of this text is avai~~l~~ contains the following topics:

Calculus and Its Applications: Expanded Version
(ISBN: 978-0-134-12349-3)

Chapter 11   (online only) Systems and Matrices

Chapter 12   (online only) Discrete Probability

Preface

Calculus and Its Applications strives to be the most student-oriented applied calculus text on the market, and this eleventh edition continues to improve in that regard. The authors believe that appealing to students' intuition and speaking in a direct, down-to-earth manner make this text accessible to any student possessing the prerequisite math skills. By presenting more topics in a conceptual and often visual manner and adding student self-assessment and teaching aids, this revision addresses students' needs better than ever before. Tapping into areas of student interest, the authors provide motivation through an abundant supply of examples and exercises rich in real-world data from business, economics, environmental studies, health care, and the life sciences.

New examples cover applications ranging from monthly cell phone traffic (in exabytes) to the growth of Facebook membership. Found in every chapter, realistic applications draw students into the discipline and help them to generalize the material and apply it to new situations. To further spark student interest, hundreds of meticulously rendered graphs and illustrations appear throughout the text, making it a favorite among students who are visual learners.

Appropriate for a one-term course, this text is an introduction to applied calculus. A course in intermediate algebra is a prerequisite, although "Appendix A: Review of Basic Algebra," together with "Chapter R: Functions, Graphs, and Models," provides a sufficient foundation to unify the diverse backgrounds of most students. For schools offering a two-term course, *Calculus and Its Applications, Expanded Version*, by the same author team, is available; it includes chapters covering trigonometric functions, differential equations, sequences and series, and probability distributions.

New to This Edition

With every revision comes the opportunity to improve the presentation of the content in a variety of ways based on feedback from users of the text and author experience. This revision is focused on providing students with *just-in-time* reminders of skills that should be familiar to them, updating and adding new applications—especially business applications—throughout the text, and fine-tuning the pedagogical design elements that make this book so user-friendly. The exercises have been carefully evaluated to be sure they align with the objectives of the text, and data analysis of MyMathLab exercises has helped guide the gradation and organization of the exercises in both the text and MyMathLab. Throughout the preface, the new elements of the text are described and specific new and modified content outlined. Below is a quick snapshot of what's new in this edition.

- Additional coverage of exponential functions has been added to Section R.5, to support students' use of these functions in applications.
- The former Section 3.6, "An Economics Application: Elasticity of Demand," has been moved and is now Section 2.7, allowing students to be introduced to the application sooner so they can use the concept throughout Chapter 3.
- A discussion of annuities has been added to Section 3.5, and a new section dedicated to amortization (with the use of Excel as an option) has been added as Section 3.6.
- Section 5.6, "Volume," now includes discussion on the use of shells, and Section 6.4, "An Application: The Least-Squares Technique," was expanded to include a derivation of an exponential regression by hand.
- Applications have been updated to reflect more current data and trends whenever possible.

- Exercise sets have been carefully evaluated to ensure appropriate gradation of level, odd/even pairing, and specific connection to the objectives being evaluated. In addition, MyMathLab usage data was analyzed to expose any exercises that needed improvement.
- MyMathLab has been greatly improved to include a vast array of new resources for both instructors and students. In addition to a greater quantity and variety of exercises, MyMathLab now includes more videos, additional levels of assessment, and interactive figures to help students gain the skills and knowledge they need to be successful in this and future courses.

Our Approach

Intuitive Presentation

Although the word *intuitive* has many meanings and interpretations, its use here means "experience based, without proof." Throughout the text, when a concept is discussed, its presentation is designed so that the students' learning process is based on their earlier mathematical experience. This is illustrated by the following situations.

- Before the formal definition of *continuity* is presented, an informal explanation is given, complete with graphs that make use of student intuition about ways in which a function could be discontinuous (see pp. 109–110).
- The definition of *derivative*, in Chapter 1, is presented in the context of a discussion of average rates of change (see p. 129). This presentation is more accessible and realistic than the strictly geometric idea of slope.
- When maximization problems involving volume are introduced (see pp. 244–246), a function is derived that is to be maximized. Instead of forging ahead with the standard calculus solution, the text first asks the student to make a table of function values, graph the function, and then estimate the maximum value. This experience provides students with more insight into the problem. They recognize not only that different dimensions yield different volumes, but also that the dimensions yielding the maximum volume may be conjectured or estimated as a result of the calculations.
- The explanation underlying the definition of the number *e* is presented in Chapter 3 both graphically and through a discussion of continuously compounded interest (see pp. 330–331).
- Within MyMathLab, students and instructors have access to **interactive figures** that illustrate concepts and allow manipulation by the user so that he or she can better predict and understand the underlying concepts. Also available within MyMathLab are questions that provide focus for student use.

Timely Help for Gaps in Algebra Skills

One of the most critical factors underlying success in this course is a strong foundation in algebra skills. We recognize that students start this course with varying degrees of skills, so we have included multiple opportunities in both the text and MyMathLab to help students target their weak areas and remediate or refresh the needed skills.

In the Text

- **Prerequisite Skills Diagnostic Test (Part A).** This portion of the diagnostic test assesses skills refreshed in Appendix A: Review of Basic Algebra. Answers to the questions reference specific examples within the appendix.
- **Appendix A: Review of Basic Algebra.** This 11-page appendix provides examples on topics such as exponents, equations, and inequalities and applied problems. It ends with an exercise set, for which answers are provided at the back of the book so students can check their understanding.
- **Prerequisite Skills Diagnostic Test (Part B).** This portion of the diagnostic test assesses skills that are reviewed in "Chapter R: Functions, Graphs, and Models," and the answers reference specific sections in that chapter. Some instructors may choose

to cover these topics thoroughly in class, making this assessment less critical. Other instructors may use all or portions of this test to determine whether there is a need to spend time remediating before moving on with Chapter 1.

■ **Chapter R: Functions, Graphs, and Models.** This chapter covers basic concepts related to functions, graphing, and modeling. It is an optional chapter based on students' prerequisite skills.

In MyMathLab

■ **Integrated Review.** You can diagnose weak prerequisite skills through built-in diagnostic quizzes. By coupling these quizzes with Personalized Homework, MyMathLab provides remediation for just those skills a student lacks. Even if you choose not to assign these quizzes with Personalized Homework, students can self-remediate through videos and practice exercises provided at the objective level. MyMathLab provides the just-in-time help that students need, so you can focus on the course content.

■ **New! Basic Skills Videos.** Videos are now available within exercises to help refresh the key algebra skill required for a specific exercise.

Exercises and Applications

There are over 3500 assignable section-level homework exercises in this edition. A large percentage of these exercises are rendered algorithmically in MyMathLab. All exercise sets are enhanced by the inclusion of real-world applications, detailed art pieces, and illustrative graphs. There are a variety of types of exercises, too, so different levels of understanding and varying approaches to problems can be assessed. In addition to applications, the exercise sets include *Thinking and Writing*, *Synthesis*, *Technology Connection*, and *Concept Reinforcement* exercises. The exercises in MyMathLab reflect the depth and variety of those in the printed text.

The authors also provide *Quick Check* exercises, following selected examples, to give students the opportunity to check their understanding of new concepts or skills as soon as they learn them and one skill at a time. Instructors may include these as part of a lecture as a means of gauging skills and gaining immediate student feedback. Answers to the Quick Check exercises are provided following the exercise set at the end of each section.

Relevant and factual applications drawn from a broad spectrum of fields are integrated throughout the text as applied examples and exercises, and are also featured in separate application sections. Applications have been updated and expanded in this edition to include even more real data. In addition, each chapter opener features an application that serves as a preview of what students will learn in the chapter.

The applications in the exercise sets in the text and within MyMathLab are grouped under headings that identify them as reflecting real-life situations: Business and Economics, Life and Physical Sciences, Social Sciences, and General Interest. This organization allows the instructor to gear the assigned exercises to specific students and also allows each student to know whether a particular exercise applies to his or her major.

Furthermore, the Index of Applications at the back of the book provides students and instructors with a comprehensive list of the many different fields considered throughout the text.

Opportunities to Incorporate Technology

This edition continues to emphasize mathematical modeling, utilizing the advantages of technology as appropriate. The use of Excel as a tool for solving problems has been expanded in this edition. Though the use of technology is optional with this text, its use meshes well with the text's more intuitive approach to applied calculus.

Technology Connections

Technology Connections are included throughout the text to illustrate the use of technology, including graphing calculators, Excel spreadsheets, and smartphone apps. Whenever appropriate, art that simulates graphs or tables generated by a graphing calculator is included as well. The goal is to take advantage of technology to which many students have access, wherever it makes sense, given the mathematical situation.

Four types of Technology Connections allow students and instructors to explore key ideas:

- **Lesson/Teaching**. These provide students with an example, followed by exercises to work within the lesson.
- **Checking**. These tell the students how to verify a solution within an example by using a graphing calculator.
- **Exploratory/Investigation**. These provide questions to guide students through an investigation.
- **Technology Connection Exercises**. Most exercise sets contain technology-based exercises identified with either an icon or the heading "Technology Connection." This type of exercise also appears in the Chapter Review Exercises, Chapter Tests, and the supplemental Printable Test Forms.

Extended Technology Applications at the end of every chapter use real applications and real data. They require a step-by-step analysis that encourages group work. More challenging in nature, the exercises in these features often involve the use of regression to create models on a graphing calculator. The data in the Extended Technology Applications has been updated wherever possible to keep the applications fresh for instructors and relevant for students.

Use of Art and Color

One of the hallmarks of this text is the pervasive use of color as a pedagogical tool. Color is used in a methodical and precise manner that enhances the readability of the text for students and instructors.

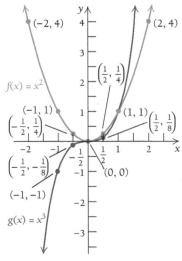

- When two curves are graphed using the same set of axes, one is usually red and the other blue, with the red graph being the curve of major importance. The equation labels are the same color as the curve for clarity (see p. 52).
- When the instructions say "Graph," the dots match the color of the curve. When dots are used for emphasis other than just merely plotting, they are black. Throughout the text, blue is used for secant lines and red for tangent lines (see p. 128).
- Red denotes substitution in equations while blue highlights the corresponding outputs, and the specific use of color is carried out in related figures (see pp. 206–207).
- Beginning with the discussion of integration, an amber color is used to highlight areas in graphs (see p. 400).

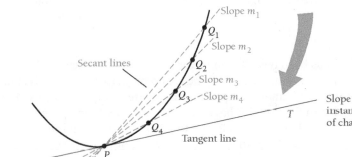

Opportunity for Review and Synthesis

Recognizing that it is often while preparing for exams that concepts gel for students, this text offers abundant opportunities for students to review, analyze, and synthesize recently learned concepts and skills.

- A **Section Summary** precedes every exercise set to assist students in identifying the key topics for each section and to serve as a mini-review.
- A **Chapter Summary** at the end of every chapter includes a section-by-section list of key definitions, concepts, and theorems, with examples for further clarification.
- **Chapter Review Exercises**, which include bracketed references to the section in which the related concept is first introduced, provide comprehensive coverage and appropriate referencing of each chapter's material.
- A **Chapter Test** at the end of every chapter and a **Cumulative Review** at the end of the text give students an authentic exam-like environment for testing their mastery. Answers to the chapter tests and the Cumulative Review are at the back of the text and include section references so students can diagnose their mistakes while preparing for exams.

New and Revised Content

In response to faculty and student feedback, we have made many changes to the text's content for this edition. New examples and exercises have been added throughout each chapter, as well as new problems to each chapter's review exercises and chapter test. Data have been updated wherever achievable, so problems use the most up-to-date information possible. Following is an overview of the major content changes in each chapter.

Chapter R

Several new exercises have been added to this chapter, including 10 in Section R.2 that address how to describe functions verbally and translate them algebraically. In Section R.5, a subsection and several exercises were added that cover exponential functions and their graphs to help bridge the gap in student understanding of those functions. Section R.6 has expanded discussion of exponential functions, along with four new exercises involving exponential models. Throughout, data-driven examples were updated when possible.

Chapter 1

The goal for Chapter 1 was to update the data-based examples and consolidate similar exercises into a more manageable number. Section 1.8 has changed the most, with the addition of examples and exercises designed to help students visualize acceleration and velocity. In addition, l'Hôpital's Rule is briefly covered in a synthesis exercise.

Chapter 2

In Section 2.5, Example 3 has been rewritten to factor in cost, spreadsheet use has been added to show how a minimum or maximum can be found numerically, a new Technology Connection has been added, and Examples 6 and 7 were integrated into a single example. Several examples in Section 2.6 have been consolidated, and a new Quick Check exercise has been added. The main change to Chapter 2 is the addition of the expanded and updated Section 2.7, "Elasticity." This new location is a more natural fit than its former position as Section 3.6. The former Section 2.7, "Implicit Differentiation and Related Rates," has become Section 2.8.

Chapter 3

New material on exponential functions has been added to Section 3.1 based on the expanded content in Section R.5. In Section 3.2, there is more emphasis on the general antiderivative for $1/x$, for all x except $x = 0$, through additional examples and exercises. The Rule of 70 is now included in Section 3.3, which also has a new Technology Connection. Section 3.5 has been expanded to include a discussion on annuities. New Section 3.6 covers the topic of amortization and includes some Excel spreadsheet applications.

Chapter 4

Application examples and exercises were added and updated throughout Chapter 4. In addition, new material on Simpson's Rule was added to Section 4.2, and the topic of recursion was moved to a synthesis exercise in Section 4.6.

Chapter 5

Topics throughout Chapter 5 were expanded, allowing for over 80 new exercises and applications. Improper integration at a vertical asymptote was added to Section 5.3, and finding volume by shells was added to Section 5.6.

Chapter 6

The main changes in Chapter 6 are the addition of exponential regression to Section 6.4 and the addition of average value of a two-variable function to Section 6.6. New application exercises were also added, and data-driven examples and exercises were updated throughout.

Appendix A

New material on the Principle of Square Roots was added as a reference for students.

Supplements

STUDENT SUPPLEMENTS	INSTRUCTOR SUPPLEMENTS

Student's Solutions Manual
(ISBN: 0-321-99905-3/978-0-321-99905-4)
- Provides detailed solutions to all odd-numbered section exercises, with the exception of the Thinking and Writing exercises

Graphing Calculator Manual for Applied Mathematics (downloadable)
- By Victoria Baker, Nicholls State University
- Contains detailed instruction for using the TI-83/TI-83+/TI-84+C
- Instructions are organized by topic.
- Downloadable from within MyMathLab

Excel Spreadsheet Manual for Applied Mathematics (downloadable)
- By Stela Pudar-Hozo, Indiana University-Northwest
- Contains detailed instruction for using Excel 2013
- Instructions are organized by topic.
- Downloadable from within MyMathLab

Video Lectures with optional captioning (online)
- Complete set of digitized videos for student use anywhere
- Example-level and lecture-level videos available
- Available in MyMathLab

Annotated Instructor's Edition
(ISBN: 0-321-99903-7/978-0-321-99903-0)
- Includes numerous Teaching Tips
- Includes all of the answers, usually on the same page as the exercises, for quick reference

Instructor's Solutions Manual (downloadable)
- Provides complete solutions to all text exercises
- Available to qualified instructors through the Pearson Instructor Resource Center, **www.pearsonhighered.com/irc**, and MyMathLab

Printable Test Forms (downloadable)
- Contains four alternative tests per chapter
- Contains four comprehensive final exams
- Includes answer keys
- Available to qualified instructors through the Pearson Instructor Resource Center, **www.pearsonhighered.com/irc**, and MyMathLab

PowerPoint Lecture Presentations
- Classroom presentation software oriented specifically to the text's topic sequence
- Available to qualified instructors through the Pearson Instructor Resource Center, **www.pearsonhighered.com/irc**, and MyMathLab

TECHNOLOGY RESOURCES

MyMathLab® Online Course (access code required)
MyMathLab from Pearson is the world's leading online resource in mathematics, integrating interactive homework, assessment, and media in a flexible, easy-to-use format.

MyMathLab delivers **proven results** in helping individual students succeed.

- MyMathLab has a consistently positive impact on student retention, subsequent success, and overall achievement. MyMathLab can be successfully implemented in any environment—lab-based, hybrid, fully online, or traditional.
- MyMathLab's comprehensive online gradebook automatically tracks students' results on tests, quizzes, homework, and in the study plan. You can use the gradebook to quickly intervene if your students have trouble, or to provide positive feedback on a job well done.

MyMathLab provides **engaging experiences** that personalize, stimulate, and measure learning for each student.

- **Personalized Learning:** MyMathLab's personalized homework and adaptive study plan features allow your students to work on just what they need to learn when it makes the most sense.
  - Chapter skills check quizzes are available (at the chapter level and course-wide) to help students recognize what prerequisite skills they may need to brush up on.
  - The results of the chapter skills check quiz can be tied to personalized homework so that each student is given targeted skills to practice prior to starting course-level work.
- **Exercises:** The homework and practice exercises in MyMathLab are correlated to the exercises in the textbook, and they regenerate algorithmically to give students unlimited opportunity for practice and mastery. The software offers immediate, helpful feedback when students enter incorrect answers.
- **Multimedia Learning Aids:** Exercises include guided solutions, sample problems, animations, videos, and eText access for extra help at point-of-use.
  - Videos include section-level, lecture-style videos as well as example-level videos. Both are helpful resources when instructors or tutors are not available.
  - *MathTalk* videos show how the math the students are learning now may apply to their future careers. These videos could be used to kick off a lecture, in a flipped classroom setting, or as a way to motivate students.
  - Videos can be assigned as homework or as a prerequisite to students getting started on the homework. Premade questions are available for the MathTalk videos.
  - *Interactive figures* illustrate concepts and allow manipulation, so the user can better predict, visualize, and understand the underlying concept. Questions are available within MyMathLab to provide focus for student use.

- **MyMathLab Accessibility:** MyMathLab is compatible with the JAWS screen reader, and enables problems to be read and interacted with via keyboard controls and math notation input. MyMathLab also works with screen enlargers, including ZoomText, MAGic, and SuperNova. And all MyMathLab videos for this course have closed captioning. More information on this functionality is available at **mymathlab.com/accessibility**.

And, MyMathLab comes from an **experienced partner** with educational expertise and an eye on the future. Whether you are just getting started with MyMathLab, or have a question along the way, we're here to help you learn about our technologies and how to incorporate them into your course. Contact us at **www.mymathlab.com**.

MyMathLab® Integrated Review Course (access code required)
These new courses provide students with all the same great MyMathLab features, but make it easier for instructors to get started. Each course includes pre-assigned homework and quizzes to make creating a course even simpler. You can find more details at **www.mymathlab.com**.

MyLabsPlus
MyLabsPlus combines proven results and engaging experiences from MyMathLab® with convenient management tools and a dedicated services team. Designed to support growing math programs, it includes additional features such as:

- **Batch Enrollment:** Your school can create the login name and password for every student and instructor, so everyone can be ready to start class on the first day. Automation of this process is also possible through integration with your school's Student Information System.
- **Login from your campus portal:** You and your students can link directly from your campus portal into your MyLabsPlus courses. A Pearson service team works with your institution to create a single sign-on experience for instructors and students.
- **Advanced Reporting:** MyLabsPlus's advanced reporting allows instructors to review and analyze students' strengths and weaknesses by tracking their performance on tests, assignments, and tutorials. Administrators can review grades and assignments across all courses on your MyLabsPlus campus for a broad overview of program performance.
- **24/7 Support:** Students and instructors receive 24/7 support, 365 days a year, by email or online chat.

MyLabsPlus is available to qualified adopters. For more information, visit our website at **www.mylabsplus.com** or contact your Pearson representative.

MathXL® Online Course (access code required)
MathXL® is the homework and assessment engine that runs MyMathLab. With MathXL, instructors can:

- Create, edit, and assign online homework and tests using algorithmically generated exercises correlated at the objective level to the textbook.
- Create and assign their own online exercises and import TestGen tests for added flexibility.
- Maintain records of all student work tracked in MathXL's online gradebook.

With MathXL, students can:

- Take chapter tests in MathXL and receive personalized study plans and/or personalized homework assignments based on their test results.
- Use the study plan and/or the homework to link directly to tutorial exercises for the objectives they need to study.

- Access supplemental animations and video clips directly from selected exercises.

MathXL is available to qualified adopters. For more information, visit our website at **www.mathxl.com**, or contact your Pearson representative.

TestGen®
TestGen® (**www.pearsoned.com/testgen**) enables instructors to build, edit, print, and administer tests using a computerized bank of questions developed to cover all the objectives of the text. TestGen is algorithmically based, allowing instructors to create multiple but equivalent versions of the same question or test with the click of a button. Instructors can also modify test bank questions or add new questions. The software and testbank are available for instructors to download from Pearson Education's online catalog.

Acknowledgments

As authors, we have taken many steps to ensure the accuracy of this text. Many devoted individuals comprised the team that was responsible for monitoring the revision and production process in a manner that makes this a work of which we can all be proud. We are thankful for our publishing team at Pearson, as well as all of the Pearson representatives who share our book with educators across the country. Many thanks to Michelle Christian, who was instrumental in getting Scott Surgent's first book printed and in bringing him to the attention of the Pearson team. We would like to thank Jane Hoover for her many helpful suggestions, proofreading, and checking of art. Jane's attention to detail and pleasant demeanor made our work as low in stress as humanly possible, given the demands of the production process. Geri Davis deserves credit for both the attractive design of the text and the coordination of the many illustrations, photos, and graphs. She is always a distinct pleasure to work with and sets the standard by which all other art editors are measured. Many thanks also to Jennifer Blue, Lisa Collette, and John Morin for their careful checking of the manuscript and typeset pages. We are grateful to all those who have contributed to the improvements of this text over the years, including those who were instrumental in helping us to shape this 11th edition.

The following individuals provided terrific insights and meaningful suggestions for improving this text. We thank them:

Fernanda Botelho, *University of Memphis*
Hugh Cornell, *University of North Florida*
Marvin Stick, *University of Massachusetts, Lowell*
Timothy D. Sullivan, *Northern Illinois University*
Kimberly Walters, *Mississippi State University*

Prerequisite Skills Diagnostic Test

To the Student and the Instructor

Part A of this diagnostic test covers basic algebra concepts, such as properties of exponents, multiplying and factoring polynomials, equation solving, and applied problems. Part B covers topics, discussed in Chapter R, such as graphs, slope, equations of lines, and functions, most of which come from a course in intermediate or college algebra. This diagnostic test does not cover regression, though it is considered in Chapter R and used throughout the text. This test can be used to assess student needs for this course. Students who miss most of the questions in part A should study Appendix A before moving to Chapter R. Those who miss most of the questions in part B should study Chapter R. Students who miss just a few questions might study the related topics in either Appendix A or Chapter R before continuing with the calculus chapters.

Part A

Answers and locations of worked-out solutions appear on p. A-39.

Express each of the following without an exponent.

1. 4^3 2. $(-2)^5$ 3. $\left(\frac{1}{2}\right)^3$ 4. $(-2x)^1$ 5. e^0

Express each of the following without a negative exponent.

6. x^{-5} 7. $\left(\frac{1}{4}\right)^{-2}$ 8. t^{-1}

Multiply. Express each answer without a negative exponent.

9. $x^5 \cdot x^6$ 10. $x^{-5} \cdot x^6$ 11. $2x^{-3} \cdot 5x^{-4}$

Divide. Express each answer without a negative exponent.

12. $\dfrac{a^3}{a^2}$ 13. $\dfrac{e^3}{e^{-4}}$

Simplify. Express each answer without a negative exponent.

14. $(x^{-2})^3$ 15. $(2x^4 y^{-5} z^3)^{-3}$

Multiply.

16. $3(x - 5)$ 17. $(x - 5)(x + 3)$

18. $(a + b)(a + b)$

19. $(2x - t)^2$ 20. $(3c + d)(3c - d)$

Factor.

21. $2xh + h^2$ 22. $x^2 - 6xy + 9y^2$

23. $x^2 - 5x - 14$ 24. $6x^2 + 7x - 5$

25. $x^3 - 7x^2 - 4x + 28$

Solve.

26. $-\frac{5}{6}x + 10 = \frac{1}{2}x + 2$ 27. $3x(x - 2)(5x + 4) = 0$

28. $4x^3 = x$ 29. $\dfrac{2x}{x - 3} - \dfrac{6}{x} = \dfrac{18}{x^2 - 3x}$

30. $17 - 8x \geq 5x - 4$

31. After a 5% gain in weight, a grizzly bear weighs 693 lb. What was the bear's original weight?

32. Raggs, Ltd., a clothing firm, determines that its total revenue, in dollars, from the sale of x suits is given by $200x + 50$. Determine the number of suits the firm must sell to ensure that its total revenue will be more than $70,050.

Part B

Answers and locations of worked-out solutions appear on p. A-39.

Graph.

1. $y = 2x + 1$ 2. $3x + 5y = 10$

3. $y = x^2 - 1$ 4. $x = y^2$

5. A function f is given by $f(x) = 3x^2 - 2x + 8$. Find each of the following: $f(0), f(-5)$, and $f(7a)$.

6. A function f is given by $f(x) = (x + 3)^2 - 4$. Find all x such that $f(x) = 0$.

7. Graph the function f defined as follows:
$$f(x) = \begin{cases} 4, & \text{for } x \leq 0, \\ 3 - x^2, & \text{for } 0 < x \leq 2, \\ 2x - 6, & \text{for } x > 2. \end{cases}$$

8. Write interval notation for $\{x | -4 < x \leq 5\}$.

9. Find the domain: $f(x) = \dfrac{3}{2x - 5}$.

10. Find the slope and y-intercept of $2x - 4y - 7 = 0$.

11. Find an equation of the line that has slope 3 and contains the point $(-1, -5)$.

12. Find the slope of the line containing the points $(-2, 6)$ and $(-4, 9)$.

Graph.

13. $f(x) = x^2 - 2x - 3$ 14. $f(x) = x^3$ 15. $f(x) = \dfrac{1}{x}$

16. $f(x) = |x|$ 17. $f(x) = -\sqrt{x}$

18. Suppose that $1000 is invested at 5%, compounded annually. How much is the investment worth at the end of 2 yr?

Credits

Chapter R   **p. 1:** The Washington Post/Getty Images. **p. 2:** Berents/Shutterstock. **p. 7:** The Washington Post/Getty Images. **p. 10:** (upper) ZUMA Press, Inc./Alamy; (lower) Bo Bridges/PR Newswire/AP Images. **p. 36:** Felinda/Fotolia. **p. 39:** Kruwt/Fotolia. **p. 41:** Scott Surgent. **p. 46:** Karramba Production/Fotolia. **p. 53:** Graphicus, Serafim Chekalkin. **p. 59:** Kyslynskyy/Fotolia. **p. 70:** Monkey Business Images/Shutterstock. **p. 72:** Brian Jackson/Fotolia. **p. 73:** Blend Images/Shutterstock. **p. 90:** Stephen Coburn/Shutterstock.

Chapter 1   **p. 92:** Scott Boehm/Associated Press. **p. 110:** Bastos/Fotolia. **p. 117:** Kunal Mehta/Shutterstock. **p. 127:** Oliver Hausen/Fotolia. **p. 134:** Graphicus, Serafim Chekalkin. **p. 148:** (upper) Kushnirov Avraham/Fotolia; (lower) Scott Boehm/ Associated Press. **p. 152:** Federicocandonifoto/Shutterstock. **p. 155:** Bildagentur Zoonar GmbH/Shutterstock. **p. 159:** Brian Spurlock. **p. 162:** Robnroll/Shutterstock. **p. 174:** Dotshock/Shutterstock. **p. 186:** Bikeriderlondon/Shutterstock. **p. 187:** New York Daily News Archive/Getty Images.

Chapter 2   **p. 188:** Stephen Shepherd/Alamy. **p. 216:** Graphicus, Serafim Chekalkin. **p. 219:** gpointstudio/Shutterstock. **p. 232:** uss Reed/Globe Photos/ZUMAPRESS/Alamy. **p. 243:** Scott Surgent. **p. 247:** (upper) Stephen Shepherd/Alamy; (lower) Screenshots from Microsoft® Excel®. Used by permission of Microsoft Corporation. **p. 253:** Screenshots from Microsoft® Excel®. Used by permission of Microsoft Corporation. **p. 257:** Mi.Ti./Fotolia. **p. 269:** Losevsky Pavel/Alamy. **p. 278:** Minerva Studio/Fotolia. **p. 280:** (left) francesco de marco/Shutterstock; (right) 3D4Medical/Science Source. **p. 292:** Mike Thomas/Fotolia. **p. 293:** (left) njsphotography/Fotolia; (right) mattjeppson/Fotolia.

Chapter 3   **p. 294:** Dragon Images/Shutterstock. **p. 305:** Peter Bernik/Shutterstock. **p. 325:** (left) Glow Images; (right) Dragon Images/Shutterstock. **p. 327:** UPI/Heritage Auctions/Newscom. **p. 332:** (left) Vladimir Mucibabic/Fotolia; (right) EZIO PETERSEN/UPI/Newscom. **p. 333:** Edelweiss/Fotolia. **p. 334:** Chuck Crow/The Plain Dealer/Landov. **p. 335:** Mike Blake/Reuters. **p. 339:** UPI Photo/Debbie Hill/Newscom. **p. 344:** Josemaria Toscano/Fotolia. **p. 348:** Ethan Daniels/Shutterstock. **p. 354:** Tommy E Trenchard/Alamy. **p. 370:** Photos 12/Alamy. **p. 371:** (upper left) PIXAR ANIMATION STUDIOS/WALT DISNEY PICTURES/Alb/ Album/Superstock; (bottom right) Mim Friday/Alamy.

Chapter 4   **p. 372:** Transtock/Superstock. **p. 379:** Nenetus/Shutterstock. **p. 380:** Michael Jung/Shutterstock. **p. 383:** PicturenetCorp/Fotolia. **p. 384:** Sira Anamwong/Shutterstock. **p. 399:** Transtock/Superstock. **p. 404:** Karichs/Fotolia. **p. 445:** NASA. **p. 447:** (bottom left) 06photo/Shutterstock; (top right) Nik Wheeler/Alamy. **p. 448:** (top left) Wassiliy/Fotolia; (bottom right) estherpoon/Shutterstock.

Chapter 5   **p. 449:** Anekoho/Fotolia. **p. 455:** Darryl Leniuk/Getty Images. **p. 463:** Sergey Volkov/Fotolia. **p. 466:** Anekoho/ Fotolia. **p. 479:** SeanPavonePhoto/Fotolia. **p. 481:** Tetra Images/Alamy. **p. 492:** Jens Kalaene/dpa/picture-alliance/Newscom. **p. 494:** Brian Spurlock. **p. 497:** dvande/Shutterstock. **p. 498:** fotogrammi3/Fotolia. **p. 500:** mirec/Fotolia. **p. 501:** John Elk/Getty Images. **p. 502:** Chris VanLennep Photo/Fotolia. **p. 505:** Popperfoto/Getty Images. **p. 524:** Vladimir Salman/Shutterstock.

Chapter 6   **p. 525:** Tom Grill/Corbis. **p. 528:** aigarsr/Fotolia. **pp. 530–531:** Quick Graph, Kz Labs. **p. 532:** (left) Tom Grill/ Corbis; (right) lafoto/Shutterstock. **p. 533:** Corbis. **p. 536:** VIEW Pictures Ltd/Alamy. **p. 541:** Maisie Paterson/Getty Images. **p. 544:** Rick Hanston/Latent Images. **p. 555:** H. Ruckemann UPI Photo Service/Newscom. **p. 560:** ZUMA Press, Inc/Alamy. **p. 565:** picsfive/Fotolia. **p. 579:** Suzanne Tucker/Shutterstock.

Appendix B   **pp. 598–599:** Screenshots from Microsoft® Excel®. Used by permission of Microsoft Corporation.

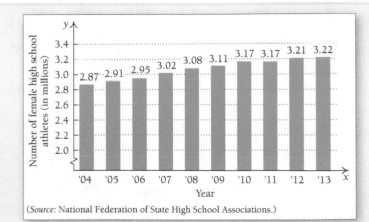

R Functions, Graphs, and Models

What You'll Learn

R.1 Graphs and Equations
R.2 Functions and Models
R.3 Finding Domain and Range
R.4 Slope and Linear Functions
R.5 Nonlinear Functions and Models
R.6 Mathematical Modeling and Curve Fitting

Why It's Important

This chapter introduces functions and covers their notation, graphs, and applications. Also presented are many topics considered often throughout the text: supply and demand; total cost, revenue, and profit; the concept of a mathematical model; and curve fitting.

Skills in using a graphing calculator are introduced in optional Technology Connections. Details on keystrokes are given in the *Graphing Calculator Manual* (GCM).

Part A of the diagnostic test (p. xv), on basic algebra concepts, allows students to determine whether they need to review Appendix A (p. 585) before studying this chapter. Part B, on college algebra topics, assesses the need to study this chapter before the calculus chapters.

Where It's Used

Participation of Females in High School Athletes: What is the predicted number of female high school athletes in 2017? (*This problem appears as Example 5 in Section R.1.*)

(*Source:* National Federation of State High School Associations.)

Graphs and Equations

What Is Calculus?

- Graph equations.
- Use graphs as mathematical models to make predictions.
- Carry out calculations involving compound interest.

What is calculus? This is a common question at the start of a course like this. Let's consider a simplified answer for now.

The common food can comes in many sizes, as the photo at the left illustrates. The following is a typical problem from an algebra course. Try to solve it. (If you need some algebra review, refer to Appendix A at the end of the book.)

Algebra Problem

A soup can contains a volume of 250 cm^3. If the height of the can is twice the length of the radius of the base, find the dimensions of the can.

From geometry, the volume of a cylinder is $V = \pi r^2 h$, where r is the radius of the circular base in centimeters and h is the height in centimeters. Since $V = 250$ and $h = 2r$, we have $\pi r^2 (2r) = 250$, or $2\pi r^3 = 250$. Solving for r, we find that the soup can has a radius of approximately 3.4 cm and a height of 6.8 cm.

The following is a calculus problem that a manufacturer of cans might need to solve:

Calculus Problem

A soup can is to contain a volume of 250 cm^3. If the cost of the material for the two circular ends is $0.0008 per square centimeter and the cost of the material for the side is $0.0015 per square centimeter, what dimensions will minimize the cost of the can?

One way to solve this problem might be to choose several sets of dimensions that give a volume for the can of 250 cm^3, compute the resulting costs, and determine which is the lowest. For any r, we must have $h = 250/\pi r^2$. Using a computer spreadsheet, we could create a table such as the one below. We let $r =$ radius in centimeters and $h =$ height in centimeters.

	A	B	C	
1				
2	Radius	Height	Cost	
3	r	h	C	
4	3.5	6.495277933	0.275868914	
5	3.6	6.139440947	0.273485845	
6	3.7	5.812063892	0.271525071	
7	3.8	5.510190767	0.269961189	
8	3.9	5.231239624	0.268771404	
9	4	4.972947167	0.2679352	
10	4.1	4.733322705	0.267434061	
11	4.2	4.510609676	0.267251237	←— Possible lowest cost
12	4.3	4.303253363	0.267371533	
13	4.4	4.109873692	0.267781137	
14	4.5	3.929242206	0.268467467	

From the data in the table, we might conclude that the lowest cost is about $0.26725 per can when the can's radius is 4.2 cm and its height is 4.51 cm. But how can we be certain that no other dimensions will give a lower cost? We need the tools of calculus to answer this. In Chapter 2, we will study such maximum–minimum problems, including a complete solution to this one, which appears as Example 3 in Section 2.5.

Other topics we will consider in calculus are the slope of a curve at a point, rates of change, area under a curve, accumulations of quantities, and some statistical applications.

Graphs

The study of graphs is an essential aspect of calculus. A graph offers the opportunity to visualize relationships. For instance, the graph below shows how life expectancy has changed over time in the United States. One topic that we consider later in calculus is how a change on one axis affects the change on another.

ESTIMATED LIFE EXPECTANCY OF U.S. NEWBORNS BY YEAR OF BIRTH, 1929–2013

(*Source*: U.S. National Center for Health Statistics.)

Ordered Pairs and Graphs

Each point in a plane corresponds to an ordered pair of numbers. Note in the figure at the right that the point corresponding to the pair $(2, 5)$ is different from the point corresponding to the pair $(5, 2)$. This is why we call a pair like $(2, 5)$ an *ordered pair*. The first number is called the *first coordinate* of the point, and the second number is called the *second coordinate*. Together these are the *coordinates of the point*. The horizontal line is often labeled as the *x-axis*, and the vertical line is often labeled as the *y-axis*. The two axes intersect at the *origin*, $(0, 0)$.

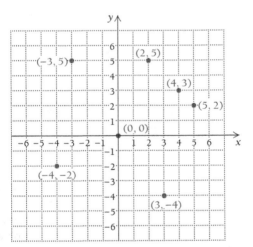

Graphs of Equations

A **solution** of an equation in two variables is an ordered pair of numbers that, when substituted for the variables, forms a true statement. If not directed otherwise, we usually take the variables in *alphabetical* order. For example, $(-1, 2)$ is a solution of the equation $3x^2 + y = 5$, because when we substitute -1 for x and 2 for y, we get a true statement:

$$\begin{array}{c|c}
\multicolumn{2}{c}{3x^2 + y = 5} \\
\hline
3(-1)^2 + 2 \;?\; 5 & \\
3 + 2 & 5 \\
5 & 5 \quad \text{TRUE}
\end{array}$$

> **DEFINITION**
> The **graph** of an equation is a drawing that represents all ordered pairs that are solutions of the equation.

We obtain the graph of an equation by plotting enough ordered pairs (that are solutions) to see a pattern.

EXAMPLE 1   Graph: $y = 2x + 1$.

Solution   We first find some ordered pairs that are solutions and arrange them in a table. To find an ordered pair, we can choose any number for x and then determine y. For example, if we choose -2 for x and substitute that value in $y = 2x + 1$, we find that $y = 2(-2) + 1 = -4 + 1 = -3$. Thus, $(-2, -3)$ is a solution. We select both negative numbers and positive numbers, as well as 0, for x.

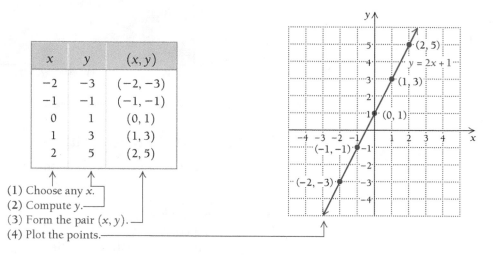

x	y	(x, y)
-2	-3	$(-2, -3)$
-1	-1	$(-1, -1)$
0	1	$(0, 1)$
1	3	$(1, 3)$
2	5	$(2, 5)$

(1) Choose any x.
(2) Compute y.
(3) Form the pair (x, y).
(4) Plot the points.

Quick Check 1 ☑

Graph: $y = 3 - x$.

After we plot the points, we look for a pattern in the graph. In this case, the points suggest a solid line. We draw the line with a straightedge and label it $y = 2x + 1$.

1 ☑

EXAMPLE 2   Graph: $3x + 5y = 10$.

Solution   We could choose x-values, substitute, and solve for y-values, but we first solve for y to ease the calculations.*

$$3x + 5y = 10$$
$$3x + 5y - 3x = 10 - 3x \qquad \text{Subtracting } 3x \text{ from both sides}$$
$$5y = 10 - 3x \qquad \text{Simplifying}$$
$$\tfrac{1}{5} \cdot 5y = \tfrac{1}{5} \cdot (10 - 3x) \qquad \text{Multiplying both sides by } \tfrac{1}{5}, \text{ or dividing both sides by 5}$$
$$y = \tfrac{1}{5} \cdot (10) - \tfrac{1}{5} \cdot (3x) \qquad \text{Using the distributive law}$$
$$= 2 - \tfrac{3}{5}x \qquad \text{Simplifying}$$
$$= -\tfrac{3}{5}x + 2$$

Next we use $y = -\tfrac{3}{5}x + 2$ to find some ordered pairs, choosing multiples of 5 for x to avoid fractions.

———————

*Be sure to consult Appendix A, as needed, for a review of algebra.

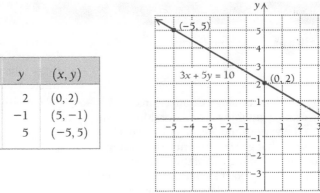

x	y	(x, y)
0	2	$(0, 2)$
5	−1	$(5, -1)$
−5	5	$(-5, 5)$

Quick Check 2 ☑

Graph: $3x - 5y = 10$.

We plot the points, draw the line, and label the graph as shown.   **2** ☑

Examples 1 and 2 show graphs of linear equations. Such graphs are considered in greater detail in Section R.4.

EXAMPLE 3   Graph: $y = x^2 - 1$.

Solution

x	y	(x, y)
−2	3	$(-2, 3)$
−1	0	$(-1, 0)$
0	−1	$(0, -1)$
1	0	$(1, 0)$
2	3	$(2, 3)$

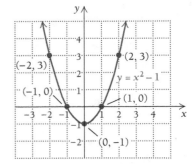

Quick Check 3 ☑

Graph: $y = 2 - x^2$.

This time the pattern of the points is a curve called a *parabola*. We plot enough points to see a pattern and draw the graph.   **3** ☑

EXAMPLE 4   Graph: $x = y^2$.

Solution   In this case, x is expressed in terms of the variable y. Thus, we first choose numbers for y and then compute x.

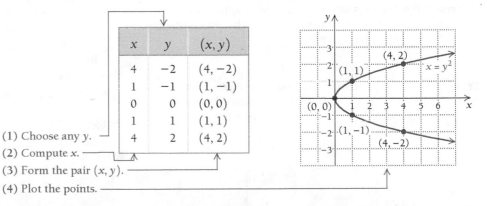

x	y	(x, y)
4	−2	$(4, -2)$
1	−1	$(1, -1)$
0	0	$(0, 0)$
1	1	$(1, 1)$
4	2	$(4, 2)$

(1) Choose any y.

(2) Compute x.

(3) Form the pair (x, y).

(4) Plot the points.

Quick Check 4 ☑

Graph: $x = 1 + y^2$.

We plot these points, keeping in mind that x is still the first coordinate and y the second. We look for a pattern and complete the graph by connecting the points.   **4** ☑

Introduction to the Use of a Graphing Calculator: Windows and Graphs

Viewing Windows

In this first of the optional Technology Connections, we begin to create graphs using a graphing calculator. Most of the coverage will refer to the various models of TI-83 and TI-84 calculators but in a somewhat generic manner, discussing features common to most graphing calculators. Although some keystrokes will be listed, exact keystrokes can be found in the owner's manual for your calculator or in the *Graphing Calculator Manual* (GCM) that accompanies this text.

The **viewing window** is a feature common to all graphing calculators. This is the rectangular screen in which a graph appears. Windows are described by four numbers in the format [L, R, B, T], representing the Left and Right endpoints of the *x*-axis and the Bottom and Top endpoints of the *y*-axis. A WINDOW feature can be used to set these dimensions. Below is a window setting of $[-20, 20, -5, 5]$ with axis scaling denoted as Xscl = 5 and Yscl = 1, which means that there are 5 units between tick marks extending from -20 to 20 on the *x*-axis and 1 unit between tick marks extending from -5 to 5 on the *y*-axis.

Scales should be chosen with care, since tick marks become blurred and indistinguishable when too many appear. On most graphing calculators, a window setting of $[-10, 10, -10, 10]$, Xscl = 1, Yscl = 1, Xres = 1 is considered **standard**.

Graphs are made up of black rectangular dots called **pixels.** The setting xres allows users to set pixel resolution at 1 through 8 for graphs of equations. At Xres = 1, equations are evaluated and graphed at each pixel on the *x*-axis. At Xres = 8, equations are evaluated and graphed at every eighth pixel on the *x*-axis. The resolution is better for smaller Xres values than for larger ones.

Graphs

Let's use a graphing calculator to graph the equation $y = x^3 - 5x + 1$. The equation can be entered by pressing Y= and entering x^3–5x+1. We obtain the following graph in the standard viewing window.

It is often necessary to change viewing windows in order to best reveal the curvature of a graph. For example, each of the following is a graph of $y = 3x^5 - 20x^3$, but with a different viewing window. Which do you think best displays the curvature of the graph?

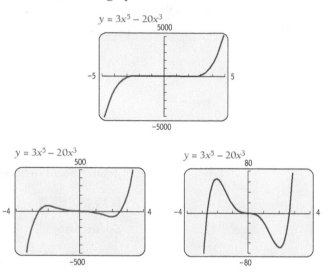

In general, choosing a window that best reveals a graph's characteristics involves some trial and error and, in some cases, some knowledge about the shape of the graph.

To graph an equation like $3x + 5y = 10$, most calculators require that the equation be solved for *y*. Thus, we must rewrite the equation and enter it as

$$y = \frac{-3x + 10}{5}, \quad \text{or} \quad y = -\frac{3}{5}x + 2.$$

(See Example 2.) Its graph is shown below.

To graph an equation like $x = y^2$, we solve for *y* and get $y = \sqrt{x}$ or $y = -\sqrt{x}$. We then graph both equations, $y_1 = \sqrt{x}$ and $y_2 = -\sqrt{x}$.

EXERCISES

Graph each of the following equations. Select the standard window, $[-10, 10, -10, 10]$, with Xscl = 1 and Yscl = 1.

1. $y = x + 3$ **2.** $y = x - 5$

3. $y = 2x - 1$ **4.** $y = 3x + 1$

5. $y = -\frac{2}{3}x + 4$ **6.** $y = -\frac{4}{5}x + 3$

7. $2x - 3y = 18$ **8.** $5y + 3x = 4$

(continued)

9. $y = x^2$

10. $y = (x + 4)^2$

11. $y = 8 - x^2$

12. $y = 4 - 3x - x^2$

13. $y + 10 = 5x^2 - 3x$

14. $y - 2 = x^3$

15. $y = x^3 - 7x - 2$

16. $y = x^4 - 3x^2 + x$

17. $y = |x|$ (On most calculators, this is entered as $y = \text{abs}(x)$.)

18. $y = |x - 5|$

19. $y = |x| - 5$

20. $y = 9 - |x|$

Mathematical Models

When a real-world situation is described using mathematics, the description is a **mathematical model.** For example, the natural numbers constitute a mathematical model for situations in which counting is essential. Also, the speed at which a body falls due to gravity can be described using a mathematical model.

Mathematical models are abstracted from real-world situations. A mathematical model may give results that allow us to predict what will happen in the real-world situation. If the predictions are too inaccurate or the results of experimentation do not conform to the model, the model must be changed or discarded.

CREATING A MATHEMATICAL MODEL

1. Recognize a real-world problem. → 2. Collect data. → 3. Analyze the data. → 4. Construct a model. → 5. Test and refine the model. → 6. Explain and predict.

Mathematical modeling is often an ongoing process. For example, finding a mathematical model that will provide an accurate prediction of population growth is not a simple task. Any population model that can be devised will need to be reshaped as further information is acquired.

EXAMPLE 5 The graph below shows participation by females in high school athletics from 2004 to 2013.

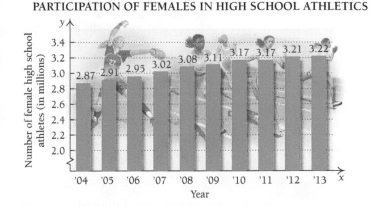

PARTICIPATION OF FEMALES IN HIGH SCHOOL ATHLETICS

Number of female high school athletes (in millions): 2.87, 2.91, 2.95, 3.02, 3.08, 3.11, 3.17, 3.17, 3.21, 3.22

Year: '04, '05, '06, '07, '08, '09, '10, '11, '12, '13

(*Source*: National Federation of State High School Associations.)

Use the model $N = 0.041t + 2.88$, where t is the number of years after 2004 and N is the number of participants, in millions, to predict the number of female high school athletes in 2017.

Quick Check 5 ✔

Using the model in Example 5, determine the year in which the number of female high school athletes will reach 3.5 million.

Solution Since 2017 is 13 years after 2004, we substitute 13 for t:

$$N = 0.041t + 2.88 = 0.041(13) + 2.88 = 3.41.$$

According to this model, in 2017, approximately 3.41 million females will participate in high school athletics.

5 ✔

As is the case with many kinds of models, the model in Example 5 is not perfect. For example, for $t = 1$, we get $N = 2.921$, a number slightly different from the 2.91 in the original data. But, for purposes of estimating, the model is adequate. The cubic model $N = -0.00043t^3 + 0.003t^2 + 0.044t + 2.87$ also fits the data, at least in the short term: For $t = 1$, we get $N \approx 2.92$, close to the given data value. But for $t = 13$, we have $N = 3.00$, which is quite different from the prediction in Example 5. The difficulty with a cubic model here is that, eventually, its predictions become undependable. For example, the model in Example 5 predicts that there will be 3.54 million female high school athletes in 2020, but the cubic model predicts only 2.58 million. We always have to subject our models to careful scrutiny.

Compound Interest

One important model that is extremely precise involves **compound interest**. Suppose we invest P dollars at interest rate r, expressed as a decimal, and compounded annually. The amount A_1 in the account at the end of the first year, is given by

$$A_1 = P + Pr = P(1 + r).$$ The original amount invested, P, is called the principal.

Going into the second year, we have $P(1 + r)$ dollars, so by the end of the second year, we will have the amount A_2 given by

$$A_2 = A_1 \cdot (1 + r) = [P(1 + r)](1 + r) = P(1 + r)^2.$$

Going into the third year, we have $P(1 + r)^2$ dollars, so by the end of the third year, we will have the amount A_3 given by

$$A_3 = A_2 \cdot (1 + r) = [P(1 + r)^2](1 + r) = P(1 + r)^3.$$

In general, we have the following theorem.

THEOREM 1

If an amount P is invested at interest rate r, expressed as a decimal, and compounded annually, in t years it will grow to the amount A given by

$$A = P(1 + r)^t.$$

EXAMPLE 6 **Business: Compound Interest.** Suppose $1000 is invested in Fibonacci Investment Fund at 5%, compounded annually. How much is in the account at the end of 2 yr?

Solution We substitute 1000 for P, 0.05 for r, and 2 for t into the equation $A = P(1 + r)^t$ and get

$$
\begin{aligned}
A &= 1000(1 + 0.05)^2 & &\text{Substituting} \\
&= 1000(1.05)^2 & &\text{Adding terms in parentheses} \\
&= 1000(1.1025) & &\text{Squaring} \\
&= \$1102.50. & &\text{Multiplying}
\end{aligned}
$$

Quick Check 6 ☑

Business. Repeat Example 6 for an interest rate of 6%.

There is $1102.50 in the account after 2 yr.   **6** ☑

For interest that is compounded quarterly (four times per year), we can find a formula like the one above, as illustrated in the following diagram.

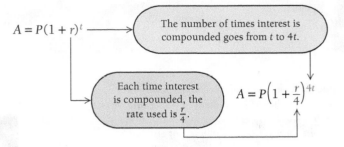

The number of times interest is compounded goes from t to $4t$.

Each time interest is compounded, the rate used is $\frac{r}{4}$.

$A = P(1 + r)^t$

$A = P\left(1 + \dfrac{r}{4}\right)^{4t}$

"Compounded quarterly" means that the interest is divided by 4 and compounded four times per year. In general, the following theorem applies.

THEOREM 2

If a principal P is invested at interest rate r, expressed as a decimal, and compounded n times a year, in t years it will grow to an amount A given by

$$A = P\left(1 + \frac{r}{n}\right)^{nt}.$$

EXAMPLE 7 **Business: Compound Interest.** Suppose \$1000 is invested in Wellington Investment Fund at 5%, compounded quarterly. How much is in the account at the end of 3 yr?

Solution We use the equation $A = P(1 + r/n)^{nt}$, substituting 1000 for P, 0.05 for r, 4 for n (compounding quarterly), and 3 for t. Then we get

$$A = 1000\left(1 + \frac{0.05}{4}\right)^{4 \cdot 3} \qquad \text{Substituting}$$

$$= 1000(1 + 0.0125)^{12}$$

$$= 1000(1.0125)^{12}$$

$$= 1000(1.160754518) \qquad \text{Using a calculator to approximate } (1.0125)^{12}$$

$$= 1160.754518$$

$$\approx \$1160.75. \qquad \text{The symbol} \approx \text{means "approximately equal to."}$$

There is \$1160.75 in the account after 3 yr. **7** ✓

Quick Check 7 ✓

Business: Compound Interest.
Repeat Example 7 for an interest rate of 6%.

A calculator with a $\boxed{y^x}$ or $\boxed{\wedge}$ key and a ten-digit readout was used to find $(1.0125)^{12}$ in Example 7. The number of places on a calculator may affect the accuracy of the answer. Thus, you may occasionally find that your answers do not agree with those at the back of the book, which were found on a calculator with a ten-digit readout. In general, when using a calculator, do all computations and round only at the end, as in Example 7. Usually, your answer will agree to at least four digits. It is a good idea to consult with your instructor about the accuracy required.

Section Summary

- Most graphs can be created by plotting points and looking for patterns. A graphing calculator can create graphs rapidly.
- Mathematical equations can serve as models of many kinds of applications.

- An example of mathematical model is the formula for compound interest. If P dollars are invested at interest rate r, compounded n times a year for t years, then the amount A at the end of the t years is given by

$$A = P\left(1 + \frac{r}{n}\right)^{nt}.$$

R.1 | Exercise Set

Exercises designated by the symbol ↘ are Thinking and Writing Exercises. They should be answered using one or two English sentences. Because answers to many such exercises will vary, solutions are not given at the back of the book.

Graph. (Unless directed otherwise, assume that "Graph" means "Graph by hand.")

1. $y = x - 1$

2. $y = x + 4$

3. $y = -\frac{1}{4}x$

4. $y = -3x$

5. $y = -\frac{5}{3}x + 3$

6. $y = \frac{2}{3}x - 4$

7. $x + y = 5$

8. $x - y = 4$

9. $6x + 3y = -9$

10. $8y - 2x = 4$

11. $2x + 5y = 10$

12. $5x - 6y = 12$

13. $y = x^2 - 5$

14. $y = x^2 - 3$

15. $x = y^2 + 2$

16. $x = 2 - y^2$

17. $y = |4 - x|$

18. $y = |x|$

19. $y = 7 - x^2$

20. $y = 5 - x^2$

21. $y - 7 = x^3$

22. $y + 1 = x^3$

APPLICATIONS

23. Medicine. Ibuprofen is a medication used to relieve pain. The function

$$A = 0.5t^4 + 3.45t^3 - 96.65t^2 + 347.7t, \ 0 \le t \le 6,$$

can be used to estimate the number of milligrams, A, of ibuprofen in the bloodstream t hours after 400 mg of the medication has been swallowed. (*Source*: Based on data from Dr. P. Carey, Burlington, VT.) How many milligrams of ibuprofen are in the bloodstream 2 hr after 400 mg has been swallowed?

24. Running records. According to at least one study, the world record in any running race can be modeled by a linear equation. In particular, the world record R, in minutes, for the mile run in year x can be modeled by

$$R = -0.006x + 15.714.$$

Use this model to estimate the world records for the mile run in 1954, 2000, and 2015. Round your answers to the nearest hundredth of a minute.

25. Snowboarding in the half-pipe. Shaun White, "The Flying Tomato," won a gold medal in the 2010 Winter Olympics for snowboarding in the half-pipe. He soared an unprecedented 25 ft above the edge of the half-pipe. His speed $v(t)$, in miles per hour, upon reentering the pipe can be approximated by $v(t) = 10.9t$, where t is the number of seconds for which he was airborne. White was airborne for 2.5 sec. (*Source*: "White Rides to Repeat in Halfpipe, Lago Takes Bronze," Associated Press, 2/18/2010.) How fast was he going when he reentered the half-pipe?

26. Skateboard bomb drop. The distance $s(t)$, in feet, traveled by a body falling freely from rest in t seconds is approximated by

$$s(t) = 16t^2.$$

On April 6, 2006, pro skateboarder Danny Way smashed the world record for the "bomb drop" by free-falling 28 ft from the Fender Stratocaster guitar atop the Hard Rock Hotel & Casino in Las Vegas onto a ramp below. (*Source*: www.skateboardingmagazine.com.) How long did it take until he hit the ramp?

27. Hearing-impaired Americans. The number N, in millions, of hearing-impaired Americans of age x can be approximated by the graph that follows.

(*Source*: Better Hearing Institute.)

Use the graph to answer the following.

a) Approximate the number of hearing-impaired Americans of ages 20, 40, 50, and 60.

b) For what ages is the number of hearing-impaired Americans approximately 4 million?

c) Estimate the age for which the greatest number of Americans is hearing-impaired.

d) What difficulty do you have in making this determination?

28. Life science: incidence of breast cancer. The following graph approximates the incidence of breast cancer y, per 100,000 women, as a function of age x, where x represents ages 25 to 102.

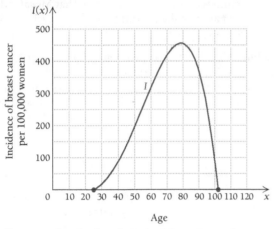

Age

(*Source*: Based on data from the National Cancer Institute.)

a) What is the incidence of breast cancer in 40-yr-old women?

b) For what ages is the incidence of breast cancer about 400 per 100,000 women?

c) Examine the graph and try to determine the age at which the largest incidence of breast cancer occurs.

d) What difficulty do you have making this determination?

29. Compound interest. Southside Investments purchases a $100,000 certificate of deposit from Newton Bank, at 2.8%. How much is the investment worth (rounded to the nearest cent) at the end of 1 yr, if interest is compounded:

a) annually?   **b)** semiannually?
c) quarterly?   **d)** daily (use 365 days
e) hourly?   for 1 yr)?

30. Compound interest. Greenleaf Investments purchases a $300,000 certificate of deposit from Descartes Bank, at 2.2%. How much is the investment worth (rounded to the nearest cent) at the end of 1 yr, if interest is compounded:

a) annually?   **b)** semiannually?
c) quarterly?   **d)** daily (use 365 days
e) hourly?   for 1 yr)?

31. Compound interest. Stateside Brokers deposit $30,000 in Godel Municipal Bond Funds, at 4%. How much is the

investment worth (rounded to the nearest cent) at the end of 3 yr, if interest is compounded:

a) annually?   **b)** semiannually?
c) quarterly?   **d)** daily (use 365 days
e) hourly?   for 1 yr)?

32. Compound interest. The Kims deposit $1000 in Wiles Municipal Bond Funds, at 5%. How much is the investment worth (rounded to the nearest cent) at the end of 4 yr, if interest is compounded:

a) annually?   **b)** semiannually?
c) quarterly?   **d)** daily (use 365 days
e) hourly?   for 1 yr)?

Determining monthly loan payments.   *If P dollars are borrowed at an annual interest rate r, the payment M made each month for a total of n months is*

$$M = P \frac{\frac{r}{12}\left(1 + \frac{r}{12}\right)^n}{\left(1 + \frac{r}{12}\right)^n - 1}.$$

33. Fermat's Last Bank makes a car loan of $18,000, at 6.4% interest and with a loan period of 3 yr. What is the monthly payment?

34. At Haken Bank, Ken Appel takes out a $100,000 mortgage at an interest rate of 4.8% for a loan period of 30 yr. What is the monthly payment?

Annuities.   *If P dollars are invested annually in an annuity (investment fund), after n years, the annuity will be worth*

$$W = P\left[\frac{(1 + r)^n - 1}{r}\right],$$

where r is the interest rate, compounded annually.

35. Kate invests $3000 annually in an annuity from Mersenne Fund that earns 6.57% interest. How much is the investment worth after 18 yr? Round to the nearest cent.

36. Paulo establishes an annuity that earns $7\frac{1}{4}$% interest and wants it to be worth $50,000 in 20 yr. How much will he need to invest annually to achieve this goal?

37. Condor population. The condor population in California and Arizona from 2002 to 2012 is approximated in the graph below.

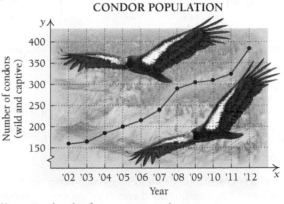

CONDOR POPULATION

Year

(*Source*: Based on data from esasuccess.org.)

a) In what years was the condor population at or above 230?
b) In what year was the condor population at 200?
c) In what year was the condor population the highest?
d) In what year was the condor population the lowest?

38. Speculate as to why the condor population in California and Arizona experienced such a dramatic rise in 2007–2008.

SYNTHESIS

Retirement account. *Sally makes deposits into a retirement account every year from the age of 30 until she retires at age 65.*

39. a) If Sally deposits $1200 per year and the account earns interest at a rate of 4% per year, compounded annually, how much will she have in the account when she retires? (*Hint:* Use the annuity formula given for Exercises 35 and 36.)
b) How much of that total amount is from Sally's deposits? How much is interest?

40. a) Sally plans to take regular monthly distributions from her retirement account from the time she retires until she is 80 years old, when the account will have a value of $0. How much should she take each month? Assume the interest rate is 4% per year, compounded monthly. (*Hint:* Use the formula given for Exercises 33 and 34 that calculates the monthly payments on a loan.)
b) What is the total of the payments she will receive? How much of the total will be her own money (see part b of Exercise 39), and how much will be interest?

Annual yield. *The annual interest rate r, when compounded more than once a year, results in a slightly higher yearly interest rate; this is called the* annual (or effective) yield *and denoted as Y. For example, $1000 deposited at 5%, compounded monthly for 1 yr (12 months), will have a value of* $A = 1000(1 + \frac{0.05}{12})^{12} = \$1051.16$. *The interest earned is $51.16/$1000, or 0.05116, which is 5.116% of the original deposit. Thus, we say this account has a yield of Y = 0.05116, or 5.116%. The formula for annual yield depends on the annual interest rate r and the compounding frequency n:*

$$Y = \left(1 + \frac{r}{n}\right)^n - 1.$$

For Exercises 41–48, find the annual yield as a percentage, to two decimal places, given the annual interest rate and the compounding frequency.

41. Annual interest rate of 5.3%, compounded monthly

42. Annual interest rate of 4.1%, compounded quarterly

43. Annual interest rate of 3.75%, compounded weekly

44. Annual interest rate of 4%, compounded daily

45. Lena is considering two savings accounts: Western Bank offers 4.5%, compounded annually, on saving accounts,

while Commonwealth Savings offers 4.43%, compounded monthly.

a) Find the annual yield for both accounts.
b) Which account has the higher annual yield?

46. Chris is considering two savings accounts: Sierra Savings offers 5%, compounded annually, on savings accounts, while Foothill Bank offers 4.88%, compounded weekly.

a) Find the annual yield for both accounts.
b) Which account has the higher annual yield?

47. Stockman's Bank will pay 4.2%, compounded annually, on a savings account. A competitor, Mesalands Savings, offers monthly compounding on savings accounts. What is the minimum annual interest rate that Mesalands needs to pay to make its annual yield exceed that of Stockman's?

48. Belltown Bank offers a certificate of deposit at 3.75%, compounded annually. Shea Savings offers savings accounts with interest compounded quarterly. What is the minimum annual interest rate that Shea needs to pay to make its annual yield exceed that of Belltown?

TECHNOLOGY CONNECTION

The Technology Connection heading indicates exercises designed to provide practice using a graphing calculator.

Graph.

49. $y = x - 150$ **50.** $y = 25 - |x|$

51. $y = x^3 + 2x^2 - 4x - 13$

52. $y = \sqrt{23 - 7x}$ **53.** $9.6x + 4.2y = -100$

54. $y = -2.3x^2 + 4.8x - 9$

55. $x = 4 + y^2$ **56.** $x = 8 - y^2$

Answers to Quick Checks

1. $y = 3 - x$ **2.** $3x - 5y = 10$

3. $y = 2 - x^2$ **4.** $x = 1 + y^2$

5. 2019   **6.** There is $1123.60 in the account after 2 yr.
7. There is $1195.62 in the account after 3 yr.

- Determine whether a correspondence is a function.
- Find function values.
- Graph functions and determine whether a graph is that of a function.
- Graph functions that are piecewise-defined.

Functions and Models

Identifying Functions

The idea of a *function* is one of the most important concepts in mathematics. Put simply, a function is a special kind of correspondence between two sets. Let's look at the following.

> To each letter on a telephone keypad there corresponds a number.
>
> To each model of television in a store there corresponds its price.
>
> To each real number there corresponds the cube of that number.

In each of these examples, the first set is called the *domain* and the second set is called the *range*. Given a member of the domain, there is *exactly one* member of the range to which it corresponds. This type of correspondence is called a *function*.

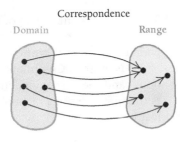

Correspondence

Domain   Range

DEFINITION

A **function** is a correspondence between a first set, called the **domain,** and a second set, called the **range,** such that each member of the domain corresponds to *exactly one* member of the range.

EXAMPLE 1   Determine whether or not each correspondence is a function.

a) *Cumulative number of iPhones sold*

Domain	Range
2009 ⟶	20,400,000
2010 ⟶	40,000,000
2011 ⟶	72,000,000
2012 ⟶	125,400,000

(*Source:* Apple Inc.)

b) *Squaring*

Domain	Range
3 ⟶	9
4 ⟶	16
5 ↘	
−5 ⟶	25

c) *Basketball teams*

Domain	Range
New York ⟶	Knicks
Los Angeles ⟶	Lakers
↘	Clippers
Atlanta ⟶	Hawks

d) *Basketball teams*

Domain	Range
Knicks ⟶	New York
Lakers ⟶	Los Angeles
Clippers ↗	
Hawks ⟶	Atlanta

Solution

a) The correspondence *is* a function because each member of the domain corresponds (is matched) to only one member of the range.

b) The correspondence *is* a function because each member of the domain corresponds to only one member of the range, even though two members of the domain correspond to 25.

c) The correspondence *is not* a function because one member of the domain, Los Angeles, corresponds to two members of the range, the Lakers and the Clippers.

d) The correspondence *is* a function because each member of the domain corresponds to only one member of the range, even though two members of the domain correspond to Los Angeles.   ■

Quick Check 1 ✔

Determine whether or not each correspondence is a function.

a) The domain is the books in a library, the range is the set of positive integers, and the correspondence is the page count of each book.

b) The domain is the letters of the alphabet, the range is the set of people listed in the white pages of the New York City phone book, and the correspondence is the first letter of a person's last name.

EXAMPLE 2   Determine whether or not each correspondence is a function.

Domain	Correspondence	Range
a) A family	Each person's weight	A set of positive numbers
b) The integers $\{\dots, -3, -2, -1, 0, 1, 2, 3, \dots\}$	Each number's square	A set of nonnegative integers: $\{0, 1, 4, 9, 16, 25, \dots\}$
c) The set of all states	Each state's U.S. Senators	The set of all 100 U.S. Senators

Solution

a) The correspondence is a function because each person has *only one* weight.

b) The correspondence is a function because each integer has *only one* square.

c) The correspondence is *not* a function because each state has *two* U.S. Senators.   **1** ✔

Consistent with the definition on p. 13, we regard a function as a set of ordered pairs, such that no two pairs have the same first coordinate paired with different second coordinates. The domain is the set of all first coordinates, and the range is the set of all second coordinates. Function names are usually represented by lowercase letters. Thus, if f represents the function in Example 1(b), we have

$$f = \{(3, 9), (4, 16), (5, 25), (-5, 25)\}$$

and

Domain of $f = \{3, 4, 5, -5\}$;   Range of $f = \{9, 16, 25\}$.

Finding Function Values

Many functions can be described by an equation like $y = 2x + 3$ or $y = 4 - x^2$. To graph the function given by $y = 2x + 3$, we find ordered pairs by performing calculations for selected x values.

for $x = 4, y = 2x + 3 = 2 \cdot 4 + 3 = 11$;   The graph includes $(4, 11)$.

for $x = -5, y = 2x + 3 = 2 \cdot (-5) + 3 = -7$;   The graph includes $(-5, -7)$.

for $x = 0, y = 2x + 3 = 2 \cdot 0 + 3 = 3$; and so on.   The graph includes $(0, 3)$.

For $y = 2x + 3$, the **inputs** (members of the domain) are the values of x substituted into the equation. The **outputs** (members of the range) are the resulting values of y. If we call the function f, we can use x to represent an arbitrary input and $f(x)$, read "f of x" or "f at x" or "the value of f at x," to represent the corresponding output. In this notation, the function given by $y = 2x + 3$ is written as $f(x) = 2x + 3$, and the calculations above can be written more concisely as

$$f(4) = 2 \cdot 4 + 3 = 11;$$
$$f(-5) = 2 \cdot (-5) + 3 = -7;$$
$$f(0) = 2 \cdot 0 + 3 = 3; \text{ and so on.}$$

Thus, instead of writing "when $x = 4$, the value of y is 11," we can simply write "$f(4) = 11$," which is most commonly read as "f of 4 is 11."

It helps to think of a function as a machine. Think of $f(4) = 11$ as the result of putting a member of the domain (an input), 4, into the machine. The machine knows the correspondence $f(x) = 2x + 3$, computes $2 \cdot 4 + 3$, and produces a member of the range (the output), 11.

Function: $f(x) = 2x + 3$

Input	Output
4	11
−5	−7
0	3
t	$2t + 3$
$a + h$	$2(a + h) + 3$

Remember that $f(x)$ *does not mean* "f times x" and should never be read that way.

EXAMPLE 3   The squaring function f is given by

$$f(x) = x^2.$$

Find $f(-3), f(1), f(k), f(\sqrt{k}), f(1 + t)$, and $f(x + h)$.

Solution   We have

$$f(-3) = (-3)^2 = 9;$$
$$f(1) = 1^2 = 1;$$
$$f(k) = k^2;$$
$$f(\sqrt{k}) = (\sqrt{k})^2 = k;$$
$$f(1 + t) = (1 + t)^2 = 1 + 2t + t^2;$$

For a review of algebra, see Appendix A on p. 585.

$$f(x + h) = (x + h)^2 = x^2 + 2xh + h^2.$$

To find $f(x + h)$, remember what the function does: It squares the input. Thus, $f(x + h) = (x + h)^2 = x^2 + 2xh + h^2$. This amounts to replacing x on both sides of $f(x) = x^2$ with $x + h$.   **2** ✔

Quick Check 2 ✔

A function f is given by $f(x) = 3x + 5$. Find $f(4), f(-5), f(0), f(a),$ and $f(a + h)$.

EXAMPLE 4   A function f is given by $f(x) = 3x^2 - 2x + 8$. Find $f(0), f(-5),$ and $f(7a)$.

Solution   One way to find function values when a formula is given is to think of the formula with blanks, or placeholders, as follows:

$$f(\ \square\ ) = 3 \cdot \square^2 - 2 \cdot \square + 8.$$

To find an output for a given input, we think: "Whatever goes in the blank on the left goes in the blank(s) on the right."

$$f(0) = 3 \cdot 0^2 - 2 \cdot 0 + 8 = 8$$
$$f(-5) = 3(-5)^2 - 2 \cdot (-5) + 8 = 3 \cdot 25 + 10 + 8 = 75 + 10 + 8 = 93$$
$$f(7a) = 3(7a)^2 - 2(7a) + 8 = 3 \cdot 49a^2 - 14a + 8 = 147a^2 - 14a + 8$$

3 ✔

Quick Check 3 ✔

A function f is given by $f(x) = 3x^2 + 2x - 7$. Find $f(4), f(-5), f(0), f(a),$ and $f(5a)$.

TECHNOLOGY CONNECTION

The TABLE Feature

The TABLE feature is one way to find ordered pairs of inputs and outputs of functions. To see how, consider the function given by $f(x) = x^3 - 5x + 1$. We enter it as $y_1 = x^3 - 5x + 1$. To use the TABLE feature, we access the TABLE SETUP screen and enter the x-value at which the table will start and an increment for the x-value. For this equation, let's set TblStart = 0.3 and ΔTbl = 1. (Other values can be chosen.) This means that the table's x-values will start at 0.3 and increase by 1.

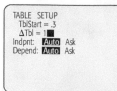

We next set Indpnt and Depend to Auto and then press TABLE. The result is shown below.

X	Y1	
.3	−.473	
1.3	−3.303	
2.3	1.667	
3.3	20.437	
4.3	59.007	
5.3	123.38	
6.3	219.55	

X = .3

The arrow keys, ⌃ and ⌄, allow us to scroll up and down the table and extend it to other values not initially shown.

X	Y1	
12.3	1800.4	
13.3	2287.1	
14.3	2853.7	
15.3	3506.1	
16.3	4250.2	
17.3	5092.2	
18.3	6038	

X = 18.3

EXERCISES

Use the function given by $f(x) = x^3 - 5x + 1$ for Exercises 1 and 2.

1. Use the TABLE feature to construct a table starting with $x = 10$ and ΔTbl = 5. Find the value of y when x is 10. Then find the value of y when x is 35.

2. Adjust the table settings to Indpnt: Ask. How does the table change? Enter a number of your choice and see what happens. Use this setting to find the value of y when x is 28.

EXAMPLE 5 A function f subtracts the square of an input from the input:

$$f(x) = x - x^2.$$

Find $f(4), f(x + h)$, and $\dfrac{f(x + h) - f(x)}{h}$.

Solution We have

$$f(4) = 4 - 4^2 = 4 - 16 = -12;$$

and

$$f(x + h) = (x + h) - (x + h)^2$$
$$= x + h - (x^2 + 2xh + h^2) \quad \text{Squaring the binomial}$$
$$= x + h - x^2 - 2xh - h^2.$$

For the expression $\dfrac{f(x + h) - f(x)}{h}$, we have

$$\frac{f(x + h) - f(x)}{h} = \frac{\overbrace{x + h - x^2 - 2xh - h^2}^{f(x+h),\text{ found above}} - \overbrace{(x - x^2)}^{f(x)}}{h}$$

$$= \frac{h - 2xh - h^2}{h} \quad \text{Simplifying}$$

$$= \frac{h(1 - 2x - h)}{h} \quad \text{Factoring}$$

$$= 1 - 2x - h, \quad \text{for } h \neq 0. \qquad 4 ✔$$

Quick Check 4 ✔

A function f is given by $f(x) = 2x - x^2$. Find $f(4), f(x + h)$, and $\dfrac{f(x + h) - f(x)}{h}$.

Graphs of Functions

Consider again the function given by $f(x) = x^2$. The input 3 is associated with the output 9. The input–output pair $(3, 9)$ is one point on the *graph* of this function.

> **DEFINITION**
>
> The **graph** of a function f is a drawing that represents all the input–output pairs $(x, f(x))$. In cases where the function is given by an equation, the graph of the function is the graph of the equation $y = f(x)$.

It is customary to locate input values (the domain) on the horizontal axis and output values (the range) on the vertical axis.

EXAMPLE 6 Graph: $f(x) = x^2 - 1$.

Solution

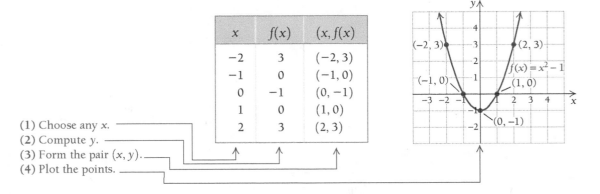

x	$f(x)$	$(x, f(x))$
-2	3	$(-2, 3)$
-1	0	$(-1, 0)$
0	-1	$(0, -1)$
1	0	$(1, 0)$
2	3	$(2, 3)$

(1) Choose any x.
(2) Compute y.
(3) Form the pair (x, y).
(4) Plot the points.

Quick Check 5 ✔

Graph: $f(x) = 2 - x^2$.

We plot the input–output pairs from the table and, in this case, draw a curve to complete the graph.

5 ✔

TECHNOLOGY CONNECTION

Graphs and Function Values

We graphed equations in the Technology Connection in Section R.1. To graph a function, we use the same procedure, after changing the "$f(x) =$" notation to "$y =$." Thus, to graph $f(x) = 2x^2 + x$, we key in $y_1 = 2x^2 + x$.

There are several ways to find function values. One is to use the TABLE feature, as previously discussed. Another is

to use the TRACE feature. To do so, graph the function, press TRACE, and either move the cursor or enter any x-value that is in the window. The corresponding y-value appears automatically. Function values can also be found using the VALUE or Y-VARS feature. Consult an owner's manual or the GCM for details.

EXERCISES

1. Graph $f(x) = x^2 + 3x - 4$. Then find $f(-5), f(-4.7)$, $f(11)$, and $f(2/3)$. (*Hint:* To find $f(11)$, be sure that the window dimensions for the x-values include $x = 11$.)

2. Graph $f(x) = 3.7 - x^2$. Then find $f(-5), f(-4.7), f(11)$, and $f(2/3)$.

3. Graph $f(x) = 4 - 1.2x - 3.4x^2$. Then find $f(-5)$, $f(-4.7), f(11)$, and $f(2/3)$.

The Vertical-Line Test

Let's now determine how to look at a graph and decide whether it represents a function. In the graph at the right, note that the input x_1 has *two* outputs. Since a function has exactly *one* output for every input, this graph cannot represent a function. Note that a vertical line can intersect the graph in more than one place.

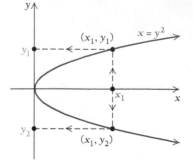

The Vertical-Line Test

A graph represents a function if it is impossible to draw a vertical line that intersects the graph more than once.

EXAMPLE 7   Determine whether each of the following is the graph of a function.

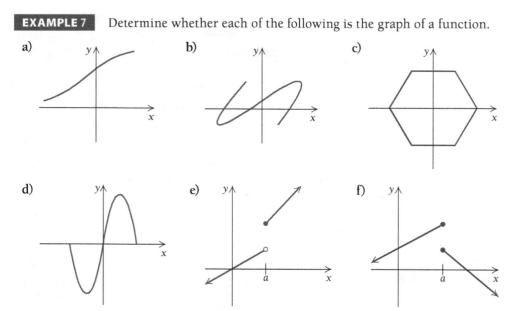

Quick Check 6 ☑

Determine whether each of the following is the graph of a function.

Solution

a) The graph is that of a function. It is impossible to draw a vertical line that intersects the graph more than once.

b) The graph is not that of a function. A vertical line (in fact, many) can intersect the graph more than once.

c) The graph is not that of a function.

d) The graph is that of a function.

e) The graph is that of a function. Note that a vertical line at $x = a$ would intersect the graph once.

f) The graph is not that of a function. Note that a vertical line at $x = a$ would intersect the graph more than once.

6 ☑

Functions Defined Piecewise

Sometimes functions are defined *piecewise,* using different output formulas for different parts of the domain, as in parts (e) and (f) of Example 7. To graph a piecewise-defined function, we usually work from left to right, using the correspondence specified for the x-values on each part of the horizontal axis.

EXAMPLE 8   Graph the function defined as follows:

$$f(x) = \begin{cases} 4, & \text{for } x \le 0, \\ 3 - x^2, & \text{for } 0 < x \le 2, \\ 2x - 6, & \text{for } x > 2. \end{cases}$$

This means that for any input x less than or equal to 0, the output is 4.

This means that for any input x greater than 0 and less than or equal to 2, the output is $3 - x^2$.

This means that for any input x greater than 2, the output is $2x - 6$.

Solution   Working from left to right, note that for all x-values less than or equal to 0, the graph is the horizontal line $y = 4$. Thus,

$$f(-2) = 4;$$
$$f(-1) = 4;$$
and $$f(0) = 4.$$

The solid dot indicates that $(0, 4)$ is part of the graph.

Next, observe that for x-values greater than 0 but not greater than 2, the graph is a portion of the parabola given by $y = 3 - x^2$. Note that for $f(x) = 3 - x^2$,

$$f(0.5) = 3 - 0.5^2 = 2.75;$$
$$f(1) = 2;$$
and $$f(2) = -1.$$

The open dot at $(0, 3)$ indicates that this point is *not* part of the graph.

Finally, note that for x-values greater than 2, the graph is the line $y = 2x - 6$.

$$f(2.5) = 2 \cdot 2.5 - 6 = -1;$$
$$f(4) = 2;$$
and $$f(5) = 4.$$

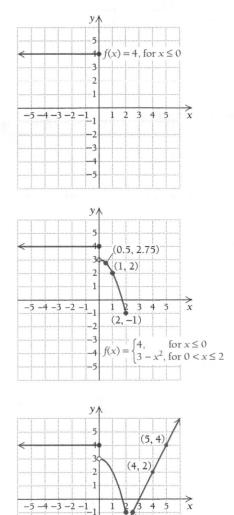

Quick Check 7 ☑

Graph the function defined as follows:

$$f(x) = \begin{cases} 4, & \text{for } x \le 0, \\ 4 - x^2, & \text{for } 0 < x \le 2, \\ 2x - 6, & \text{for } x > 2. \end{cases}$$

7 ☑

EXAMPLE 9   Graph the function defined as follows:

$$g(x) = \begin{cases} 3, & \text{for } x = 1, \\ -x + 2, & \text{for } x \ne 1. \end{cases}$$

Solution   The function is defined such that $g(1) = 3$ and for all other x-values (that is, for $x \ne 1$), we have $g(x) = -x + 2$. Thus, to graph this function, we graph the line given by $y = -x + 2$, but with an open dot at the point corresponding to $x = 1$. To complete the graph, we plot the point $(1, 3)$ since $g(1) = 3$.

x	$g(x)$	$(x, g(x))$
-3	$-(-3) + 2$	$(-3, 5)$
0	$-0 + 2$	$(0, 2)$
1	3	$(1, 3)$
2	$-2 + 2$	$(2, 0)$
3	$-3 + 2$	$(3, -1)$

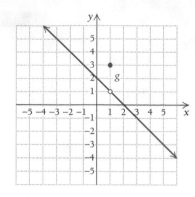

Quick Check 8 ✔

Graph the function defined as follows:

$$f(x) = \begin{cases} 1, & \text{for } x = -2, \\ 2 - x, & \text{for } x \neq -2. \end{cases}$$

8 ✔

TECHNOLOGY CONNECTION

Graphing Functions Defined Piecewise

Graphing functions defined piecewise generally involves the use of inequality symbols, which are often accessed using the TEST menu. The function in Example 8 can be entered as follows:

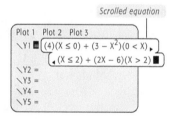

Scrolled equation

The graph is shown below.

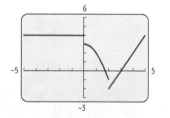

Note that most graphing calculators do not display solid or open dots.

EXERCISES

Graph.

1. $f(x) = \begin{cases} -x - 2, & \text{for } x < -2, \\ 4 - x^2, & \text{for } -2 \leq x < 2, \\ x + 3, & \text{for } x \geq 2 \end{cases}$

2. $f(x) = \begin{cases} x^2 - 2, & \text{for } x \leq 3, \\ 1, & \text{for } x > 3 \end{cases}$

3. $f(x) = \begin{cases} x + 3, & \text{for } x \leq -2, \\ 1, & \text{for } -2 < x \leq 3, \\ x^2 - 10, & \text{for } x > 3 \end{cases}$

Some Final Remarks

We sometimes use the terminology *y is a function of x*. This means that x is an input and y is an output. It also means that x is the **independent variable** because it represents inputs and y is the **dependent variable** because it represents outputs. We may refer to "a function $y = x^2$" without naming it using a letter f.

Section Summary

- *Functions* are a key concept in mathematics.

- The essential trait of a function is that to each number in the *domain* there corresponds one and only one number in the *range*.

R.2 Exercise Set

Note: *A review of algebra can be found in Appendix A on p. 585.*

Determine whether each correspondence is a function.

1. Domain → Range
5 → 3
−3 → 7
7 →
−7

2. Domain → Range
5 → 4
7 → 8
9

3. Domain → Range
−5 → 1
5 →
8

4. Domain → Range
6 → −6
7 → −7
3 → −3

5. Sandwich prices.

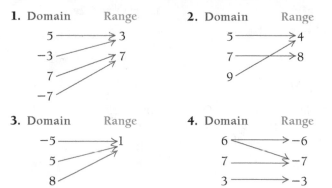

DOMAIN	RANGE
Hamburger	→ $0.99
Cheeseburger	→ $1.29
Filet-O-Fish®	→ $3.49
Quarter Pounder® with cheese	→ $3.69
Big Mac®	→ $3.99
Crispy Chicken	→ $4.29
Chicken McNuggets®	
Double Quarter Pounder® with cheese	→ $4.69

(*Source:* www.mcdonalds.com.)

6. Sandwich calorie content.

DOMAIN	RANGE
Hamburger	→ 250
Cheeseburger	→ 300
Quarter Pounder®	→ 410
Double Cheeseburger®	→ 440
Filet-O-Fish®	→ 380
Big Mac®	→ 540
Double Quarter Pounder® with cheese	→ 740

(*Source:* www.mcdonalds.com.)

Determine whether each of the following is a function.

Domain	Correspondence	Range
7. A set of iPods	Each iPod's memory in gigabytes	A set of numbers
8. A set of iPods	Each iPod's serial number	A set of alphanumeric codes
9. A set of iPods	The number of songs on each iPod	A set of numbers
10. A set of iPods	The number of Avril Lavigne songs on each iPod	A set of numbers
11. The set of all real numbers	The square of a number, to which 8 is added	The set of all positive numbers greater than or equal to 8
12. The set of all real numbers	The fourth power of a number	The set of all nonnegative numbers.
13. A set of females	Each person's biological mother	A set of females
14. A set of males	Each person's biological father	A set of males
15. A set of avenues	An intersecting road	A set of cross streets
16. A set of textbooks	An even-numbered page in each book	A set of pages
17. A set of shapes	The area of each shape	A set of area measurements
18. A set of shapes	The perimeter of each shape	A set of length measurements

19. A function f is given by

$$f(x) = 4x - 3.$$

This function takes a number x, multiplies it by 4, and subtracts 3.

a) Complete this table.

x	5.1	5.01	5.001	5
$f(x)$				

b) Find $f(4), f(3), f(-2), f(k), f(1 + t)$, and $f(x + h)$.

20. A function f is given by

$$f(x) = 3x + 2.$$

This function takes a number x, multiplies it by 3, and adds 2.

a) Complete this table.

x	4.1	4.01	4.001	4
$f(x)$				

b) Find $f(5), f(-1), f(k), f(1 + t)$, and $f(x + h)$.

21. A function g is given by

$$g(x) = x^2 - 3.$$

This function takes a number x, squares it, and subtracts 3. Find $g(-1), g(0), g(1), g(5), g(u), g(a + h)$, and $\dfrac{g(a + h) - g(a)}{h}$.

22. A function g is given by

$$g(x) = x^2 + 4.$$

This function takes a number x, squares it, and adds 4. Find $g(-3), g(0), g(-1), g(7), g(v), g(a + h)$, and $\dfrac{g(a + h) - g(a)}{h}$.

23. A function f is given by

$$f(x) = \frac{1}{(x + 3)^2}.$$

This function takes a number x, adds 3, squares the result, and takes the reciprocal of that result.

a) Find $f(4), f(0), f(a), f(t + 4), f(x + h)$, and $\dfrac{f(x + h) - f(x)}{h}$.

b) Note that f could also be given by

$$f(x) = \frac{1}{x^2 + 6x + 9}.$$

Explain what this does to an input number x.

24. A function f is given by

$$f(x) = \frac{1}{(x - 5)^2}.$$

This function takes a number x, subtracts 5 from it, squares the result, and takes the reciprocal of the square.

a) Find $f(3), f(-1), f(k), f(t - 1), f(t - 4)$, and $f(x + h)$.

b) Note that f could also be given by

$$f(x) = \frac{1}{x^2 - 10x + 25}.$$

Explain what this does to an input number x.

25. A function f takes a number x, multiplies it by 4, and adds 2.

a) Write f as an equation.
b) Graph f.

26. A function g takes a number x, multiplies it by -3, and subtracts 4.

a) Write g as an equation.
b) Graph g.

27. A function h takes a number x, squares it, and adds x.

a) Write h as an equation.
b) Graph h.

28. A function k takes a number x, squares it, and subtracts 3 times x.

a) Write k as an equation.
b) Graph k.

Graph each function.

29. $f(x) = 2x - 5$

30. $f(x) = 3x - 1$

31. $g(x) = -4x$

32. $g(x) = -2x$

33. $f(x) = x^2 - 2$

34. $f(x) = x^2 + 4$

35. $f(x) = 6 - x^2$

36. $g(x) = -x^2 + 1$

37. $g(x) = x^3$

38. $g(x) = \frac{1}{2}x^3$

Use the vertical-line test to determine whether each graph is that of a function. (In Exercises 47–50 and 52, the dashed lines are not part of the graphs.)

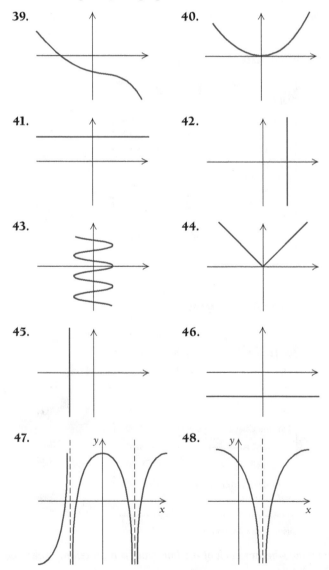

39.   **40.**

41.   **42.**

43.   **44.**

45.   **46.**

47.   **48.**

49.

50.

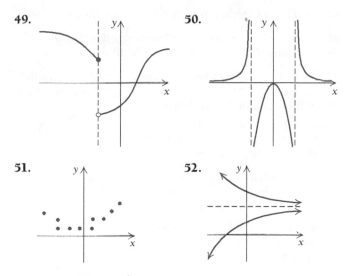

51.

52.

53. a) Graph $x = y^2 - 2$.
   b) Is this a function?

54. a) Graph $x = y^2 - 3$.
   b) Is this a function?

55. For $f(x) = x^2 - 3x$, find $\dfrac{f(x + h) - f(x)}{h}$.

56. For $f(x) = x^2 + 4x$, find $\dfrac{f(x + h) - f(x)}{h}$.

For Exercises 57–60, consider the function f given by

$$f(x) = \begin{cases} -2x + 1, & \text{for } x < 0, \\ 17, & \text{for } x = 0, \\ x^2 - 3, & \text{for } 0 < x < 4, \\ \frac{1}{2}x + 1, & \text{for } x \geq 4. \end{cases}$$

57. Find $f(-1)$ and $f(1)$.

58. Find $f(-3)$ and $f(3)$.

59. Find $f(0)$ and $f(10)$.

60. Find $f(-5)$ and $f(5)$.

Graph.

61. $f(x) = \begin{cases} 1, & \text{for } x < 0, \\ -1, & \text{for } x \geq 0 \end{cases}$

62. $f(x) = \begin{cases} 2, & \text{for } x \leq 3, \\ -2, & \text{for } x > 3 \end{cases}$

63. $f(x) = \begin{cases} 6, & \text{for } x = -2, \\ x^2, & \text{for } x \neq -2 \end{cases}$

64. $f(x) = \begin{cases} 5, & \text{for } x = 1, \\ x^3, & \text{for } x \neq 1 \end{cases}$

65. $g(x) = \begin{cases} -x, & \text{for } x < 0, \\ 4, & \text{for } x = 0, \\ x + 2, & \text{for } x > 0 \end{cases}$

66. $g(x) = \begin{cases} 2x - 3, & \text{for } x < 1, \\ 5, & \text{for } x = 1, \\ x - 2, & \text{for } x > 1 \end{cases}$

67. $g(x) = \begin{cases} \frac{1}{2}x - 1, & \text{for } x < 2, \\ -4, & \text{for } x = 2, \\ x - 3, & \text{for } x > 2 \end{cases}$

68. $g(x) = \begin{cases} x^2, & \text{for } x < 0, \\ -3, & \text{for } x = 0, \\ -2x + 3, & \text{for } x > 0 \end{cases}$

69. $f(x) = \begin{cases} -7, & \text{for } x = 2, \\ x^2 - 3, & \text{for } x \neq 2 \end{cases}$

70. $f(x) = \begin{cases} -6, & \text{for } x = -3, \\ -x^2 + 5, & \text{for } x \neq -3 \end{cases}$

Compound interest. *The amount of money, $A(t)$, in a savings account that pays 3% interest, compounded quarterly for t years, with an initial investment of P dollars, is given by*

$$A(t) = P\left(1 + \frac{0.03}{4}\right)^{4t}.$$

71. If \$500 is invested at 3%, compounded quarterly, how much will the investment be worth after 2 yr?

72. If \$800 is invested at 3%, compounded quarterly, how much will the investment be worth after 3 yr?

Chemotherapy. *In computing the dosage for chemotherapy, the measure of a patient's body surface area is needed. A good approximation of this area s, in square meters (m^2), is given by*

$$s = \sqrt{\frac{hw}{3600}},$$

where w is the patient's weight in kilograms (kg) and h is the patient's height in centimeters (cm). (Source: U.S. Oncology.) Use this information for Exercises 73 and 74. Round your answers to the nearest thousandth.

73. Assume that a patient's height is 170 cm. Find the patient's approximate surface area assuming that:

   a) The patient's weight is 70 kg.
   b) The patient's weight is 100 kg.
   c) The patient's weight is 50 kg.

74. Assume that a patient's weight is 70 kg. Approximate the patient's surface area assuming that:

   a) The patient's height is 150 cm.
   b) The patient's height is 180 cm.

75. Scaling stress factors. In psychology a process called *scaling* is used to attach numerical ratings to a group of life experiences. In the following table, various events have been rated on a scale from 1 to 100 according to their stress levels.

EVENT	SCALE OF IMPACT
Death of spouse	100
Divorce	73
Jail term	63
Marriage	50
Lost job	47
Pregnancy	40
Death of close friend	37
Loan over $10,000	31
Child leaving home	29
Change in schools	20
Loan less than $10,000	17
Christmas	12

(*Source:* Thomas H. Holmes, University of Washington School of Medicine.)

a) Does the table represent a function? Why or why not?

b) What are the inputs? What are the outputs?

SYNTHESIS

Solve for y in terms of x, and determine if the resulting equation represents a function.

76. $2x + y - 16 = 4 - 3y + 2x$

77. $2y^2 + 3x = 4x + 5$

78. $(4y^{2/3})^3 = 64x$

79. $(3y^{3/2})^2 = 72x$

80. Explain why the vertical-line test works.

81. Is 4 in the domain of f in Exercises 57–60? Explain why or why not.

TECHNOLOGY CONNECTION

In Exercises 82 and 83, use the TABLE *feature to construct a table for the function under the given conditions.*

82. $f(x) = x^3 + 2x^2 - 4x - 13$; TblStart $= -3$; ΔTbl $= 2$

83. $f(x) = \dfrac{3}{x^2 - 4}$; TblStart $= -3$; ΔTbl $= 1$

84. A function f is given by
$$f(x) = |x - 2| + |x + 1| - 5.$$
Find $f(-3), f(-2), f(0),$ and $f(4)$.

85. Graph the function in each of Exercises 82–84.

86. Use the TRACE feature to find several ordered-pair solutions of the function $f(x) = \sqrt{10 - x^2}$.

87. A function f takes a number x, adds 2, and then multiplies the result by 5, while a function g takes a number x, multiplies it by 5, and then adds 2.

a) Write f and g as equations.
b) Graph f and g on the same axes.
c) Are f and g the same function?

88. A function h takes a number x, subtracts 4, and then squares the result, while a function k takes a number x, squares it, and then subtracts 4.

a) Write h and k as equations.
b) Graph h and k on the same axes.
c) Are h and k the same function?

89. A function f takes a number x, multiplies it by 3, and then adds 6, while a function g takes a number x, adds a to it, and then multiplies the result by 3. Find a if f and g are the same function.

90. A function h takes a number x, adds 3, and then squares the result, while a function k takes a number x, squares it, adds 6 times x, and then adds a to the result. Find a if h and k are the same function.

Answers to Quick Checks

1. **(a)** The correspondence is a function since each book has one page count associated with it. **(b)** The correspondence is not a function since more than one person will have a last name that starts with any particular letter. That is, each letter has more than one last name associated with it. **2.** $17, -10, 5, 3a + 5, 3a + 3h + 5$
3. $49, 58, -7, 3a^2 + 2a - 7, 75a^2 + 10a - 7$
4. $-8, 2x + 2h - x^2 - 2xh - h^2, 2 - 2x - h$
5. $f(x) = 2 - x^2$ **6.** **(a)** The graph is not that of a function. **(b)** The graph is that of a function.

7.

8.

- Write interval notation for a set of points.
- Find the domain and the range of a function.

Finding Domain and Range

Set Notation

A **set** is a collection of objects. The set we consider most in calculus is the set of **real numbers**, $\mathbb{R}$. There is a real number for every point on the number line.

The set consisting of $-\frac{9}{25}$, 0, and $\sqrt{2}$ can be written $\left\{-\frac{9}{25}, 0, \sqrt{2}\right\}$. This method of describing sets is known as the **roster method**. It lists every member of the set. We describe larger sets using **set-builder notation**, which specifies conditions under which an object is in the set. For example, the set of all real numbers less than 4 can be described as follows in set-builder notation:

$$\{x | x \text{ is a real number less than } 4\} \text{ or } \{x | x < 4\}.$$

The set of
all x
such that
x is a real number less than 4.

Interval Notation

We can also describe certain sets using **interval notation.** If a and b are real numbers, with $a < b$, we define the interval (a, b) as the set of all numbers between but not including a and b, that is, the set of all x for which $a < x < b$. Thus,

$$(a, b) = \{x | a < x < b\}.$$

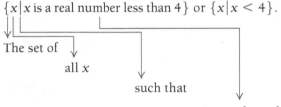

The points a and b are the **endpoints** of the interval. The parentheses indicate that the endpoints are *not* included in the interval.

The interval $[a, b]$ is defined as the set of all x for which $a \le x \le b$. Thus,

$$[a, b] = \{x | a \le x \le b\}.$$

The brackets indicate that the endpoints *are* included in the interval.*

Be careful not to confuse the *interval* (a, b) with the *ordered pair* (a, b) used to represent a point in the plane, as in Section R.1. The context in which the notation appears makes the meaning clear.

Intervals like $(-2, 3)$, in which neither endpoint is included, are called **open intervals**; intervals like $[-2, 3]$, which include both endpoints, are said to be **closed intervals.** Thus, $[a, b]$ is read "the closed interval a, b" and (a, b) is read "the open interval a, b."

An open interval

A closed interval

---

*Some books use the representations ──●──●── and ──●──●── instead of, respectively, ──(───)── and ──[───]──.

Some intervals are **half-open** and include one endpoint but not the other:

$(a, b] = \{x | a < x \leq b\}$.   The graph excludes a and includes b.

$$\underset{a \qquad\qquad b}{\overset{(a, b]}{\longmapsto}}$$

$[a, b) = \{x | a \leq x < b\}$.   The graph includes a and excludes b.

$$\underset{a \qquad\qquad b}{\overset{[a, b)}{\longmapsto}}$$

Some intervals extend without bound in one or both directions. We use the symbols ∞, read "infinity," and $-\infty$, read "negative infinity," to name these intervals. The notation $(5, \infty)$ represents the set of all real numbers greater than 5. That is,

$(5, \infty) = \{x | x > 5\}$. $\underset{5}{\overset{(5, \infty)}{\longrightarrow}}$

Similarly, the notation $(-\infty, 5)$ represents the set of all real numbers less than 5. That is,

$(-\infty, 5) = \{x | x < 5\}$. $\underset{5}{\overset{(-\infty, 5)}{\longleftarrow}}$

The notations $[5, \infty)$ and $(-\infty, 5]$ are used when we want to include an endpoint. The interval $(-\infty, \infty)$ names the set of all real numbers.

$$(-\infty, \infty) = \{x | x \text{ is a real number}\}$$
$$\longleftrightarrow$$

Interval notation is summarized in the following table. Note that the symbols ∞ and $-\infty$ always have a parenthesis next to them; neither of these represents a real number.

Intervals: Notation and Graphs

INTERVAL NOTATION	SET NOTATION	GRAPH
(a, b)	$\{x | a < x < b\}$	
$[a, b]$	$\{x | a \leq x \leq b\}$	
$[a, b)$	$\{x | a \leq x < b\}$	
$(a, b]$	$\{x | a < x \leq b\}$	
(a, ∞)	$\{x | x > a\}$	
$[a, \infty)$	$\{x | x \geq a\}$	
$(-\infty, b)$	$\{x | x < b\}$	
$(-\infty, b]$	$\{x | x \leq b\}$	
$(-\infty, \infty)$	$\{x | x \text{ is a real number}\}$	

EXAMPLE 1   Write interval notation for each set or graph:

a) $\{x \mid -4 < x < 5\}$

b) $\{x \mid x \geq -2\}$

c)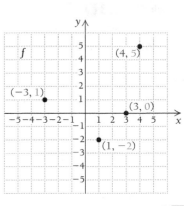

d)

Quick Check 1 ☑

Write interval notation for each set, and show it on a graph.

a) $\{x \mid -2 \leq x \leq 5\}$
b) $\{x \mid -2 \leq x < 5\}$
c) $\{x \mid -2 < x \leq 5\}$
d) $\{x \mid -2 < x < 5\}$

Solution

a) $\{x \mid -4 < x < 5\} = (-4, 5)$

b) $\{x \mid x \geq -2\} = [-2, \infty)$

c) $(-2, 4]$

d) $(-\infty, -1)$

1 ☑

Finding Domain and Range

Recall that when a set of ordered pairs is such that no two different pairs share a common first coordinate, we have a function. The **domain** is the set of all first coordinates, and the **range** is the set of all second coordinates.

EXAMPLE 2   For the function f shown to the right, determine the domain and the range.

Solution   This function consists of just four ordered pairs and can be written as

$$f = \{(-3, 1), (1, -2), (3, 0), (4, 5)\}.$$

We can determine the domain and the range by reading the x- and the y-values directly from the graph.

The domain is the set of all first coordinates, $\{-3, 1, 3, 4\}$. The range is the set of all second coordinates, $\{1, -2, 0, 5\}$.

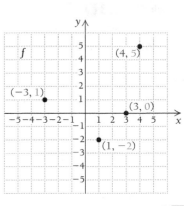

2 ☑

Quick Check 2 ☑

For the function shown below, determine the domain and the range.

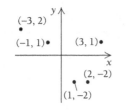

EXAMPLE 3   For the function f shown to the right, determine each of the following.

a) The number in the range that is paired with the input 1. That is, find $f(1)$.

b) The domain of f

c) The number(s) in the domain that is (are) paired with the output 1. That is, find all x-values for which $f(x) = 1$.

d) The range of f

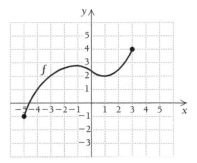

Solution

a) To determine which number is paired with the input 1, we locate 1 on the horizontal axis. Next, we identify the point on the graph of f for which 1 is the first coordinate. From that point, we look to the vertical axis to find the corresponding y-coordinate, 2. The input 1 has the output 2— that is, $f(1) = 2$.

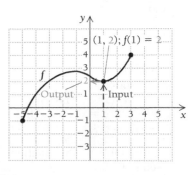

b) The domain of the function is the set of all x-values, or inputs, of the points on the graph. These extend from −5 to 3 and can be viewed as the curve's shadow, or *projection,* onto the x-axis. Thus, the domain is the set $\{x\,|\,-5 \le x \le 3\}$, or, in interval notation, $[-5, 3]$.

The domain of f is $\{x\,|\,-5 \le x \le 3\}$, or $[-5, 3]$

c) To determine which number(s) in the domain is (are) paired with the output 1, we locate 1 on the vertical axis. From there, we look left and right to the graph of f to identify any points for which 1 is the second coordinate. One such point exists: $(-4, 1)$. For this function, we note that $x = -4$ is the only member of the domain paired with the range value 1. For other functions, there might be more than one member of the domain paired with a member of the range.

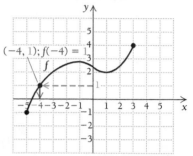

$(-4, 1); f(-4) = 1$

d) The range of the function is the set of all y-values, or outputs, of the points on the graph. These extend from −1 to 4 and can be viewed as the curve's shadow, or projection, onto the y-axis. Thus, the range is the set $\{y\,|\,-1 \le y \le 4\}$, or, in interval notation, $[-1, 4]$.

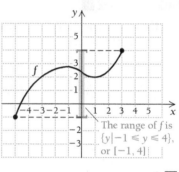

The range of f is $\{y\,|\,-1 \le y \le 4\}$, or $[-1, 4]$

3 ✔

Quick Check 3 ✔

For the function f, shown below, determine each of the following: $f(-1), f(1)$, the domain, and the range.

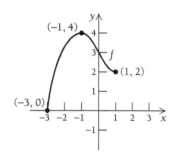

Consider the function given by $f(x) = 1/(x - 3)$. The table below was obtained with ΔTbl set at 0.25. Note that the calculator cannot calculate $f(3)$.

ΔTbl = 0.25

X	Y1
2	−1
2.25	−1.333
2.5	−2
2.75	−4
3	ERR:
3.25	4
3.5	2
3.75	1.3333

X = 2

EXERCISES

1. Make a table for $f(x) = 1/(x^2 - 4)$ from $x = -3$ to $x = 0$ and with ΔTbl set at 0.5.

2. Create a table for the function given in Example 5.

When a function is given by an equation or formula, the domain is understood to be the largest set of real numbers (inputs) for which function values (outputs) can be calculated. That is, the domain is the set of all allowable inputs into the formula. To find the domain, think, "For what input values does the function have an output?"

EXAMPLE 4   Find the domain: $f(x) = |x|$.

Solution   We ask, "What can we substitute?" Is there any number x for which we cannot calculate $|x|$? The answer is no. Thus, the domain of f is the set of all real numbers. ■

EXAMPLE 5   Find the domain: $f(x) = \dfrac{3}{2x - 5}$.

Solution   We recall that a denominator cannot equal zero and ask, "What can we substitute?" Is there any number x for which we cannot calculate $3/(2x - 5)$? Since $3/(2x - 5)$ cannot be calculated when the denominator, $2x - 5$, is 0, we solve $2x - 5 = 0$ to find those real numbers that must be excluded from the domain of f:

$$2x - 5 = 0 \qquad \text{Setting the denominator equal to 0}$$
$$2x = 5 \qquad \text{Adding 5 to both sides}$$
$$x = \tfrac{5}{2}. \qquad \text{Dividing both sides by 2}$$

Thus, $\frac{5}{2}$ is not in the domain, whereas all other real numbers are. We say that f is *not defined at* $\frac{5}{2}$, or $f(\frac{5}{2})$ *does not exist*.

The domain of f is $\{x \mid x$ is a real number *and* $x \neq \frac{5}{2}\}$, or, in interval notation, $\left(-\infty, \frac{5}{2}\right) \cup \left(\frac{5}{2}, \infty\right)$. The symbol $\cup$ indicates the *union* of two sets and means that all elements in both sets are included in the domain. ■

EXAMPLE 6   Find the domain: $f(x) = \sqrt{4 + 3x}$.

Solution   We ask, "Is there any number x for which we can't calculate $\sqrt{4 + 3x}$?" Since radicands in even roots cannot be negative, $\sqrt{4 + 3x}$ is not a real number when $4 + 3x$ is negative. The domain is all real numbers for which $4 + 3x \geq 0$. We find the domain by solving the inequality. (See Appendix A for a review of solving inequalities.)

$$4 + 3x \geq 0$$
$$3x \geq -4 \qquad \text{Adding } -4 \text{ to both sides}$$
$$x \geq -\tfrac{4}{3} \qquad \text{Dividing both sides by 3}$$

The domain is $\{x \mid -\frac{4}{3} \leq x < \infty\}$, or, in interval notation, $\left[-\frac{4}{3}, \infty\right)$.   **4** ✓

Quick Check 4 ✓

Find the domain of each function. Express each answer using interval notation.

a) $f(x) = \dfrac{5}{x - 8}$

b) $f(x) = x^3 + |2x|$

c) $f(x) = \sqrt{2x - 8}$

TECHNOLOGY CONNECTION

Determining Domain and Range

Graph each function in the given viewing window. Then determine the domain and the range.

a) $f(x) = 3 - |x|$, $[-10, 10, -10, 10]$

b) $f(x) = x^3 - x$, $[-3, 3, -4, 4]$

c) $f(x) = \dfrac{3}{x - 2}$, $[-14, 14, -14, 14]$

d) $f(x) = x^4 - 2x^2 - 3$, $[-4, 4, -6, 6]$

We have the following.

a)

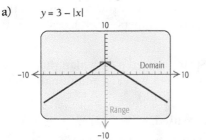

Domain = $\mathbb{R}$ (the real numbers), or $(-\infty, \infty)$
Range = $(-\infty, 3]$

b)

Domain = $\mathbb{R}$
Range = $\mathbb{R}$

c)

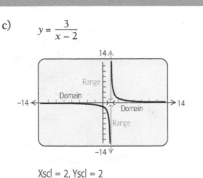

Xscl = 2, Yscl = 2

The number 2 is excluded as an input.
Domain = $\{x \mid x$ is a real number *and* $x \neq 2\}$, or $(-\infty, 2) \cup (2, \infty)$;
Range = $\{y \mid y$ is a real number *and* $y \neq 0\}$, or $(-\infty, 0) \cup (0, \infty)$

d)

Domain = $\mathbb{R}$
Range = $[-4, \infty)$

We can confirm our results using the TRACE feature, moving the cursor along the curve or entering any x-value in which we have interest. We can also use the TABLE feature. In Example (d), the domain might not appear to be the set of all real numbers because the graph seems "thin," but careful examination of the formula shows that we can indeed substitute any real number.

(continued)

Determining Domain and Range (*continued*)

EXERCISES

Graph each function in the given viewing window. Then determine the domain and the range.

1. $f(x) = |x| - 4$, $[-10, 10, -10, 10]$

2. $f(x) = 2 + 3x - x^3$, $[-5, 5, -5, 5]$

3. $f(x) = \dfrac{-3}{x + 1}$, $[-20, 20, -20, 20]$

4. $f(x) = x^4 - 2x^2 - 7$, $[-4, 4, -9, 9]$

5. $f(x) = \sqrt{x + 4}$, $[-8, 8, -8, 8]$

6. $f(x) = \sqrt{9 - x^2}$, $[-5, 5, -5, 5]$

7. $f(x) = -\sqrt{9 - x^2}$, $[-5, 5, -5, 5]$

8. $f(x) = x^3 - 5x^2 + x - 4$, $[-10, 10, -20, 10]$

Domains and Ranges in Applications

The domain and the range of a function given by a formula are sometimes affected by the context of an application. Let's look at an example similar to Exercises 71 and 72 in Section R.2.

EXAMPLE 7   **Business: Compound Interest.**   Suppose $500 is invested at 2.5%, compounded quarterly for t years. From Theorem 2 in Section R.1, we know that the amount in the account is given by

$$A(t) = 500\left(1 + \frac{0.025}{4}\right)^{4t}$$
$$= 500(1.00625)^{4t}.$$

The amount A is a function of the number of years t for which the money is invested. Determine the domain of A.

Solution   We can substitute any real number for t into the formula, but a negative number of years is not meaningful. The context of the application excludes negative numbers. Thus, the domain is the set of all nonnegative numbers, $[0, \infty)$.   ■

EXAMPLE 8   **iPhone Data Plans.**   Recently, Sprint offered a data plan that allows a customer 450 min per month for $80 and charges $0.45 for each additional minute (or part thereof). (*Source*: www.sprint.com, November 2013.)

a) Find the amount of a customer's bill if 500 min are used.

b) Find the range of possible monthly charges if a customer uses up to 500 min.

Solution

a) Since 500 min is 50 min more than 450 min, the customer will be charged $80 + 0.45(50) = 102.50.

b) The range is the set of outputs, in this case, the possible monthly charges. The charge amounts rise in increments of $0.45; that is, the amounts can be $80.00, $80.45, $80.90, $81.35, and so on, up through $102.50. Thus, the range is the set $\{80.00, 80.45, 80.90, 81.35, \ldots, 102.50\}$. The ellipses (...) indicate that the pattern continues up to and including a charge of $102.50.

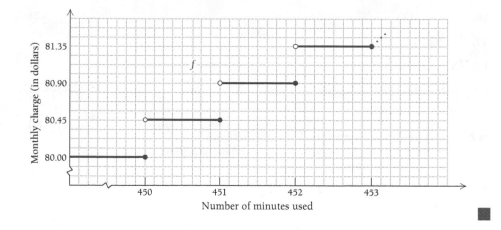

Number of minutes used

Section Summary

The following is a review of function terminology from Sections R.1–R.3.

Function Concepts

- Formula for f: $f(x) = x^2 - 7$
- For every input of f, there is exactly one output.
- For the input 1, the output is -6.
- $f(1) = -6$
- The point $(1, -6)$ is on the graph.
- Domain = the set of all inputs
       = the set of all real numbers, $\mathbb{R}$
- Range = the set of all outputs
       = $[-7, \infty)$

Graph

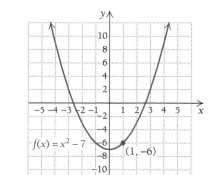

R.3 Exercise Set

In Exercises 1–10, write interval notation for each graph.

1.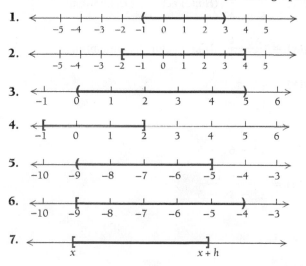

2.

3.

4.

5.

6.

7.

8.

9.

10.

Write interval notation for each of the following. Then graph the interval on a number line.

11. The set of all numbers x such that $-2 \le x \le 2$

12. The set of all numbers x such that $-5 < x < 5$

13. $\{x \mid 6 < x \le 20\}$

14. $\{x \mid -4 \le x < -1\}$

15. $\{x \mid x > -3\}$

16. $\{x | x \le -2\}$

17. $\{x | -2 < x \le 3\}$

18. $\{x | -10 \le x < 4\}$

19. $\{x | x \ge 12.5\}$

20. $\{x | x < 12.5\}$

In Exercises 21–32, each graph is that of a function.
Determine (a) $f(1)$; (b) the domain; (c) all x-values such that
$f(x) = 2$; and (d) the range.

21. **22.**

23. **24.**

25. **26.**

27. **28.**

29. **30.**

31. **32.**

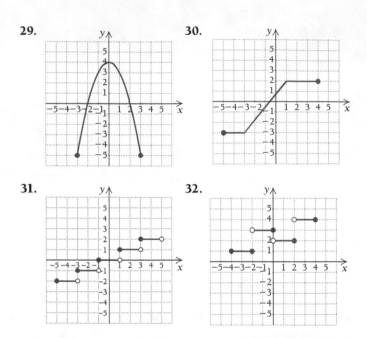

Find the domain of each function given below.

33. $f(x) = \dfrac{6}{2 - x}$ **34.** $f(x) = \dfrac{2}{x + 3}$

35. $f(x) = \sqrt{2x}$ **36.** $f(x) = \sqrt{x - 2}$

37. $f(x) = x^2 - 2x + 3$ **38.** $f(x) = x^2 + 3$

39. $f(x) = \dfrac{x - 2}{6x - 12}$ **40.** $f(x) = \dfrac{8}{3x - 6}$

41. $f(x) = |x - 4|$ **42.** $f(x) = |x| - 4$

43. $f(x) = \dfrac{3x - 1}{7 - 2x}$ **44.** $f(x) = \dfrac{2x - 1}{9 - 2x}$

45. $g(x) = \sqrt{4 + 5x}$ **46.** $g(x) = \sqrt{2 - 3x}$

47. $g(x) = x^2 - 2x + 1$

48. $g(x) = 4x^3 + 5x^2 - 2x$

49. $g(x) = \dfrac{2x}{x^2 - 25}$ (*Hint:* Factor the denominator.)

50. $g(x) = \dfrac{x - 1}{x^2 - 36}$ (*Hint:* Factor the denominator.)

51. $g(x) = |x| + 1$

52. $g(x) = |x + 7|$

53. $g(x) = \dfrac{2x - 6}{x^2 - 6x + 5}$

54. $g(x) = \dfrac{3x - 10}{x^2 - 4x - 5}$

55. For the function f shown to the right, find all x-values for which $f(x) \leq 0$.

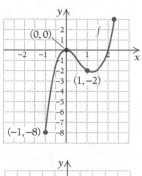

56. For the function g shown to the right, find all x-values for which $g(x) = 1$.

APPLICATIONS

Business and Economics

57. Compound interest. Suppose $5000 is invested at 3.1% interest, compounded semiannually, for t years.

   a) The amount A in the account is a function of time. Find an equation for this function.

   b) Determine the domain of A.

58. Compound interest. Suppose $3000 is borrowed as a college loan, at 5% interest, compounded daily, for t years.

   a) The amount A that is owed is a function of time. Find an equation for this function.

   b) Determine the domain of A.

Life and Physical Sciences

59. Incidence of breast cancer. The following graph (considered in Exercise 28 of Exercise Set R.1 without an equation) approximates the incidence of breast cancer I, per 100,000 women, as a function of age x. The equation for this graph is

$$I(x) = -0.0000554x^4 + 0.0067x^3 - 0.0997x^2 - 0.84x - 0.25.$$

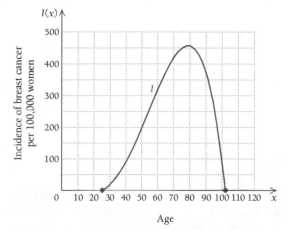

(*Source*: Based on data from the National Cancer Institute.)

   a) Use the graph to determine the domain of I.

   b) Use the graph to determine the range of I.

   c) What 10-yr age interval sees the greatest increase in the incidence of breast cancer? Explain how you determined this.

60. Hearing-impaired Americans. The following graph (considered in Exercise Set R.1) approximates the number N, in millions, of hearing-impaired Americans who are x years old. The equation for this graph is

$$N(x) = -0.000065x^3 + 0.0072x^2 - 0.133x + 2.062.$$

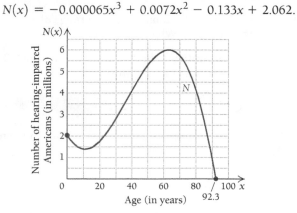

(*Source*: Better Hearing Institute.)

   a) Use the graph to determine the domain of N.

   b) Use the graph to determine the range of N.

   c) If you were marketing a new type of hearing aid, at what age group (expressed as a 10-yr interval) would you target advertisements? Why?

61. Lung cancer. The following graph approximates the incidence of lung and bronchus cancer L, per 100,000 males, as a function of t, the number of years since 1940. The equation for this graph is

$$L(t) = -0.00054t^3 + 0.02917t^2 + 1.2329t + 8.$$

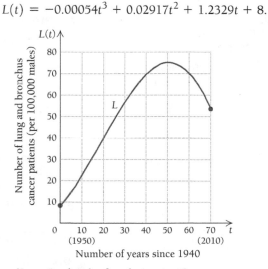

(*Source*: Based on data from the American Cancer Society Surveillance Research, 2005.)

   a) Use the graph to estimate the domain of L.

   b) Use the graph to estimate the range of L.

62. See Exercise 61.

    a) Use the graph to approximate all the *x*-values (years since 1940) for which the cancer rate is 50 per 100,000.

    b) Use the graph to approximate all the *x*-values (years since 1940) for which the cancer rate is 70 per 100,000.

    c) Use the formula to approximate the lung and bronchus cancer rate in 2010.

SYNTHESIS

63. Is it possible for the domain and the range of a function to be the same set? Why or why not?

64. Is there an infinite number of functions for which 3 is not in the domain? Explain why or why not.

TECHNOLOGY CONNECTION

65. Determine the range of each of the functions in Exercises 33, 35, 39, 40, and 47.

66. Determine the range of each of the functions in Exercises 34, 36, 48, 51, and 54.

Answers to Quick Checks

1. (a) $[-2, 5]$,

(b) $[-2, 5)$,

(c) $(-2, 5]$,

(d) $(-2, 5)$,

2. Domain is $\{-3, -1, 1, 2, 3\}$, and range is $\{-2, 1, 2\}$.

3. $f(-1) = 4, f(1) = 2$; domain is $[-3, 1]$, and range is $[0, 4]$ **4. (a)** $(-\infty, 8) \cup (8, \infty)$ **(b)** $(-\infty, \infty)$ **(c)** $[4, \infty)$

Slope and Linear Functions

Horizontal and Vertical Lines

Let's consider graphs of equations $y = c$ and $x = a$, where c and a are real numbers.

- Graph equations of the form $y = f(x) = c$ and $x = a$.
- Graph linear functions.
- Find an equation of a line when given the slope and one point on the line and when given two points on the line.
- Solve applied problems involving slope and linear functions.

EXAMPLE 1

a) Graph $y = 4$.

b) Decide whether the graph represents a function.

Solution

a) The graph consists of all ordered pairs whose second coordinate is 4. To see how a pair such as $(-2, 4)$ could be a solution of $y = 4$, we can write $y = 4$ as

$$y = 0x + 4.$$

Then $(-2, 4)$ is a solution because

$$0(-2) + 4 = 4$$

is true.

b) The vertical-line test holds. Thus, the graph represents a function. ■

EXAMPLE 2

a) Graph $x = -3$.

b) Decide whether the graph represents a function.

Solution

a) The graph consists of all ordered pairs whose first coordinate is -3. To see how a pair such as $(-3, 4)$ could be a solution of $x = -3$, we can write the equation as

$$x + 0y = -3.$$

Then $(-3, 4)$ is a solution because

$$(-3) + 0(4) = -3$$

is true.

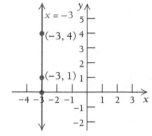

Quick Check 1 ✔

Graph each equation:

a) $x = 4$;
b) $y = -3$.

b) This graph does not represent a function because it fails the vertical-line test. A vertical line at $x = -3$ meets the graph more than once—in fact, infinitely many times. **1** ✔

In general, we have the following.

> **THEOREM 3**
>
> The graph of $y = c$, or $f(x) = c$, a horizontal line, is the graph of a function. Such a function is referred to as a **constant function**. The graph of $x = a$ is a vertical line, and $x = a$ is not a function.

TECHNOLOGY CONNECTION

Visualizing Slope

Exploratory: Squaring A Viewing Window

The standard $[-10, 10, -10, 10]$ viewing window shown below is not scaled identically on both axes. Note that the intervals on the y-axis are about two-thirds the length of those on the x-axis.

If we change the dimensions of the window to $[-6, 6, -4, 4]$, we get a graph for which the units are visually about the same on both axes.

Creating such a window is called **squaring the window**. On many calculators, this is accomplished automatically by selecting the zsquare option of the zoom menu.

Each of the following is a graph of $y = 2x - 3$, but with different viewing windows. When the window is squared, as shown in the final graph, we get the typical representation of a *slope* of 2.

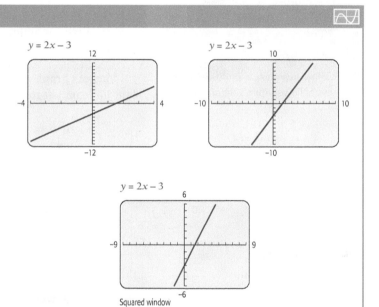

Squared window

EXERCISES

Use a squared viewing window for each of these exercises.

1. Graph $y = x + 1$, $y = 2x + 1$, $y = 3x + 1$, and $y = 10x + 1$. What do you think the graph of $y = 247x + 1$ looks like?

2. Graph $y = x$, $y = \frac{7}{8}x$, $y = 0.47x$, and $y = \frac{2}{31}x$. What do you think the graph of $y = 0.000018x$ looks like?

3. Graph $y = -x$, $y = -2x$, $y = -5x$, and $y = -10x$. What do you think the graph of $y = -247x$ looks like?

4. Graph $y = -x - 1$, $y = -\frac{3}{4}x - 1$, $y = -0.38x - 1$, and $y = -\frac{5}{32}x - 1$. What do you think the graph of $y = -0.000043x - 1$ looks like?

The Equation $y = mx$

Consider the following table of numbers and look for a pattern.

x	1	-1	$-\frac{1}{2}$	2	-2	3	-7	5
y	3	-3	$-\frac{3}{2}$	6	-6	9	-21	15

Note that the ratio of the y-value to the x-value is 3 to 1. That is,

$$\frac{y}{x} = 3, \quad \text{or} \quad y = 3x.$$

Ordered pairs from the table can be used to graph the equation $y = 3x$ (see the figure at the left). Note that this is a function.

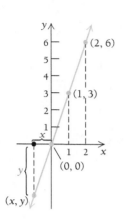

The rows of flowers form lines of equal slope.

> **THEOREM 4**
>
> The graph of the function given by
>
> $$y = mx \qquad \text{or} \qquad f(x) = mx$$
>
> is the straight line through the origin $(0, 0)$ and the point $(1, m)$. The constant m is called the **slope** of the line.

Various graphs of $y = mx$ for $m > 0$ are shown on the left below. Such graphs slant up from left to right and rise faster when m is larger.

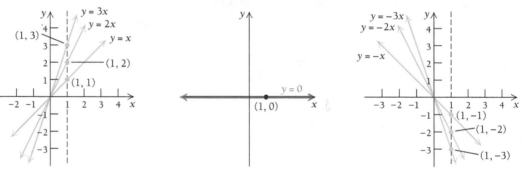

Quick Check 2 ✔

Graph each equation:

a) $y = \frac{1}{2}x$;

b) $y = -\frac{1}{2}x$.

When $m = 0$, we have $y = 0x$, or $y = 0$. In the middle above is a graph of $y = 0$. Note that this is both the x-axis and a horizontal line. Graphs of $y = mx$ for negative values of m are shown on the right above. Note that such graphs slant down from left to right. **2** ✔

Direct Variation

Many applications involve equations like $y = mx$, with $m > 0$. In such situations, we say that we have **direct variation**, and m is the **variation constant**, or **constant of proportionality**. Generally, we assume $x \geq 0$.

> **DEFINITION**
>
> The variable y **varies directly** with x if there is some positive constant m such that $y = mx$. We also say that y is **directly proportional** to x.

EXAMPLE 3 **Life Science: Weight on Earth and the Moon.** The weight M, in pounds, of an object on the moon is directly proportional to the weight E of that object on Earth. An astronaut who weighs 180 lb on Earth will weigh 28.8 lb on the moon.

a) Find an equation of variation.

b) An astronaut weighs 120 lb on Earth. How much will the astronaut weigh on the moon?

Solution

a) The equation has the form $M = mE$. To find m, we substitute:

$$M = mE$$
$$28.8 = m \cdot 180$$
$$\frac{28.8}{180} = m$$
$$0.16 = m.$$

Thus, $M = 0.16E$ is the equation of variation.

b) To find the weight on the moon of an astronaut who weighs 120 lb on Earth, we substitute 120 for E in the equation of variation,

$$M = 0.16 \cdot 120 \quad \text{Substituting 120 for } E$$
$$M = 19.2.$$

Thus, an astronaut who weighs 120 lb on Earth weighs 19.2 lb on the moon. **3** ✔

Quick Check 3 ✔

Measurements in inches and centimeters are directly proportional. For example, a length of 12 in. is the same as a length of 30.48 cm.
a) Find an equation of variation.
b) The height of a table is 90 cm. Find this measurement in inches.

The Equation $y = mx + b$

Compare the graphs of the equations

$$y = 3x \quad \text{and} \quad y = 3x - 2$$

(see the following figure). Note that the graph of $y = 3x - 2$ is a shift 2 units down of the graph of $y = 3x$, and that $y = 3x - 2$ has the y-intercept $(0, -2)$. Both graphs represent functions.

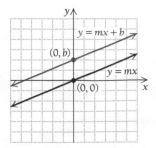

DEFINITION

A **linear function** is any function that can be written in the form

$$y = mx + b \quad \text{or} \quad f(x) = mx + b.$$

Its graph has the same slope, m, as the graph of $y = mx$ and crosses the y-axis at $(0, b)$. The point $(0, b)$ is called the **y-intercept**. (See the figure at the left.)

Two lines that have the same slope but different y-intercepts are **parallel**. The lines $y = mx$ and $y = mx + b$ are examples of parallel lines.

Quick Check 4 ✔

Find the slope and the y-intercept of the graph of $3x - 6y - 7 = 0$.

The Slope–Intercept Equation

Every nonvertical line is uniquely determined by its slope m and its y-intercept $(0, b)$. In other words, the slope describes the "slant" of the line, and the y-intercept locates the point at which the line crosses the y-axis. Thus, we have the following.

> **DEFINITION**
>
> $y = mx + b$ is called the **slope–intercept equation** of a line.

EXAMPLE 4   Find the slope and the y-intercept of the graph of $2x - 4y - 7 = 0$.

Solution   We solve for y:

$$2x - 4y - 7 = 0$$
$$4y = 2x - 7 \qquad \text{Adding } 4y \text{ to both sides and reversing the equation}$$
$$y = \frac{2}{4}x - \frac{7}{4} \qquad \text{Dividing both sides by 4}$$

Slope: $\frac{1}{2}$ y-intercept: $\left(0, -\frac{7}{4}\right)$ 4 ✔

The Point–Slope Equation

Suppose we know the slope of a line and any point on the line. We can use these to find an equation of the line.

EXAMPLE 5   Find an equation of the line with slope 3 containing the point $(-1, -5)$.

Solution   The slope is given as $m = 3$. From the slope–intercept equation, we have

$$y = 3x + b. \tag{1}$$

To determine b, we substitute -5 for y and -1 for x:

$$-5 = 3(-1) + b$$
$$-5 = -3 + b,$$
so $-2 = b$

Then, replacing b in equation (1) with -2, we get $y = 3x - 2$.   ■

More generally, if a point (x_1, y_1) is on the line given by

$$y = mx + b, \tag{2}$$

it follows that

$$y_1 = mx_1 + b. \tag{3}$$

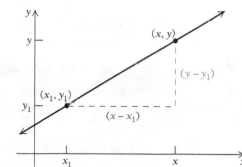

Subtracting the left and right sides of equation (3) from the left and right sides, respectively, of equation (2), we have

$$y - y_1 = (mx + b) - (mx_1 + b)$$
$$= mx + b - mx_1 - b \qquad \text{Simplifying}$$
$$= mx - mx_1 \qquad \text{Combining like terms}$$
$$= m(x - x_1). \qquad \text{Factoring}$$

DEFINITION

$y - y_1 = m(x - x_1)$ is called the **point–slope equation** of a line. The point is (x_1, y_1), and the slope is m.

This definition allows us to write an equation of a line given its slope and the coordinates of *any* point on the line.

EXAMPLE 6   Find an equation of the line with slope $\frac{2}{3}$ containing the point $(-1, -5)$.

Solution   Substituting in

$$y - y_1 = m(x - x_1),$$

we get

$$y - (-5) = \tfrac{2}{3}\big[x - (-1)\big]$$
$$y + 5 = \tfrac{2}{3}(x + 1)$$
$$y + 5 = \tfrac{2}{3}x + \tfrac{2}{3} \qquad \text{Using the distributive law}$$
$$y = \tfrac{2}{3}x + \tfrac{2}{3} - 5 \qquad \text{Subtracting 5 from both sides}$$
$$y = \tfrac{2}{3}x + \tfrac{2}{3} - \tfrac{15}{3}$$
$$y = \tfrac{2}{3}x - \tfrac{13}{3}. \qquad \text{Combining like terms} \qquad 5\ ✔$$

Quick Check 5 ✔

Find the equation of the line with slope $-\frac{2}{3}$ containing the point $(-3, 6)$.

Which lines have the same slope?

Computing Slope

We now determine a method of computing the slope of a line when we know the coordinates of two of its points. Suppose (x_1, y_1) and (x_2, y_2) are the coordinates of two different points, P_1 and P_2, respectively, on a line that is not vertical. Consider a right triangle with legs parallel to the axes, as shown in the following figure.

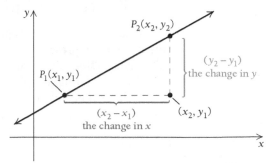

Note that the change in y is $y_2 - y_1$ and the change in x is $x_2 - x_1$. The ratio of these changes is the slope. To see this, consider the point–slope equation,

$$y - y_1 = m(x - x_1).$$

Since (x_2, y_2) is on the line, it must follow that

$$y_2 - y_1 = m(x_2 - x_1). \qquad \text{Substituting}$$

Since the line is not vertical, the two *x*-coordinates differ; so $x_2 - x_1$ is nonzero, and we can divide the preceding equation by it to get the following theorem.

THEOREM 5

The **slope** of a line containing points (x_1, y_1) and (x_2, y_2) is

$$m = \frac{y_2 - y_1}{x_2 - x_1} = \frac{\text{change in } y}{\text{change in } x}.$$

EXAMPLE 7   Find the slope of the line containing the points $(-2, 6)$ and $(-4, 9)$.

Solution   We have

$$m = \frac{y_2 - y_1}{x_2 - x_1} = \frac{6 - 9}{-2 - (-4)} \qquad \text{Regarding } (-2, 6) \text{ as } P_2 \text{ and } (-4, 9) \text{ as } P_1$$

$$= \frac{-3}{2} = -\frac{3}{2}.$$

It does not matter which point is taken first, as long as we subtract the coordinates in the same order. Thus, we can also find *m* as follows:

$$m = \frac{9 - 6}{-4 - (-2)} = \frac{3}{-2} = -\frac{3}{2}. \qquad \text{Here, } (-4, 9) \text{ serves as } P_2,$$
$$\text{and } (-2, 6) \text{ serves as } P_1. \qquad \textbf{6} ✔$$

Quick Check 6 ✔

Find the slope of the line containing the points $(2, 3)$ and $(1, -4)$.

If a line is horizontal, the change in *y* for any two points is 0. Thus, a horizontal line has slope 0. If a line is vertical, the change in *x* for any two points is 0. In this case, the slope is *not defined* because we cannot divide by 0. A vertical line has undefined slope. Thus, "0 slope" and "undefined slope" are two very different concepts.

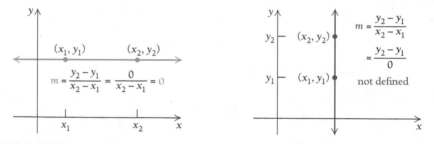

Applications of Slope

Slope has many real-world applications. For example, numbers like 2%, 3%, and 6% are often used to represent the *grade* of a road, a measure of how steep a road on a hill is. A 3% grade $(3\% = \frac{3}{100})$ means that for every horizontal distance of 100 ft, the road rises 3 ft. In architecture, the *pitch* of a roof is a measure of how steeply it is angled—a steep pitch sheds more snow than a shallow pitch. Wheelchair-ramp design also involves slope: Building codes rarely allow the steepness of a wheelchair ramp to exceed $\frac{1}{12}$.

Road grade $= \frac{a}{b}$
(expressed as a percent)

Ski trail difficulty ratings, or *gradients*, are yet another application of slope. The following table presents examples.

Ski Trail Difficulty Ratings in North America

TRAIL RATING	SYMBOL	LEVEL OF DIFFICULTY	DESCRIPTION
Green Circle	●	Easiest	A Green Circle trail is the easiest. These trails typically have slope gradients ranging from 6% to 25% (a 100% slope is a 45° angle).
Blue Square	■	Intermediate	A Blue Square trail is of intermediate difficulty. These trails have gradients ranging from 25% to 40%.
Black Diamond	◆	Difficult	Black Diamond trails tend to be steep—typically 40% and up.

Frenchman Mountain near Las Vegas, Nevada.

To estimate a gradient, hold your arm parallel to the ground out from your side—that is a 0% gradient. Hold it at a 45° angle—that is a 100% gradient. A 22.5° angle is a 41% gradient. And, surprisingly, an angle of only 3.5° constitutes a 6% gradient. What do you think is the slope of the steep road near the top of the mountain in the photo?*

Slope can also be considered as an **average rate of change.**

EXAMPLE 8 **Life Science: Amount Spent on Cancer Research.** The amount spent on cancer research has increased steadily over the years and is approximated in the following graph. Find the average rate of change of the amount spent on the research.

CANCER RESEARCH

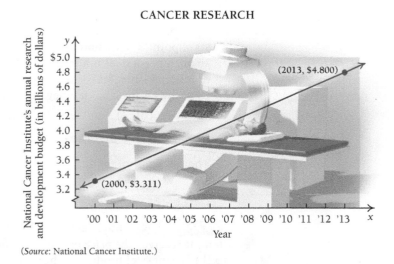

(*Source*: National Cancer Institute.)

Solution First, we determine the coordinates of two points on the graph. Here, they are given as (2000, $3.311) and (2013, $4.800). Then we compute the slope, or rate of change, as follows:

$$\text{Slope} = \text{average rate of change} = \frac{\text{change in } y}{\text{change in } x}$$

$$= \frac{\$4.800 - \$3.311}{2013 - 2000} = \frac{1.489}{13} \approx \$0.1145 \text{ billion/yr.}$$

---

*The road's slope is about 0.35, or a 35% gradient, or an angle of about 20.3°.

Applications of Linear Functions

Many applications are modeled by linear functions.

EXAMPLE 9   Business: Total Cost.   Raggs, Ltd., a clothing firm, has **fixed costs** of $10,000 per year. These costs, such as rent, maintenance, and so on, must be paid no matter how much the company produces. To produce x units of a certain kind of suit, it costs $20 per suit (unit) in addition to the fixed costs. That is, the **variable costs** for producing x of these suits are $20x$ dollars. These costs are due to the amount produced and cover material, wages, fuel, and so on. The **total cost** $C(x)$ of producing x suits in a year is given by

$$C(x) = (\text{Variable costs}) + (\text{Fixed costs}) = 20x + 10{,}000.$$

a) Graph the variable-cost, fixed-cost, and total-cost functions.

b) What is the total cost of producing 100 suits? 400 suits?

Solution

a) The variable-cost and fixed-cost functions appear in the graph on the left below.

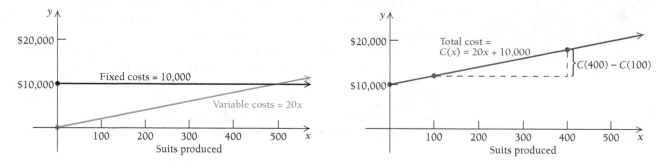

The total-cost function is shown in the graph on the right. From a practical standpoint, the domains of these functions are nonnegative integers 0, 1, 2, 3, and so on, since it does not make sense to make either a negative number or a fractional number of suits. It is common practice to draw such graphs as though the domains were the entire set of nonnegative real numbers.

b) The total cost of producing 100 suits is

$$C(100) = 20 \cdot 100 + 10{,}000 = \$12{,}000.$$

The total cost of producing 400 suits is

$$C(400) = 20 \cdot 400 + 10{,}000 = \$18{,}000. \qquad \blacksquare$$

EXAMPLE 10   Business: Profit-and-Loss Analysis.   When a business sells an item, it receives the *price* paid by the consumer (this is normally greater than the *cost* to the business of producing the item).

a) The **total revenue** that a business receives is the product of the number of items sold and the price paid per item. Thus, if Raggs, Ltd., sells x suits at $80 per suit, the total revenue $R(x)$, in dollars, is given by

$$R(x) = \text{Unit price} \cdot \text{Quantity sold} = 80x.$$

If $C(x) = 20x + 10{,}000$ (see Example 9), graph R and C using the same set of axes.

b) The **total profit** that a business makes is the amount left after all costs have been subtracted from the total revenue. Thus, if $P(x)$ represents the total profit when x items are produced and sold, we have

$$P(x) = (\text{Total revenue}) - (\text{Total costs}) = R(x) - C(x).$$

Determine $P(x)$, and draw its graph using the same set of axes used for the graph in part (a).

c) The company will *break even* at that value of x for which $P(x) = 0$ (that is, no profit and no loss). This is the point at which $R(x) = C(x)$. Find the **break-even value** of x.

Solution

a) The graphs of $R(x) = 80x$ and $C(x) = 20x + 10{,}000$ are shown below. When $C(x)$ is above $R(x)$, a loss will occur. This is shown by the region shaded red. When $R(x)$ is above $C(x)$, a gain will occur. This is shown by the region shaded gray.

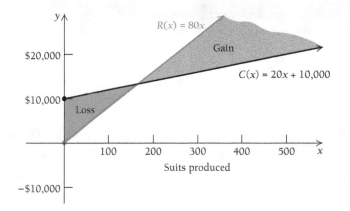

b) To find P, the profit function, we have

$$P(x) = R(x) - C(x) = 80x - (20x + 10{,}000)$$
$$= 60x - 10{,}000.$$

The graph of $P(x)$ is shown by the heavy line. The red portion of the line shows a "negative" profit, or loss. The black portion of the heavy line shows a "positive" profit, or gain.

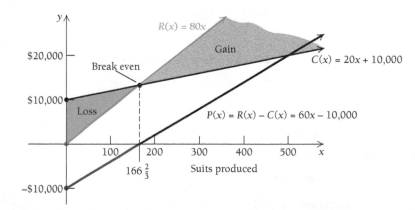

c) To find the break-even value, we solve $R(x) = C(x)$:

$$R(x) = C(x)$$
$$80x = 20x + 10{,}000$$
$$60x = 10{,}000$$
$$x = 166\tfrac{2}{3}.$$

How do we interpret the fractional answer, since it is not possible to produce $\tfrac{2}{3}$ of a suit? We simply round up to 167. Estimates of break-even values are usually sufficient since companies want to operate well away from those values in order to maximize profit.

7 ✔

Quick Check 7 ✔

Business. Suppose that in Examples 9 and 10 fixed costs are increased to $20,000. Find:

a) the total-cost, total-revenue, and total-profit functions;

b) the break-even value.

Section Summary

- Graphs of functions that are straight lines (*linear functions*) are characterized by an equation of the type $f(x) = mx + b$, where m is the slope and $(0, b)$ is the *y-intercept*, the point at which the graph crosses the *y*-axis.

- The *point–slope equation* of a line is $y - y_1 = m(x - x_1)$, where (x_1, y_1) is a point on the line and m is the slope.

R.4 | Exercise Set

Graph.

1. $x = 5$

2. $x = 3$

3. $y = -4$

4. $y = -2$

5. $x = -1.5$

6. $x = -4.5$

7. $y = 2.25$

8. $y = 3.75$

Graph. List the slope and y-intercept.

9. $y = -2x$

10. $y = -3x$

11. $f(x) = -0.5x$

12. $f(x) = 0.5x$

13. $y = 3x - 4$

14. $y = 2x - 5$

15. $g(x) = x - 2.5$

16. $g(x) = -x + 3$

17. $y = 7$

18. $y = -5$

Find the slope and y-intercept.

19. $y - 4x = 1$

20. $y - 3x = 6$

21. $2x + y - 3 = 0$

22. $2x - y + 3 = 0$

23. $3x - 3y + 6 = 0$

24. $2x + 2y + 8 = 0$

25. $x = 3y + 7$

26. $x = -4y + 3$

Find an equation of the line:

27. with $m = 7$, containing $(1, 7)$.

28. with $m = -5$, containing $(-2, -3)$.

29. with $m = -2$, containing $(2, 3)$.

30. with $m = -3$, containing $(5, -2)$.

31. with slope -5, containing $(5, 0)$.

32. with slope 2, containing $(3, 0)$.

33. with y-intercept $(0, -6)$ and slope $\frac{1}{2}$.

34. with y-intercept $(0, 7)$ and slope $\frac{4}{3}$.

35. with slope 0, containing $(4, 8)$.

36. with slope 0, containing $(2, 3)$.

Find the slope of the line containing the given pair of points. If a slope is undefined, state that fact.

37. $(5, -3)$ and $(-2, 1)$

38. $(-2, 1)$ and $(6, 3)$

39. $(-3, -5)$ and $(1, -6)$

40. $(2, -3)$ and $(-1, -4)$

41. $(3, -7)$ and $(3, -9)$

42. $(-4, 2)$ and $(-4, 10)$

43. $\left(-\frac{3}{16}, -\frac{1}{2}\right)$ and $\left(\frac{5}{8}, -\frac{3}{4}\right)$

44. $\left(\frac{4}{5}, -3\right)$ and $\left(\frac{1}{2}, \frac{2}{5}\right)$

45. $(2, 3)$ and $(-1, 3)$

46. $\left(-6, \frac{1}{2}\right)$ and $\left(-7, \frac{1}{2}\right)$

47. $(x, 4x)$ and $(x + h, 4(x + h))$

48. $(x, 3x)$ and $(x + h, 3(x + h))$

49. $(x, 2x + 3)$ and $(x + h, 2(x + h) + 3)$

50. $(x, 3x - 1)$ and $(x + h, 3(x + h) - 1)$

51–60. Find an equation of the line containing the pair of points in each of Exercises 37–46.

61. Find the slope (or grade) of the treadmill.

62. Find the slope of the skateboard ramp.

63. Find the slope (or head) of the river. Express the answer as a percentage.

APPLICATIONS

Business and Economics

64. Highway tolls. It has been suggested that since heavier vehicles are responsible for more wear and tear on highways, drivers should pay tolls in direct proportion to the weight of their vehicles. Suppose a Toyota Camry weighing 3350 lb was charged $2.70 for traveling an 80-mile stretch of highway.

a) Find an equation of variation that expresses the amount of the toll T as a function of the vehicle's weight w.

b) What would the toll be if a 3700-lb Jeep Cherokee drove the same stretch of highway?

65. Inkjet cartridges. A registrar's office finds that the number of inkjet cartridges, I, required each year for its copiers and printers varies directly with the number of students enrolled, s.

a) Find an equation of variation that expresses I as a function of s, if the office requires 16 cartridges when 2800 students enroll.

b) How many cartridges would be required if 3100 students enrolled?

66. Profit-and-loss analysis. Boxowitz, Inc., a computer firm, is planning to sell a new graphing calculator. For the first year, the fixed costs for setting up the new production line are $100,000. The variable costs for each calculator are $20. The sales department projects that 150,000 calculators will be sold during the first year at a price of $45 each.

a) Find and graph $C(x)$, the total cost of producing x calculators.

b) Using the same axes as in part (a), find and graph $R(x)$, the total revenue from the sale of x calculators.

c) Using the same axes as in part (a), find and graph $P(x)$, the total profit from the production and sale of x calculators.

d) What profit or loss will the firm realize if the expected sale of 150,000 calculators occurs?

e) How many calculators must the firm sell in order to break even?

67. Profit-and-loss analysis. Red Tide is planning a new line of skis. For the first year, the fixed costs for setting up production are $45,000. The variable costs for producing each pair of skis are estimated at $80, and the selling price will be $450 per pair. It is projected that 3000 pairs will sell the first year.

a) Find and graph $C(x)$, the total cost of producing x pairs of skis.

b) Find and graph $R(x)$, the total revenue from the sale of x pairs of skis. Use the same axes as in part (a).

c) Using the same axes as in part (a), find and graph $P(x)$, the total profit from the production and sale of x pairs of skis.

d) What profit or loss will the company realize if the expected sale of 3000 pairs occurs?

e) How many pairs must the company sell in order to break even?

68. Profit-and-loss analysis. Jamal decides to mow lawns to earn money. The initial cost of his lawnmower is $250. Gasoline and maintenance costs are $4 per lawn.

a) Formulate a function $C(x)$ for the total cost of mowing x lawns.

b) Jamal determines that the total-profit function for the lawn-mowing business is given by $P(x) = 9x - 250$. Find a function for the total revenue from mowing x lawns. How much does Jamal charge per lawn?

c) How many lawns must Jamal mow before he begins making a profit?

69. Straight-line depreciation. Quick Copy buys an office machine for $5200 on January 1 of a given year. The machine is expected to last for 8 yr, at the end of which time its *salvage value* will be $1100. If the company figures the decline in value to be the same each year, then the *straight-line depreciation value*, $V(t)$, after t years, $0 \le t \le 8$, is given by

$$V(t) = C - t\left(\frac{C - S}{N}\right),$$

where C is the original cost of the item, N is the number of years of expected life, and S is the salvage value. $V(t)$ is also called the *book value*.

a) Find the linear function for the straight-line depreciation of the machine.

b) Find the book value of the machine after 0 yr, 1 yr, 2 yr, 3 yr, 4 yr, 7 yr, and 8 yr.

70. Straight-line depreciation. (See Exercise 69.) Hanna's Photography spends $40 per square foot on improvements to a 25,000-ft² office space. Under IRS guidelines for straight-line depreciation, these improvements will depreciate completely—that is, have zero salvage value—after 39 yr. Find the depreciated value of the improvements after 10 yr.

71. Straight-line depreciation. The Video Game Wizard buys a new computer system for $60,000 and projects that its book value will be $2000 after 5 yr. Using straight-line depreciation, find the book value after 3 yr.

72. Straight-line depreciation. Tyline Electric uses the function $B(t) = -700t + 3500$ to find the book value, $B(t)$, in dollars, of a photocopier t years after its purchase.

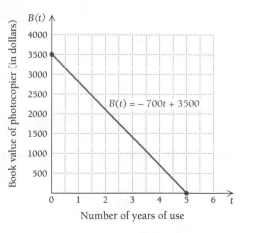

a) What do the numbers −700 and 3500 signify?
b) How long will it take the copier to depreciate completely?
c) What is the domain of B? Explain.

General Interest

73. Stair requirements. A North Carolina state law requires that stairs have minimum treads of 9 in. and maximum risers of 8.25 in. (*Source:* North Carolina Office of the State Fire Marshal.) According to this law, what is the maximum grade of stairs in North Carolina?

74. Health insurance premiums. Find the average rate of change in the annual premium for a family's health insurance.

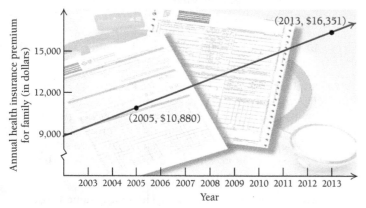

(*Source:* The Kaiser Family Foundation; Health Research and Education Trust.)

75. Health insurance premiums. Find the average rate of change in the annual premium for a single person.

(*Source:* The Kaiser Family Foundation; Health Research and Education Trust.)

76. Two-year college tuitions. Find the average rate of change of the tuition and fees at public two-year colleges.

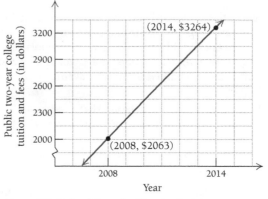

(*Source:* U.S. National Center for Education Statistics, *Digest of Education Statistics*, annual.)

77. Organic food sales. Find the average rate of change of organic food sales in the United States.

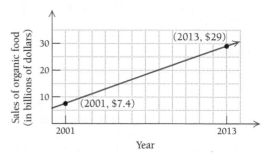

(*Source:* Big Green Opportunity Report, 2013.)

78. Energy conservation. The R-factor of home insulation is directly proportional to its thickness T.

a) Find an equation of variation if $R = 12.51$ when $T = 3$ in.
b) What is the R-factor for insulation that is 6 in. thick?

79. Nerve impulse speed. Impulses in nerve fibers travel at a speed of 293 ft/sec. The distance D, in feet, traveled in t sec is given by $D = 293t$. How long would it take an impulse to travel from the brain to the toes of a person who is 6 ft tall?

80. Muscle weight. The weight M of a person's muscles is directly proportional to the person's body weight W.

Muscle weight is directly proportional to body weight.

a) It is known that a person weighing 200 lb has 80 lb of muscles. Find an equation of variation expressing M as a function of W.

b) Express the variation constant as a percentage, and interpret the resulting equation.

c) What is the muscle weight of a person weighing 120 lb?

81. Brain weight.   The weight B of a person's brain is directly proportional to the person's body weight W.

a) It is known that a person weighing 120 lb has a brain that weighs 3 lb. Find an equation of variation expressing B as a function of W.

b) Express the variation constant as a percentage, and interpret the resulting equation.

c) What is the weight of the brain of a person weighing 160 lb?

82. Stopping distance on glare ice.   The stopping distance (at some fixed speed) of regular tires on glare ice is a linear function of the air temperature F,

$$D(F) = 2F + 115,$$

where $D(F)$ is the stopping distance, in feet, when the air temperature is F, in degrees Fahrenheit.

a) Find $D(0°), D(-20°), D(10°)$, and $D(32°)$.

b) Explain why the domain should be restricted to the interval $[-57.5°, 32°]$.

83. Reaction time.   While driving a car, you see a child suddenly crossing the street. Your brain registers the emergency and sends a signal to your foot to hit the brake. The car travels a reaction distance D, in feet, during this time, where D is a function of the speed r, in miles per hour, that the car is traveling when you see the child. That reaction distance is a linear function given by

$$D(r) = \frac{11r + 5}{10}.$$

a) Find $D(5), D(10), D(20), D(50)$, and $D(65)$.

b) Graph $D(r)$.

c) What is the domain of the function? Explain.

84. Estimating heights.   An anthropologist can use certain linear functions to estimate the height of a male or female, given the length of certain bones. The *humerus* is the bone from the elbow to the shoulder. Let x = the length of the humerus, in centimeters. Then the height, in centimeters, of a male with a humerus of length x is given by

$$M(x) = 2.89x + 70.64.$$

The height, in centimeters, of a female with a humerus of length x is given by

$$F(x) = 2.75x + 71.48.$$

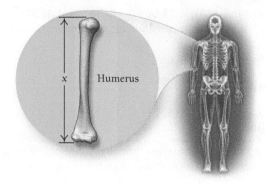

A 26-cm humerus was uncovered in some ruins.

a) If we assume it was from a male, how tall was he?

b) If we assume it was from a female, how tall was she?

85. Percentage of young adults using social networking sites.   In 2006, the percentage of 18- to 29-year-olds who used social networking sites was 49%. In 2013, that percentage had risen to 89%. (*Source:* pewresearch.org.)

a) Use the year as the x-coordinate and the percentage as the y-coordinate. Find the equation of the line that contains the data points.

b) Use the equation in part (a) to estimate the percentage of young adults using social networking sites in 2014.

c) Use the equation in part (a) to estimate the year in which the percentage of young adults using social networking sites will reach 100%.

d) Explain why a linear equation cannot be used for years after the year found in part (c).

86. Manatee population.   In January 2005, 3143 manatees were counted in an aerial survey of Florida. In January 2011, 4834 manatees were counted. (*Source*: Florida Fish and Wildlife Conservation Commission.)

a) Using the year as the x-coordinate and the number of manatees as the y-coordinate, find an equation of the line that contains the two data points.

b) Use the equation in part (a) to estimate the number of manatees counted in January 2010.

c) The actual number counted in January 2010 was 5067. Does the equation found in part (a) give an accurate representation of the number of manatees counted each year? Why or why not?

87. Urban population.   The population of Woodland is P. After growing 2%, the new population is N.

a) Assuming that N is directly proportional to P, find an equation of variation.

b) Find N when $P = 200{,}000$.

c) Find P when $N = 367{,}200$.

88. Median age of women at first marriage.   In general, people in our society are marrying at a later age. The median age, $A(t)$, of women at first marriage can be approximated by

$$A(t) = 0.08t + 19.7,$$

where t is the number of years after 1950. Thus, $A(0)$ is the median age of women at first marriage in 1950, $A(50)$ is the median age in 2000, and so on.

a) Find $A(0), A(1), A(10), A(30)$, and $A(50)$.

b) What was the median age of women at first marriage in 2008?

c) Graph $A(t)$.

SYNTHESIS

89. Suppose $(2, 5), (4, 13)$, and $(7, y)$ all lie on the same line. Find y.

90. Describe one situation in which you would use the slope–intercept equation rather than the point–slope equation.

91. Business: daily sales.   Match each sentence below with the most appropriate of the following graphs (I, II, III, or IV).

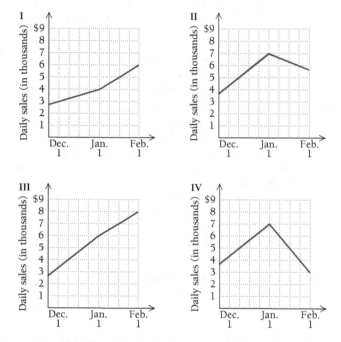

a) After January 1, daily sales continued to rise, but at a slower rate.

b) After January 1, sales decreased faster than they ever grew.

c) The rate of growth in daily sales doubled after January 1.

d) After January 1, daily sales decreased at half the rate that they grew in December.

92. Business: depreciation.   A large crane is being depreciated according to the model $V(t) = 900 - 60t$, where $V(t)$ is in thousands of dollars and t is the number of years since 2005. If the crane is to be depreciated until its value is $0, what is the domain of this model?

TECHNOLOGY CONNECTION

93. Graph some of the total-revenue, total-cost, and total-profit functions in this exercise set using the same set of axes. Identify regions of profit and loss.

Answers to Quick Checks

1. (a)   **(b)**

2. (a)   **(b)**

3. (a) Let x be a measurement in inches and y be a measurement in centimeters. Then $y = 2.54x$ or $x = 0.39y$.   **(b)** 35.1 in.

4. $m = \frac{1}{2}$, y-intercept: $(0, -\frac{7}{6})$ **5.** $y = -\frac{2}{3}x + 4$ **6.** $m = 7$

7. (a) $C(x) = 20x + 20{,}000$; $R(x) = 80x$;
$P(x) = R(x) - C(x) = 60x - 20{,}000$;   **(b)** 333 suits

R.5

Nonlinear Functions and Models

Many functions have graphs that are not lines. In this section, we study some of these **nonlinear functions** that we will use throughout this course.

- Graph nonlinear functions and solve applied problems.
- Manipulate radical expressions and rational exponents.
- Determine the domain of a rational function and graph certain rational functions.
- Find the equilibrium point given a supply function and a demand function.

Quadratic Functions

DEFINITION

A **quadratic function** f is given by

$$f(x) = ax^2 + bx + c, \quad \text{where } a \neq 0.$$

We have already encountered some quadratic functions—for example, $f(x) = x^2$ and $g(x) = x^2 - 1$. We can create hand-drawn graphs of quadratic functions using the following information.

> The graph of a quadratic function $f(x) = ax^2 + bx + c$ is called a **parabola.**
>
> **a)** It is always a cup-shaped curve, like those in Examples 1 and 2 that follow.
>
> **b)** It opens upward if $a > 0$ and opens downward if $a < 0$.
>
> **c)** It has a turning point, or **vertex**, whose first coordinate is $x = -\dfrac{b}{2a}$.
>
> **d)** The vertical line $x = -b/(2a)$ is the line of symmetry, although it is not part of the graph.

EXAMPLE 1 Graph: $f(x) = x^2 - 2x - 3$.

Solution Note that for $f(x) = 1x^2 - 2x - 3$, we have $a = 1, b = -2$, and $c = -3$. Since $a > 0$, the graph opens upward. The x-coordinate of the vertex is

$$x = -\frac{b}{2a}$$

$$= -\frac{-2}{2(1)} = 1.$$

Substituting 1 for x, we find the second coordinate of the vertex, $f(1)$:

$$f(1) = 1^2 - 2(1) - 3$$
$$= 1 - 2 - 3$$
$$= -4.$$

The vertex is $(1, -4)$, and the line $x = 1$ is the line of symmetry of the graph. We choose some x-values on each side of the vertex, compute y-values, plot the points, and graph the parabola.

x	$f(x)$	
1	-4	←Vertex
0	-3	←y-intercept
2	-3	
3	0	
4	5	
-1	0	
-2	5	

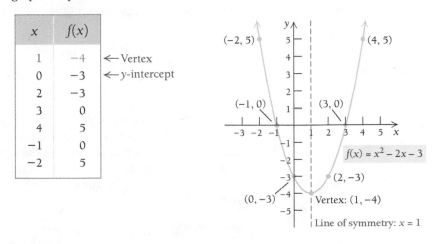

EXAMPLE 2 Graph: $f(x) = -2x^2 + 10x - 7$.

Solution Note that $a = -2$, and since $a < 0$, the graph will open downward. The x-coordinate of the vertex is

$$x = -\frac{b}{2a}$$

$$= -\frac{10}{2(-2)} = \frac{5}{2}.$$

EXERCISES

Using the procedure of Examples 1 and 2, graph each of the following by hand, using the TABLE feature to create an input–output table for each function. Then press GRAPH to check your sketch.

1. $f(x) = x^2 - 6x + 4$

2. $f(x) = -2x^2 + 4x + 1$

Quick Check 1 ✔

Graph each function:

a) $f(x) = x^2 + 2x - 3$;

b) $f(x) = -2x^2 - 10x - 5$.

Substituting $\frac{5}{2}$ for x in the equation, we find the second coordinate of the vertex:

$$y = f\left(\tfrac{5}{2}\right) = -2\left(\tfrac{5}{2}\right)^2 + 10\left(\tfrac{5}{2}\right) - 7$$
$$= -2\left(\tfrac{25}{4}\right) + 25 - 7$$
$$= \tfrac{11}{2}.$$

The vertex is $\left(\frac{5}{2}, \frac{11}{2}\right)$, and the line of symmetry is $x = \frac{5}{2}$. We choose some x-values on each side of the vertex, compute y-values, plot the points, and graph the parabola:

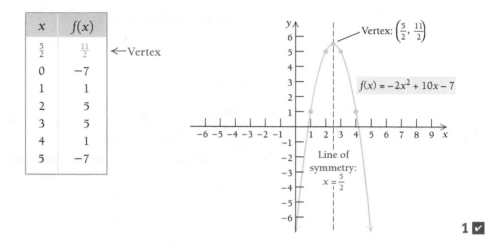

x	$f(x)$	
$\frac{5}{2}$	$\frac{11}{2}$	←Vertex
0	-7	
1	1	
2	5	
3	5	
4	1	
5	-7	

1 ✔

First coordinates of points at which a quadratic function intersects the x-axis (x-intercepts), if they exist, can be found by solving the quadratic equation, $ax^2 + bx + c = 0$. If real-number solutions exist, they can be found using the *quadratic formula*. See Appendix A at the end of the book for additional review of this important result.

THEOREM 6   The Quadratic Formula

The solutions of any quadratic equation $ax^2 + bx + c = 0, a \neq 0$, are given by

$$x = \frac{-b \pm \sqrt{b^2 - 4ac}}{2a}.$$

To solve a quadratic equation, first try to factor and use the Principle of Zero Products (see Appendix A). When factoring is not possible or seems difficult, use the quadratic formula. It will always give the solutions. When $b^2 - 4ac < 0$, there are no real-number solutions and thus no x-intercepts. There are solutions in an expanded number system called the *complex numbers*. In this text, we will work only with real numbers.

EXAMPLE 3   Solve: $3x^2 - 4x = 2$.

Solution   We first write an equivalent equation of the form $ax^2 + bx + c = 0$, and then determine $a, b,$ and c:

$$3x^2 - 4x - 2 = 0,$$
$$a = 3, \quad b = -4, \quad c = -2.$$

We then use the quadratic formula:

$$x = \frac{-b \pm \sqrt{b^2 - 4ac}}{2a}$$

$$= \frac{-(-4) \pm \sqrt{(-4)^2 - 4(3)(-2)}}{2 \cdot 3} \quad \text{Substituting}$$

$$= \frac{4 \pm \sqrt{16 + 24}}{6} = \frac{4 \pm \sqrt{40}}{6} \quad \text{Simplifying}$$

$$= \frac{4 \pm \sqrt{4 \cdot 10}}{6} = \frac{4 \pm 2\sqrt{10}}{6}$$

$$= \frac{2\left(2 \pm \sqrt{10}\right)}{2 \cdot 3} \quad \text{Factoring}$$

$$= \frac{2 \pm \sqrt{10}}{3}.$$

The solutions are $\left(2 + \sqrt{10}\right)/3$ and $\left(2 - \sqrt{10}\right)/3$, or approximately 1.721 and -0.387, respectively. **2 ✔**

Quick Check 2 ✔

Solve: $3x^2 + 2x = 7$.

Algebraic–Graphical Connection

Let's make an algebraic–graphical connection between the solutions of a quadratic equation and the x-intercepts of a quadratic function.

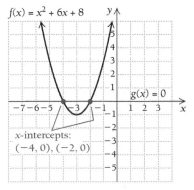
$f(x) = x^2 + 6x + 8$
$g(x) = 0$
x-intercepts: $(-4, 0), (-2, 0)$

We just graphed equations of the form $f(x) = ax^2 + bx + c, a \neq 0$. Let's look at the graph of $f(x) = x^2 + 6x + 8$ and its x-intercepts, shown to the right.

The **x-intercepts**, $(-4, 0)$ and $(-2, 0)$, are the points at which the graph crosses the x-axis. These pairs are also the points of intersection of the graphs of $f(x) = x^2 + 6x + 8$ and $g(x) = 0$ (the x-axis). The x-values, -4 and -2, can be found by solving $f(x) = g(x)$:

$$x^2 + 6x + 8 = 0$$
$$(x + 4)(x + 2) = 0 \quad \text{Factoring; there is no need for the quadratic formula here.}$$
$$x + 4 = 0 \quad \text{or} \quad x + 2 = 0 \quad \text{Principle of Zero Products}$$
$$x = -4 \quad \text{or} \quad x = -2.$$

The solutions of $x^2 + 6x + 8 = 0$ are -4 and -2, which are the first coordinates of the x-intercepts, $(-4, 0)$ and $(-2, 0)$, of the graph of $f(x) = x^2 + 6x + 8$. A brief review of factoring can be found in Appendix A at the end of the book.

Polynomial Functions

Linear and quadratic functions are part of a general class of *polynomial functions*.

> **DEFINITION**
>
> A **polynomial function** f is given by
> $$f(x) = a_n x^n + a_{n-1} x^{n-1} + \cdots + a_2 x^2 + a_1 x^1 + a_0,$$
> where n is a nonnegative integer and $a_n, a_{n-1}, \ldots, a_1, a_0$ are real numbers, called the **coefficients**.

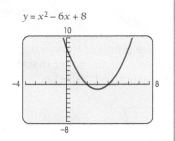

The following are examples of polynomial functions:

$$f(x) = -5, \qquad \text{(A constant function)}$$
$$f(x) = 4x + 3, \qquad \text{(A linear function)}$$
$$f(x) = -x^2 + 2x + 3, \qquad \text{(A quadratic function)}$$
$$f(x) = 2x^3 - 4x^2 + x + 1. \qquad \text{(A cubic, or third-degree, function)}$$

In general, creating graphs of polynomial functions other than linear and quadratic functions is difficult without a calculator. We use calculus to sketch such graphs in Chapter 2. However, some **power functions**, of the form

$$f(x) = ax^n,$$

are relatively easy to graph.

EXAMPLE 4   Using the same set of axes, graph $f(x) = x^2$ and $g(x) = x^3$.

Solution   We set up a table of values, plot the points, and then draw the graphs.

x	x^2	x^3
-2	4	-8
-1	1	-1
$-\frac{1}{2}$	$\frac{1}{4}$	$-\frac{1}{8}$
0	0	0
$\frac{1}{2}$	$\frac{1}{4}$	$\frac{1}{8}$
1	1	1
2	4	8

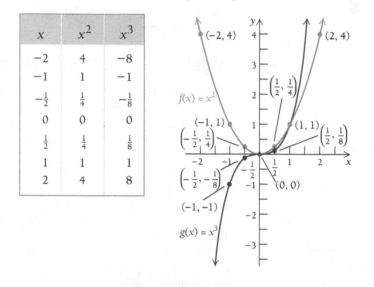

Quick Check 3 ☑

Graph each function using the same set of axes:

$f(x) = 4 - x^2$ and
$g(x) = x^3 - 1$.

3 ☑

Solving Polynomial Equations

The INTERSECT Feature

Solving $x^3 = 3x + 1$ amounts to finding the x-coordinates of the point(s) of intersection of the graphs of

$$f(x) = x^3 \quad \text{and} \quad g(x) = 3x + 1.$$

We enter the functions as

$$y_1 = x^3 \quad \text{and} \quad y_2 = 3x + 1$$

and then graph. We use a $[-3, 3, -5, 8]$ window to see the curvature and possible points of intersection.

There appear to be at least three points of intersection. Using the INTERSECT feature in the CALC menu, we see that the point of intersection on the left is about $(-1.53, -3.60)$.

In a similar manner, we approximate the other points of intersection as $(-0.35, -0.04)$ and $(1.88, 6.64)$. The solutions of $x^3 = 3x + 1$ are the x-coordinates of these points, approximately

$$-1.53, \ -0.35, \ \text{and} \ 1.88.$$

The ZERO Feature

The ZERO, or ROOT, feature can be used to solve an equation. The word "zero" in this context refers to an input, or x-value,

(continued)

for which the output of a function is 0. That is, c is a **zero** of the function f if $f(c) = 0$.

To use such a feature requires a 0 on one side of the equation. Thus, to solve $x^3 = 3x + 1$, we obtain $x^3 - 3x - 1 = 0$ by subtracting $3x + 1$ from both sides. Graphing $y = x^3 - 3x - 1$ and using the ZERO feature to find the zeros, we view a screen like the following.

We see that $x^3 - 3x - 1 = 0$ when $x \approx -1.53$, so -1.53 is an approximate solution of $x^3 = 3x + 1$. In a similar manner, we can approximate the other solutions as -0.35 and 1.88. Note that the points of intersection of the graphs of f and g have the same x-values as the zeros of $x^3 - 3x - 1$.

EXERCISES

Using the INTERSECT feature, solve each equation.

1. $x^2 = 10 - 3x$ **2.** $2x + 24 = x^2$

3. $x^3 = 3x - 2$

4. $x^4 - 2x^2 = 0$

Using the ZERO feature, solve each equation.

5. $0.4x^2 = 280x$
(*Hint:* Use $[-200, 800, -100,000, 200,000]$.)

6. $\frac{1}{3}x^3 - \frac{1}{2}x^2 = 2x - 1$

7. $x^2 = 0.1x^4 + 0.4$

8. $0 = 2x^4 - 4x^2 + 2$

Find the zeros of each function.

9. $f(x) = 3x^2 - 4x - 2$

10. $f(x) = -x^3 + 6x^2 + 5$

11. $g(x) = x^4 + x^3 - 4x^2 - 2x + 4$

12. $g(x) = -x^4 + x^3 + 11x^2 - 9x - 18$

TECHNOLOGY CONNECTION

App for the iPhone: Graphicus

The advent of the iPhone and other sophisticated mobile devices has made available many inexpensive mathematics applications. One popular and useful app is Graphicus. It has a more visually appealing display than most graphing calculators, but it does have some limitation. For example, it does not do regression, as described in Section R.6.

Graphicus can graph most of the functions we encounter in this text. It can find roots and intersections, and it excels at many aspects of calculus. Let's look again at the function $f(x) = 2x^3 - x^4$.

To graph and find roots, first open Graphicus. Touch the blank rectangle at the top of the screen and enter the function as y(x)=2x^3-x^4. Press ⊕ in the upper right, and you will see the graph in Fig. 1. Notice the seven icons at the bottom. The one at the far left is for zooming. The fourth icon from the left is for finding roots. Touch it and the roots of the function are highlighted (Fig. 2). Touch the symbol marking each root, and a box appears with its value; see Figs. 3 and 4.

FIGURE 1

FIGURE 2

FIGURE 3

FIGURE 4

(continued)

Piecewise-defined functions cannot be entered. The graph of a function with a missing point, such as $f(x) = \dfrac{x^2 - 9}{x + 3}$, will not show the hole at $x = -3$. Graphicus can graph more than one function on the same set of axes. Graph $g(x) = x^3 - 1$ and $f(x) = 2x^3 - x^4$, and then press the fourth icon to find the points of intersection. Press some of the other icons to further explore Graphicus.

For more information, consult the Graphicus page at the iTunes Store.

EXERCISES

Using Graphicus, repeat Exercises 1–12 in the Technology Connection on page 53.

Rational Functions

DEFINITION

Functions given by the quotient, or ratio, of two polynomials are called **rational functions.**

The following are examples of rational functions:

$$f(x) = \frac{x^2 - 9}{x - 3}, \qquad h(x) = \frac{x - 3}{x^2 - x - 2},$$

$$g(x) = \frac{3x^2 - 4x}{2x + 10}, \qquad k(x) = \frac{x^3 - 2x + 7}{1} = x^3 - 2x + 7.$$

As the function k illustrates, every polynomial function is also a rational function.

The domain of a rational function cannot include any input value that results in division by zero. Thus, for f above, the domain consists of all real numbers except 3. To determine the domain of h, we set the denominator equal to 0 and solve:

$$x^2 - x - 2 = 0$$
$$(x + 1)(x - 2) = 0$$
$$x = -1 \quad or \quad x = 2.$$

Neither -1 nor 2 is in the domain of h. The domain of h is the real numbers except -1 and 2. The numbers -1 and 2 "split," or "separate," the intervals in the domain.

Graphing rational functions can be complicated and is best done using tools of calculus that we will develop in Chapters 1 and 2. For now, we focus on graphs that are fairly basic.

EXAMPLE 5   Graph: $f(x) = \dfrac{x^2 - 9}{x - 3}$.

Solution   This particular function can be simplified before we graph it. We do so by factoring the numerator and removing a factor equal to 1 as follows:

$$f(x) = \frac{x^2 - 9}{x - 3} \qquad \text{Noting that 3 is not in the domain of } f$$

$$= \frac{(x - 3)(x + 3)}{x - 3}$$

$$= \frac{x - 3}{x - 3} \cdot \frac{x + 3}{1} \qquad \text{Noting that } \frac{x - 3}{x - 3} = 1$$

$$= x + 3, \quad x \neq 3. \qquad \text{We must specify } x \neq 3.$$

If $y_1 = (x^2 - 9)/(x - 3)$ and $y_2 = x + 3$ are both graphed, the two graphs appear indistinguishable. To see this, graph both lines and use the arrow keys, ⌃ and ⌄, and the TRACE feature to move the cursor from line to line.

EXERCISES

1. Compare the results of using TRACE and entering the value 3 with y_1 and y_2.

2. Use the TABLE feature with TblStart set at -1 and ΔTbl set at 1. How do y_1 and y_2 differ in the resulting table?

This simplification assumes that x is not 3. By writing $x \neq 3$, we indicate that for any x-value other than 3, the equation $f(x) = x + 3$ is used:

$$f(x) = x + 3, \quad x \neq 3.$$

To find function values, we substitute any value for x other than 3. We make calculations as in the following table and draw the graph. The open dot at $(3, 6)$ indicates that this point is *not* part of the graph.

x	$f(x)$
-3	0
-2	1
-1	2
0	3
1	4
2	5
4	7

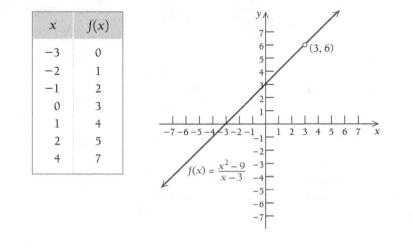

One important class of rational functions is given by $f(x) = k/x$, where k is a constant.

EXAMPLE 6 Graph: $f(x) = 1/x$.

Solution We make a table of values, plot the points, and then draw the graph.

x	$f(x)$
-3	$-\frac{1}{3}$
-2	$-\frac{1}{2}$
-1	-1
$-\frac{1}{2}$	-2
$-\frac{1}{4}$	-4
$\frac{1}{4}$	4
$\frac{1}{2}$	2
1	1
2	$\frac{1}{2}$
3	$\frac{1}{3}$

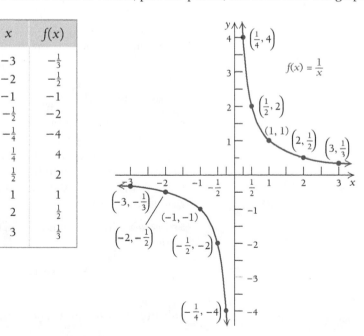

Quick Check 4 ✔

Graph each function:

a) $f(x) = \dfrac{x^2 - 9}{x + 3}$;

b) $f(x) = -\dfrac{1}{x}$.

4 ✔

TECHNOLOGY CONNECTION

Graphs of Rational Functions

Consider two graphs of the function given by

$$f(x) = \frac{2x + 1}{x - 3}.$$

CONNECTED mode: DOT mode:

Use of CONNECTED mode leads to an *incorrect* graph in this case. Because, in CONNECTED mode, points are joined with line segments, both branches of the graph are connected, making the vertical line $x = 3$ appear as part of the graph.

On the other hand, in DOT mode, the calculator simply plots dots representing coordinates of points. When graphing rational functions, it is usually best to use DOT mode.

EXERCISES

Graph each of the following using DOT mode.

1. $f(x) = \dfrac{4}{x - 2}$ 2. $f(x) = \dfrac{x}{x + 2}$

3. $f(x) = \dfrac{x^2 - 1}{x^2 + x - 6}$ 4. $f(x) = \dfrac{x^2 - 4}{x - 1}$

5. $f(x) = \dfrac{10}{x^2 + 4}$ 6. $f(x) = \dfrac{8}{x^2 - 4}$

7. $f(x) = \dfrac{2x + 3}{3x^2 + 7x - 6}$ 8. $f(x) = \dfrac{2x^3}{x^2 + 1}$

In Example 6, note that 0 is not in the domain of f because it would yield a denominator of zero. The function given by $f(x) = 1/x$ is an example of **inverse variation**.

> **DEFINITION**
>
> y **varies inversely** with x if there is some positive number k for which $y = k/x$. We also say that y is **inversely proportional** to x.

EXAMPLE 7   **Business: Stocks and Gold.**   Certain economists theorize that stock prices are inversely proportional to the price of gold. That is, when gold prices go up, stock prices go down, and when gold prices go down, stock prices go up. Assume that the Dow Jones Industrial Average D, an index of the overall prices of stocks, is inversely proportional to the price of gold G, in dollars per ounce. If D was 10,619.70 when G was $1129.60 per ounce, find the Dow Jones Industrial Average if the price of gold rises to $1400.

Solution   We assume $D = k/G$, so $10{,}619.7 = k/1129.6$ and $k = 11{,}996{,}013.12$. Thus,

$$D = \frac{11{,}996{,}013.12}{G}.$$

Substituting 1400 for G and computing D, we have

$$D = \frac{11{,}996{,}013.12}{1400}$$
$$\approx 8568.6.$$

Price of gold (in dollars per ounce)

Business: Stocks and Gold.
Suppose in Example 7 that the price of gold drops to $1000 per ounce. Predict what happens to the Dow Jones Industrial Average. Then compute the value of D.

Warning! Do not put too much "stock" in the equation of this example. It is meant only to give an idea of economic relationships. An equation for predicting the stock market accurately has not been found!   **5** ✔

Absolute-Value Functions

The absolute value of a number is its distance from 0 on the number line. We denote the absolute value of a number x as $|x|$. The absolute-value function, given by $f(x) = |x|$, is very important in calculus, and its graph has a distinctive V shape.

EXAMPLE 8   Graph: $f(x) = |x|$.

Solution   We make a table of values, plot the points, and then draw the graph.

x	$f(x)$
-3	3
-2	2
-1	1
0	0
1	1
2	2
3	3

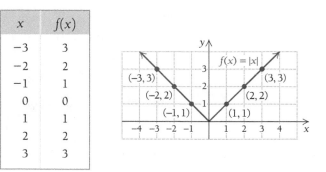

We can think of this function as being defined piecewise by considering the definition of absolute value:

$$f(x) = |x| = \begin{cases} x, & \text{if } x \geq 0, \\ -x, & \text{if } x < 0. \end{cases}$$

Square-Root Functions

The following is an example of a square-root function and its graph.

EXAMPLE 9   Graph: $f(x) = -\sqrt{x}$.

Solution   The domain of this function is the set of all nonnegative numbers—the interval $[0, \infty)$. You can find approximate values of square roots on your calculator.

We make a table of values, plot the points, and then draw the graph.

x	0	1	2	3	4	5
$f(x) = -\sqrt{x}$	0	-1	-1.4	-1.7	-2	-2.2

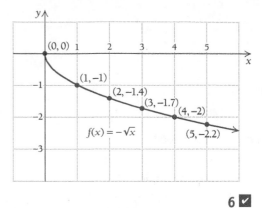

Quick Check 6 ✔

Graph each function:
a) $f(x) = |x + 2|$;
b) $f(x) = \sqrt{x} + 4$.

6 ✔

Power Functions with Rational Exponents

We are motivated to define rational exponents so that the following laws of exponents still hold (also see Appendix A):

> For any nonzero real number a and any integers n and m,
> $$a^n \cdot a^m = a^{n+m}; \quad \frac{a^n}{a^m} = a^{n-m}; \quad (a^n)^m = a^{n \cdot m}; \quad a^{-m} = \frac{1}{a^m}.$$

This suggests that $a^{1/2}$ be defined so that $(a^{1/2})^2 = a^{(1/2) \cdot 2} = a^1$. Thus, we define $a^{1/2}$ as $\sqrt{a}$. Similarly, in order to have $(a^{1/3})^3 = a^{(1/3) \cdot 3} = a^1$, we define $a^{1/3}$ as $\sqrt[3]{a}$. In general,

$$a^{1/n} = \sqrt[n]{a}, \quad \text{provided } \sqrt[n]{a} \text{ is defined.}$$

Again, for the laws of exponents to hold, and assuming that $\sqrt[n]{a}$ exists, we have

$$a^{m/n} = (a^m)^{1/n} = \sqrt[n]{a^m} = (\sqrt[n]{a})^m.$$

Similarly, $a^{-m/n}$ is defined by

$$a^{-m/n} = \frac{1}{a^{m/n}} = \frac{1}{\sqrt[n]{a^m}}.$$

EXAMPLE 10 Rewrite each of the following as an equivalent expression using radical notation: **a)** $x^{1/3}$; **b)** $t^{6/7}$; **c)** $x^{-2/3}$; **d)** $r^{-1/4}$.

Solution

a) $x^{1/3} = \sqrt[3]{x}$

b) $t^{6/7} = \sqrt[7]{t^6}$

c) $x^{-2/3} = \dfrac{1}{x^{2/3}} = \dfrac{1}{\sqrt[3]{x^2}}$

d) $r^{-1/4} = \dfrac{1}{r^{1/4}} = \dfrac{1}{\sqrt[4]{r}}, \quad r > 0$ ∎

EXAMPLE 11 Rewrite each of the following as an equivalent expression with rational exponents:

a) $\sqrt[4]{x}$, for $x \geq 0$

b) $\sqrt[3]{r^2}$

c) $\sqrt{x^{10}}$, for $x \geq 0$

d) $\dfrac{1}{\sqrt[3]{b^5}}$, for $b \neq 0$

Solution

a) $\sqrt[4]{x} = x^{1/4}$ $x \geq 0$

b) $\sqrt[3]{r^2} = r^{2/3}$

c) $\sqrt{x^{10}} = x^{10/2} = x^5$, $x \geq 0$

d) $\dfrac{1}{\sqrt[3]{b^5}} = \dfrac{1}{b^{5/3}} = b^{-5/3}$, $b \neq 0$ ■

EXAMPLE 12 Simplify: **a)** $8^{5/3}$; **b)** $81^{3/4}$.

Solution

a) $8^{5/3} = \left(8^{1/3}\right)^5 = \left(\sqrt[3]{8}\right)^5 = 2^5 = 32$

b) $81^{3/4} = \left(81^{1/4}\right)^3 = \left(\sqrt[4]{81}\right)^3 = 3^3 = 27$ ■

Because even roots (square roots, fourth roots, sixth roots, and so on) of negative numbers are not real numbers, the domain of a radical function may have restrictions.

EXAMPLE 13 Find the domain of the function given by
$$f(x) = \sqrt[4]{2x - 10}.$$

Solution For $f(x)$ to be a real number, $2x - 10$ cannot be negative. Thus, to find the domain of f, we solve the inequality $2x - 10 \geq 0$:

$2x - 10 \geq 0$

$2x \geq 10$ Adding 10 to both sides

$x \geq 5$.   Dividing both sides by 2

The domain of f is $\{x \mid x \geq 5\}$, or, in interval notation, $[5, \infty)$.   **7** ✔

Quick Check 7 ✔

Find the domain of the function given by
$$f(x) = \sqrt{x + 3}.$$

Power functions of the form $f(x) = ax^k$, with k a fraction, occur in many applications.

A lynx in its territorial area.

EXAMPLE 14 **Life Science: Home Range.** The *home range* of an animal is defined as the region to which the animal confines its movements. It has been shown that for carnivorous mammals the area of that region can be approximated by
$$H(w) = 0.11w^{1.36},$$

where w is the mass of the animal, in grams, and $H(w)$ is the area of the home range, in hectares. Graph the function. (*Source*: Based on information in Emlen, J. M., *Ecology: An Evolutionary Approach*, p. 200 (Reading, MA: Addison-Wesley, 1973), and Harestad, A. S., and Bunnel, F. L., "Home Range and Body Weight—A Reevaluation," *Ecology*, Vol. 60, No. 2 (April, 1979), pp. 389–402.)

Solution We can approximate function values using a power key, usually labeled ⌃ or y^x. Note that $w^{1.36} = w^{136/100} = \sqrt[100]{w^{136}}$.

w	0	700	1400	2100	2800	3500
$H(w)$	0	814.2	2089.9	3627.5	5364.5	7266.5

The graph is shown below. Note that function values increase from left to right. As body weight increases, the area over which the animal moves increases.

$$H(w) = 0.11w^{1.36}$$

Home range (in hectares) — H(w)

Mass (in grams) — w

Exponential Functions

Sometimes, we consider expressions in which a constant (called the *base*) has a variable exponent. Such expressions are used in *exponential functions*.

DEFINITION

An **exponential function** f is given by

$$f(x) = a_0 \cdot a^x,$$

where x is any real number and $a > 0$ and $a \neq 1$. The number a is the **base**.

The following are examples of exponential functions:

$$f(x) = 2^x, \quad f(x) = \left(\frac{1}{2}\right)^x, \quad f(x) = 3(0.4)^x.$$

Note that in contrast to a power function like $y = x^2$, an exponential function has the variable in the exponent, not the base. Let's consider the graphs of exponential functions.

EXAMPLE 15 Graph: $y = f(x) = 2^x$.

Solution First, we find some function values. Note that 2^x is always positive:

$$x = 0, \quad y = 2^0 = 1;$$
$$x = \frac{1}{2}, \quad y = 2^{1/2} = \sqrt{2} \approx 1.4;$$
$$x = 1, \quad y = 2^1 = 2;$$
$$x = 2, \quad y = 2^2 = 4;$$
$$x = 3, \quad y = 2^3 = 8;$$
$$x = -1, \quad y = 2^{-1} = \frac{1}{2};$$
$$x = -2, \quad y = 2^{-2}$$
$$= \frac{1}{2^2} = \frac{1}{4}.$$

In this part of the curve, $f(x)$ gets larger without bound.

$f(x) = 2^x$

This part of the curve comes very close to the x-axis, but does not touch or cross it.

y-intercept: (0, 1)

x	0	$\frac{1}{2}$	1	2	3	-1	-2
$y = f(x) = 2^x$	1	1.4	2	4	8	$\frac{1}{2}$	$\frac{1}{4}$

Quick Check 8 ✔

For $f(x) = 3^x$, complete this table of function values.

x	$f(x) = 3^x$
0	
1	
2	
3	
-1	
-2	
-3	

Graph $f(x) = 3^x$.

8 ✔

EXAMPLE 16   Graph: $y = g(x) = 3 \cdot \left(\frac{1}{2}\right)^x$.

Solution   We find some function values:

$$x = 0, \quad y = 3 \cdot \left(\frac{1}{2}\right)^0 = 3;$$

$$x = \frac{1}{2}, \quad y = 3 \cdot \left(\frac{1}{2}\right)^{1/2} \approx 2.1;$$

$$x = 1, \quad y = 3 \cdot \left(\frac{1}{2}\right)^1 = \frac{3}{2};$$

$$x = 2, \quad y = 3 \cdot \left(\frac{1}{2}\right)^2 = \frac{3}{4};$$

$$x = -1, \quad y = 3 \cdot \left(\frac{1}{2}\right)^{-1} = 3 \cdot 2 = 6;$$

$$x = -2, \quad y = 3 \cdot \left(\frac{1}{2}\right)^{-2} = 3 \cdot 4 = 12;$$

$$x = -3, \quad y = 3 \cdot \left(\frac{1}{2}\right)^{-3} = 3 \cdot 8 = 24.$$

$g(x) = 3 \cdot \left(\frac{1}{2}\right)^x$

y-intercept: (0, 3)

Quick Check 9 ✔

For $g(x) = 2 \cdot \left(\frac{1}{3}\right)^x$, complete this table of function values.

x	$g(x) = 2 \cdot \left(\frac{1}{3}\right)^x$
0	
1	
2	
3	
−1	
−2	
−3	

Graph $g(x) = 2 \cdot \left(\frac{1}{3}\right)^x$.

x	0	$\frac{1}{2}$	1	2	−1	−2	−3
$y = f(x) = 3 \cdot \left(\frac{1}{2}\right)^x$	3	2.1	$\frac{3}{2}$	$\frac{3}{4}$	6	12	24

9 ✔

In general, when $0 < a < 1$, as x gets larger, $f(x)$ gets smaller. When $a > 1$, as x gets larger, $f(x)$ also gets larger. The domain of an exponential function is all of the real numbers (this is discussed further in Section 3.1). The range is $y > 0$. Note that when $x = 0$, we have $f(0) = a_0 \cdot a^0 = a_0 \cdot 1 = a_0$. Thus, the y-intercept is $(0, a_0)$, and there are no x-intercepts.

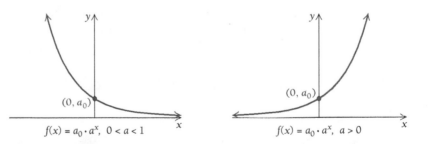

$(0, a_0)$

$f(x) = a_0 \cdot a^x, \ 0 < a < 1$

$(0, a_0)$

$f(x) = a_0 \cdot a^x, \ a > 0$

Supply and Demand Functions

In economics, *demand* is modeled by a decreasing function; that is, as the price x gets larger, the demand $D(x)$ gets smaller. However, *supply* is modeled by an increasing function: As the price x gets larger, so does the supply, $S(x)$.

Demand Functions

Suppose the relationship between the price x of a 5-lb bag of sugar and the quantity q of bags that consumers will demand at that price is given in the table and graph below.

Demand Schedule

Price, x, per 5-lb Bag	Quantity, q, of 5-lb Bags (in millions)
$5	4
4	5
3	7
2	10
1	15

Note that the quantity consumers demand is inversely proportional to the price. As the price goes up, the quantity demanded goes down.

Supply Functions

Furthermore, suppose the relationship between the price x of a 5-lb bag of sugar and the quantity q of bags that sellers are willing to supply, or sell, at that price is given in the table and graph below.

Supply Schedule

Price, x, per 5-lb Bag	Quantity, q, of 5-lb Bags (in millions)
$1	0
2	10
3	16
4	20
5	22

Note that sellers will supply greater quantities at higher prices, and consumers will demand greater quantities at lower prices.

Let's now look at these curves together. As price increases, supply increases and demand decreases; and as price decreases, demand increases but supply decreases. The point of intersection (x_E, q_E) is called the **equilibrium point**. The equilibrium price x_E (in this case, $2 per bag) corresponds to an equilibrium quantity q_E (in this case, 10 million bags). Sellers are willing to sell 10 million bags at $2 per bag, and consumers are willing to buy 10 million bags at that price. The situation is a bit like a buyer and a seller haggling over the price of an item. The equilibrium point, or selling price, is what they finally agree on.

EXAMPLE 17 **Economics: Equilibrium Point.** Find the equilibrium point for the demand and supply functions for the Ultra-Fine coffee maker. Here q represents the number of coffee makers produced, in hundreds, and x is the price of a coffee maker, in dollars.

$$\text{Demand: } q = 50 - \frac{1}{4}x$$

$$\text{Supply: } q = x - 25$$

Solution To find the equilibrium point, the quantity demanded must match the quantity produced:

$$50 - \frac{1}{4}x = x - 25 \qquad \text{Setting demand equal to supply}$$

$$50 + 25 = x + \frac{1}{4}x \qquad \text{Adding } 25 + \frac{1}{4}x \text{ to both sides}$$

$$75 = \frac{5}{4}x$$

$$75 \cdot \frac{4}{5} = x \qquad \text{Multiplying both sides by } \frac{4}{5}$$

$$60 = x.$$

Thus, $x_E = 60$. To find q_E, we substitute x_E into either function. We select the supply function:

$$q_E = x_E - 25 = 60 - 25 = 35.$$

Thus, the equilibrium quantity is 3500 units, and the equilibrium point is ($60, 3500$).   **10 ✔**

Quick Check 10 ✔

Economics: Equilibrium Point.
Repeat Example 17 for the following functions:

Demand: $q = 70 - \frac{1}{5}x$

Supply: $q = x - 20$

Section Summary

- Many types of functions have graphs that are not straight lines; among these are *quadratic functions, polynomial functions, power functions, rational functions, the absolute-value function, square-root functions,* and *exponential functions.*

- Demand is modeled by a decreasing function; that is, as the price x gets larger, the demand $D(x)$ gets smaller. Supply is modeled by an increasing function; that is, as the price x gets larger, so does the supply, $S(x)$. The point of intersection of graphs of demand and supply functions for the same product is called the *equilibrium point.*

R.5 Exercise Set

Graph each pair of equations on one set of axes.

1. $y = \frac{1}{4}x^2$ and $y = -\frac{1}{4}x^2$

2. $y = \frac{1}{2}x^2$ and $y = -\frac{1}{2}x^2$

3. $y = x^2$ and $y = x^2 - 1$

4. $y = x^2$ and $y = x^2 - 3$

5. $y = -3x^2$ and $y = -3x^2 + 2$

6. $y = -2x^2$ and $y = -2x^2 + 1$

7. $y = |x|$ and $y = |x - 3|$

8. $y = |x|$ and $y = |x - 1|$

9. $y = x^3$ and $y = x^3 + 1$

10. $y = x^3$ and $y = x^3 + 2$

11. $y = \sqrt{x}$ and $y = \sqrt{x - 1}$

12. $y = \sqrt{x}$ and $y = \sqrt{x - 2}$

For each of the following, state whether the graph of the function is a parabola. If the graph is a parabola, find its vertex.

13. $f(x) = x^2 + 4x - 7$

14. $f(x) = x^3 - 2x + 3$

15. $g(x) = 2x^4 - 4x^2 - 3$

16. $g(x) = 3x^2 - 6x$

Graph.

17. $y = x^2 - 6x + 5$

18. $y = x^2 - 4x + 3$

19. $y = -x^2 + 2x - 1$

20. $y = -x^2 - x + 6$

21. $f(x) = 3x^2 - 6x + 4$

22. $f(x) = 2x^2 - 6x + 1$

23. $g(x) = -3x^2 - 4x + 5$

24. $g(x) = -2x^2 - 3x + 7$

25. $y = \dfrac{3}{x}$

26. $y = \dfrac{2}{x}$

27. $y = -\dfrac{2}{x}$

28. $y = \dfrac{-3}{x}$

29. $y = \dfrac{1}{x - 1}$

30. $y = \dfrac{1}{x^2}$

31. $y = \sqrt[3]{x}$

32. $y = \dfrac{1}{|x|}$

33. $g(x) = \dfrac{x^2 + 7x + 10}{x + 2}$

34. $f(x) = \dfrac{x^2 + 5x + 6}{x + 3}$

35. $f(x) = \dfrac{x^2 - 1}{x - 1}$

36. $g(x) = \dfrac{x^2 - 25}{x - 5}$

37. $f(x) = (1.25)^x$

38. $g(x) = (1.5)^x$

39. $f(x) = (0.4)^x$

40. $g(x) = (0.25)^x$

41. $f(x) = 3 \cdot (1.1)^x$

42. $g(x) = 2 \cdot (1.45)^x$

43. $f(x) = 4 \cdot (0.8)^x$

44. $g(x) = 2.5 \cdot (0.33)^x$

Solve.

45. $x^2 - 2x = 2$

46. $x^2 - 2x + 1 = 5$

47. $x^2 + 6x = 1$

48. $x^2 + 4x = 3$

49. $4x^2 = 4x + 1$

50. $-4x^2 = 4x - 1$

51. $3y^2 + 8y + 2 = 0$

52. $2p^2 - 5p = 1$

53. $x + 7 + \dfrac{9}{x} = 0$ (*Hint:* Multiply both sides by x.)

54. $1 - \dfrac{1}{w} = \dfrac{1}{w^2}$

Rewrite each of the following as an equivalent expression using radical notation.

55. $x^{1/5}$

56. $t^{1/7}$

57. $y^{2/3}$

58. $t^{2/5}$

59. $t^{-2/5}$

60. $y^{-2/3}$

61. $b^{-1/3}$

62. $b^{-1/5}$

63. $(x^2 - 3)^{-1/2}$

64. $(y^2 + 7)^{-1/4}$

Rewrite each of the following as an equivalent expression with rational exponents.

65. $\sqrt{x^3}$

66. $\sqrt{x^5}$

67. $\sqrt[5]{a^3}$

68. $\sqrt[4]{b^2}, \quad b \geq 0$

69. $\sqrt[4]{x^{12}}, \quad x \geq 0$

70. $\sqrt[3]{t^6}$

71. $\dfrac{1}{\sqrt{t^5}}$

72. $\dfrac{1}{\sqrt{m^4}}$

73. $\dfrac{1}{\sqrt{x^2 + 7}}$

74. $\sqrt{x^3 + 4}$

Simplify.

75. $9^{3/2}$

76. $16^{5/2}$

77. $64^{2/3}$

78. $8^{2/3}$

Determine the domain of each function.

79. $f(x) = \dfrac{x^2 - 25}{x - 5}$

80. $f(x) = \dfrac{x^2 - 4}{x + 2}$

81. $f(x) = \dfrac{x^3}{x^2 - 5x + 6}$

82. $f(x) = \dfrac{x^4 + 7}{x^2 + 6x + 5}$

83. $f(x) = \sqrt{5x + 4}$

84. $f(x) = \sqrt{2x - 6}$

85. $f(x) = \sqrt[4]{7 - x}$

86. $f(x) = \sqrt[6]{5 - x}$

APPLICATIONS

Business and Economics

Find the equilibrium point for each pair of demand and supply functions.

87. Demand: $q = 1000 - 10x$; Supply: $q = 250 + 5x$

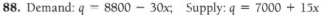

88. Demand: $q = 8800 - 30x$; Supply: $q = 7000 + 15x$

89. Demand: $q = \dfrac{5}{x}$; Supply: $q = \dfrac{x}{5}$

90. Demand: $q = \dfrac{4}{x}$; Supply: $q = \dfrac{x}{4}$

91. Demand: $q = (x - 3)^2$; Supply: $q = x^2 + 2x + 1$
(assume $x \le 3$)

92. Demand: $q = (x - 4)^2$; Supply: $q = x^2 + 2x + 6$
(assume $x \le 4$)

93. Demand: $q = 5 - x$; Supply: $q = \sqrt{x + 7}$

94. Demand: $q = 7 - x$; Supply: $q = 2\sqrt{x + 1}$

95. Price of admission.   The number of tickets sold for a fund-raiser is inversely proportional to the price of a ticket, p. If 175 tickets can be sold for \$20 each, how many tickets will be sold if the price is \$25 each?

96. Demand. The quantity sold x of a high-definition TV is inversely proportional to the price p. If 85,000 high-definition TVs sold for $1200 each, how many will be sold if the price is $850 each?

Life and Physical Sciences

97. Radar range. The function given by

$$R(x) = 11.74x^{0.25}$$

can be used to approximate the maximum range, $R(x)$, in miles, of ARSR-3 surveillance radar with a peak power of x watts.

a) Determine the maximum radar range when the peak power is 40,000 watts, 50,000 watts, and 60,000 watts.

b) Graph the function.

98. Home range. Refer to Example 14. The home range, in hectares, of an omnivorous mammal of mass w grams is given by

$$H(w) = 0.059w^{0.92}.$$

(*Source*: Harestad, A. S., and Bunnel, F. L., "Home Range and Body Weight—A Reevaluation," *Ecology*, Vol. 60, No. 2 (April, 1979), pp. 389–402.) Complete the table of approximate function values and graph the function.

w	0	1000	2000	3000	4000	5000	6000	7000
$H(w)$	0	34.0						

99. Life science: pollution control. Pollution control has become an important concern worldwide. The function

$$P(t) = 12.85t^{-0.077}$$

describes the average pollution, in micrograms per cubic meter of air, t years after 2000. (*Source*: epa.gov/airtrends/pm.html)

a) Predict the pollution in 2015, 2020, and 2025.

b) Graph the function over the interval [0, 50].

100. Surface area and mass. The surface area of a person whose mass is 75 kg can be approximated by

$$f(h) = 0.144h^{1/2},$$

where $f(h)$ is measured in square meters and h is the person's height in centimeters. (*Source*: U.S. Oncology.)

a) Find the approximate surface area of a person whose mass is 75 kg and whose height is 180 cm.

b) Find the approximate surface area of a person whose mass is 75 kg and whose height is 170 cm.

c) Graph the function f for $0 \le h \le 200$.

SYNTHESIS

101. Zipf's Law. According to Zipf's Law, the number of cities N with a population greater than S is inversely proportional to S. In 2012, there were 285 U.S. cities with a population greater than 100,000. Estimate the number of U.S. cities with a population between 350,000 and 500,000; between 300,000 and 600,000.

102. At most, how many y-intercepts can a function have? Why?

103. What is the difference between a rational function and a polynomial function?

TECHNOLOGY CONNECTION

Use the ZERO *feature or the* INTERSECT *feature to approximate the zeros of each function to three decimal places.*

104. $f(x) = x^3 - x$
(Also use algebra to find the zeros of this function.)

105. $f(x) = 2x^3 - x^2 - 14x - 10$

106. $f(x) = \frac{1}{2}(|x - 4| + |x - 7|) - 4$

107. $f(x) = x^4 + 4x^3 - 36x^2 - 160x + 300$

108. $f(x) = \sqrt{7 - x^2} - 1$

109. $f(x) = |x + 1| + |x - 2| - 5$

110. $f(x) = |x + 1| + |x - 2|$

111. $f(x) = |x + 1| + |x - 2| - 3$

112. $f(x) = x^8 + 8x^7 - 28x^6 - 56x^5 + 70x^4 + 56x^3 - 28x^2 - 8x + 1$

113. Find the equilibrium point for the following demand and supply functions, where q is the quantity, in thousands of units, and x is the price per unit, in dollars.

Demand: $q = 15 \cdot (0.95)^x$

Supply: $q = 2.5 \cdot (1.13)^x$

Answers to Quick Checks

1. (a)

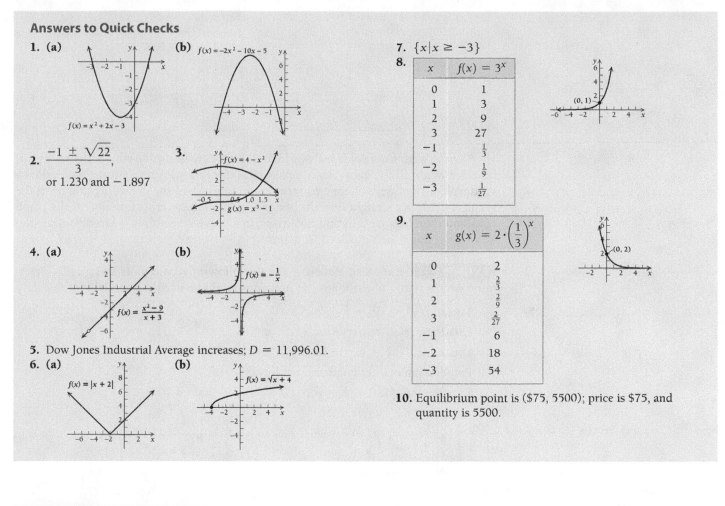

$f(x) = x^2 + 2x - 3$

(b) $f(x) = -2x^2 - 10x - 5$

2. $\dfrac{-1 \pm \sqrt{22}}{3}$, or 1.230 and -1.897

3. $f(x) = 4 - x^2$ $g(x) = x^3 - 1$

4. (a) $f(x) = \dfrac{x^2 - 9}{x + 3}$

(b) $f(x) = -\dfrac{1}{x}$

5. Dow Jones Industrial Average increases; $D = 11{,}996.01$.

6. (a) $f(x) = |x + 2|$

(b) $f(x) = \sqrt{x + 4}$

7. $\{x \mid x \geq -3\}$

8.

x	$f(x) = 3^x$
0	1
1	3
2	9
3	27
-1	$\frac{1}{3}$
-2	$\frac{1}{9}$
-3	$\frac{1}{27}$

$(0, 1)$

9.

x	$g(x) = 2 \cdot \left(\dfrac{1}{3}\right)^x$
0	2
1	$\frac{2}{3}$
2	$\frac{2}{9}$
3	$\frac{2}{27}$
-1	6
-2	18
-3	54

$(0, 2)$

10. Equilibrium point is ($75, 5500$); price is $75, and quantity is 5500.

Mathematical Modeling and Curve Fitting

R.6

- Use curve fitting to find a mathematical model for a set of data and use the model to make predictions.

Fitting Functions to Data

We now have a library of functions that can serve as models for applications, and they are shown below. Cubic and quartic functions are covered in detail in Chapter 2, but we show them for reference. We will not consider rational functions in this section.

Linear function:
$f(x) = mx + b$

Quadratic function:
$f(x) = ax^2 + bx + c, \ a > 0$

Quadratic function:
$f(x) = ax^2 + bx + c, \ a < 0$

Absolute-value function:
$f(x) = |x|$

Cubic function:
$f(x) = ax^3 + bx^2 + cx + d, \ a > 0$

Quartic function:
$f(x) = ax^4 + bx^3 + cx^2 + dx + e, \ a > 0$

Exponential growth:
$f(x) = a_0 \cdot a^x, \ a > 1$

Exponential decay:
$f(x) = a_0 \cdot a^x, \ 0 < a < 1$

Now let's consider some real-world data. How can we decide which, if any, type of function might fit the data? One simple way is to examine a graph of the data called a **scatterplot.** Then we look for a pattern resembling one of the preceding graphs. If the graph resembles a straight line, the best model might be a linear function. If the graph rises and then falls, or falls and then rises, in a curve resembling a parabola, then the best model might be a quadratic function.

EXAMPLE 1   **Choosing Models.**   For the following scatterplots and graphs, determine which, if any, of the following functions might be used as a model for the data.

Linear, $f(x) = mx + b$

Quadratic, $f(x) = ax^2 + bx + c, \quad a > 0$

Quadratic, $f(x) = ax^2 + bx + c, \quad a < 0$

Polynomial, neither quadratic nor linear

Exponential, $f(x) = a_0 \cdot a^x, \quad 0 < a < 1 \quad \text{or} \quad a > 1$

a)

b)

c)

d)

DRIVER FATALITIES BY AGE

(*Source*: Based on data from the American Automobile Association, 2012.)

e)

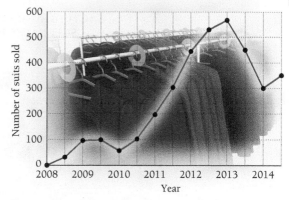

ACTUAL AND PROJECTED ANNUAL
SUIT SALES FOR RAGGS LTD.

(Source: Business Week annual executive pay surveys.)

Solution

a) The data rise and then fall in a curved manner fitting a quadratic function,

$$f(x) = ax^2 + bx + c, \quad a < 0.$$

b) The data seem to fit a linear function,

$$f(x) = mx + b.$$

c) The data rise in a manner fitting the right-hand side of a quadratic function,

$$f(x) = ax^2 + bx + c, \quad a > 0.$$

The data may also fit an expontential growth function,

$$f(x) = a_0 \cdot a^x, \quad a > 1.$$

d) The data fall and then rise in a curved manner suggesting a quadratic function,

$$f(x) = ax^2 + bx + c, \quad a > 0.$$

DRIVER FATALITIES BY AGE

Age of drivers (in years)

(Source: Based on data from the American Automobile Association, 2012.)

e) The data rise and fall more than once, so they do not fit a linear or quadratic function but might fit a polynomial function that is neither quadratic nor linear.

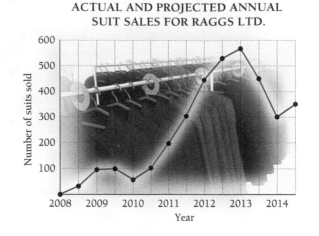

ACTUAL AND PROJECTED ANNUAL SUIT SALES FOR RAGGS LTD.

It is sometimes possible to find a mathematical model by graphing a set of data as a scatterplot, inspecting the graph to see if a known type of function seems to fit, and then using the data points to derive the equation of a specific function.

EXAMPLE 2   **Business: High-Speed Internet Subscribers.**   The following table and scatterplot show the number of U.S. households with high-speed Internet service. It appears that the data can be modeled by a linear function.

Years since 2005, x	Number of Households with High-Speed Internet Service (in millions), y	Scatterplot
2005, 0	25.4	
2006, 1	28.9	
2007, 2	35.7	
2008, 3	39.3	
2009, 4	41.8	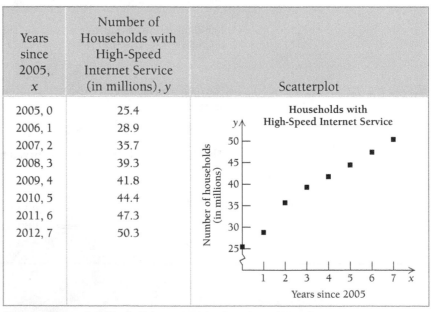
2010, 5	44.4	
2011, 6	47.3	
2012, 7	50.3	

(*Source*: National Cable & Telecommunications Association.)

a) Find a linear function that fits the data.

b) Use the model to predict the number of households with high-speed Internet service in 2018.

Solution

a) We can choose any two data points to determine an equation. Let's use $(2, 35.7)$ and $(7, 50.3)$.

We first determine the slope of the line:

$$m = \frac{50.3 - 35.7}{7 - 2} = \frac{14.6}{5} = 2.92.$$

We substitude 2.92 for m and either of the points $(2, 35.7)$ or $(7, 50.3)$ for (x_1, y_1) in the point–slope equation. Using $(7, 50.3)$ we get

$$y - 50.3 = 2.92(x - 7),$$

which simplifies to

$$y = 2.92x + 29.86,$$

where x is the number of years after 2005 and y is in millions. We can then graph the linear equation $y = 2.92x + 29.86$ on the scatterplot to see how it fits the data.

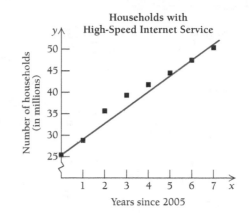

b) We can predict the number of households with high-speed Internet in 2018 by substituting 13 for x (since $2018 - 2005 = 13$) in the model:

$$y = 2.92x + 29.86 \qquad \text{Model}$$
$$= 2.92(13) + 29.86 \qquad \text{Substituting}$$
$$\approx 67.82.$$

Quick Check 1 ✔

Business. Repeat Example 2 using the data points $(1, 28.9)$ and $(5, 44.4)$. Are the model and the result different from those in Example 2?

We can then predict that there will be about 67.82 million households with high-speed Internet in 2018.   **1** ✔

Different pairs of points yield different linear models, and *regression* is used to find a line of *best* fit.

TECHNOLOGY CONNECTION

Linear Regression: Fitting a Linear Function to Data

We now consider **linear regression**, the preferred method for fitting a linear function to a set of data. Although the complete basis for this method is discussed in Section 6.4, we consider it here because we can carry out the procedure easily using technology. One advantage of linear regression is that it uses *all* data points rather than just two.

EXAMPLE **Business: High-Speed Internet Subscribers.** Consider the data in Example 2.

a) Find the equation of the regression line for the given data. Then graph both the regression line and the data.

b) Use the model to predict the number of households with high-speed Internet in 2018. Compare your answer to that found in Example 2.

Solution

a) To fit a linear function using regression, we select the EDIT option of the STAT menu. We then enter the data, entering the first coordinate for L1 and the second coordinate for L2.

$$(0, 25.4), (1, 28.9), (2, 35.7), (3, 39.3),$$
$$(4, 41.8), (5, 44.4), (6, 47.3), (7, 50.3)$$

(continued)

To view the data points, we turn on PLOT1 by pressing ENTER from y_1 at the Y= screen and then pressing GRAPH. To set the window, we could select the ZoomStat option of ZOOM. Instead, we select a $[-1, 15, 0, 80]$ window.

To find the line that best fits the data, we press STAT, select CALC, then LinReg(ax+b), and then press ENTER.

```
LinReg
  y = ax + b
  a = 3.510714286
  b = 26.85
```

A convenient way to copy a regression function, in full detail, onto the Y= screen is to press Y=, move the cursor to Y2 (or wherever the function is to appear), press VARS, and select STATISTICS and then EQ and RegEq.

```
Plot 1  Plot 2  Plot 3
\Y1 = 3.510714286X + 26.85
\Y2 =
\Y3 =
\Y4 =
```

b) To find, or predict, the number of U.S. households with high-speed Internet service in 2018, we press 2ND, CALC, 1, and enter 13.

Note that the result, 72.49 million, is more than the 67.96 million found in Example 2. Statisticians might give more credence to the regression value because more data points were used to construct the equation.

EXERCISE

1. Study time and test scores. The data in the following table relate study time and test scores.

Study Time (in hours)	Test Grade (in percent)
7	83
8	85
9	88
10	91
11	?

a) Make a scatterplot of the data, fit a regression line to the data, and graph the line with the scatterplot.

b) Use the linear model to predict the test score received when one has studied for 11 hr.

c) Discuss the limitations of a linear model for this application.

EXAMPLE 3 **Life Science: Hours of Sleep and Death Rate.** From a study by Dr. Harold J. Morowitz of Yale University, the following data show the relationship between the death rate of men and the average number of hours per day that the men slept.

Average Number of Hours of Sleep, x	Death Rate per 100,000 Males, y
5	1121
6	805
7	626
8	813
9	967

(*Source:* Morowitz, Harold J., "Hiding in the Hammond Report," *Hospital Practice.*)

a) Make a scatterplot of the data, and determine whether the data seem to fit a quadratic function.

b) Find a quadratic function that fits the data.

c) Use the model to find the death rate for males who sleep 2 hr, 8 hr, and 10 hr.

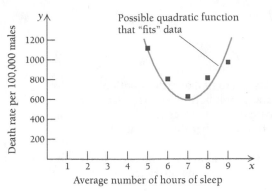

Average number of hours of sleep

Solution

a) The scatterplot is shown to the left. Note that the rate drops and then rises, which suggests that a quadratic function might fit the data.

b) We consider the quadratic model,

$$y = ax^2 + bx + c. \tag{1}$$

To determine the constants a, b, and c, we choose three of the data points: $(5, 1121)$, $(7, 626)$, and $(9, 967)$. Since these points are to be solutions of equation (1), it follows that

$$1121 = a \cdot 5^2 + b \cdot 5 + c, \quad \text{or} \quad 1121 = 25a + 5b + c,$$
$$626 = a \cdot 7^2 + b \cdot 7 + c, \quad \text{or} \quad 626 = 49a + 7b + c,$$
$$967 = a \cdot 9^2 + b \cdot 9 + c, \quad \text{or} \quad 967 = 81a + 9b + c.$$

We solve this system of three equations in three variables using procedures of algebra and get

$$a = 104.5, \quad b = -1501.5, \quad \text{and} \quad c = 6016.$$

Substituting these values into equation (1), we get the following quadratic function:

$$y = 104.5x^2 - 1501.5x + 6016.$$

c) The death rate for males who sleep 2 hr is

$$y = 104.5(2)^2 - 1501.5(2) + 6016 = 3431 \text{ deaths per 100,000 males.}$$

The death rate for males who sleep 8 hr is

$$y = 104.5(8)^2 - 1501.5(8) + 6016 = 692 \text{ deaths per 100,000 males.}$$

The death rate for males who sleep 10 hr is

$$y = 104.5(10)^2 - 1501.5(10) + 6016 = 1451 \text{ deaths per 100,000 males.}$$

2 ✔

Quick Check 2 ✔

Life Science. See the data on live births in the following Technology Connection. Use the data points $(16, 15.4)$, $(27, 107.2)$, and $(37, 47.2)$ to find a quadratic function that fits the data. Use the model to predict the average number of live births to women age 20.

TECHNOLOGY CONNECTION

Mathematical Modeling Using Regression: Fitting Quadratic and Other Polynomial Functions to Data

Regression extends to quadratic, cubic, and quartic polynomial functions.

EXAMPLE **Life Science: Live Births to Women of Age x.** The chart below relates the average number of live births to women of a particular age.

Age, x (in years)	Average Number of Live Births per 1000 women
16	15.4
18.5	54.1
22	85.3
27	107.2
32	96.5
37	47.2
42	10.3

(*Source: CDC, National Vital Statistics*, Vol. 62, No. 1, June 28, 2013.)

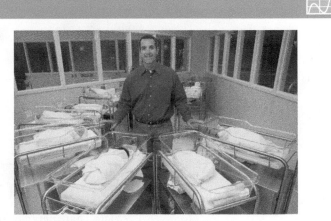

a) Fit a quadratic function to the data using REGRESSION. Then make a scatterplot of the data and graph the quadratic function with the scatterplot.

b) Fit a cubic function to the data using REGRESSION. Then make a scatterplot of the data and graph the cubic function with the scatterplot.

c) Which function seems to fit the data better?

d) Use the function from part (c) to estimate the average number of live births to women of ages 20 and 30.

(continued)

Mathematical Modeling Using Regression (*continued*)

Solution   We proceed as follows.

a) To fit a quadratic function using REGRESSION, the procedure is similar to what is outlined in the preceding Technology Connection. We enter the data but select QuadReg instead of LinReg(ax + b). In this case, we use ZoomStat to set the window. Here y_1 uses approximations of a, b, and c from the QuadReg screen.

$$y_1 = -0.54x^2 + 30.56x - 329.5$$

b) To fit a cubic function, we select CubicReg and obtain the following, which we enter as y_2.

$$y_2 = 0.0140646004x^3$$
$$- 1.765413134x^2$$
$$+ 64.29927316x$$
$$- 620.3338007$$

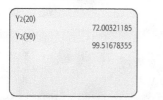

c) The cubic function fits better.

d) We press **2ND** **QUIT** to leave the graph screen. Pressing **VARS** and selecting Y-VARS and then FUNCTION and Y2, we have $y_2(20) \approx 72$ and $y_2(30) \approx 99.5$ as shown.

```
Y2(20)
              72.00321185
Y2(30)
              99.51678355
```

The TRACE feature can also be used. Thus, the average number of live births is 72 per 1000 women age 20 and 99.5 per 1000 women age 30.

EXERCISES

1. Life science: live births.

a) Use REGRESSION to fit a quartic equation to the live-birth data. Graph both the scatterplot of the data and the quartic function. Does the quartic function give a better fit than either the quadratic or the cubic function?

b) Explain why the domain of the cubic live-birth function should probably be restricted to the interval $[15, 45]$.

2. Business: median household income by age.

Age, x	Median Income in 2003
19.5	$27,053
29.5	44,779
39.5	55,044
49.5	60,242
59.5	49,215
65	23,787

(*Source:* Based on data in the *Statistical Abstract of the United States, 2005.*)

a) Make a scatterplot of the data and fit a quadratic function to the data using QuadReg. Then graph the quadratic function with the scatterplot.

b) Fit a cubic function to the data using CubicReg. Then graph the cubic function with the scatterplot.

c) Fit a quartic function to the data using QuartReg. Then graph the quartic function with the scatterplot.

d) Which of the quadratic, cubic, or quartic functions seems to best fit the data?

e) Use the function from part (d) to estimate the median household income of people age 25; of people age 45.

3. Life science: hours of sleep and death rate. Solve Example 3 using quadratic regression.

Exponential Models

Data that increase quickly as x increases may fit an exponential model of the form $f(x) = a_0 \cdot a^x$, where $a > 1$. If the data decrease in such a way that they "level off" as x increases, then the exponential model $f(x) = a_0 \cdot a^x$, where $0 < a < 1$, may fit.

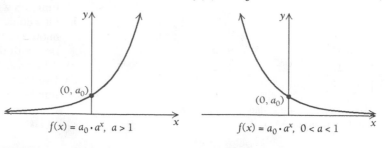

EXAMPLE 4   Business: Annual Sales of Compact Discs. The graph below illustrates the annual sales (in millions of dollars, rounded to the nearest $250 million) of compact discs in the United States between 2007 and 2012.

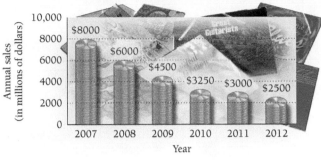

ANNUAL SALES OF COMPACT DISCS

(*Source:* Based on data from the RIAA.)

a) Find a quadratic model, $f(x) = ax^2 + bx + c$, that fits the data, and use it to estimate annual sales in 2017.

b) Find an exponential model, $f(x) = a_0 \cdot a^x$, that fits the data, and use it to estimate annual sales in 2017.

c) Which model better predicts future annual sales of compact discs?

Solution

a) We find that $f(x) = 223.214x^2 - 2194.643x + 7982.143$ fits this data. Since 2017 is 10 years after 2007, we use $x = 10$. The estimate of annual sales of compact discs for 2017 is $f(10) = 8357.1$, or approximately $8357 million.

b) We find that $f(x) = 7503.176 \cdot (0.791)^x$ also fits the data. Using this model, the annual sales of compact discs for 2017 is $f(10) = 716.47$, or approximately $716.5 million.

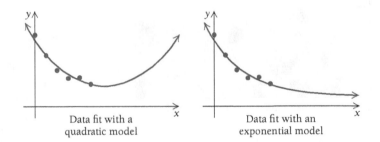

Data fit with a quadratic model

Data fit with an exponential model

c) With the quadratic model, annual sales increase as x (time) increases, so it is probably not a very accurate model for predicting future sales of compact discs. The exponential model yields decreasing sales as x increases. Thus, it is probably a more accurate predictor of future sales of compact discs. ∎

R.6   Exercise Set

Choosing models. *For the scatterplots and graphs in Exercises 1–9, determine which, if any, of the following functions might be the best model for the data:*

Linear, $f(x) = mx + b$

Quadratic, $f(x) = ax^2 + bx + c, a > 0$

Quadratic, $f(x) = ax^2 + bx + c, a < 0$

Polynomial, neither quadratic nor linear

Exponential, $f(x) = a_0 \cdot a^x, 0 < a < 1$ or $a > 1$

1.

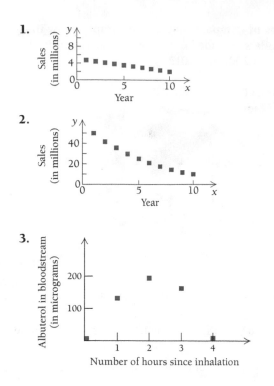

2.

3.

Business and Economics

4.

U.S. TRADE DEFICIT WITH JAPAN

(*Source*: U.S. Census Bureau, Foreign Trade Statistics.)

5.

MEDIAN INCOME

(*Source*: U.S. Census Bureau.)

6.

NBA AVERAGE SALARY

(*Source*: *The Compendium of Professional Basketball*, by Robert D. Bradley, Xaler Press, 2010; personal communication with author, 2013.)

7.

AVERAGE MONTHLY TEMPERATURE IN DALLAS

(*Source*: www.weather.com, Dallas, TX, 75235.)

8.

CABLE VIDEO CUSTOMERS

(*Source*: www.ncta.org.)

APPLICATIONS

Business and Economics

9. Cable video customers.

a) For the data shown in Exercise 8, find a linear function that fits the data using the values given for 2006 and 2012. Let x represent the number of years since 2006.

b) Use the linear function to estimate the number of cable video customers in 2018.

10. Average salary in NBA. Use the data from the bar graph in Exercise 6.

    a) Find a linear function that fits the data using the average salaries given for the years 2006 and 2013. Use 0 for 2006 and 7 for 2013.

    b) Use the linear function to predict average salaries in 2018 and 2025.

    c) In what year will the average salary reach 7.0 million?

Life and Physical Sciences

11. Absorption of an asthma medication. Use the data from Exercise 3.

    a) Find a quadratic function that fits the data using the data points $(0, 0)$, $(2, 200)$, and $(3, 167)$.

    b) Use the function to estimate the amount of albuterol in the bloodstream 4 hr after inhalation.

    c) Does it make sense to use this function for $t = 6$? Why or why not?

12. Median income. Use the data given in Exercise 5.

    a) Find a quadratic function that fits the data using the data points $(21, 14483)$, $(41, 50168)$, and $(61, 49615)$.

    b) Use the function to estimate the median income of Americans who were 55 in 2012.

13. Braking distance.

    a) Find a quadratic function that fits the following data.

TRAVEL SPEED (mph)	BRAKING DISTANCE (ft)
20	25
40	105
60	300

(*Source:* New Jersey Department of Law and Public Safety.)

    b) Use the function to estimate the braking distance of a car traveling at 50 mph.

    c) Does it make sense to use this function when speeds are less than 15 mph? Why or why not?

14. Daytime accidents.

    a) Find a quadratic function that fits the following data.

TRAVEL SPEED (in km/h)	NUMBER OF DAYTIME ACCIDENTS (for every 200 million km driven)
60	100
80	130
100	200

    b) Use the function to estimate the number of daytime accidents that occur at 50 km/h for every 200 million km driven.

15. High blood pressure in women.

    a) Choose two points from the following data and find a linear function that fits the data.

AGE OF FEMALE	PERCENTAGE OF FEMALES WITH HIGH BLOOD PRESSURE
30	1.4
40	8.5
50	19.1
60	31.9
70	53.0

(*Source:* Based on data from Health United States 2005, CDC/NCHS.)

    b) Graph the scatterplot and the function on the same set of axes.

    c) Use the function to estimate the percentage of 55-yr-old women with high blood pressure.

16. High blood pressure in men.

    a) Choose two points from the following data and find a linear function that fits the data.

AGE OF MALE	PERCENTAGE OF MALES WITH HIGH BLOOD PRESSURE
30	7.3
40	12.1
50	20.4
60	24.8
70	34.9

(*Source:* Based on data from Health United States 2005, CDC/NCHS.)

    b) Graph the scatterplot and the function on the same set of axes.

    c) Use the function to estimate the percent of 55-yr-old men with high blood pressure.

In Exercises 17–20, give the numbers in the exponential function to three decimal places.

17. Population.

    a) Find the exponential function that best fits the following data.

YEARS SINCE 1970	POPULATION OF TEXAS (in millions)
0	11.2
10	14.2
20	17.0
30	20.9
43	26.4

(*Source:* www.census.gov.)

    b) Graph the scatterplot and the function on the same set of axes.

    c) Use the function to estimate the population of Texas in 2020.

18. Population.

a) Find the exponential function that best fits the following data.

YEARS SINCE 1970	POPULATION OF DETROIT (in millions)
0	1.5
10	1.2
20	1.0
30	0.95
40	0.71

(*Source:* www.census.gov.)

b) Graph the scatterplot and the function on the same set of axes.

c) Use the function to estimate the population of Detroit in 2020.

19. Buying power.

a) Find the exponential function that best fits the following data.

YEARS SINCE 1980	EQUIVALENT BUYING POWER OF $100 (in 1980 dollars)
0	$100.00
10	$158.62
20	$208.98
30	$264.63
33	$282.85

(*Source:* http://data.bls.gov/cgi-bin/cpicalc.pl.)

b) Graph the scatterplot and the function on the same set of axes.

c) Use the function to estimate the equivalent buying power of $100 (in 1980 dollars) in 2020.

d) What other models also fit this data? Which model best predicts the equivalent buying power of $100 (in 1980 dollars) for future years? Why?

20. Stock prices.

a) Find the exponential function that best fits the following data.

YEARS SINCE 2010	PRICE OF ONE SHARE OF STARBUCKS STOCK AT BEGINNING OF JANUARY
0	$20.59
1	$30.21
2	$46.61
3	$55.39
4	$76.17

(*Source:* yahoo.finance; Nasdaq.)

b) Graph the scatterplot and the function on the same set of axes.

c) Use the function to estimate the price of one share of Starbucks stock in 2018.

d) What other models also fit this data? Which model best predicts the price of one share of Starbucks stock in future years? Why?

SYNTHESIS

21. Under what conditions might it make better sense to use a linear function rather than a quadratic or cubic function that fits a few data points more closely?

22. For modeling the number of hours of daylight for the dates April 22 to August 22, which would be a better choice: a linear function or a quadratic function? Why?

23. What restrictions should be placed on the domain of the quadratic function found in Exercise 11? Why are such restrictions needed?

24. What restrictions should be placed on the domain of the quadratic function found in Exercise 12? Why are such restrictions needed?

TECHNOLOGY CONNECTION

25. Business: cable video customers.

a) Use regression to fit a linear function to the data shown in Exercise 8.

b) Use the function to estimate the number of cable video customers in 2018.

c) Compare your answer for part (b) to that found in Exercise 9. Which is more accurate?

d) Fit an exponential function to the data and use it to estimate the number of cable video customers in 2018.

e) Is a linear or an exponential model more appropriate for this set of data? Why.

26. Business: trade deficit with Japan.

a) Use regression to fit a cubic function to the data in Exercise 4. Let x be the number of years after 2006.

b) Use the function to estimate the trade deficit with Japan in 2017.

c) Why might a linear function be a more logical choice than a cubic function for modeling this set of data?

Answers to Quick Checks

1. $y = 3.875x + 25.025$; 59.9 million high-speed internet subscribers. The model is different, and the prediction is higher.   **2.** $y = -0.683x^2 + 37.719x - 413.234$; 67.9 live births per 1000 women age 20.

KEY TERMS AND CONCEPTS

EXAMPLES

SECTION R.1

In an **ordered pair** (x, y), the first number is called the **first coordinate** and the second number is called the **second coordinate**. Together, they are the **coordinates** of the point.

A **solution** of an equation in two variables is an ordered pair of numbers that, when substituted for the variables, forms a true equation. The **graph** of an equation is a drawing that represents all ordered pairs that are solutions of the equation.

This is the graph of the equation $y = x^4 - 2x^2$.

The mathematics used to represent the essential features of an applied problem comprise a **mathematical model**.

Business. The equation

$$A = \$1000\left(1 + \frac{r}{4}\right)^{7 \cdot 4}$$

is used to estimate the amount A, in dollars, to which $1000 will grow in 7 years, at interest rate r, compounded quarterly.

SECTION R.2

A **function** is a correspondence between a first set, called a **domain**, and a second set, called a **range**, for which each member of the domain corresponds to *exactly one* member of the range.

A graph represents a function if it is impossible to draw a vertical line that crosses the graph more than once.

Not a function   A function

Function notation permits us to easily determine what **output**, or member of the range, is paired with a given **input**, or member of the domain.

The function given by $f(x) = x^2 - 5x - 8$ allows us to determine what member of the range is paired with the number 2 of the domain:

$$f(x) = x^2 - 5x - 8$$
$$f(2) = 2^2 - 5(2) - 8$$
$$= 4 - 10 - 8$$
$$= -14.$$

(continued)

KEY TERMS AND CONCEPTS	EXAMPLES

SECTION R.2 (*continued*)

In calculus, it is important to be able to simplify an expression like

$$\frac{f(x + h) - f(x)}{h}.$$

For $f(x) = x^2 - 5x - 8$,

$$\frac{f(x + h) - f(x)}{h} = \frac{[(x + h)^2 - 5(x + h) - 8] - f(x)}{h}$$

$$= \frac{x^2 + 2xh + h^2 - 5x - 5h - 8 - [x^2 - 5x - 8]}{h}$$

$$= \frac{x^2 + 2xh + h^2 - 5x - 5h - 8 - x^2 + 5x + 8}{h}$$

$$= \frac{2xh + h^2 - 5h}{h}$$

$$= \frac{h(2x + h - 5)}{h}$$

$$= 2x + h - 5, \ h \neq 0.$$

A function that is defined **piecewise** specifies different rules for parts of the domain.

To graph

$$g(x) = \begin{cases} \dfrac{1}{3}x + 3, & \text{for } x < 3, \\ -x, & \text{for } x \geq 3, \end{cases}$$

we plot $\dfrac{1}{3}x + 3$ for all inputs x less than 3 and $-x$ for all inputs x greater than or equal to 3.

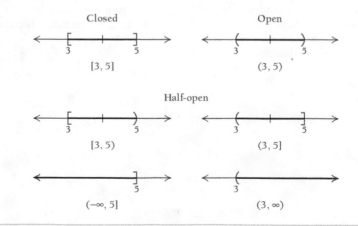

$g(x) = \frac{1}{3}x + 3$, for $x < 3$

$g(x) = -x$, for $x \geq 3$

SECTION R.3

The domain of any function is a **set**, or collection of objects. In this book, the domain is usually a subset of the real numbers.

There are three ways of describing sets:

Roster Notation: $\{-2, 5, 9, \pi\}$

Set-Builder Notation: $\{x | x \text{ is a real number and } x \geq 3\}$

Interval Notation:

Closed
[3, 5]

Open
(3, 5)

Half-open
[3, 5)

(3, 5]

(−∞, 5]

(3, ∞)

KEY TERMS AND CONCEPTS	EXAMPLES

SECTION R.3 (*continued*)

For a function given by an equation or formula, the domain is the largest set of real numbers (inputs) for which function values (outputs) can be calculated.	**Function** **Domain**

$$f(x) = \frac{8x}{x^2 - 9} = \frac{8x}{(x-3)(x+3)}$$ All real numbers except -3 and 3.

$$g(x) = \sqrt{10 - 5x}$$ All real numbers x for which $10 - 5x \geq 0$ or $10 \geq 5x$ or $2 \geq x$. The domain is $(-\infty, 2]$.

$$h(x) = |x - 3| + 5x^2$$ All real numbers, $\mathbb{R}$.

SECTION R.4

The **slope m** of the line containing the points (x_1, y_1) and (x_2, y_2) is given by
$$m = \frac{y_2 - y_1}{x_2 - x_1}$$
and can be regarded as **average rate of change**. An equation of the form $f(x) = mx + b$ is said to be in **slope–intercept form**. Its graph has slope m and y-intercept $(0, b)$.

An equation of the form $y - y_1 = m(x - x_1)$ is said to be in **point–slope form**. Its graph is a line with slope m passing through the point (x_1, y_1).

The graph of a **constant function**, given by $f(x) = c$, is a horizontal line.

The graph of an equation of the form $x = a$ is a vertical line and is not a function.

The variable y **varies directly** with x if there exists some positive constant m for which $y = mx$. We say that m is the **variation constant**.

$$y = 3.14x, \qquad A = 1.08t, \qquad I = kR, \qquad y = \frac{1}{3}x$$

Total profit is the difference between **total revenue** and **total cost**.

The value x for which $P(x) = 0$ is the **break-even value**.

For $P(x) = R(x) - C(x)$, $R(x) = 84x$, and $C(x) = 28x + 56{,}000$, the break-even value is found as follows:

$$R(x) = C(x)$$
$$84x = 28x + 56{,}000$$
$$56x = 56{,}000$$
$$x = 10{,}000.$$

(continued)

KEY TERMS AND CONCEPTS	EXAMPLES

SECTION R.5

The graph of a **quadratic function** $f(x) = ax^2 + bx + c$ is a **parabola** with a **vertex** at $\left(-\dfrac{b}{2a}, f\left(-\dfrac{b}{2a}\right)\right)$. The graph opens **upward** if $a > 0$ and **downward** if $a < 0$. It is an example of a nonlinear function.

The vertical line $x = -\dfrac{b}{2a}$ is the **line of symmetry**.

The **x-intercepts** of the graph of a quadratic equation, $f(x) = ax^2 + bx + c$, are the solutions of $ax^2 + bx + c = 0$ and are given by the quadratic formula

$$x = \frac{-b \pm \sqrt{b^2 - 4ac}}{2a}.$$

The x-intercepts of $f(x) = x^2 - 6x - 10$ are found by solving $x^2 - 6x - 10 = 0$. They are

$$\frac{-b + \sqrt{b^2 - 4ac}}{2a} = \frac{-(-6) + \sqrt{(-6)^2 - 4(1)(-10)}}{2(1)} = 3 + \sqrt{19}, \text{ and}$$

$$\frac{-b - \sqrt{b^2 - 4ac}}{2a} = \frac{-(-6) - \sqrt{(-6)^2 - 4(1)(-10)}}{2(1)} = 3 - \sqrt{19}.$$

A **polynomial function** is a function like those shown at the right.

$f(x) = -8$, constant;
$g(x) = 3x - 7$, linear;
$h(x) = x^2 - 6x - 10$, quadratic;
$p(x) = 2x^3 - 7x^2 + 0.23x - 10$, cubic.

Power functions are polynomial functions of the form $f(x) = ax^n$, where n is a positive integer.

A **rational function** is a function that can be expressed as the quotient of two polynomials.

$$g(x) = \frac{x^2 - 9}{x + 3}, \quad h(x) = \frac{x^3 - 4x^2 + x - 5}{x^2 - 6x - 10},$$

$$f(x) = \frac{x^3 - 4x^2 + x - 5}{1} = x^3 - 4x^2 + x - 5.$$

KEY TERMS AND CONCEPTS	EXAMPLES
SECTION R.5 (*continued*)	

The domain of a rational function is restricted to those input values that do not result in division by zero.

For $f(x) = \dfrac{1}{x-3}$, the domain is the set of all real numbers except 3, or $(-\infty, 3) \cup (3, \infty)$.

$f(x) = \dfrac{1}{x-3}$

An **absolute-value** function is described using absolute value symbols.

$f(x) = |x|$ $g(x) = |x+2|$

A **square-root function** is a function described using a square root symbol.

$f(x) = \sqrt{x}$ $g(x) = \sqrt{x+3}$

An **exponential function** can be written in the form $f(x) = a_0 \cdot a^x$, $a > 0$, $a \neq 1$. The domain of an exponential function is all real numbers.

The range is $y > 0$, and the y-intercept is $(0, a_0)$. There is no x-intercept.

$(0, 2)$ $(0, 3)$

$f(x) = 2(1.2)^x$ $g(x) = 3(0.8)^x$

The point at which demand and supply are the same is called an **equilibrium point**.

Demand

Supply

Quantity

Equilibrium point

Price

(*continued*)

KEY TERMS AND CONCEPTS	EXAMPLES

SECTION R.6

When real-world data are available, we can form a **scatterplot** and decide which, if any, of the graphs in this chapter best models the situation. Then we can use an appropriate model to make predictions.

Business.

Average Gasoline Prices, 2003–2013

YEARS SINCE 2003	PRICE PER GALLON
0	1.52
1	1.81
2	2.25
3	2.53
4	2.77
5	3.21
6	2.33
7	2.74
8	3.48
9	3.55
10	3.45

(*Source*: eia.gov/petroleum/gasprices.)

CHAPTER R
Review Exercises

These review exercises are for test preparation. They can also serve as a practice test. Answers are at the back of the book. Red bracketed section references indicate the part(s) of the chapter to restudy if your answer is incorrect.

CONCEPT REINFORCEMENT

For each equation in column A, select the most appropriate graph in column B. [R.1, R.4, R.5]

Column A

Column B

1. $y = |x|$ **a)**

2. $f(x) = x^2 - 1$ **b)**

3. $y = -2x - 1$ **c)**

4. $y = x$ **d)**

5. $g(x) = \sqrt{x}$ **e)**

6. $f(x) = 0.5(1.2)^x$ **f)**

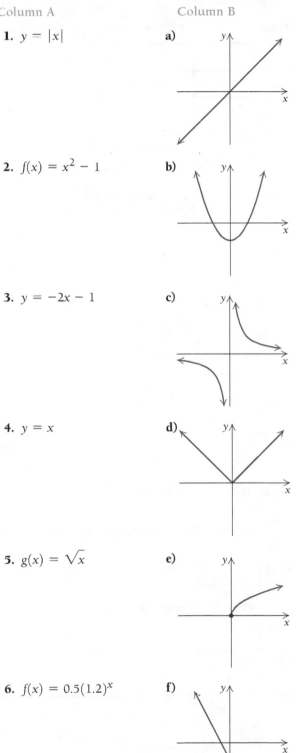

7. $f(x) = \dfrac{1}{x}$ **g)**

In Exercises 8–14, classify each statement as either true or false.

8. The graph of an equation represents all ordered pairs that are solutions of the equation. [R.1]

9. If $f(-3) = 5$ and $f(3) = 5$, then f cannot be a function. [R.2]

10. The notation $(3, 7)$ can represent a point or an interval. [R.3]

11. An equation of the form $y - y_1 = m(x - x_1)$ has a graph that is a line of slope m passing through (x_1, y_1). [R.4]

12. The graph of an equation of the form $f(x) = ax^2 + bx + c$ has its vertex at $x = b/(2a)$. [R.5]

13. A scatterplot is a random collection of points near a line. [R.6]

14. Unless stated otherwise, the domain of a polynomial function is the set of all real numbers. [R.5]

REVIEW EXERCISES

15. Hearing-impaired Americans. The following graph shows the number of hearing-impaired Americans who are x years old. (*Source:* Better Hearing Institute.) [R.1, R.5]

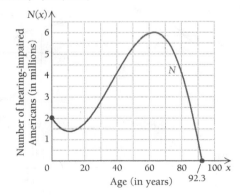

a) What is the number of hearing-impaired Americans aged 40?

b) For what age(s) are about 3,000,000 Americans hearing-impaired?

c) What is a reasonable estimate of the domain of this function? Why?

16. Finance: compound interest. Sam borrows $4000 at 12%, compounded annually. How much does she owe at the end of 2 yr? [R.1]

17. Business: compound interest. Suppose $1100 is invested at 5%, compounded semiannually. How much is in the account at the end of 4 yr? [R.1]

18. Is the following correspondence a function? Why or why not? [R.2]

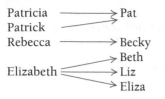

19. A function is given by $f(x) = -x^2 + x$. Find each of the following. [R.2]

a) $f(3)$ **b)** $f(-5)$
c) $f(a)$ **d)** $f(x + h)$

Graph. [R.5]

20. $f(x) = (x - 2)^2$ **21.** $y = |x + 1|$

22. $f(x) = \dfrac{x^2 - 16}{x + 4}$ **23.** $g(x) = \sqrt{x} + 1$

Use the vertical-line test to determine whether each of the following is the graph of a function. [R.2]

24.   **25.**

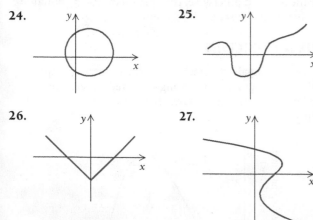

26.   **27.**

28. For the graph of function f shown to the right, determine **(a)** $f(2)$; **(b)** the domain; **(c)** all x-values for which $f(x) = 2$; and **(d)** the range. [R.3]

29. Consider the function given by

$$f(x) = \begin{cases} -x^2 + 2, & \text{for } x < 1, \\ 4, & \text{for } 1 \le x < 2, \\ \frac{1}{2}x, & \text{for } x \ge 2. \end{cases}$$

a) Find $f(-1), f(1.5)$, and $f(6)$. [R.2]

b) Graph the function. [R.2]

30. Write interval notation for each graph. [R.3]

31. Write interval notation for each of the following. Then graph each interval on a number line. [R.3]

a) $\{x \mid -4 \le x < 5\}$ **b)** $\{x \mid x > 2\}$

32. For the function graphed below, determine **(a)** $f(-3)$; **(b)** the domain; **(c)** all x-values for which $f(x) = 4$; **(d)** the range. [R.3]

33. Find the domain of f. [R.3, R.5]

a) $f(x) = \dfrac{7}{2x - 10}$

b) $f(x) = \sqrt{x + 6}$

34. What are the slope and the y-intercept of $y = -3x + 2$? [R.4]

35. Find an equation of the line with slope $\frac{1}{4}$, containing the point $(8, -5)$. [R.4]

36. Find the slope of the line containing the points $(2, -5)$ and $(-3, 10)$. [R.4]

Find the average rate of change. [R.4]

37.

38.

Number of days spent reading

39. Business: shipping charges.   The amount A that Pet-Treats-to-U charges for shipping is directly proportional to the value V of the item(s) being shipped. If the business charges $2.10 to ship a $60 gift basket, find an equation of variation expressing A as a function of V. [R.4]

40. Business: profit-and-loss analysis.   The band Soul Purpose has fixed costs of $4000 for producing a new CD. Thereafter, the variable costs are $0.50 per CD, and the CD will sell for $10. [R.4]

a) Find and graph $C(x)$, the total cost of producing x CDs.

b) Find and graph $R(x)$, the total revenue from the sale of x CDs. Use the same axes as in part (a).

c) Find and graph $P(x)$, the total profit from the production and sale of x CDs. Use the same axes as in part (b).

d) How many CDs must the band sell in order to break even?

41. Graph each pair of equations on one set of axes. [R.5]

a) $y = \sqrt{x}$ and $y = \sqrt{x} - 3$

b) $y = x^3$ and $y = (x - 1)^3$

42. Graph each of the following. If the graph is a parabola, identify the vertex. [R.5]

a) $f(x) = x^2 - 6x + 8$ **b)** $g(x) = \sqrt[3]{x} + 2$

c) $y = -\dfrac{1}{x}$ **d)** $y = \dfrac{x^2 + x - 6}{x - 2}$

43. Solve each of the following. [R.5]

a) $5 + x^2 = 4x + 2$

b) $2x^2 = 4x + 3$

44. Rewrite each of the following as an equivalent expression with a rational exponent. [R.5]

a) $\sqrt[5]{x^4}$ **b)** $\sqrt{t^8}$

c) $\dfrac{1}{\sqrt[3]{m^2}}$ **d)** $\dfrac{1}{\sqrt{x^2 - 9}}$

45. Rewrite each of the following as an equivalent expression using radical notation. [R.5]

a) $x^{2/5}$ **b)** $m^{-3/5}$

c) $(x^2 - 5)^{1/2}$ **d)** $\dfrac{1}{t^{-1/3}}$

46. Determine the domain of the function given by $f(x) = \sqrt[8]{2x - 9}$. [R.5]

47. Graph each of the following, and identify the y-intercept. [R.5]

a) $y = \dfrac{1}{2} \cdot (4)^x$ **b)** $y = 3 \cdot \left(\dfrac{1}{4}\right)^x$

48. Economics: equilibrium point.   Find the equilibrium point for the given demand and supply functions. [R.5]

Demand: $q = (x - 7)^2$

Supply: $q = x^2 + x + 4$ (assume $x \le 7$)

Price per item (in dollars)

49. Trail maintenance.   The amount of time required to maintain a section of the Appalachian Trail varies inversely with the number of volunteers working. If a particular section of trail can be cleared in 4 hr by 9 volunteers, how long would it take 11 volunteers to clear the same section? [R.5]

50. Life science: maximum heart rate.   A person exercising should not exceed a maximum heart rate, which depends on his or her gender, age, and resting heart rate. The following table shows data relating resting heart rate and maximum heart rate for a 20-yr-old woman. [R.6]

RESTING HEART RATE, r (in beats per minute)	MAXIMUM HEART RATE, M (in beats per minute)
50	170
60	172
70	174
80	176

(*Source*: American Heart Association.)

a) Using the data points $(50, 170)$ and $(80, 176)$, find a linear function that fits the data.

b) Graph the scatterplot and the function on the same set of axes.

c) Use the function to predict the maximum heart rate of a woman whose resting heart rate is 67.

51. Business: ticket profits.   The Spring Valley Drama Troupe is performing a new play. Data relating daily profit P to the number of days after opening night appear below. [R.6]

DAYS, x	0	9	18	27	36	45
PROFIT, P (in dollars)	870	548	−100	−100	510	872

a) Make a scatterplot of the data.

b) Do the data seem to fit a quadratic function?

c) Using the data points $(0, 870)$, $(18, -100)$, and $(45, 872)$, find a quadratic function that fits the data.

d) Use the function from part (c) to estimate the profit made on the 30th day.

e) Make an estimate of the domain of this function. Why must it have restrictions?

SYNTHESIS

52. Economics: demand.   The demand function for Clifton Cheddar Cheese is given by

Demand: $q = 800 - x^3, \quad 0 \le x \le 9.28,$

where x is the price per pound and q is in thousands of pounds. [R.5]

a) Find the number of pounds sold when the price per pound is $6.50.

b) Find the price per pound when 720,000 lb are sold.

TECHNOLOGY CONNECTION

Graph each function and find the zeros, the domain, and the range. [R.5]

53. $f(x) = x^3 - 9x^2 + 27x + 50$

54. $f(x) = \sqrt[3]{|4 - x^2|} + 1$

55. Approximate the point(s) of intersection of the graphs of the two functions in Exercises 53 and 54. [R.5]

56. Life science: maximum heart rate.   Use the data in Exercise 50. [R.6]

a) Use regression to fit a linear function to the data.

b) Use the linear function to predict the maximum heart rate of a woman whose resting heart rate is 67.

c) Compare your answer to that found in Exercise 50. Are the answers equally reliable? Why or why not?

57. Business: ticket profits.   Use the data in Exercise 51. [R.6]

a) Use regression to fit a quadratic function to the data.

b) Use the function to estimate the profit made on the 30th day.

c) What factors might cause the Spring Valley Drama Troupe's profit to drop and then rise?

58. Social sciences: time spent on home computer.   The data in the table below relate A, the average number of minutes spent per month on a home computer, to a person's age, x, in years. [R.6]

a) Use regression to fit linear, quadratic, cubic, and quartic functions to the data.

b) Make a scatterplot of the data, and graph each function on the scatterplot.

c) Which function provides the best model for the data? Why?

AGE (in years)	AVERAGE USE (in minutes per month)
6.5	363
14.5	645
21	1377
29.5	1727
39.5	1696
49.5	2052
55	2299

(*Source:* Media Matrix; The PC Meter Company.)

CHAPTER R
Test

1. Business: compound interest.   Cecilia invests funds at 6.5% compounded annually. The investment grows to $798.75 in 1 yr. How much was originally invested?

2. A function is given by $f(x) = -x^2 + 5$. Find:

a) $f(-3)$;

b) $f(a + h)$.

3. Find the slope and the y-intercept of the graph of $y = \frac{4}{5}x - \frac{2}{3}$.

4. Find an equation of the line with slope $\frac{1}{4}$, containing the point $(-3, 7)$.

5. Find the slope of the line containing the points $(-9, 2)$ and $(3, -4)$.

Find the average rate of change.

6.
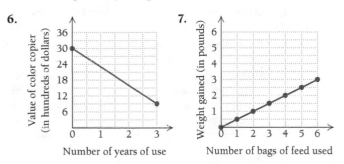

7.

8. Life science: body fluids. The weight F of fluids in a human is directly proportional to body weight W. It is known that a 180-lb person has 120 lb of fluids. Find an equation of variation expressing F as a function of W.

9. Business: profit-and-loss analysis. A printing shop has fixed costs of \$8000 for producing a newly designed note card. The variable costs are \$0.08 per card. The revenue from each card will be \$0.50.

a) Find $C(x)$, the total cost of producing x cards.
b) Find $R(x)$, the total revenue from the sale of x cards.
c) Find $P(x)$, the total profit from the production and sale of x cards.
d) How many cards must the company sell in order to break even?

10. Economics: equilibrium point. Find the equilibrium point for these demand and supply functions:

Demand: $q = (x - 8)^2$, $0 \le x \le 8$,

Supply: $q = x^2 + x + 13$,

given that x is the unit price, in dollars, and q is the quantity demanded or supplied, in thousands.

Use the vertical-line test to determine whether each of the following is the graph of a function.

11.

12.

13. For the following graph of a quadratic function f, determine **(a)** $f(1)$; **(b)** the domain; **(c)** all x-values for which $f(x) = 4$; and **(d)** the range.

14. Graph: $f(x) = 8/x$.

15. Convert to a rational exponent: $1/\sqrt{t}$.

16. Convert to radical notation: $t^{-3/5}$.

17. Graph: $f(x) = \dfrac{x^2 - 1}{x + 1}$.

Determine the domain of each function.

18. $f(x) = \dfrac{x^2 + 20}{x^2 + 5x - 14}$

19. $f(x) = \dfrac{x}{\sqrt{3x + 6}}$

20. Write interval notation for the following graph.

21. Graph:
$$f(x) = \begin{cases} x^2 + 2, & \text{for } x \ge 0, \\ x^2 - 2, & \text{for } x < 0. \end{cases}$$

22. Graph, and identify the y-intercept:
$$f(x) = \frac{1}{2} \cdot (3)^x.$$

23. Nutrition. As people age, their daily caloric needs change. The following table shows data for physically active females, relating age, in years, to number of calories needed daily.

AGE	NUMBER OF CALORIES NEEDED DAILY
6	1800
11	2200
16	2400
24	2400
41	2200

(*Source*: Based on data from U.S. Department of Agriculture.)

a) Make a scatterplot of the data.
b) Do the data appear to fit a quadratic function?
c) Using the data points $(6, 1800)$, $(16, 2400)$, and $(41, 2200)$, find a quadratic function that fits the data.
d) Use the function from part (c) to predict the number of calories needed daily by a physically active 30-yr-old woman.
e) What restrictions are reasonable for the domain of the function from part (c)? Why?

SYNTHESIS

24. Simplify: $(64^{4/3})^{-1/2}$.

25. Find the domain and the zeros of the function given by
$$f(x) = (5 - 3x)^{1/4} - 7.$$

26. Write an equation that has exactly three solutions: -3, 1, and 4. Answers may vary.

27. A function's average rate of change over the interval $[1, 5]$ is $-\frac{3}{7}$. If $f(1) = 9$, find $f(5)$.

TECHNOLOGY CONNECTION

28. Graph f and find its zeros, domain, and range:
$$f(x) = \sqrt[3]{|9 - x^2|} - 1.$$

29. Nutrition.   Use the data in Exercise 23.

a) Use REGRESSION to fit a quadratic function to the data.

b) Use the function from part (a) to predict the number of calories needed daily by a physically active 30-yr-old woman.

c) Compare your answer from part (b) with that from part (d) of Exercise 23. Which answer do you feel is more accurate? Why?

EXTENDED TECHNOLOGY APPLICATION

Average Price of a Movie Ticket

Extended Technology Applications occur at the ends of all chapters. They consider certain applications in greater depth, make use of calculator skills, and allow for possible group or collaborative learning.

Have you noticed that the price of a movie ticket seems to increase over time? The table and graph that follow show the average price of a movie ticket for the years 1950 to 2010.

How much did you pay the last time you went to an evening movie? The average prices in the table may seem low, but they reflect discounts for matinees, children, and senior citizens. Let's use REGRESSION to analyze the data.

YEAR, t	AVERAGE TICKET PRICE, $P(t)$
1950, 0	$0.46
1955, 5	0.58
1960, 10	0.76
1965, 15	1.01
1970, 20	1.55
1975, 25	2.05
1980, 30	2.69
1985, 35	3.55
1990, 40	4.23
1995, 45	4.35
2000, 50	5.39
2005, 55	6.41
2010, 60	8.01

(*Source:* Motion Picture Association of America.)

Exercises

1. a) Using REGRESSION, find a linear function that fits the data.
   b) Graph the linear function.
   c) Use the linear function to predict the average price of a movie ticket in 2015 and in 2020. Do these estimates appear reasonable?
   d) Use the function to predict the year when the average price of a ticket will reach $20. Does this estimate seem reasonable?

2. a) Using REGRESSION, find a quadratic function,
$$y = ax^2 + bx + c,$$
   that fits the data.
   b) Graph the quadratic function.
   c) Use the quadratic function to predict the average price of a movie ticket in 2015 and in 2020. Do these estimates appear reasonable?
   d) Use the function to predict the year when the average price of a ticket will reach $20. Does this estimate seem reasonable?

3. a) Using REGRESSION, find a cubic function,
$$y = ax^3 + bx^2 + cx + d,$$
   that fits the data.
   b) Graph the cubic function.
   c) Use the cubic function to predict the average price of a movie ticket in 2015 and in 2020. Do these estimates appear reasonable?
   d) Use the function to predict the year when the average price of a ticket will reach $20. Does this estimate seem reasonable?

4. a) Using REGRESSION, find a quartic function,
$$y = ax^4 + bx^3 + cx^2 + dx + e,$$
   that fits the data.
   b) Graph the quartic function.
   c) Use the quartic function to predict the average price of a movie ticket in 2015 and in 2020. Do these estimates appear reasonable?
   d) Use the function to predict the year when the average price of a ticket will reach $20. Does this estimate seem reasonable?

5. a) Using REGRESSION, find an exponential function,
$$y = a_0 \cdot a^x,$$
   that fits the data.
   b) Graph the exponential function.
   c) Use the exponential function to predict the average price of a movie ticket in 2015 and 2020. Do these estimates appear reasonable?
   d) Use the function to predict the year when the average price of a ticket will reach $20. Does this estimate seem reasonable?

6. You are a research statistician assigned the task of making an accurate prediction of movie ticket prices.
   a) Why might you not use the linear function?
   b) Why might you use the quadratic function rather than the linear function?
   c) Why might you use the exponential function rather than the quadratic function?

There are yet other procedures a statistician uses to choose predicting functions but they are beyond the scope of this text.

1 Differentiation

What You'll Learn

Why It's Important

With this chapter, we begin our study of calculus. The first concepts we consider are *limits* and *continuity*. We apply those concepts to establishing the first of the two main building blocks of calculus: differentiation.

Consider *differentiation*, a process that takes a formula for a function and derives another function, called a *derivative*. A derivative represents an instantaneous rate of change. Throughout the chapter, we develop techniques for finding derivatives and explore their many applications.

Where It's Used

Ticket Prices: The price, *p*, of a ticket to the Super Bowl *t* years after 1967 can be estimated by the model shown in the graph. Find the rate of change of the ticket price with respect to the year, dp/dt. (*This model appears in Exercise 94 in Section 1.5.*)

$$p(t) = 0.696t^2 - 13.290t + 61.857$$

Price (in dollars)

Number of years after 1967

(*Source*: Based on data from extramustard.si.com.)

1.1

- Find limits of functions, if they exist, using numerical or graphical methods.

Limits: A Numerical and Graphical Approach

In this section, we discuss the concept of a *limit*. The discussion is intuitive—that is, it relies on prior experience and lacks formal proof.

Suppose a football team has the ball on its own 10-yard line. Then, because of a penalty, the referee moves the ball back half the distance to the goal line; the ball is now on the 5-yard line. If the penalty is repeated, the ball will again be moved half the distance to the goal line, to the 2.5-yard line. If the penalty is repeated over and over again, the ball will move steadily *closer* to the goal line but never be placed *on* the goal line. We say that the *limit* of the distance between the ball and the goal line is zero.

Limits

One important aspect of calculus is analysis of how function values (outputs) change as input values change. Basic to this study is the notion of a limit. Suppose a function *f* is given and we have *x*-values (the inputs) that are increasingly close to some number *a*. If the corresponding values of *f*(*x*) get closer and closer to some number *L*, then that number is called the *limit* of *f*(*x*) as *x* approaches *a*.

For example, let $f(x) = 2x + 3$ and select *x*-values that get closer and closer to 4. In the table and graph below, we see that as input values approach 4 from the left (that is, are less than 4), output values approach 11, and as input values approach 4 from the right (that is, are greater than 4), output values also approach 11. Thus, we say:

As *x* approaches 4 from either side, the function $f(x) = 2x + 3$ approaches 11.

Limit Graphically

Limit Numerically

These input values approach 4 from the left.				These input values approach 4 from the right.		
x	3.9	3.99	3.999	4	4.001	4.01	4.1
$f(x)$	10.8	10.98	10.998	11	11.002	11.02	11.2

These output values approach 11.

These output values approach 11.

An arrow, →, is often used to stand for the words "approaches from either side." Thus, the statement above can be written:

As $x \rightarrow 4$, $2x + 3 = 11$.

The number 11 is said to be the *limit* of $2x + 3$ as x approaches 4 from either side. We can abbreviate this statement as follows:

$$\lim_{x \to 4} (2x + 3) = 11.$$

This is read: "The limit, as x approaches 4, of $2x + 3$ is 11."

DEFINITION

As x approaches a, the **limit** of $f(x)$ is L, written

$$\lim_{x \to a} f(x) = L,$$

if all values of $f(x)$ are close to L for values of x that are sufficiently close, but not necessarily equal, to a. The limit L, if it exists, must be a unique real number.

When we write $\lim_{x \to a} f(x)$, we are indicating that x is approaching a from both sides. If we want to specify the side from which x-values approach a, we write

$\lim_{x \to a^-} f(x)$ to indicate the limit from the left (that is, where $x < a$),

or $\lim_{x \to a^+} f(x)$ to indicate the limit from the right (that is, where $x > a$).

These are called *left-hand* and *right-hand limits*, respectively. For a limit to exist, both the left-hand and right-hand limits must exist and be the same.

THEOREM

As x approaches a, the limit of $f(x)$ is L if the limit from the left exists and the limit from the right exists and both limits are L. That is,

$$\text{if } \lim_{x \to a^+} f(x) = \lim_{x \to a^-} f(x) = L, \text{ then } \lim_{x \to a} f(x) = L.$$

The converse of this theorem is also true: if $\lim_{x \to a} f(x) = L$, then it follows that both the left-hand limit, $\lim_{x \to a^-} f(x)$, and the right-hand limit, $\lim_{x \to a^+} f(x)$, exist and are equal to L.

We showed earlier that as x approaches 4, the value of $2x + 3$ approaches 11, summarized as $\lim_{x \to 4} (2x + 3) = 11$. You may have thought "Why not just substitute 4 into the function to get 11?" In the next section, we see that we can use such shortcuts in certain cases, but keep in mind that we are curious about the behavior of the function $f(x) = 2x + 3$ for values of x close to 4, not at 4 itself. Let's summarize:

● For values of x close to 4, the corresponding values of $f(x)$ are close to 11; this is the *limit* we have been discussing.

● At $x = 4$, the function value is 11, corresponding to the point $(4, 11)$ on the graph of f.

Limits can help us understand the behavior of some functions more clearly. Consider the following example.

EXAMPLE 1   Let $f(x) = \dfrac{x^2 - 1}{x - 1}$.

a) Find $f(1)$, if it exists.   **b)** What is the limit of $f(x)$ as x approaches 1?

Solution

a) $f(1)$ does not exist, since 1 is not in the domain of f.

b) Selecting x-values close to 1 on either side (see the following tables), we see that the function values get close to 2. Thus, the limit of $f(x)$ as x approaches 1 is 2:
$\lim_{x \to 1} f(x) = 2$.

TECHNOLOGY CONNECTION

Finding Limits Using the TABLE and TRACE Features

Consider the function given by $f(x) = 3x - 1$. Let's use the TABLE feature to complete the following table. Note that the inputs do not have the same increment from one to the next, and they approach 6 from both the left and the right. We use TblSet and select Indpnt and Ask mode. Then we enter the inputs shown and use the corresponding outputs to complete the table.

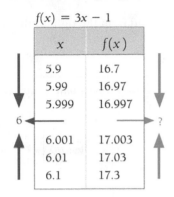

$$f(x) = 3x - 1$$

x	f(x)
5.9	16.7
5.99	16.97
5.999	16.997
6.001	17.003
6.01	17.03
6.1	17.3

Now we set the table in Auto mode and, starting (TblStart) with a number near 6, make tables for some increments (ΔTbl) like 0.1, 0.01, −0.1, −0.01, and so on, to determine $\lim\limits_{x \to 6} f(x)$.

As an alternative, graphical approach, let's use TRACE. We move the cursor from left to right so that the x-coordinate

approaches 6 from the left, zooming as needed, to see what happens. In general, TRACE is not an efficient way to find limits, but it will help in visualizing the limit process at this early stage.

Using TABLE and TRACE, we have

$$\lim_{x \to 6^+} f(x) = \boxed{17} \quad \text{and} \quad \lim_{x \to 6^-} f(x) = \boxed{17}.$$

Thus,

$$\lim_{x \to 6} f(x) = \boxed{17}.$$

EXERCISES

Let $f(x) = 3x - 1$. Use TABLE and TRACE to find each of the following.

1. $\lim\limits_{x \to 2} f(x)$ **2.** $\lim\limits_{x \to -1} f(x)$

Let $g(x) = x^3 - 2x - 2$ for Exercises 3–5.

3. Complete the following table.

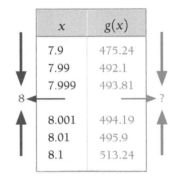

x	g(x)
7.9	475.24
7.99	492.1
7.999	493.81
8.001	494.19
8.01	495.9
8.1	513.24

Use TABLE and TRACE to find each of the following.

4. $\lim\limits_{x \to 8} g(x)$ **5.** $\lim\limits_{x \to -1} g(x)$

The graph has a "hole" at the point $(1, 2)$. Thus, even though the function is not defined at $x = 1$, the limit *does* exist as $x \to 1$.

Quick Check 1 ✔

Let

$$f(x) = \frac{x^2 - 9}{x - 3}.$$

(See Example 5 in Section R.5.)

a) What is $f(3)$?

b) What is the limit of f as x approaches 3?

Limit Numerically

$x \to 1^-$ $(x < 1)$	$f(x)$
0.9	1.9
0.99	1.99
0.999	1.999

$x \to 1^+$ $(x > 1)$	$f(x)$
1.1	2.1
1.01	2.01
1.001	2.001

Limit Graphically

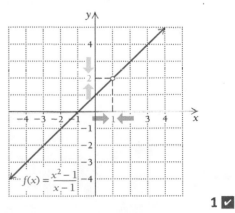

$$f(x) = \frac{x^2 - 1}{x - 1}$$

1 ✔

Limits are also useful when discussing piecewise-defined functions.

EXAMPLE 2 Consider the function H given by

$$H(x) = \begin{cases} 2x + 2, & \text{for } x < 1, \\ 2x - 4, & \text{for } x \geq 1. \end{cases}$$

Graph the function and find the following limits, if they exist, both numerically and graphically.

a) $\lim\limits_{x \to 1} H(x)$ **b)** $\lim\limits_{x \to -3} H(x)$

Solution We check the limits from the left and from the right both numerically, with an input–output table, and graphically.

a)

Limit Numerically Limit Graphically

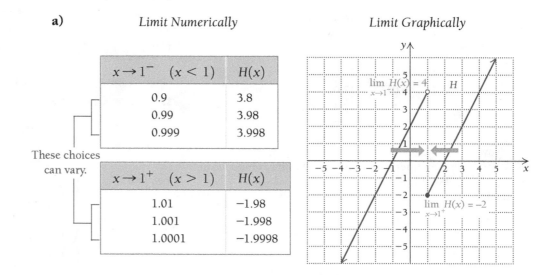

$x \to 1^-$ $\;(x < 1)$	$H(x)$
0.9	3.8
0.99	3.98
0.999	3.998

These choices can vary.

$x \to 1^+$ $\;(x > 1)$	$H(x)$
1.01	−1.98
1.001	−1.998
1.0001	−1.9998

As inputs x approach 1 from the left (see the upper table), outputs $H(x)$ approach 4. Thus, the limit from the left is 4. That is,

$$\lim\limits_{x \to 1^-} H(x) = 4.$$

But as inputs x approach 1 from the right (see the lower table), outputs $H(x)$ approach −2. Thus, the limit from the right is −2. That is,

$$\lim\limits_{x \to 1^+} H(x) = -2.$$

Since the limit from the left, 4, is not the same as the limit from the right, −2, we say that

$$\lim\limits_{x \to 1} H(x) \text{ does not exist.}$$

Note that $H(1) = -2$. In this example, the function value exists for $x = 1$, but the limit as $x \to 1$ does not exist.

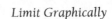

Exploratory

Check the results of Examples 1 and 2 using the TABLE feature. See Section R.2 to recall how to graph functions defined piecewise.

Note: Each Technology Connection labeled "Exploratory" is designed to lead you through a discovery process. Because of this, answers are not provided.

Quick Check 2 ✔

Let

$$k(x) = \begin{cases} -x + 4, & \text{for } x \leq 3, \\ 2x + 1, & \text{for } x > 3. \end{cases}$$

Find these limits:

a) $\lim\limits_{x \to 3^-} k(x)$, $\lim\limits_{x \to 3^+} k(x)$, and $\lim\limits_{x \to 3} k(x)$;

b) $\lim\limits_{x \to 1} k(x)$.

b)   *Limit Numerically*   *Limit Graphically*

$x \to -3^-$ $(x < -3)$	$H(x)$
-3.1	-4.2
-3.01	-4.02
-3.001	-4.002

$x \to -3^+$ $(x > -3)$	$H(x)$
-2.9	-3.8
-2.99	-3.98
-2.999	-3.998

As inputs x approach -3 from the left, outputs $H(x)$ approach -4, so the limit from the left is -4. That is,

$$\lim_{x \to -3^-} H(x) = -4.$$

As inputs x approach -3 from the right, outputs $H(x)$ approach -4, so the limit from the right is -4. That is,

$$\lim_{x \to -3^+} H(x) = -4.$$

Since the limits from the left and the right exist and are the same, we have

$$\lim_{x \to -3} H(x) = -4.$$ **2** ✔

> The limit of $f(x)$ at a number a *does not depend* on the function value at a or even on whether $f(a)$ exists. That is, the existence of a limit at a has *nothing* to do with the function value $f(a)$.

The "Wall" Method

An alternative approach for Example 2 is to draw a "wall" at $x = 1$, as shown in blue on the graph below. We then trace the graph from left to right with a pencil until we hit the wall and mark the location with an ✕, assuming it can be determined. Then we trace the graph from right to left until we hit the wall and mark that location with an ✕. If the locations are the same, as in the graph to the right below, a limit exists. Thus, for Example 2,

$$\lim_{x \to 1} H(x) \text{ does not exist,} \quad \text{and} \quad \lim_{x \to -3} H(x) = -4.$$

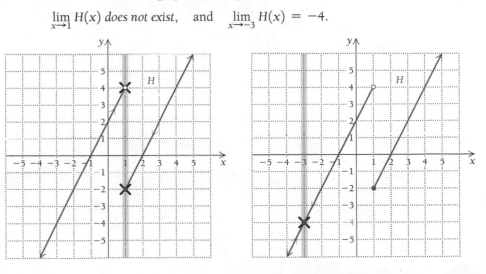

EXAMPLE 3   Consider the function defined as follows:

$$G(x) = \begin{cases} 5, & \text{for } x = 1, \\ x + 1, & \text{for } x \neq 1. \end{cases}$$

Graph the function, and find each of the following limits, if they exist.

a) $\lim_{x \to 1} G(x)$

b) $\lim_{x \to -2} G(x)$

Solution   The graph of G follows.

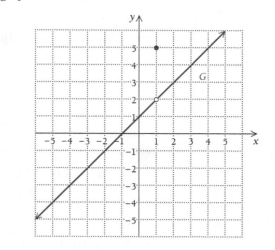

a) As inputs x approach 1 from the left, outputs $G(x)$ approach 2, so the limit from the left is 2. As inputs x approach 1 from the right, outputs $G(x)$ also approach 2, so the limit from the right is 2. Both limits are the same, so

$$\lim_{x \to 1} G(x) = 2.$$

Note that the limit, 2, is not the same as the function value at 1, which is $G(1) = 5$.

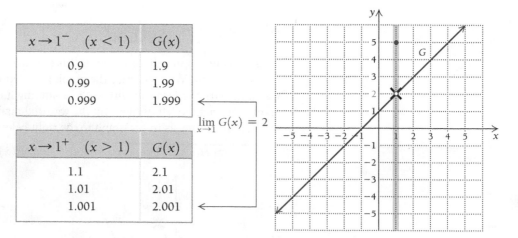

Limit Numerically

$x \to 1^-$ $(x < 1)$	$G(x)$
0.9	1.9
0.99	1.99
0.999	1.999

$$\lim_{x \to 1} G(x) = 2$$

$x \to 1^+$ $(x > 1)$	$G(x)$
1.1	2.1
1.01	2.01
1.001	2.001

Limit Graphically

b) Using the same approach as in part (a), we have

$$\lim_{x \to -2} G(x) = -1.$$

Note that in this case, the limit, -1, is the same as the function value, $G(-2)$.

Quick Check 3 ✔

Calculate the following limits based on the graph of f.

a) $\lim\limits_{x \to 2^-} f(x)$

b) $\lim\limits_{x \to 2^+} f(x)$

c) $\lim\limits_{x \to 2} f(x)$

Limit Numerically   *Limit Graphically*

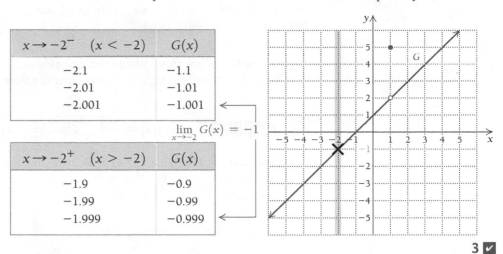

$x \to -2^-$ $(x < -2)$	$G(x)$
−2.1	−1.1
−2.01	−1.01
−2.001	−1.001

$\lim\limits_{x \to -2} G(x) = -1$

$x \to -2^+$ $(x > -2)$	$G(x)$
−1.9	−0.9
−1.99	−0.99
−1.999	−0.999

3 ✔

Limits Involving Infinity

Limits also help us understand the role of infinity with respect to some functions. Consider the following example.

EXAMPLE 4   Let $f(x) = \dfrac{1}{x - 2}$.

a) Find $\lim\limits_{x \to 2^-} f(x)$.

b) Find $\lim\limits_{x \to 2^+} f(x)$.

c) Use the information from parts (a) and (b) to form a conclusion about $\lim\limits_{x \to 2} f(x)$.

Solution   Note first that $f(2)$ does not exist, since 2 is not in the domain of f.

Limit Numerically   *Limit Graphically*

$x \to 2^-$ $(x < 2)$	$f(x)$
1.9	−10
1.99	−100
1.999	−1,000
1.9999	−10,000

$x \to 2^+$ $(x > 2)$	$f(x)$
2.1	10
2.01	100
2.001	1,000
2.0001	10,000

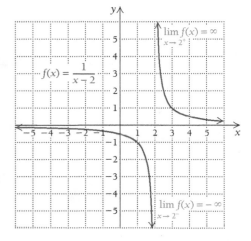

a) The table and graph show that as x approaches 2 from the left, $f(x)$ decreases without bound. We conclude that the left-hand limit is negative infinity; that is, $\lim\limits_{x \to 2^-} f(x) = -\infty$. We symbolize the notion of "infinity" with ∞. The symbol ∞ *does not represent* a real number.

b) The table and graph show that as x approaches 2 from the right, $f(x)$ increases without bound toward positive infinity. The right-hand limit is positive infinity; that is, $\lim\limits_{x \to 2^+} f(x) = \infty$.

c) Since the left-hand and right-hand limits are not equal (and are not finite), $\lim\limits_{x \to 2} f(x)$ does not exist. ■

Sometimes we need to determine limits as inputs approach positive or negative infinity. In such cases, we are finding *limits at infinity*. Such a limit is expressed as

$$\lim_{x \to \infty} f(x) \qquad \text{or} \qquad \lim_{x \to -\infty} f(x).$$

These limits are approached from one side only: from the left if approaching positive infinity or from the right if approaching negative infinity.

EXAMPLE 5 Let $f(x) = \dfrac{1}{x-3}$. Find $\lim_{x \to \infty} f(x)$ and $\lim_{x \to -\infty} f(x)$.

Solution The table shows that as x increases toward positive infinity, $f(x)$ approaches 0. Thus, $\lim_{x \to \infty} f(x) = 0$. As x decreases toward negative infinity, $f(x)$ again approaches 0. Thus, $\lim_{x \to -\infty} f(x) = 0$.

Limit Numerically   *Limit Graphically*

$x \to \infty$	$f(x)$
100	0.0103 . . .
1,000	0.001003 . . .
10,000	0.00010003 . . .

$$\lim_{x \to \infty} f(x) = 0$$

$x \to -\infty$	$f(x)$
−100	−0.0097 . . .
−1,000	−0.000997 . . .
−10,000	−0.00009997 . . .

$$\lim_{x \to -\infty} f(x) = 0$$

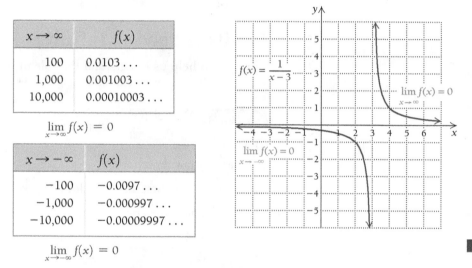

EXAMPLE 6 Consider the function f given by

$$f(x) = \frac{1}{x-2} + 3.$$

Graph the function, and find each of the following limits, if they exist.

a) $\lim_{x \to 3} f(x)$ **b)** $\lim_{x \to 2} f(x)$

Solution Note that the graph of f is the same as the graph of $f(x) = \dfrac{1}{x}$ but shifted 2 units to the right and 3 units up.

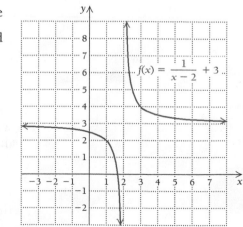

a) As x approaches 3 from the left, $f(x)$ approaches 4, so the limit from the left is 4. As x approaches 3 from the right, $f(x)$ also approaches 4. Since the limit from the left, 4, is the same as the limit from the right, we have

$$\lim_{x \to 3} f(x) = 4.$$

Limit Numerically

Limit Graphically

$x \to 3^-$ $(x < 3)$	$f(x)$
2.9	4.1
2.99	4.$\overline{01}$
2.999	4.$\overline{001}$

$$\lim_{x \to 3^-} f(x) = 4$$

$x \to 3^+$ $(x > 3)$	$f(x)$
3.1	3.$\overline{90}$
3.01	3.$\overline{9900}$
3.001	3.$\overline{999000}$

$$f(x) = \frac{1}{x - 2} + 3$$

b) As inputs x approach 2 from the left, outputs $f(x)$ become more and more negative, without bound. These numbers do not approach any real number, although it might be said that the limit from the left is negative infinity, $-\infty$. That is,

$$\lim_{x \to 2^-} f(x) = -\infty.$$

As inputs x approach 2 from the right, outputs $f(x)$ become larger and larger, without bound. These numbers do not approach any real number, although it might be said that the limit from the right is infinity, ∞. That is,

$$\lim_{x \to 2^+} f(x) = \infty.$$

Because the left-sided limit differs from the right-sided limit,

$$\lim_{x \to 2} f(x) \text{ does not exist.}$$

Limit Numerically

Limit Graphically

$x \to 2^-$ $(x < 2)$	$f(x)$
1.9	-7
1.99	-97
1.999	-997

$$\lim_{x \to 2} f(x) \text{ does not exist.}$$

$x \to 2^+$ $(x > 2)$	$f(x)$
2.1	13
2.01	103
2.001	1003

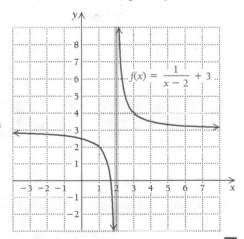

$$f(x) = \frac{1}{x - 2} + 3$$

EXAMPLE 7   Consider again the function in Example 6, given by

$$f(x) = \frac{1}{x - 2} + 3.$$

Find $\lim_{x \to \infty} f(x)$.

Solution   As x gets larger and larger, $f(x)$ gets closer and closer to 3. Thus,

$$\lim_{x \to \infty} f(x) = 3.$$

Limit Numerically   *Limit Graphically*

$x \to \infty$	$f(x)$
10	3.125
100	3.0102 ...
1000	3.0010 ...

$\lim_{x \to \infty} f(x) = 3$

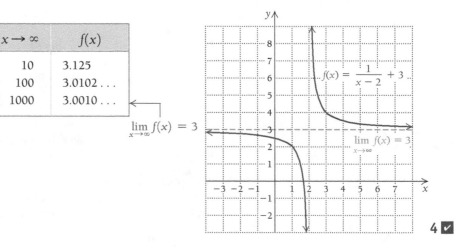

Quick Check 4 ✔

Let $h(x) = \dfrac{1}{1 - x} + 6$. Find

these limits:

a) $\lim_{x \to 1} h(x)$;   **b)** $\lim_{x \to 2} h(x)$;

c) $\lim_{x \to \infty} h(x)$.

4 ✔

Section Summary

- The *limit* of a function f, as x approaches a, is written $\lim_{x \to a} f(x) = L$. This means that as the values of x approach a, the corresponding values of $f(x)$ approach L. The value L must be a unique real number.
- A *left-hand limit* is written $\lim_{x \to a^-} f(x)$. The values of x are approaching a from the left, that is, $x < a$.
- A *right-hand limit* is written $\lim_{x \to a^+} f(x)$. The values of x are approaching a from the right, that is, $x > a$.
- If the left-hand and right-hand limits (as x approaches a) are *not* equal, the limit does *not* exist. On the other

hand, if the left-hand and right-hand limits are equal and not infinite, the limit does exist.
- A limit $\lim_{x \to a} f(x)$ may exist even though the function value $f(a)$ does not exist. (See Example 1.)
- A limit $\lim_{x \to a} f(x)$ may exist and be different from the function value $f(a)$. (See Example 3a.)
- Graphs and tables are useful tools in determining limits.

1.1   Exercise Set

Complete each of the following statements.

1. As x approaches _____, the value of $-3x$ approaches 6.

2. As x approaches _____, the value of $x - 2$ approaches 5.

3. The notation $\lim_{x \to 4} f(x)$ is read _____.

4. The notation $\lim_{x \to 1} g(x)$ is read _____.

5. The notation $\lim_{x \to 5^-} F(x)$ is read _____.

6. The notation $\lim_{x \to 4^+} G(x)$ is read _____.

7. The notation _____ is read "the limit, as x approaches 2 from the right."

8. The notation _____ is read "the limit, as x approaches 3 from the left."

9. The notation _____ is read "the limit as x approaches 5."

10. The notation _____ is read "the limit as x approaches $\frac{1}{2}$."

For Exercises 11 and 12, consider the function f given by

$$f(x) = \begin{cases} x - 2, & \text{for } x \le 3, \\ x - 1, & \text{for } x > 3. \end{cases}$$

If a limit does not exist, state that fact.

11. Find (a) $\lim_{x \to 3^-} f(x)$; (b) $\lim_{x \to 3^+} f(x)$; (c) $\lim_{x \to 3} f(x)$.

12. Find (a) $\lim_{x \to -1^-} f(x)$; (b) $\lim_{x \to -1^+} f(x)$; (c) $\lim_{x \to -1} f(x)$.

For Exercises 13 and 14, consider the function g given by

$$g(x) = \begin{cases} x + 6, & \text{for } x < -2, \\ -\frac{1}{2}x + 1, & \text{for } x \ge -2. \end{cases}$$

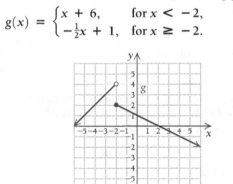

If a limit does not exist, state that fact.

13. Find (a) $\lim_{x \to -2^-} g(x)$; (b) $\lim_{x \to -2^+} g(x)$; (c) $\lim_{x \to -2} g(x)$.

14. Find (a) $\lim_{x \to 4^-} g(x)$; (b) $\lim_{x \to 4^+} g(x)$; (c) $\lim_{x \to 4} g(x)$.

For Exercises 15–22, use the following graph of F to find each limit. When necessary, state that the limit does not exist.

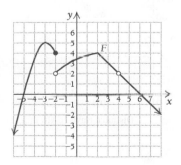

15. $\lim_{x \to 2} F(x)$

16. $\lim_{x \to -3} F(x)$

17. $\lim_{x \to -5} F(x)$

18. $\lim_{x \to -2} F(x)$

19. $\lim_{x \to 6} F(x)$

20. $\lim_{x \to 4} F(x)$

21. $\lim_{x \to -2^-} F(x)$

22. $\lim_{x \to -2^+} F(x)$

For Exercises 23–30, use the following graph of G to find each limit. When necessary, state that the limit does not exist.

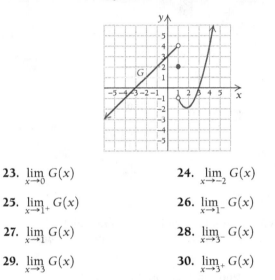

23. $\lim_{x \to 0} G(x)$

24. $\lim_{x \to -2} G(x)$

25. $\lim_{x \to 1^+} G(x)$

26. $\lim_{x \to 1^-} G(x)$

27. $\lim_{x \to 1} G(x)$

28. $\lim_{x \to 3^-} G(x)$

29. $\lim_{x \to 3} G(x)$

30. $\lim_{x \to 3^+} G(x)$

For Exercises 31–40, use the following graph of H to find each limit. When necessary, state that the limit does not exist.

31. $\lim_{x \to -2^-} H(x)$

32. $\lim_{x \to -3} H(x)$

33. $\lim_{x \to -2} H(x)$

34. $\lim_{x \to -2^+} H(x)$

35. $\lim_{x \to 1^+} H(x)$

36. $\lim_{x \to 1^-} H(x)$

37. $\lim_{x \to 1} H(x)$

38. $\lim_{x \to 3^-} H(x)$

39. $\lim_{x \to 3} H(x)$

40. $\lim_{x \to 3^+} H(x)$

For Exercises 41–50, use the following graph of f to find each limit. When necessary, state that the limit does not exist.

41. $\lim\limits_{x \to 2} f(x)$

42. $\lim\limits_{x \to -1} f(x)$

43. $\lim\limits_{x \to 0} f(x)$

44. $\lim\limits_{x \to -3} f(x)$

45. $\lim\limits_{x \to 1} f(x)$

46. $\lim\limits_{x \to 3} f(x)$

47. $\lim\limits_{x \to -2} f(x)$

48. $\lim\limits_{x \to -4} f(x)$

49. $\lim\limits_{x \to -\infty} f(x)$

50. $\lim\limits_{x \to \infty} f(x)$

For Exercises 51–68, graph each function and then find the specified limits. When necessary, state that the limit does not exist.

51. $f(x) = |x|$;   find $\lim\limits_{x \to 0} f(x)$ and $\lim\limits_{x \to -2} f(x)$.

52. $f(x) = x^2$;   find $\lim\limits_{x \to -1} f(x)$ and $\lim\limits_{x \to 0} f(x)$.

53. $g(x) = x^2 - 5$;   find $\lim\limits_{x \to 0} g(x)$ and $\lim\limits_{x \to -1} g(x)$.

54. $g(x) = |x| + 1$;   find $\lim\limits_{x \to -3} g(x)$ and $\lim\limits_{x \to 0} g(x)$.

55. $G(x) = \dfrac{1}{x + 2}$;   find $\lim\limits_{x \to -1} G(x)$ and $\lim\limits_{x \to -2} G(x)$.

56. $F(x) = \dfrac{1}{x - 3}$;   find $\lim\limits_{x \to 3} F(x)$ and $\lim\limits_{x \to 4} F(x)$.

57. $f(x) = \dfrac{1}{x} - 2$;   find $\lim\limits_{x \to \infty} f(x)$ and $\lim\limits_{x \to 0} f(x)$.

58. $f(x) = \dfrac{1}{x} + 3$;   find $\lim\limits_{x \to \infty} f(x)$ and $\lim\limits_{x \to 0} f(x)$.

59. $g(x) = \dfrac{1}{x - 3} + 2$;   find $\lim\limits_{x \to \infty} g(x)$ and $\lim\limits_{x \to 3} g(x)$.

60. $g(x) = \dfrac{1}{x + 2} + 4$;   find $\lim\limits_{x \to \infty} g(x)$ and $\lim\limits_{x \to -2} g(x)$.

61. $F(x) = \begin{cases} 2x + 1, & \text{for } x < 1, \\ x, & \text{for } x \geq 1. \end{cases}$

Find $\lim\limits_{x \to 1^-} F(x), \lim\limits_{x \to 1^+} F(x)$, and $\lim\limits_{x \to 1} F(x)$.

62. $G(x) = \begin{cases} -x + 3, & \text{for } x < 2, \\ x + 1, & \text{for } x \geq 2. \end{cases}$

Find $\lim\limits_{x \to 2^-} G(x), \lim\limits_{x \to 2^+} G(x)$, and $\lim\limits_{x \to 2} G(x)$.

63. $g(x) = \begin{cases} -x + 4, & \text{for } x < 3, \\ x - 3, & \text{for } x > 3. \end{cases}$

Find $\lim\limits_{x \to 3^-} g(x), \lim\limits_{x \to 3^+} g(x)$, and $\lim\limits_{x \to 3} g(x)$.

64. $f(x) = \begin{cases} 3x - 4, & \text{for } x < 1, \\ x - 2, & \text{for } x > 1. \end{cases}$

Find $\lim\limits_{x \to 1^-} f(x), \lim\limits_{x \to 1^+} f(x)$, and $\lim\limits_{x \to 1} f(x)$.

65. $F(x) = \begin{cases} -2x - 3, & \text{for } x < -1, \\ x^3, & \text{for } x > -1. \end{cases}$ Find $\lim\limits_{x \to -1} F(x)$.

66. $G(x) = \begin{cases} x^2, & \text{for } x < -1, \\ x + 2, & \text{for } x > -1. \end{cases}$ Find $\lim\limits_{x \to -1} G(x)$.

67. $H(x) = \begin{cases} x + 1, & \text{for } x < 0, \\ 2, & \text{for } 0 \leq x < 1, \\ 3 - x, & \text{for } x \geq 1. \end{cases}$

Find $\lim\limits_{x \to 0} H(x)$ and $\lim\limits_{x \to 1} H(x)$.

68. $G(x) = \begin{cases} 2 + x, & \text{for } x \leq -1, \\ x^2, & \text{for } -1 < x < 3, \\ 9, & \text{for } x \geq 3. \end{cases}$

Find $\lim\limits_{x \to -1} G(x)$ and $\lim\limits_{x \to 3} G(x)$.

APPLICATIONS

Business and Economics

Taxicab fares.   *In New York City, taxicabs charge passengers $2.50 for entering a cab and then $0.50 for each one-fifth of a mile (or fraction thereof) traveled. (There are additional charges for slow traffic and idle times, but these are not considered in this problem.) If x represents the distance traveled in miles, then C(x) is the cost of the taxi fare, where*

$$C(x) = \$2.50, \quad \text{if} \quad x = 0,$$
$$C(x) = \$3.00, \quad \text{if} \quad 0 < x \leq 0.2,$$
$$C(x) = \$3.50, \quad \text{if} \quad 0.2 < x \leq 0.4,$$
$$C(x) = \$4.00, \quad \text{if} \quad 0.4 < x \leq 0.6,$$

and so on. The graph of C is shown below. (Source: New York City Taxi and Limousine Commission.)

Using the graph of the taxicab fare function, find each of the following limits, if it exists.

69. $\lim\limits_{x\to0.25^-} C(x)$, $\lim\limits_{x\to0.25^+} C(x)$, $\lim\limits_{x\to0.25} C(x)$

70. $\lim\limits_{x\to0.2^-} C(x)$, $\lim\limits_{x\to0.2^+} C(x)$, $\lim\limits_{x\to0.2} C(x)$

71. $\lim\limits_{x\to0.6^-} C(x)$, $\lim\limits_{x\to0.6^+} C(x)$, $\lim\limits_{x\to0.6} C(x)$

The postage function.   *The cost of sending a large envelope via U.S. first-class mail in 2014 was $0.98 for the first ounce and $0.21 for each additional ounce (or fraction thereof). (Source: www.usps.com.) If x represents the weight of a large envelope, in ounces, then p(x) is the cost of mailing it, where*

$$p(x) = \$0.98, \quad \text{if} \quad 0 < x \le 1,$$
$$p(x) = \$1.19, \quad \text{if} \quad 1 < x \le 2,$$
$$p(x) = \$1.40, \quad \text{if} \quad 2 < x \le 3,$$

and so on, up through 13 ounces. The graph of p is shown below.

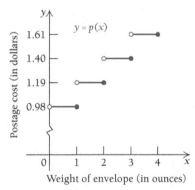

Using the graph of the postage function, find each of the following limits, if it exists.

72. $\lim\limits_{x\to1^-} p(x)$, $\lim\limits_{x\to1^+} p(x)$, $\lim\limits_{x\to1} p(x)$

73. $\lim\limits_{x\to2^-} p(x)$, $\lim\limits_{x\to2^+} p(x)$, $\lim\limits_{x\to2} p(x)$

74. $\lim\limits_{x\to2.6^-} p(x)$, $\lim\limits_{x\to2.6^+} p(x)$, $\lim\limits_{x\to2.6} p(x)$

75. $\lim\limits_{x\to3} p(x)$

76. $\lim\limits_{x\to3.4} p(x)$

Tax rate schedule.   *The federal tax rate for single filers is given as a percentage of taxable income in the graph below. (Source: troweprice.com, 2013.)*

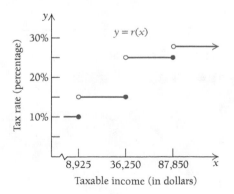

Use the graph for Exercises 77–79.

77. Find $\lim\limits_{x\to8925^-} r(x)$, $\lim\limits_{x\to8925^+} r(x)$, and $\lim\limits_{x\to8925} r(x)$.

78. Find $\lim\limits_{x\to10,000^-} r(x)$, $\lim\limits_{x\to10,000^+} r(x)$, and $\lim\limits_{x\to10,000} r(x)$.

79. Find $\lim\limits_{x\to50,000} r(x)$ and $\lim\limits_{x\to87,850} r(x)$.

Tax rate schedule.   *The federal tax rate for heads of household is given in the graph below. (Source: troweprice.com, 2013.)*

Use the graph for Exercises 80–82.

80. Find $\lim\limits_{x\to9000^-} r(x)$, $\lim\limits_{x\to9000^+} r(x)$, and $\lim\limits_{x\to9000} r(x)$.

81. Find $\lim\limits_{x\to48,600^-} r(x)$, $\lim\limits_{x\to48,600^+} r(x)$, and $\lim\limits_{x\to48,600} r(x)$.

82. Find $\lim\limits_{x\to60,000} r(x)$ and $\lim\limits_{x\to12,570} r(x)$.

SYNTHESIS

In Exercises 83–85, fill in each blank so that $\lim\limits_{x\to2} f(x)$ exists.

83. $f(x) = \begin{cases} \frac{1}{2}x + \underline{\hspace{1em}}, & \text{for } x < 2, \\ -x + 6, & \text{for } x > 2 \end{cases}$

84. $f(x) = \begin{cases} -\frac{1}{2}x + 1, & \text{for } x < 2, \\ \frac{3}{2}x + \underline{\hspace{1em}}, & \text{for } x > 2 \end{cases}$

85. $f(x) = \begin{cases} x^2 - 9, & \text{for } x < 2, \\ -x^2 + \underline{\hspace{1em}}, & \text{for } x > 2 \end{cases}$

TECHNOLOGY CONNECTION

86. Graph the function f given by

$$f(x) = \begin{cases} -3, & \text{for } x = -2, \\ x^2, & \text{for } x \ne -2. \end{cases}$$

Use GRAPH and TRACE to find each of the following limits. When necessary, state that the limit does not exist.

a) $\lim\limits_{x\to-2^+} f(x)$ **b)** $\lim\limits_{x\to-2^-} f(x)$

c) $\lim\limits_{x\to-2} f(x)$ **d)** $\lim\limits_{x\to2^+} f(x)$

e) $\lim\limits_{x\to2^-} f(x)$

f) Does $\lim\limits_{x\to-2} f(x) = f(-2)$?

g) Does $\lim\limits_{x\to2} f(x) = f(2)$?

In Exercises 87–89, use GRAPH *and* TRACE *to find each limit. When necessary, state that the limit does not exist.*

87. For $f(x) = \begin{cases} x^2 - 2, & \text{for } x < 0, \\ 2 - x^2, & \text{for } x \geq 0, \end{cases}$

find $\lim\limits_{x \to 0} f(x)$ and $\lim\limits_{x \to -2} f(x)$.

88. For $g(x) = \dfrac{20x^2}{x^3 + 2x^2 + 5x}$,

find $\lim\limits_{x \to \infty} g(x)$ and $\lim\limits_{x \to -\infty} g(x)$.

89. For $f(x) = \dfrac{x - 5}{x^2 - 4x - 5}$, find $\lim\limits_{x \to -1} f(x)$ and $\lim\limits_{x \to 5} f(x)$.

Answers to Quick Checks

1. (a) $f(3)$ does not exist; **(b)** 6   **2. (a)** 1, 7, does not exist; **(b)** 3   **3. (a)** 3; **(b)** 3; **(c)** 3   **4. (a)** Limit does not exist; **(b)** 5; **(c)** 6

1.2

• Develop and use the Limit Properties to calculate limits.

• Determine whether a function is continuous at a point.

Algebraic Limits and Continuity

Using numerical and graphical methods for finding limits can be time-consuming. In this section, we develop methods to more quickly evaluate limits for a wide variety of functions. We then use limits to study *continuity*, a concept of great importance in calculus.

Algebraic Limits

Consider the functions given by $f(x) = x$, $g(x) = 3$, and $F(x) = x + 3$, displayed in the following graphs. Note that function F is the sum of functions f and g.

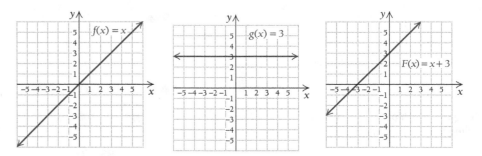

Suppose we are interested in the limits of $f(x)$, $g(x)$, and $F(x)$ as x approaches 2. In Section 1.1, we learned numerical and graphical techniques that can be used to show that

$$\lim_{x \to 2} f(x) = 2, \quad \lim_{x \to 2} g(x) = 3, \quad \text{and} \quad \lim_{x \to 2} F(x) = 5.$$

These techniques work equally well for any value of a. For example, if we choose $a = -1$, we can compute the following limits:

$$\lim_{x \to -1} f(x) = -1, \quad \lim_{x \to -1} g(x) = 3, \quad \text{and} \quad \lim_{x \to -1} F(x) = 2.$$

From these results, the following observations can be made:

1. For any real number a, $\lim\limits_{x \to a} x = a$.
2. For any real number a, $\lim\limits_{x \to a} 3 = 3$.

Recalling that $F(x) = f(x) + g(x)$, we make this reasonable conclusion:

3. For any real number a, $\lim\limits_{x \to a} (x + 3) = a + 3$.

We determined the limits of these functions by observing basic behaviors and making a reasonable generalization. The following list summarizes common limit properties that allow us to calculate limits much more efficiently.

Limit Properties

If $\lim_{x \to a} f(x) = L$ and $\lim_{x \to a} g(x) = M$, and c is any constant, then we have the following limit properties.

L1. The limit of a constant is the constant:

$$\lim_{x \to a} c = c.$$

L2. The limit of a power is the power of that limit, and the limit of a root is the root of that limit:

$$\lim_{x \to a} [f(x)]^m = [\lim_{x \to a} f(x)]^m = L^m, \text{ where } m \text{ is any integer;}$$

$$\lim_{x \to a} \sqrt[n]{f(x)} = \sqrt[n]{\lim_{x \to a} f(x)} = \sqrt[n]{L}, \text{ where } n \geq 2.$$

In the case of the power, we must have $L \neq 0$ if m is negative, and in the case of the root, we must have $L \geq 0$ if n is an even integer.

L3. The limit of a sum or difference is the sum or difference of the limits:

$$\lim_{x \to a} [f(x) \pm g(x)] = \lim_{x \to a} f(x) \pm \lim_{x \to a} g(x) = L \pm M.$$

L4. The limit of a product is the product of the limits:

$$\lim_{x \to a} [f(x) \cdot g(x)] = [\lim_{x \to a} f(x)] \cdot [\lim_{x \to a} g(x)] = L \cdot M.$$

L5. The limit of a quotient is the quotient of the limits:

$$\lim_{x \to a} \frac{f(x)}{g(x)} = \frac{\lim_{x \to a} f(x)}{\lim_{x \to a} g(x)} = \frac{L}{M}, \quad \text{assuming } M \neq 0.$$

L6. The limit of a constant times a function is the constant times the limit of the function:

$$\lim_{x \to a} c \cdot f(x) = c \cdot \lim_{x \to a} f(x) = c \cdot L.$$

Property L6 combines L1 and L4 but is stated separately because it is used so frequently.

EXAMPLE 1   Use the Limit Properties to find $\lim_{x \to 4} (x^2 - 3x + 7)$.

Solution   We know that $\lim_{x \to 4} x$ is 4.

By Limit Property L2,

$$\lim_{x \to 4} x^2 = [\lim_{x \to 4} x]^2 = 4^2 = 16,$$

by Limit Property L6,

$$\lim_{x \to 4} (-3x) = -3 \cdot \lim_{x \to 4} x = -3 \cdot 4 = -12,$$

and by Limit Property L1,

$$\lim_{x \to 4} 7 = 7.$$

Using Limit Property L3 to combine these results, we have

$$\lim_{x \to 4} (x^2 - 3x + 7) = 16 - 12 + 7 = 11.$$

∎

The result of Example 1 is extended in the following theorem.

> **THEOREM   Limits of Rational Functions**
>
> For any rational function F, with a in the domain of F,
>
> $$\lim_{x \to a} F(x) = F(a).$$

Rational functions include all polynomial functions (which include constant functions and linear functions) and ratios composed of such functions (see Section R.5). Thus, the Limit Properties allow us to evaluate limits of rational functions very quickly without tables or graphs, as illustrated by the following examples.

EXAMPLE 2   Find $\lim_{x \to 2} (x^4 - 5x^3 + x^2 - 7)$.

Solution   It follows from the Theorem on Limits of Rational Functions that we can find the limit by substitution:

$$\lim_{x \to 2} (x^4 - 5x^3 + x^2 - 7) = 2^4 - 5 \cdot 2^3 + 2^2 - 7$$
$$= 16 - 40 + 4 - 7$$
$$= -27.$$

Quick Check 1 ✔

Find these limits and note the Limit Property you use at each step.

a) $\lim_{x \to 1} 2x^3 + 3x^2 - 6$

b) $\lim_{x \to 4} \dfrac{2x^2 + 5x - 1}{3x - 2}$

c) $\lim_{x \to -2} \sqrt{1 + 3x^2}$

EXAMPLE 3   Find $\lim_{x \to 0} \sqrt{x^2 - 3x + 2}$.

Solution   The Theorem on Limits of Rational Functions and Limit Property L2 tell us that we can substitute to find the limit:

$$\lim_{x \to 0} \sqrt{x^2 - 3x + 2} = \sqrt{0^2 - 3 \cdot 0 + 2}$$
$$= \sqrt{2}.$$

1 ✔

In the following example, a is not in the domain of the function, since it would result in a zero in the denominator. Nevertheless, we can still find the limit.

EXAMPLE 4   Let $r(x) = \dfrac{x^2 - x - 12}{x + 3}$. Find $\lim_{x \to -3} r(x)$.

Solution   We note that $r(-3)$ does not exist, since -3 is not in the domain of r. Since it is impossible to determine this limit by direct evaluation (the assumption for Limit Property L5 is not met), we use a table and a graph. Although $x \neq -3$, x can approach -3 as closely as we wish:

Limit Numerically

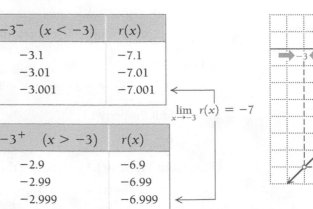

$x \to -3^-$ $(x < -3)$	$r(x)$
-3.1	-7.1
-3.01	-7.01
-3.001	-7.001

$\lim_{x \to -3} r(x) = -7$

$x \to -3^+$ $(x > -3)$	$r(x)$
-2.9	-6.9
-2.99	-6.99
-2.999	-6.999

Limit Graphically

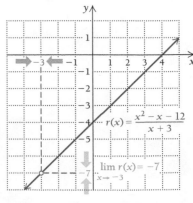

Both the table and the graph suggest that the limit is

$$\lim_{x \to -3}\left(\frac{x^2 - x - 12}{x + 3}\right) = -7.$$

Limit Algebraically. The function is simplified by factoring and noting that the factor $x + 3$ is present in both numerator and denominator. As long as $x \neq -3$, the expression can be simplified:

$$\frac{x^2 - x - 12}{x + 3} = \frac{(x + 3)(x - 4)}{(x + 3)} = x - 4, \quad \text{for } x \neq -3.$$

We then evaluate the limit using the simplified form:

$$\lim_{x \to -3}(x - 4) = (-3) - 4 = -7.$$

As shown on p. 108, the graph of r is a line with a "hole" at the point $(-3, -7)$. Even though $r(-3)$ does not exist, the limit *does* exist since we are only concerned about the behavior of $r(x)$ as x approaches -3. The decision to simplify was made by noting that $[(-3)^2 - (-3) - 12]/[(-3) + 3] = 0/0$. This *indeterminate form* indicates that the polynomials in the numerator and the denominator share a common factor, in this case, $x + 3$. The 0/0 form is a hint that a limit may exist. Look for ways to simplify algebraically, or use a table or a graph to determine such a limit.   **2** ✔

Quick Check 2 ✔

Using a table, a graph, and algebra, find

$$\lim_{x \to 2}\frac{x^2 + 4x - 12}{x^2 - 4}.$$

A common error in determining limits is to assume that all limits can be found by direct evaluation. A student may attempt to find the limit of a function like the one in Example 4, get a zero in the denominator, and then mistakenly assume that the limit does not exist. Remember, finding a limit as $x \to a$ focuses on x *close* to a, not at a. As Example 4 shows, the function may not be defined at a certain a-value, but its limit as $x \to a$ may still exist.

EXAMPLE 5   Find $\lim_{h \to 0}(3x^2 + 3xh + h^2)$.

Solution   We treat x as a constant since we are interested only in the way in which the expression varies when h approaches 0. We use the Limit Properties to find that

$$\lim_{h \to 0}(3x^2 + 3xh + h^2) = 3x^2 + 3x(0) + 0^2$$
$$= 3x^2. \quad \blacksquare$$

Continuity

The following are examples of graphs of functions that are *continuous* over the whole real number line, that is, over $(-\infty, \infty)$.

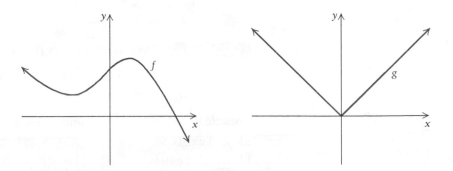

TECHNOLOGY CONNECTION 〰

EXERCISES

Find each limit, if it exists, using the TABLE feature.

1. $\lim_{x \to -2}(x^4 - 5x^3 + x^2 - 7)$

2. $\lim_{x \to 1}\sqrt{x^2 + 3x + 4}$

3. $\lim_{x \to 5}\dfrac{x - 5}{x^2 - 6x + 5}$

4. $\lim_{x \to 3}\dfrac{x - 3}{x^2 - 9}$

Note that there are no "jumps" or "holes" in the graphs. An intuitive definition of continuity is that a function is **continuous over**, or **on, some interval** if its graph can be traced without lifting pencil from paper. If there is any point in an interval where a "jump" or a "hole" occurs, then the function is *not continuous* over that interval. The graphs of *F*, *G*, and *H* below show functions that are *not* continuous over $(-\infty, \infty)$.

$$F(x) = \frac{1}{x-3}$$

$$G(x) = \begin{cases} 5, & \text{for } x = 2 \\ x+1, & \text{for } x \neq 2 \end{cases}$$

$$H(x) = \begin{cases} 2x+2, & \text{for } x < 1 \\ 2x-2, & \text{for } x \geq 1 \end{cases}$$

In each case, the graph *cannot* be traced without lifting pencil from paper. However, each case represents a different situation:

- *F* is not continuous over $(-\infty, \infty)$ because 3 is not in the domain. Thus, there is no point to trace at $x = 3$. Note that *F* is continuous over the intervals $(-\infty, 3)$ and $(3, \infty)$.
- *G* is not continuous over $(-\infty, \infty)$ because it is not continuous at $x = 2$. To see this, note that, as *x* approaches 2 from either side, $G(x)$ approaches 3. However, *at* $x = 2$, $G(x)$ *jumps* up to 5. Note that *G* is continuous over $(-\infty, 2)$ and $(2, \infty)$.
- *H* is not continuous over $(-\infty, \infty)$ because it is not continuous at $x = 1$. To see this, trace the graph and note that, as *x* approaches 1 from the left, $H(x)$ approaches 4. However, as *x* approaches 1 from the right, $H(x)$ approaches 0. Note that *H* is continuous over $(-\infty, 1)$ and $(1, \infty)$.

Each of the above graphs has a *point of discontinuity*. The graph of *F* is discontinuous at 3, because $x = 3$ is not in the domain of *F*; *G* is discontinuous at 2, because $\lim_{x \to 2} G(x) \neq G(2)$; and *H* is discontinuous at 1, because $\lim_{x \to 1} H(x)$ does not exist.

A continuous curve.

DEFINITION

A function *f* is **continuous** at $x = a$ if:

a) $f(a)$ exists,   (The output at *a* exists.)

b) $\lim_{x \to a} f(x)$ exists,   (The limit as $x \to a$ exists.)

and

c) $\lim_{x \to a} f(x) = f(a)$.   (The limit is the same as the output.)

A function is **continuous over an interval *I*** if it is continuous at each point *a* in *I*. If *f* is not continuous at $x = a$, we say that *f* is **discontinuous**, or has a **discontinuity**, at $x = a$.

A visualization of the function in Example 6

EXAMPLE 6   Determine whether the function given by

$$f(x) = 2x + 3$$

is continuous at $x = 4$.

Solution   This function is continuous at $x = 4$ because:

a) $f(4)$ exists,   ($f(4) = 11$)

b) $\lim_{x \to 4} f(x)$ exists,   ($\lim_{x \to 4} f(x) = 11$ was found on pp. 93–94.)

and

c) $\lim_{x \to 4} f(x) = 11 = f(4)$.

In fact, $f(x) = 2x + 3$ is continuous over the entire real number line. ■

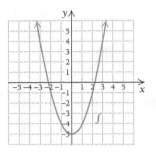

A visualization of the function in Example 7

A visualization of the function in Example 8

Quick Check 3 ✔

Let

$$g(x) = \begin{cases} 3x - 5, & \text{for } x < 2, \\ 2x + 1, & \text{for } x \geq 2. \end{cases}$$

Is g continuous at $x = 2$? Why or why not?

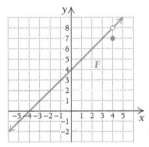

A visualization of the function in Example 9

EXAMPLE 7   Is the function f given by

$$f(x) = x^2 - 5$$

continuous at $x = 3$? Why or why not?

Solution   By the Theorem on Limits of Rational Functions, we have

$$\lim_{x \to 3} f(x) = 3^2 - 5 = 9 - 5 = 4.$$

Since

$$f(3) = 3^2 - 5 = 4,$$

we have

$$\lim_{x \to 3} f(x) = f(3).$$

Since all three parts of the definition of continuity are satisfied, f is continuous at $x = 3$. This function is also continuous over all real x. ∎

EXAMPLE 8   Is the function g, given by

$$g(x) = \begin{cases} \frac{1}{2}x + 3, & \text{for } x < -2, \\ x - 1, & \text{for } x \geq -2, \end{cases}$$

continuous at $x = -2$? Why or why not?

Solution   If g is continuous at -2, we must have $\lim_{x \to -2} g(x) = g(-2)$. Thus, we first note that $g(-2) = -2 - 1 = -3$. To find $\lim_{x \to -2} g(x)$, we look at left- and right-hand limits:

$$\lim_{x \to -2^-} g(x) = \frac{1}{2}(-2) + 3 = -1 + 3 = 2; \quad \lim_{x \to -2^+} g(x) = -2 - 1 = -3.$$

Since $\lim_{x \to -2^-} g(x) \neq \lim_{x \to -2^+} g(x)$, we see that $\lim_{x \to -2} g(x)$ does not exist. Thus, g is not continuous at -2.   **3** ✔

EXAMPLE 9   Is the function F, given by

$$F(x) = \begin{cases} \dfrac{x^2 - 16}{x - 4}, & \text{for } x \neq 4, \\ 7, & \text{for } x = 4, \end{cases}$$

continuous at $x = 4$? Why or why not?

Solution   For F to be continuous at 4, we must have $\lim_{x \to 4} F(x) = F(4)$. Note that $F(4) = 7$. To find $\lim_{x \to 4} F(x)$, note that, for $x \neq 4$,

$$\frac{x^2 - 16}{x - 4} = \frac{(x - 4)(x + 4)}{x - 4} = x + 4.$$

Thus,

$$\lim_{x \to 4} F(x) = 4 + 4 = 8.$$

We see that F is *not* continuous at $x = 4$ since

$$\lim_{x \to 4} F(x) \neq F(4). \qquad ∎$$

The Limit Properties and the Theorem on Limits of Rational Functions can be used to show that if f and g are two arbitrary polynomial functions, then f and g are both continuous. Furthermore, $f + g$, $f - g$, $f \cdot g$, and, assuming $g(x) \neq 0$, f/g are also continuous. We can also use the Limit Properties to show that for n, an integer greater than 1, $\sqrt[n]{f(x)}$ is continuous, provided that $f(x) \geq 0$ when n is even.

A visualization of the function in Example 10

Quick Check 4 ☑

Let

$$h(x) = \begin{cases} \dfrac{x^2 - 9}{x - 3}, & \text{for } x \neq 3, \\ 7, & \text{for } x = 3. \end{cases}$$

Is h continuous at $x = 3$? Why or why not?

EXAMPLE 10   Is the function G, given by

$$G(x) = \begin{cases} -x + 3, & \text{for } x \leq 2, \\ x^2 - 3, & \text{for } x > 2, \end{cases}$$

continuous for all x? Why or why not?

Solution   For G to be continuous, it must be continuous for all real numbers. Since $y = -x + 3$ is continuous on $(-\infty, 2)$ and $y = x^2 - 3$ is continuous on $(2, \infty)$, we need only to determine whether G is continuous at $x = 2$:

$$G(2) = -2 + 3 = 1;$$
$$\lim_{x \to 2^-} G(x) = -2 + 3 = 1 \quad \text{and} \quad \lim_{x \to 2^+} G(x) = (2)^2 - 3 = 4 - 3 = 1,$$

so $\lim_{x \to 2} G(x) = 1.$

Since $\lim_{x \to 2} G(x) = G(2)$, we have shown that G is continuous at $x = 2$, and we can conclude that G is continuous at all x.   **4** ☑

Example 10 shows that a piecewise-defined function may be continuous for all real numbers. In Example 11, we explore a real-world situation involving a piecewise function.

EXAMPLE 11   **Business: Price Breaks.**   Righteous Rocks sells decorative landscape rocks in bulk quantities. For quantities up to and including 500 lb, the company charges \$2.50 per pound. For quantities above 500 lb, it charges \$2 per pound. The price function can be stated as a piecewise function:

$$p(x) = \begin{cases} 2.50x, & \text{for } 0 < x \leq 500, \\ 2x, & \text{for } x > 500. \end{cases}$$

where p is the price in dollars and x is the quantity in pounds. Is p continuous at $x = 500$? Why or why not?

Solution   The graph of $p(x)$ follows.

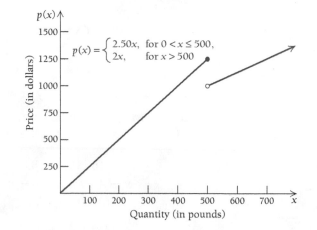

Quick Check 5 ☑

A reservoir is empty at time $t = 0$ minutes. It fills at a rate of 3 gallons of water per minute for 30 minutes. At 30 minutes, the reservoir is no longer being filled and a valve is opened, allowing water to escape at a rate of 4 gallons per minute. The volume v after t minutes is given by the function

$$v(t) = \begin{cases} 3t, & \text{for } 0 \leq t \leq 30, \\ 210 - 4t, & \text{for } t > 30. \end{cases}$$

Find $\lim_{t \to 30^-} v(t)$, $\lim_{t \to 30^+} v(t)$, and $\lim_{t \to 30} v(t)$.

As x approaches 500, we have $\lim_{x \to 500^-} p(x) = 1250$ and $\lim_{x \to 500^+} p(x) = 1000$. Since the left-hand and right-hand limits are not equal, the limit $\lim_{x \to 500} p(x)$ does not exist. Thus, the function is *not* continuous at $x = 500$. This graph literally shows a price "break."   **5** ☑

Section Summary

- For a rational function with a in its domain, the limit as x approaches a can be found by evaluating the function at a.
- When evaluating a limit leads to the *indeterminate form* $0/0$, the limit may still exist: algebraic simplification and/or a table and graph are used to find the limit.
- Informally, a function is *continuous* if its graph can be traced without lifting pencil from paper.

- Formally, a function f is continuous at $x = a$ if
  (1) the function value $f(a)$ exists,
  (2) the limit as x approaches a exists, and
  (3) the function value and the limit are equal.
  This is summarized as $\lim\limits_{x \to a} f(x) = f(a)$.
- If any part of the continuity definition fails, then the function is *discontinuous* at $x = a$.

1.2 Exercise Set

Classify each statement as either true or false.

1. $\lim\limits_{x \to 3} 7 = 3$

2. If $\lim\limits_{x \to 2} f(x) = 9$, then $\lim\limits_{x \to 2} \sqrt{f(x)} = 3$.

3. If $\lim\limits_{x \to 1} g(x) = 5$, then $\lim\limits_{x \to 1} [g(x)]^2 = 25$.

4. If $\lim\limits_{x \to 4} F(x) = 7$, then $\lim\limits_{x \to 4} [c \cdot F(x)] = 7c$.

5. If g is discontinuous at $x = 3$, then $g(3)$ must not exist.

6. If f is continuous at $x = 2$, then $f(2)$ must exist.

7. If $\lim\limits_{x \to 4} F(x)$ exists, then F must be continuous at $x = 4$.

8. If $\lim\limits_{x \to 7} G(x)$ equals $G(7)$, then G must be continuous at $x = 7$.

Use the Theorem on Limits of Rational Functions to find each limit. When necessary, state that the limit does not exist.

9. $\lim\limits_{x \to 2} (4x - 5)$

10. $\lim\limits_{x \to 1} (3x + 2)$

11. $\lim\limits_{x \to -1} (x^2 - 4)$

12. $\lim\limits_{x \to -2} (x^2 + 3)$

13. $\lim\limits_{x \to 5} (x^2 - 6x + 9)$

14. $\lim\limits_{x \to 3} (x^2 - 4x + 7)$

15. $\lim\limits_{x \to 2} (2x^4 - 3x^3 + 4x - 1)$

16. $\lim\limits_{x \to -1} (3x^5 + 4x^4 - 3x + 6)$

17. $\lim\limits_{x \to 3} \dfrac{x^2 - 25}{x^2 - 5}$

18. $\lim\limits_{x \to 3} \dfrac{x^2 - 8}{x - 2}$

For Exercises 19–30, the initial substitution of $x = a$ yields the form $0/0$. Look for ways to simplify the function algebraically, or use a table or graph to determine the limit. When necessary, state that the limit does not exist.

19. $\lim\limits_{x \to 3} \dfrac{x^2 - 9}{x - 3}$

20. $\lim\limits_{x \to 5} \dfrac{x^2 - 25}{x - 5}$

21. $\lim\limits_{x \to -2} \dfrac{x^2 - 2x - 8}{x^2 - 4}$

22. $\lim\limits_{x \to 1} \dfrac{x^2 + 5x - 6}{x^2 - 1}$

23. $\lim\limits_{x \to 2} \dfrac{3x^2 + x - 14}{x^2 - 4}$

24. $\lim\limits_{x \to -3} \dfrac{2x^2 - x - 21}{9 - x^2}$

25. $\lim\limits_{x \to 2} \dfrac{x^3 - 8}{2 - x}$

26. $\lim\limits_{x \to 1} \dfrac{x^3 - 1}{x - 1}$

27. $\lim\limits_{x \to 25} \dfrac{\sqrt{x} - 5}{x - 25}$

28. $\lim\limits_{x \to 9} \dfrac{9 - x}{\sqrt{x} - 3}$

29. $\lim\limits_{x \to 2} \dfrac{x^2 + 3x - 10}{x^2 - 4x + 4}$

30. $\lim\limits_{x \to -1} \dfrac{x^2 + 5x + 4}{x^2 + 2x + 1}$

Use the Limit Properties to find the following limits. If a limit does not exist, state that fact.

31. $\lim\limits_{x \to 5} \sqrt{x^2 - 16}$

32. $\lim\limits_{x \to 4} \sqrt{x^2 - 9}$

33. $\lim\limits_{x \to 2} \sqrt{x^2 - 9}$

34. $\lim\limits_{x \to 3} \sqrt{x^2 - 16}$

35. $\lim\limits_{x \to -4^-} \sqrt{x^2 - 16}$

36. $\lim\limits_{x \to 3^+} \sqrt{x^2 - 9}$

Determine whether each of the functions shown in Exercises 37–41 is continuous over the interval $(-6, 6)$.

37.

38.

39.

40.

41.

Use the graphs and functions in Exercises 37–41 to answer each of the following. If an expression does not exist, state that fact.

42. a) Find $\lim_{x \to 1^+} g(x)$, $\lim_{x \to 1^-} g(x)$, and $\lim_{x \to 1} g(x)$.
 b) Find $g(1)$.
 c) Is g continuous at $x = 1$? Why or why not?
 d) Find $\lim_{x \to -2} g(x)$.
 e) Find $g(-2)$.
 f) Is g continuous at $x = -2$? Why or why not?

43. a) Find $\lim_{x \to 1^+} f(x)$, $\lim_{x \to 1^-} f(x)$, and $\lim_{x \to 1} f(x)$.
 b) Find $f(1)$.
 c) Is f continuous at $x = 1$? Why or why not?
 d) Find $\lim_{x \to -2} f(x)$.
 e) Find $f(-2)$.
 f) Is f continuous at $x = -2$? Why or why not?

44. a) Find $\lim_{x \to 1} h(x)$.
 b) Find $h(1)$.
 c) Is h continuous at $x = 1$? Why or why not?
 d) Find $\lim_{x \to -2} h(x)$.
 e) Find $h(-2)$.
 f) Is h continuous at $x = -2$? Why or why not?

45. a) Find $\lim_{x \to -1} k(x)$.
 b) Find $k(-1)$.
 c) Is k continuous at $x = -1$? Why or why not?
 d) Find $\lim_{x \to 3} k(x)$.
 e) Find $k(3)$.
 f) Is k continuous at $x = 3$? Why or why not?

46. a) Find $\lim_{x \to 1} t(x)$.
 b) Find $t(1)$.
 c) Is t continuous at $x = 1$? Why or why not?
 d) Find $\lim_{x \to -2} t(x)$.
 e) Find $t(-2)$.
 f) Is t continuous at $x = -2$? Why or why not?

Answer Exercises 47 and 48 using the graphs provided.

47.

a) Find $\lim_{x \to 3^+} G(x)$.
b) Find $\lim_{x \to 3^-} G(x)$.
c) Find $\lim_{x \to 3} G(x)$.
d) Find $G(3)$.
e) Is G continuous at $x = 3$? Why or why not?
f) Is G continuous at $x = 0$? Why or why not?
g) Is G continuous at $x = 2.9$? Why or why not?

48. Consider the function

$$C(x) = \begin{cases} -1, & \text{for } x < 2, \\ 1, & \text{for } x \geq 2. \end{cases}$$

a) Find $\lim_{x \to 2^+} C(x)$.
b) Find $\lim_{x \to 2^-} C(x)$.
c) Find $\lim_{x \to 2} C(x)$.
d) Find $C(2)$.
e) Is C continuous at $x = 2$? Why or why not?
f) Is C continuous at $x = 1.95$? Why or why not?

49. Is the function given by $g(x) = x^2 - 3x$ continuous at $x = 4$? Why or why not?

50. Is the function given by $f(x) = 3x - 2$ continuous at $x = 5$? Why or why not?

51. Is the function given by $G(x) = \dfrac{1}{x}$ continuous at $x = 0$? Why or why not?

52. Is the function given by $F(x) = \sqrt{x}$ continuous at $x = -1$? Why or why not?

53. Is the function given by

$$f(x) = \begin{cases} \frac{1}{2}x + 1, & \text{for } x < 4, \\ -x + 7, & \text{for } x \geq 4, \end{cases}$$

continuous at $x = 4$? Why or why not?

54. Is the function given by

$$g(x) = \begin{cases} \frac{1}{3}x + 4, & \text{for } x \leq 3, \\ 2x - 1, & \text{for } x > 3, \end{cases}$$

continuous at $x = 3$? Why or why not?

55. Is the function given by

$$F(x) = \begin{cases} \frac{1}{3}x + 4, & \text{for } x \leq 3, \\ 2x - 5, & \text{for } x > 3, \end{cases}$$

continuous at $x = 3$? Why or why not?

56. Is the function given by

$$G(x) = \begin{cases} \frac{1}{2}x + 1, & \text{for } x < 4, \\ -x + 5, & \text{for } x > 4, \end{cases}$$

continuous at $x = 4$? Why or why not?

57. Is the function given by

$$g(x) = \begin{cases} \frac{1}{2}x + 1, & \text{for } x < 4, \\ -x + 7, & \text{for } x > 4, \end{cases}$$

continuous at $x = 4$? Why or why not?

58. Is the function given by

$$f(x) = \begin{cases} \frac{1}{3}x + 4, & \text{for } x < 3, \\ 2x - 1, & \text{for } x \geq 3, \end{cases}$$

continuous at $x = 3$? Why or why not?

59. Is the function given by

$$G(x) = \begin{cases} \dfrac{x^2 - 4}{x - 2}, & \text{for } x \neq 2, \\ 5, & \text{for } x = 2, \end{cases}$$

continuous at $x = 2$? Why or why not?

60. Is the function given by

$$F(x) = \begin{cases} \dfrac{x^2 - 1}{x - 1}, & \text{for } x \neq 1, \\ 4, & \text{for } x = 1, \end{cases}$$

continuous at $x = 1$? Why or why not?

61. Is the function given by

$$G(x) = \begin{cases} \dfrac{x^2 - 3x - 4}{x - 4}, & \text{for } x < 4, \\ 2x - 3, & \text{for } x \geq 4, \end{cases}$$

continuous at $x = 4$? Why or why not?

62. Is the function given by

$$f(x) = \begin{cases} \dfrac{x^2 - 4x - 5}{x - 5}, & \text{for } x < 5, \\ x + 1, & \text{for } x \geq 5, \end{cases}$$

continuous at $x = 5$? Why or why not?

63. Is the function given by $g(x) = \dfrac{1}{x^2 - 7x + 10}$ continuous at $x = 5$? Why or why not?

64. Is the function given by $f(x) = \dfrac{1}{x^2 - 6x + 8}$ continuous at $x = 3$? Why or why not?

65. Is the function given by $G(x) = \dfrac{1}{x^2 - 6x + 8}$ continuous at $x = 2$? Why or why not?

66. Is the function given by $F(x) = \dfrac{1}{x^2 - 7x + 10}$ continuous at $x = 4$? Why or why not?

67. Is the function given by $g(x) = \dfrac{1}{x + 5}$ continuous over the interval $(-4, 4)$? Why or why not?

68. Is the function given by $F(x) = -\dfrac{2}{x - 7}$ continuous over the interval $(-5, 5)$? Why or why not?

69. Is the function given by $G(x) = \dfrac{1}{x - 1}$ continuous over the interval $(0, \infty)$? Why or why not?

70. Is the function given by $f(x) = \dfrac{1}{x} + 3$ continuous over the interval $(-7, 7)$? Why or why not?

71. Is the function given by $g(x) = 4x^3 - 6x$ continuous on $\mathbb{R}$?

72. Is the function given by $F(x) = \dfrac{3}{x - 5}$ continuous on $\mathbb{R}$?

APPLICATIONS

Business and Economics

73. The Candy Factory sells candy by the pound, charging $1.50 per pound for quantities up to and including 20 pounds. Above 20 pounds, the Candy Factory charges $1.25 per pound for the entire quantity. If x represents the number of pounds, the price function is

$$p(x) = \begin{cases} 1.50x, & \text{for } x \leq 20, \\ 1.25x, & \text{for } x > 20. \end{cases}$$

Find $\lim\limits_{x \to 20^-} p(x)$, $\lim\limits_{x \to 20^+} p(x)$, and $\lim\limits_{x \to 20} p(x)$.

74. The Copy Shoppe charges $0.08 per copy for quantities up to and including 100 copies. For quantities above 100, the charge is $0.06 per copy. If x represents the number of copies, the price function is

$$p(x) = \begin{cases} 0.08x, & \text{for } x \leq 100, \\ 0.06x, & \text{for } x > 100. \end{cases}$$

Find $\lim\limits_{x \to 100^-} p(x)$, $\lim\limits_{x \to 100^+} p(x)$, and $\lim\limits_{x \to 100} p(x)$.

Life and Physical Sciences

75. A lab technician controls the temperature T inside a kiln. From an initial temperature of 0 degrees Celsius (°C), he allows the temperature to increase by 2°C per minute for the next 60 minutes. After the 60th minute, he allows the temperature to cool by 3°C per minute. If t is the number of minutes, the temperature T is given by

$$T(t) = \begin{cases} 2t, & \text{for } t \leq 60, \\ 300 - 3t, & \text{for } t > 60. \end{cases}$$

Find $\lim\limits_{t \to 60^-} T(t)$, $\lim\limits_{t \to 60^+} T(t)$, and $\lim\limits_{t \to 60} T(t)$.

SYNTHESIS

76. In Exercise 73, let

$$p(x) = \begin{cases} 1.50x, & \text{for } x \le 20, \\ 1.25x + k, & \text{for } x > 20. \end{cases}$$

Find k such that the price function p is continuous at $x = 20$.

77. In Exercise 74, let

$$p(x) = \begin{cases} 0.08x, & \text{for } x \le 100, \\ 0.06x + k, & \text{for } x > 100. \end{cases}$$

Find k such that the price function p is continuous at $x = 100$.

78. Find each limit, if it exists. If a limit does not exist, state that fact.

a) $\lim\limits_{x \to 0} \dfrac{|x|}{x}$

b) $\lim\limits_{x \to -2} \dfrac{x^3 + 8}{x^2 - 4}$

TECHNOLOGY CONNECTION

In Section 1.1, we used the TABLE feature to find limits. Consider

$$\lim_{x \to 0} \frac{\sqrt{1 + x} - 1}{x}.$$

Input–output tables for this function are below. The table on the left uses TblStart $= -1$ and ΔTbl $= 0.5$. By using smaller and smaller step values and beginning closer to 0, we can refine the table and obtain a better estimate of the limit. On the right is an input–output table with TblStart $= -0.03$ and ΔTbl $= 0.01$.

X	Y₁		X	Y₁
-1	1		-0.03	0.50381
-0.5	0.58579		-0.02	0.50253
0	ERROR		-0.01	0.50126
0.5	0.44949		0	ERROR
1	0.41421		0.01	0.49876
1.5	0.38743		0.02	0.49752
2	0.36603		0.03	0.49631
X = -1			X = -0.03	

It appears that the limit is 0.5. We can check by graphing

$$y = \frac{\sqrt{1 + x} - 1}{x}$$

and tracing the curve near $x = 0$, zooming in on that portion of the curve.

We see that

$$\lim_{x \to 0} \frac{\sqrt{1 + x} - 1}{x} = 0.5.$$

To verify this algebraically, multiply $\dfrac{\sqrt{1 + x} - 1}{x}$ by 1, using $\dfrac{\sqrt{1 + x} + 1}{\sqrt{1 + x} + 1}$. Then simplify the result and find the limit.

In Exercises 79–86, find each limit. Use TABLE and start with ΔTbl $= 0.1$. Then use 0.01, 0.001, and 0.0001. When you think you know the limit, graph and use TRACE to verify your assertion. Then try to verify it algebraically.

79. $\lim\limits_{x \to 1} \dfrac{\sqrt{x} - 1}{x - 1}$ **80.** $\lim\limits_{a \to -2} \dfrac{a^2 - 4}{\sqrt{a^2 + 5} - 3}$

81. $\lim\limits_{x \to 0} \dfrac{\sqrt{4 + x} - \sqrt{4 - x}}{x}$ **82.** $\lim\limits_{x \to 0} \dfrac{\sqrt{3 - x} - \sqrt{3}}{x}$

83. $\lim\limits_{x \to 0} \dfrac{\sqrt{7 + 2x} - \sqrt{7}}{x}$ **84.** $\lim\limits_{x \to 1} \dfrac{x - \sqrt[4]{x}}{x - 1}$

85. $\lim\limits_{x \to 0} \dfrac{7 - \sqrt{49 - x^2}}{x}$ **86.** $\lim\limits_{x \to 4} \dfrac{2 - \sqrt{x}}{4 - x}$

Answers to Quick Checks

1. **(a)** -1; L1, L2, L3, L6;   **(b)** $\dfrac{51}{10}$, or 5.1; L1, L2, L3, L5, L6;
(c) $\sqrt{13}$; L1, L2, L3, L6   **2.** 2   **3.** No, the limit as $x \to 2$ does not exist.   **4.** No, the limit as $x \to 3$ is 6, but $h(3) = 7$, so the limit does not equal the function value.   **5.** 90, 90, 90

1.3 Average Rates of Change

- Compute an average rate of change.
- Find a simplified difference quotient.

If a car travels 110 mi in 2 hr, its *average rate of change* (*speed*) is 110 mi/2 hr, or 55 mi/hr (55 mph). Suppose you accelerate on a freeway and, glancing at the speedometer, you see that at that instant your *instantaneous rate of change* is 55 mph. These are two quite different concepts. The first you are probably familiar with. The second involves ideas of limits and calculus. Understanding instantaneous rate of change requires a solid understanding of average rate of change.

The following graph shows total production of suits at Raggs, Ltd., during one morning of work.

EXAMPLE 1   Business: Production.   How many suits were produced at Raggs, Ltd., from 9 A.M. to 10 A.M.?

Solution   At 9 A.M., 20 suits had been produced. At 10 A.M., 55 suits had been produced. In the hour from 9 A.M. to 10 A.M., the number of suits produced was

> 55 suits − 20 suits,   or   35 suits.

Note that 35 is the slope of the line segment from *P* to *Q*.

EXAMPLE 2   Business: Average Rate of Change.   What was the average number of suits produced per hour from 9 A.M. ($t = 1$) to 11 A.M. ($t = 3$)?

Solution   We have

$$\frac{64 \text{ suits} - 20 \text{ suits}}{3 \text{ hr} - 1 \text{ hr}} = \frac{44 \text{ suits}}{2 \text{ hr}}$$

$$= 22 \frac{\text{suits}}{\text{hr}}.$$

Note that 22 is the slope of the line segment from *P* to *R*.

Quick Check 1 ✔

State the average rate of change for each situation in a short sentence. Be sure to include units.

a) It rained 4 inches over a period of 8 hours. State your answer in inches per hour.

b) Your car travels 250 miles on 10 gallons of gas. State your answer in miles per gallon.

c) At 2 P.M., the temperature was 82 degrees. At 5 P.M., the temperature was 76 degrees. State your answer in degrees per hour.

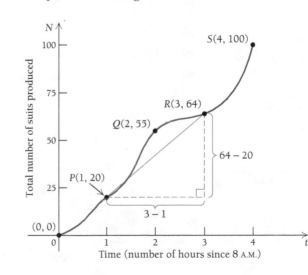

1 ✔

Let's consider a function $y = f(x)$ and two inputs x_1 and x_2. The *change in input*, or the *change in x*, is

$$x_2 - x_1.$$

The *change in output*, or the *change in y*, is

$$y_2 - y_1,$$

where $y_1 = f(x_1)$ and $y_2 = f(x_2)$.

DEFINITION

The **average rate of change of y with respect to x**, as x changes from x_1 to x_2, is the ratio of the change in output to the change in input:

$$\frac{y_2 - y_1}{x_2 - x_1}, \quad \text{where } x_2 \neq x_1.$$

If we look at a graph of the function, we see that

$$\frac{y_2 - y_1}{x_2 - x_1} = \frac{f(x_2) - f(x_1)}{x_2 - x_1},$$

which is both the average rate of change and the slope of the line from $P(x_1, y_1)$ to $Q(x_2, y_2)$.* The line passing through P and Q, denoted $\overleftrightarrow{PQ}$, is called a **secant line**.

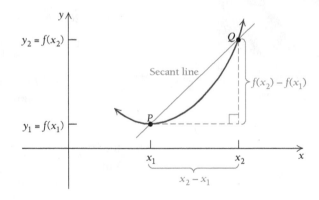

The slope of the secant line represents the average rate of change of f from x_1 to x_2.

EXAMPLE 3 For $y = f(x) = x^2 + 1$, find the average rate of change as:

a) x changes from 1 to 3;

b) x changes from 1 to 2.

Solution The graph in the margin is not necessary to the computations but gives us a look at the two secant lines whose slopes are being computed.

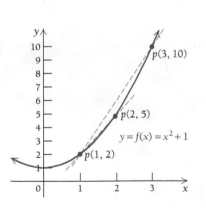

a) When $x_1 = 1$,

$$y_1 = f(x_1) = f(1) = 1^2 + 1 = 2;$$

and when $x_2 = 3$,

$$y_2 = f(x_2) = f(3) = 3^2 + 1 = 10.$$

---

*The notation $P(x_1, y_1)$ simply means that point P has coordinates (x_1, y_1).

The average rate of change is

$$\frac{y_2 - y_1}{x_2 - x_1} = \frac{f(x_2) - f(x_1)}{x_2 - x_1}$$

$$= \frac{10 - 2}{3 - 1}$$

$$= \frac{8}{2} = 4.$$

b) When $x_1 = 1$,

$$y_1 = f(x_1) = f(1) = 1^2 + 1 = 2;$$

and when $x_2 = 2$,

$$y_2 = f(x_2) = f(2) = 2^2 + 1 = 5.$$

The average rate of change is

$$\frac{5 - 2}{2 - 1} = \frac{3}{1} = 3.$$

2 ✔

Quick Check 2 ✔

For $f(x) = x^3 + 1$, find the average rate of change between:

a) $x = 1$ and $x = 4$;

b) $x = 1$ and $x = 2$.

For a linear function, the average rate of change is the same for any choice of x_1 and x_2. As we saw in Example 3, a function that is not linear has average rates of change that generally vary with choices of x_1 and x_2.

Difference Quotient as Average Rate of Change

We now develop a notation for average rate of change that does not require subscripts. Instead of x_1, we write x; in place of x_2, we write $x + h$.

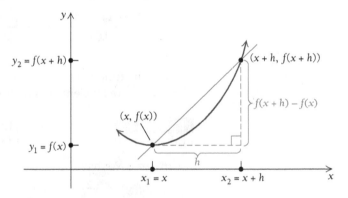

Think of h as the horizontal distance between inputs x_1 and x_2. That is, to get from x_1, or x, to x_2, we move a distance h. Thus, $x_2 = x + h$. Then the average rate of change, also called the *difference quotient,* is given by

$$\frac{y_2 - y_1}{x_2 - x_1} = \frac{f(x_2) - f(x_1)}{x_2 - x_1} = \frac{f(x + h) - f(x)}{(x + h) - x} = \frac{f(x + h) - f(x)}{h}.$$

DEFINITION

The average rate of change of $f(x)$ with respect to x is also called the **difference quotient**. It is given by

$$\frac{f(x + h) - f(x)}{h}, \quad \text{where } h \neq 0.$$

The difference quotient is equal to the slope of the secant line passing through $(x, f(x))$ and $(x + h, f(x + h))$.

EXAMPLE 4 For $f(x) = x^2$, find the difference quotient when:

a) $x = 5$ and $h = 3$.   **b)** $x = 5$ and $h = 0.1$.   **c)** $x = 5$ and $h = 0.01$.

Solution

a) We substitute $x = 5$ and $h = 3$ into the formula:

$$\frac{f(x + h) - f(x)}{h} = \frac{f(5 + 3) - f(5)}{3} = \frac{f(8) - f(5)}{3}.$$

Since $f(8) = 8^2 = 64$ and $f(5) = 5^2 = 25$, we have

$$\frac{f(8) - f(5)}{3} = \frac{64 - 25}{3} = \frac{39}{3} = 13.$$

The difference quotient is 13. It is the slope of the line passing through $(5, 25)$ and $(8, 64)$.

b) We substitute $x = 5$ and $h = 0.1$ into the formula:

$$\frac{f(x + h) - f(x)}{h} = \frac{f(5 + 0.1) - f(5)}{0.1} = \frac{f(5.1) - f(5)}{0.1}.$$

Since $f(5.1) = (5.1)^2 = 26.01$ and $f(5) = 25$, we have

$$\frac{f(5.1) - f(5)}{0.1} = \frac{26.01 - 25}{0.1} = \frac{1.01}{0.1} = 10.1.$$

c) We substitute $x = 5$ and $h = 0.01$ into the formula:

$$\frac{f(x + h) - f(x)}{h} = \frac{f(5 + 0.01) - f(5)}{0.01} = \frac{f(5.01) - f(5)}{0.01}.$$

Since $f(5.01) = (5.01)^2 = 25.1001$ and $f(5) = 25$, we have

$$\frac{f(5.01) - f(5)}{0.01} = \frac{25.1001 - 25}{0.01} = \frac{0.1001}{0.01} = 10.01.$$ ∎

For the function in Example 4, let's find a form of the difference quotient that will allow for more efficient computations.

EXAMPLE 5 For $f(x) = x^2$, find a simplified form of the difference quotient. Then evaluate the difference quotient for $x = 5$ and $h = 0.1$ and for $x = 5$ and $h = 0.01$.

Solution We have

$$f(x) = x^2,$$

so

$$f(x + h) = (x + h)^2 = x^2 + 2xh + h^2. \quad \text{Multiplying } (x + h)(x + h)$$

Then

$$f(x + h) - f(x) = (x^2 + 2xh + h^2) - x^2 = 2xh + h^2. \quad \text{The } x^2 \text{ terms add to 0.}$$

Thus,

$$\frac{f(x + h) - f(x)}{h} = \frac{2xh + h^2}{h} = \frac{h(2x + h)}{h} = 2x + h, \quad h \neq 0. \quad h/h = 1$$

This is the simplified form of this difference quotient. It is important to note that for any difference quotient, we must have $h \neq 0$.

For $x = 5$ and $h = 0.1$, we have

$$\frac{f(x + h) - f(x)}{h} = 2x + h = 2 \cdot 5 + 0.1 = 10 + 0.1 = 10.1.$$

For $x = 5$ and $h = 0.01$, we have

$$\frac{f(x + h) - f(x)}{h} = 2x + h = 2 \cdot 5 + 0.01 = 10.01.$$

Although $2x + h$ is valid only when $h \neq 0$, h can get closer and closer to 0. Perhaps you can sense what value the difference quotient will have in this example when we allow h to approach 0 as a limit. ■

Compare the results of Example 4(b) and 4(c) and Example 5. In general, computations are easier when a simplified form of a difference quotient is found before any specific calculations are performed.

EXAMPLE 6 For $f(x) = x^3$, find the simplified form of the difference quotient.

Solution For $f(x) = x^3$,

$$f(x + h) = (x + h)^3 = x^3 + 3x^2h + 3xh^2 + h^3, \qquad \text{See Appendix A.}$$
$$f(x + h) - f(x) = (x^3 + 3x^2h + 3xh^2 + h^3) - x^3 = 3x^2h + 3xh^2 + h^3,$$

and

$$\frac{f(x + h) - f(x)}{h} = \frac{3x^2h + 3xh^2 + h^3}{h} \qquad \text{It is understood that } h \neq 0.$$

$$= \frac{h(3x^2 + 3xh + h^2)}{h} \qquad \text{Factoring } h; \, h/h = 1$$

$$= 3x^2 + 3xh + h^2, \quad h \neq 0.$$

Quick Check 3 ☑

Use the result of Example 6 to calculate the slope of the secant line (average rate of change) at $x = 2$, for $h = 0.1$ and $h = 0.01$.

Again, this is true *only* for $h \neq 0$.   **3** ☑

The next two examples illustrate the development of the difference quotients for a simple rational function (Example 7) and for the square-root function (Example 8). Both forms are common in calculus.

EXAMPLE 7 For $f(x) = 1/x$, find the simplified form of the difference quotient.

Solution For $f(x) = 1/x$, we have

$$f(x + h) = \frac{1}{x + h}.$$

Then

$$f(x + h) - f(x) = \frac{1}{x + h} - \frac{1}{x}$$

$$= \frac{1}{x + h} \cdot \frac{x}{x} - \frac{1}{x} \cdot \frac{x + h}{x + h} \qquad \begin{array}{l}\text{Multiplying by 1 to get a} \\ \text{common denominator}\end{array}$$

$$= \frac{x - (x + h)}{x(x + h)} \qquad \text{Parentheses are important here.}$$

$$= \frac{x - x - h}{x(x + h)}$$

$$= \frac{-h}{x(x + h)}.$$

Thus,

$$\frac{f(x+h) - f(x)}{h} = \frac{\dfrac{-h}{x(x+h)}}{h}$$

$$= \frac{-h}{x(x+h)} \cdot \frac{1}{h} = \frac{-1}{x(x+h)}, h \neq 0.$$

This is true *only* for $h \neq 0$. ∎

EXAMPLE 8 For $f(x) = \sqrt{x}$, find the simplified form of the difference quotient.

Solution For $f(x) = \sqrt{x}$, we have $f(x+h) = \sqrt{x+h}$, so the difference quotient is

$$\frac{f(x+h) - f(x)}{h} = \frac{\sqrt{x+h} - \sqrt{x}}{h}.$$

Algebraic simplification of this difference quotient leads to

$$\frac{f(x+h) - f(x)}{h} = \frac{1}{\sqrt{x+h} + \sqrt{x}}, \quad h \neq 0.$$

Demonstration of this simplification is left as Exercise 54. This simplified difference quotient appears again in Section 1.5. ∎

In all of the above cases, the simplified difference quotient includes two variables: x and h, where h cannot be 0. Although h cannot be 0, we may let h be as small as we desire. In the next section, we take a further step: allowing h to approach 0 as a limit.

Section Summary

- An *average rate of change* is the slope of a line passing through two points. If the points are (x_1, y_1) and (x_2, y_2), then the average rate of change is $\dfrac{y_2 - y_1}{x_2 - x_1}$.
- If the two points are on the graph of f, an equivalent form of the slope formula is $\dfrac{f(x+h) - f(x)}{h}$, where h is the horizontal difference between the two x-values.

This is called the *difference quotient*. The line passing through these two points is called a *secant line*.
- The difference quotient gives the *average rate of change* between two points on a graph.
- It is preferable to simplify a difference quotient algebraically before evaluating it for particular values of x and h.

1.3 Exercise Set

For each function in Exercises 1–16, (a) find the simplified form of the difference quotient and then (b) complete the following table.

x	h	$\dfrac{f(x+h) - f(x)}{h}$
5	2	
5	1	
5	0.1	
5	0.01	

1. $f(x) = 5x^2$

2. $f(x) = 4x^2$

3. $f(x) = -5x^2$

4. $f(x) = -4x^2$

5. $f(x) = x^2 - x$

6. $f(x) = x^2 + x$

7. $f(x) = \dfrac{9}{x}$

8. $f(x) = \dfrac{2}{x}$

9. $f(x) = 2x + 3$

10. $f(x) = -2x + 5$

11. $f(x) = 12x^3$

12. $f(x) = 1 - x^3$

13. $f(x) = x^2 - 4x$

14. $f(x) = x^2 - 3x$

15. $f(x) = x^2 - 3x + 5$

16. $f(x) = x^2 + 4x - 3$

APPLICATIONS

Business and Economics

For Exercises 17–24, use each graph to estimate the average rate of change of the percentage of new employees in that type of employment from 2003 to 2007, from 2007 to 2012, and from 2003 to 2012. (Source: Bureau of Labor Statistics.)

17. Total employment.

18. Construction.

19. Professional services.

20. Health care.

21. Education.

22. Government.

23. Mining and logging.

24. Manufacturing.

25. Use the following graph to find the average rate of change in U.S. energy consumption from 1982 to 1992, from 1992 to 2002, and from 2002 to 2012.

U.S. ENERGY CONSUMPTION

Year

(*Source:* U.S. Energy Information Administration.)

26. Use the following graph to find the average rate of change of the U.S. trade deficit with Japan from 2007 to 2009, from 2009 to 2011, and from 2011 to 2013.

U.S. TRADE DEFICIT WITH JAPAN

Year

(*Source:* U.S. Census Bureau, *Statistical Abstract of the United States, 2012.*)

27. Utility. Utility is a type of function that occurs in economics. When a consumer receives x units of a product, a certain amount of pleasure, or utility U, is gained. The following represents a typical utility function.

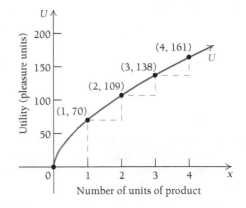

a) Find the average rate of change of U as x changes from 0 to 1; from 1 to 2; from 2 to 3; from 3 to 4.

b) Why do you think the average rates of change are decreasing as x increases?

28. Advertising results. The following graph shows a typical response to advertising. When amount a is spent on advertising, $N(a)$ units of a product are sold.

Money spent (in thousands of dollars)

a) Find the average rate of change of N as a changes from 0 to 1; from 1 to 2; from 2 to 3; from 3 to 4.

b) Why do you think the average rates of change are decreasing as x increases?

29. Baseball ticket prices. Based on data from Major League Baseball, the average price of a ticket to a major league game can be approximated by

$$p(x) = 0.06x^3 - 0.5x^2 + 1.64x + 24.76$$

where x is the number of years after 2008 and $p(x)$ is in dollars. (*Source*: Based on data from www.teammarketing .com.)

a) Find $p(4)$.

b) Find $p(6)$.

c) Find $p(6) - p(4)$.

d) Find $\dfrac{p(6) - p(4)}{6 - 4}$. What rate of change does this represent?

30. Compound interest. The amount of money, $A(t)$, in a savings account that pays 6% interest, compounded quarterly for t years, when an initial investment of $2000 is made, is given by

$$A(t) = 2000(1.015)^{4t}.$$

a) Find $A(3)$.

b) Find $A(5)$.

c) Find $A(5) - A(3)$.

d) Find $\dfrac{A(5) - A(3)}{5 - 3}$. What rate of change does this represent?

31. Population change. The population of Payton County was 5400 at the last census and decreasing at the rate of 2.5% per year. The total population of the county after t years, $P(t)$, is given by

$$P(t) = 5400(0.975)^t.$$

Find $\dfrac{P(8) - P(5)}{8 - 5}$. What rate of change does this represent?

32. Population change. The undergraduate population at Harbor College was 17,000 and increasing at the rate of 4.2% per year. The undergraduate population after t years, $P(t)$, is given by

$$P(t) = 17,000(1.042)^t.$$

Find $\dfrac{P(6) - P(2)}{6 - 2}$. What rate of change does this represent?

33. Total cost. Suppose Fast Trends determines that the cost, in dollars, of producing x iPod holders is given by

$$C(x) = -0.05x^2 + 50x.$$

Find $\dfrac{C(305) - C(300)}{305 - 300}$, and interpret the significance of this result to the company.

34. Total revenue. Suppose Fast Trends determines that the revenue, in dollars, from the sale of x iPod holders is given by

$$R(x) = -0.001x^2 + 150x.$$

Find $\dfrac{R(305) - R(300)}{305 - 300}$, and interpret the significance of this result to the company.

Life and Physical Sciences

35. Growth of a baby. The median weights of babies at age t months are graphed below.

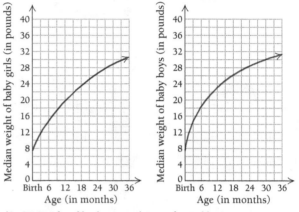

(*Source*: Developed by the National Center for Health Statistics in collaboration with the National Center for Chronic Disease Prevention and Health Promotion, 2000; checked in 2014.)

Use the graph of girls' median weight to estimate:

a) The average growth rate of a girl during her first 12 months. (Your answer should be in pounds per month.)

b) The average growth rate of a girl during her second 12 months.

c) The average growth rate of a girl during her first 24 months.

d) Based on your answers in parts (a)–(c) and the graph, estimate the growth rate of a typical 12-month-old girl, and explain how you arrived at this figure.

e) In what three-month period does a baby girl grow fastest?

36. Growth of a baby. Use the graph of boys' median weight in Exercise 35 to estimate:

a) The average growth rate of a boy during his first 15 months. (Your answer should be in pounds per month.)

b) The average growth rate of a boy during his second 15 months. (Your answer should be in pounds per month.)

c) The average growth rate of a boy during his first 30 months. (Your answer should be in pounds per month.)

d) Based on your answers in parts (a)–(c) and the graph, estimate the growth rate of a typical boy at exactly 15 months, and explain how you arrived at this figure.

37. Home range. It has been shown that the home range, in hectares, of a carnivorous mammal weighing w grams can be approximated by

$$H(w) = 0.11w^{1.36}.$$

(*Source*: Based on information in Emlen, J. M., *Ecology: An Evolutionary Approach*, p. 200, Reading, MA: Addison-Wesley, 1973; and Harestad, A. S., and Bunnel, F. L., "Home Range and Body Weight—A Reevaluation," *Ecology*, Vol. 60, No. 2, pp. 389–402.)

a) Find the average rate at which a carnivorous mammal's home range increases as the animal's weight grows from 500 g to 700 g.

b) Find $\dfrac{H(300) - H(200)}{300 - 200}$. What does this rate represent?

38. Radar range. The function given by $R(x) = 11.74x^{1/4}$ can be used to approximate the maximum range $R(x)$, in miles, of an ARSR-3 surveillance radar with a peak power of x watts (W). (*Source*: *Introduction to RADAR Techniques*, Federal Aviation Administration, 1988.)

a) Find the rate at which the maximum radar range changes as peak power increases from 40,000 W to 60,000 W.

b) Find $\dfrac{R(60{,}000) - R(50{,}000)}{60{,}000 - 50{,}000}$. What does this rate represent?

39. Memory. The total number of words, $M(t)$, that a person can memorize in t minutes is shown in the following graph.

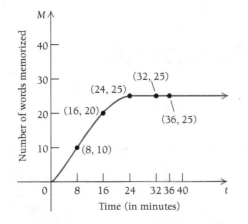

a) Find the average rate of change of M as t changes from 0 to 8; from 8 to 16; from 16 to 24; from 24 to 32; from 32 to 36.

b) Why do the average rates of change become 0 when t exceeds 24 min?

40. Gas mileage. At the beginning of a trip, the odometer on a car reads 30,680, and the car has a full tank of gas. At the end of the trip, the odometer reads 31,077. It takes 13.5 gal of gas to refill the tank.

a) What is the average rate at which the car was traveling, in miles per gallon?

b) What is the average rate of gas consumption in gallons per mile?

41. Average velocity. In t seconds, an object dropped from a certain height will fall $s(t)$ feet, where

$$s(t) = 16t^2.$$

a) Find $s(5) - s(3)$.

b) What is the average rate of change of distance with respect to time during the period from 3 to 5 sec? This is known as **average velocity,** or **speed.**

42. Average velocity. Suppose that in t hours, a truck travels $s(t)$ miles, where

$$s(t) = 10t^2.$$

a) Find $s(5) - s(2)$. What does this represent?

b) Find the average rate of change of distance with respect to time as t changes from $t_1 = 2$ to $t_2 = 5$. This is also *average velocity.*

Social Sciences

43. Population growth. The two curves below describe the numbers of people in two countries at time t, in years.

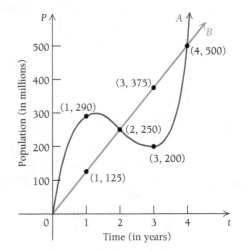

a) Find the average rate of change of each population with respect to time t as t changes from 0 to 4. This is often called the **average growth rate.**

b) If the calculations in part (a) were the only ones made, would we detect the fact that the populations were growing differently? Why or why not?

c) Find the average rates of change of each population as t changes from 0 to 1; from 1 to 2; from 2 to 3; from 3 to 4.

d) For which population does the statement "the population grew consistently at a rate of 125 million per year" convey accurate information? Why?

SYNTHESIS

44. Business: comparing rates of change. The following two graphs show the number of federally insured banks from 1987 to 2013 and the Nasdaq Composite Stock Index over a 6-month period in 2013.

DISAPPEARING BANKS

(*Source*: Federal Deposit Insurance Corp., 12/26/13.)

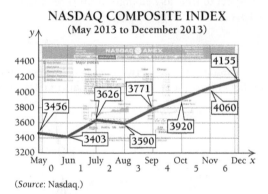

NASDAQ COMPOSITE INDEX
(May 2013 to December 2013)

(*Source*: Nasdaq.)

Explain the difference between these graphs in as many ways as you can. Be sure to mention average rates of change.

45. Rising cost of college. Like most things, the cost of a college education has gone up over time. The graph below displays the yearly costs of 4-year colleges in 2010 dollars—indicating that the costs prior to 2010 have been adjusted for inflation.

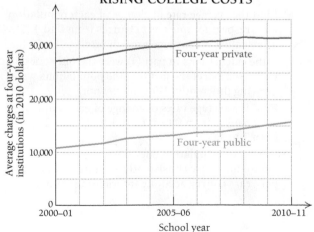

RISING COLLEGE COSTS

(*Source*: National Center for Educational Statistics, *Annual Digest of Educational, Statistics*, 2012.)

a) In what school year(s) did the cost of a private 4-year college appear to increase the most?

b) In what school year(s) did the cost of a public 4-year college appear to increase the most?

c) Assuming an annual inflation rate of 3%, calculate the cost of a year at a public and at a private 4-year college in 2000. Express the costs in 2000 dollars.

Find the simplified difference quotient for each function listed.

46. $f(x) = mx + b$　　　　**47.** $f(x) = ax^2 + bx + c$

48. $f(x) = ax^3 + bx^2$　　**49.** $f(x) = x^4$

50. $f(x) = x^5$　　　　　　**51.** $f(x) = ax^5 + bx^4$

52. $f(x) = \dfrac{1}{x^2}$　　　　**53.** $f(x) = \dfrac{1}{1-x}$

54. Below are the steps in the simplification of the difference quotient for $f(x) = \sqrt{x}$ (see Example 8). Provide a brief justification for each step.

$$\frac{f(x+h) - f(x)}{h} = \frac{\sqrt{x+h} - \sqrt{x}}{h}$$

a)
$$= \frac{\sqrt{x+h} - \sqrt{x}}{h} \cdot \left(\frac{\sqrt{x+h} + \sqrt{x}}{\sqrt{x+h} + \sqrt{x}} \right)$$

b)
$$= \frac{x + h + \sqrt{x}\sqrt{x+h} - \sqrt{x}\sqrt{x+h} - x}{h(\sqrt{x+h} + \sqrt{x})}$$

c)
$$= \frac{x + h - x}{h(\sqrt{x+h} + \sqrt{x})}$$

d)
$$= \frac{h}{h(\sqrt{x+h} + \sqrt{x})}$$

e)
$$= \frac{1}{\sqrt{x+h} + \sqrt{x}}$$

For Exercises 55 and 56, find the simplified difference quotient.

55. $f(x) = \sqrt{2x + 1}$　　　　**56.** $f(x) = \dfrac{1}{\sqrt{x}}$

Answers to Quick Checks

1. (a) It rained $1/2$ inch per hour.　(b) Your car gets 25 miles per gallon.　(c) The temperature dropped 2 degrees per hour.　**2.** (a) 21;　(b) 7　**3.** 12.61, 12.0601

- Find derivatives and values of derivatives.
- Find equations of tangent lines.

Differentiation Using Limits of Difference Quotients

The *slope of the secant line* passing through two points $(x, f(x))$ and $(x + h, f(x + h))$ on the graph of a function $y = f(x)$ represents the *average rate of change* of $f(x)$ over the interval $[x, x + h]$. This rate is given by the *difference quotient*

$$\frac{f(x + h) - f(x)}{h}, \qquad h \neq 0.$$

In Section 1.3, we simplified difference quotients for several functions. These expressions can be evaluated to calculate the slope of a secant line for given x- and h-values. Recall that h represents the horizontal distance between x and $x + h$. Although h cannot equal zero, we can consider the case in which h approaches 0.

Tangent Lines

A line that touches a circle at exactly one point is called a *tangent line*. The word "tangent" derives from the Latin *tangentem*, meaning "touch," whereas the word "secant" derives from the Latin *secantem*, meaning "cut." In the figure below, the secant line cuts through the circle, while the tangent line touches, but does not cut through, the circle.

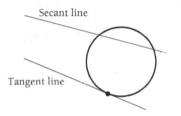

These notions extend to any smooth curve: a tangent line touches a curve at a single point, just as for the circle in the previous figure. In the figure below, the line L touches the curve at P, the *point of tangency*. Although L passes through the curve elsewhere, it is still considered a tangent line to the curve at point P.

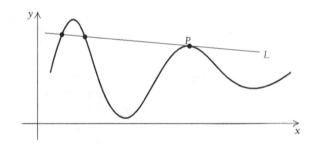

In the next figure, line M crosses the curve only at point P, but is not tangent to the curve; it does not touch the curve in the desired manner.

The four-lane highway is tangent to the access loops.

In the following figure, all of the lines except for L_1 and L_2 are tangent lines.

If a curve is smooth (has no corners or breaks), then each point on the curve has a *unique* tangent line; that is, exactly one tangent line can be drawn at any given point.

Differentiation Using Limits

We now define *tangent line* so that it makes sense for *any* curve. To do this, we use the notion of limit.

To obtain the line tangent to the curve at point P, consider secant lines through P and neighboring points Q_1, Q_2, and so on. As the Q's approach P, the secant lines approach line T. Each secant line has a slope. The slopes m_1, m_2, m_3, and so on, of the secant lines approach the slope m of line T. We *define* line T as the **tangent line,** the line that contains point P and has slope m, where m is the limit of the slopes of the secant lines as the points Q approach P.

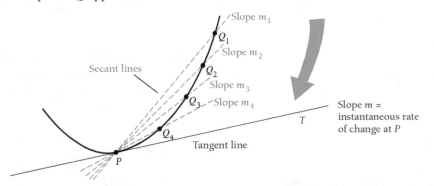

Think of the sequence of secant lines as an animation: as the points Q move closer to P, the resulting secant lines "lie down" on the tangent line.

How might we calculate the limit m? Suppose P has coordinates $(x, f(x))$. Then the first coordinate of Q is x plus some number h, or $x + h$. The coordinates of Q are $(x + h, f(x + h))$, as shown in the figure to the left below.

From Section 1.3, we know that the slope of the secant line $\overleftrightarrow{PQ}$ is given by

$$\frac{f(x + h) - f(x)}{h}.$$

Now, as shown in the figure at the bottom right on p. 128, as the Q's approach P, the values of $x + h$ approach x. That is, h approaches 0. Thus, we have the following.

The slope of the tangent line at $(x, f(x))$ is $m = \lim\limits_{h \to 0} \dfrac{f(x + h) - f(x)}{h}$.

This limit is also the **instantaneous rate of change** of $f(x)$ at x.

The formal definition of the *derivative of a function f* can now be given. We will designate the derivative at x as $f'(x)$, rather than m. The notation $f'(x)$ is read "the derivative of f at x," "f prime at x," or "f prime of x."

"Nothing in this world is so powerful as an idea whose time has come."
                                      Victor Hugo

DEFINITION

For a function $y = f(x)$, its **derivative** at x is the function f' defined by

$$f'(x) = \lim_{h \to 0} \frac{f(x + h) - f(x)}{h},$$

provided that the limit exists. If $f'(x)$ exists, then we say that f is **differentiable** at x. We sometimes call f' the **derived function**.

Let's now calculate some formulas for derivatives. That is, given a formula for a function f, we will attempt to find a formula for f'. The formula for f' can then be used to find the slope of a tangent line to $y = f(x)$ at a given x-value.

$f'(x) = $ slope at $(x, f(x))$

$(x, f(x))$

$f(x)$

x

There are three steps in calculating a derivative.

1. Write the difference quotient, $\dfrac{(f(x + h) - f(x))}{h}$.

2. Simplify the difference quotient.

3. Find the limit as h approaches 0.

EXAMPLE 1 For $f(x) = x^2$, find $f'(x)$. Then find $f'(-1)$ and $f'(2)$.

Solution We carry out the three steps.

1. $\dfrac{f(x + h) - f(x)}{h} = \dfrac{(x + h)^2 - x^2}{h}$

A visualization of Example 1

TECHNOLOGY CONNECTION 〜

Exploratory

To see exactly how the definition of derivative works and to check the results of Example 1, let $y_1 = ((-1 + x)^2 - (-1)^2)/x$ and note that we are using x in place of h. Use the TABLE feature and enter smaller and smaller values for x. Then repeat the procedure for $y_2 = ((2 + x)^2 - 2^2)/x$. How do these results confirm those in Example 1?

2. $\dfrac{f(x + h) - f(x)}{h} = \dfrac{x^2 + 2xh + h^2 - x^2}{h}$ Evaluating $f(x + h)$ and $f(x)$

$$= \frac{2xh + h^2}{h} = \frac{h(2x + h)}{h} \left.\begin{array}{c} \\ \\ \end{array}\right\} \text{Simplifying}$$

$$= 2x + h, h \neq 0$$

3. $\displaystyle\lim_{h \to 0} \dfrac{f(x + h) - f(x)}{h} = \lim_{h \to 0} (2x + h) = 2x$

Therefore, the derivative of $f(x) = x^2$ is given by

$$f'(x) = 2x.$$

Using the fact that $f'(x) = 2x$, it follows that

$$f'(-1) = 2 \cdot (-1) = -2, \quad \text{and} \quad f'(2) = 2 \cdot 2 = 4.$$

This tells us that at $x = -1$, the curve has a tangent line with slope

$$f'(-1) = -2,$$

and at $x = 2$, the tangent line has slope

$$f'(2) = 4.$$

We can also say:

- The tangent line to the curve at the point $(-1, 1)$ has slope -2.
- The tangent line to the curve at the point $(2, 4)$ has slope 4.
- The instantaneous rate of change at $x = -1$ is -2.
- The instantaneous rate of change at $x = 2$ is 4.
- f is differentiable at $x = -1$ and $x = 2$. In fact, f is differentiable for all real numbers. ■

EXAMPLE 2   For $f(x) = x^3$, find $f'(x)$. Then find $f'(-1)$ and $f'(1.5)$.

Solution

1. We have

$$\frac{f(x + h) - f(x)}{h} = \frac{(x + h)^3 - x^3}{h}.$$

2. In Example 6 of Section 1.3 (on p. 121), we showed that this simplifies to

$$\frac{f(x + h) - f(x)}{h} = 3x^2 + 3xh + h^2, \quad h \neq 0.$$

3. We then have

$$f'(x) = \lim_{h \to 0} \frac{f(x + h) - f(x)}{h} = \lim_{h \to 0} (3x^2 + 3xh + h^2) = 3x^2.$$

Thus,

$$f'(-1) = 3(-1)^2 = 3 \quad \text{and} \quad f'(1.5) = 3(1.5)^2 = 6.75. \qquad \text{1} ✔$$

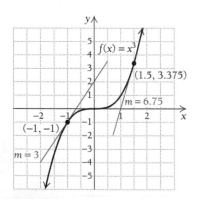

A visualization of Example 2

Quick Check 1 ✔

Use the results from Examples 1 and 2 to find the derivative of $f(x) = x^3 + x^2$, and then calculate $f'(-2)$ and $f'(4)$. Interpret these results.

EXAMPLE 3   For $f(x) = 3x - 4$, find $f'(x)$ and $f'(2)$.

Solution   We follow the three steps given above.

1. $\dfrac{f(x + h) - f(x)}{h} = \dfrac{3(x + h) - 4 - (3x - 4)}{h}$ The parentheses are important.

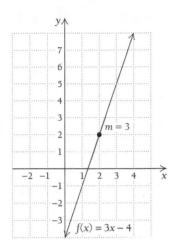

2. $\dfrac{f(x+h) - f(x)}{h} = \dfrac{3x + 3h - 4 - 3x + 4}{h}$ Using the distributive law

$$= \dfrac{3h}{h} = 3, \quad h \neq 0; \qquad \text{Simplifying}$$

3. $\displaystyle\lim_{h \to 0} \dfrac{f(x+h) - f(x)}{h} = \lim_{h \to 0} 3 = 3$, since 3 is a constant.

Thus, if $f(x) = 3x - 4$, then $f'(x) = 3$ and $f'(2) = 3$. ∎

The result of Example 3 suggests that, for the graph of any linear function, the slope of a tangent line is the slope of the line itself. That is, the derivative of

$$f(x) = mx + b$$

is $f'(x) = m$.

This formula can be verified in a manner similar to that used in Example 3.

EXAMPLE 4   For $f(x) = \dfrac{1}{x}$:

a) Find $f'(x)$.   **b)** Find $f'(2)$.

c) Find an equation of the tangent line to the curve at $x = 2$.

Solution

a) 1. We have

$$\dfrac{f(x+h) - f(x)}{h} = \dfrac{[1/(x+h)] - (1/x)}{h}.$$

2. On p. 122, we showed that this simplifies to

$$\dfrac{f(x+h) - f(x)}{h} = \dfrac{-1}{x(x+h)}, \quad h \neq 0.$$

3. We want to find

$$\lim_{h \to 0} \dfrac{f(x+h) - f(x)}{h} = \lim_{h \to 0} \dfrac{-1}{x(x+h)}.$$

As $h \to 0$, we have $x + h \to x$. Thus,

$$f'(x) = \lim_{h \to 0} \dfrac{-1}{x(x+h)} = \dfrac{-1}{x \cdot x} = -\dfrac{1}{x^2}.$$

b) Since $f'(x) = -1/x^2$, we have

$$f'(2) = -\dfrac{1}{2^2} = -\dfrac{1}{4}. \qquad \text{This is the slope of the tangent line at } x = 2.$$

c) We can find an equation of the tangent line at $x = 2$ if we know the line's slope and a point on the line. In part (b), we found that the slope at $x = 2$ is $-\frac{1}{4}$. To find a point on the line, we compute $f(2)$:

$$f(2) = \dfrac{1}{2}. \qquad \begin{array}{l} \text{CAUTION! Be careful to use } f \text{ when computing} \\ y\text{-values and } f' \text{ when computing slope.} \end{array}$$

We have

Point: $(2, \frac{1}{2})$,   This is $(x_1, f(x_1))$.

Slope: $-\frac{1}{4}$.   This is $f'(x_1)$.

TECHNOLOGY CONNECTION

Curves and Tangent Lines

EXERCISE

Find an equation of the tangent line to the graph of $f(x) = 3/x$ at $\left(-2, -\frac{3}{2}\right)$ and an equation of the tangent line to the curve at $\left(-\frac{1}{2}, -6\right)$. Then graph the curve $f(x) = 3/x$ and both tangent lines. Use ZOOM to view the graphs near the points of tangency. (You can check your equations of tangent lines by selecting Tangent from the DRAW menu and entering $x = -2$ and then $x = -\frac{1}{2}$.)

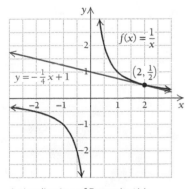

A visualization of Example 4(c)

Quick Check 2 ✔

Repeat Example 4(a) for

$f(x) = -\dfrac{2}{x}$. What are the

similarities between this solution

and that obtained for $f(x) = \dfrac{1}{x}$?

We substitute into the point–slope equation (see Section R.4):

$$y - y_1 = m(x - x_1)$$
$$y - \tfrac{1}{2} = -\tfrac{1}{4}(x - 2)$$
$$\left. \begin{aligned} y &= -\tfrac{1}{4}x + \tfrac{1}{2} + \tfrac{1}{2} \\ &= -\tfrac{1}{4}x + 1. \end{aligned} \right\} \quad \begin{aligned} &\text{Rewriting in} \\ &\text{slope–intercept form} \end{aligned}$$

The equation of the tangent line to the curve at $x = 2$ is

$$y = -\tfrac{1}{4}x + 1.$$ **2** ✔

In Example 4, note that since $f(0)$ does not exist for $f(x) = 1/x$, we cannot evaluate the difference quotient

$$\frac{f(0 + h) - f(0)}{h}.$$

Thus, $f'(0)$ does not exist. We say that "f is not differentiable at 0."

> When a function is not defined at a point, it is not differentiable at that point. In general, if a function is discontinuous at a point, it is not differentiable at that point.

Sometimes a function f is continuous at a point, but its derivative f' does not exist at this point. The function $f(x) = |x|$ is an example.

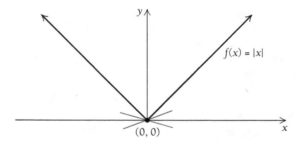

Suppose we try to draw a tangent line at $(0, 0)$. A function like this with a corner seems to have many tangent lines at $(0, 0)$, and thus many slopes. The derivative at such a point would not be unique. Let's try to calculate the derivative at 0.

Since

$$f(x) = |x| = \begin{cases} x, & \text{for } x \geq 0, \\ -x, & \text{for } x < 0, \end{cases}$$

it follows from our earlier work with lines that

$$f'(x) = \begin{cases} 1, & \text{for } x > 0, \\ -1, & \text{for } x < 0. \end{cases}$$

Then, since

$$\lim_{x \to 0^+} f'(x) \neq \lim_{x \to 0^-} f'(x),$$

it follows that $f'(0)$ does not exist.

In general, a function is not differentiable at any corners on its graph.

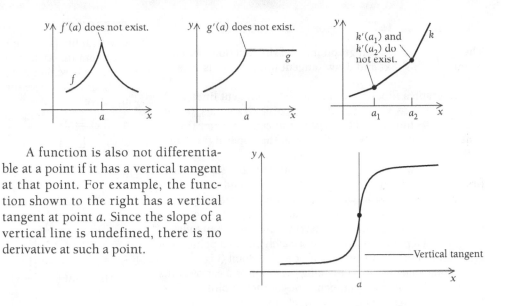

A function is also not differentiable at a point if it has a vertical tangent at that point. For example, the function shown to the right has a vertical tangent at point a. Since the slope of a vertical line is undefined, there is no derivative at such a point.

The function given by $f(x) = |x|$ illustrates the fact that although a function may be continuous at each point in an interval I, it may not be differentiable at each point in I. That is, continuity at a point does not imply differentiability at that point. However, differentiability at a point *does* guarantee continuity at that point. That is, if $f'(a)$ exists, then f is continuous at a. The function $f(x) = x^2$ is an example of a function that is differentiable over the interval $(-\infty, \infty)$ and is therefore continuous everywhere. Thus, when a function is differentiable over an interval, it is not just continuous, but is also *smooth* in the sense that there are no corners in its graph.

EXAMPLE 5 Below is the graph of a function $y = t(x)$. List the points in the graph at which the function t is not differentiable.

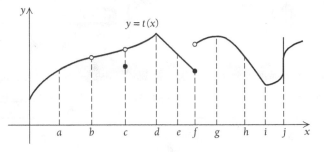

Quick Check 3 ✔

Where is $f(x) = |x + 6|$ not differentiable? Why?

Solution A function is not differentiable at a point if there is a discontinuity, a corner, or a vertical tangent at that point. Therefore, the function $y = t(x)$ is not differentiable at $x = b, x = c$, and $x = f$ since the function is discontinuous at these points; it is not differentiable at $x = d$ and $x = i$ since there are corners at these points; and it is not differentiable at $x = j$ as there is a vertical tangent line at this point (the slope is undefined). **3** ✔

Using Graphicus to Find Slopes of Tangent Lines

The app Graphicus can graph most of the functions we encounter in this text and draw tangent lines at points on a curve.

To graph a function and examine its tangent lines, let's consider $f(x) = x^4 - 2x^2$. After opening Graphicus, touch the blank rectangle at the top of the screen and enter the function as y(x)=x^4-2x^2. Press $+$ at the upper right. You will see the graph, as shown in Fig. 1.

Notice the seven icons at the bottom of the screen. The first one is for zooming. Touch it to zoom in and zoom out. Touch the screen with two fingers and move vertically or horizontally to adjust the windows and scaling. The second icon is for visualizing tangent lines. Touch it and then touch the graph at a point, and you will see a highlighted point on the graph and a tangent line to the curve at that point (Fig. 2). Move your finger left to right along the graph and various other points on the curve and tangent lines at those points will be highlighted (Figs. 3 and 4). Think about the slopes of the tangent lines as you move from left to right. When are they positive, negative, or 0?

EXERCISES

Use Graphicus to graph each function. You may need to use the zoom function to alter the window. Display tangent lines, noting where they are positive, negative, and 0. Then try to determine where the slope changes from positive to 0 to negative.

1. $f(x) = 2x^3 - x^4$ **2.** $f(x) = x(200 - x)$

3. $f(x) = x^3 - 6x^2$

4. $f(x) = -4.32 + 1.44x + 3x^2 - x^3$

5. $g(x) = x\sqrt{4 - x^2}$

6. $g(x) = \dfrac{4x}{x^2 + 1}$ **7.** $f(x) = \dfrac{x^2 - 3x}{x - 1}$

8. $f(x) = |x + 2| - 3$. What happens to the tangent line at the point $(-2, -3)$?

FIGURE 1   FIGURE 2   FIGURE 3   FIGURE 4

Section Summary

- A *tangent line* is a line that touches a smooth curve at a single point, the *point of tangency*. See the first figure on p. 128 for examples of tangent lines and lines that are not tangent lines.
- The *derivative* of a function $f(x)$ is defined by

$$f'(x) = \lim_{h \to 0} \frac{f(x + h) - f(x)}{h}.$$

- The *slope* of the tangent line to the graph of $y = f(x)$ at $x = a$ is the value of the derivative at $x = a$; that is, the slope of the tangent line at $x = a$ is $f'(a)$.
- Slopes of tangent lines are interpreted as *instantaneous rates of change*.
- The equation of a tangent line at $x = a$ is found by simplifying $y - f(a) = f'(a)(x - a)$.

- If a function is differentiable at $x = a$, then it is *continuous* at $x = a$. That is, differentiability at a point implies continuity at that point.
- However, continuity at $x = a$ does *not* imply differentiability at $x = a$. A good example is the absolute-value function, $f(x) = |x|$, or any function whose graph has

a corner. Continuity alone is not sufficient to guarantee differentiability.
- A function is not differentiable at $x = a$ if:
  (1) there is a discontinuity at $x = a$,
  (2) there is a corner at $x = a$, or
  (3) there is a vertical tangent at $x = a$.

1.4   Exercise Set

In Exercises 1–16:

a) *Graph the function.*
b) *Draw tangent lines to the graph at points whose x-coordinates are $-2, 0,$ and 1.*

c) *Find $f'(x)$ by determining $\lim\limits_{h \to 0} \dfrac{f(x + h) - f(x)}{h}$.*

d) *Find $f'(-2)$, $f'(0)$, and $f'(1)$. These slopes should match those of the lines you drew in part (b).*

1. $f(x) = \frac{1}{2}x^2$

2. $f(x) = \frac{3}{2}x^2$

3. $f(x) = -2x^2$

4. $f(x) = -3x^2$

5. $f(x) = -x^3$

6. $f(x) = x^3$

7. $f(x) = 2x + 3$

8. $f(x) = -2x + 5$

9. $f(x) = \frac{3}{4}x - 2$

10. $f(x) = \frac{1}{2}x - 3$

11. $f(x) = x^2 + x$

12. $f(x) = x^2 - x$

13. $f(x) = -5x^2 - 2x + 7$

14. $f(x) = -2x^2 + 3x - 2$

15. $f(x) = \dfrac{1}{x}$

16. $f(x) = \dfrac{2}{x}$

17. Find an equation of the tangent line to the graph of $f(x) = x^3$ at (a) $(-2, -8)$; (b) $(0, 0)$; (c) $(4, 64)$. See Example 2.

18. Find an equation of the tangent line to the graph of $f(x) = x^2$ at (a) $(3, 9)$; (b) $(-1, 1)$; (c) $(10, 100)$. See Example 1.

19. Find an equation of the tangent line to the graph of $f(x) = 2/x$ at (a) $(1, 2)$; (b) $(-1, -2)$; (c) $(100, 0.02)$. See Exercise 16.

20. Find an equation of the tangent line to the graph of $f(x) = -1/x$ at (a) $(-1, 1)$; (b) $(2, -\frac{1}{2})$; (c) $(-5, \frac{1}{5})$.

21. Find an equation of the tangent line to the graph of $f(x) = x^2 - 2x$ at (a) $(-2, 8)$; (b) $(1, -1)$; (c) $(4, 8)$.

22. Find an equation of the tangent line to the graph of $f(x) = 4 - x^2$ at (a) $(-1, 3)$; (b) $(0, 4)$; (c) $(5, -21)$.

23. Find $f'(x)$ for $f(x) = mx + b$.

24. Find $f'(x)$ for $f(x) = ax^2 + bx$.

For Exercises 25–28, list the points in the graph at which each function is not differentiable.

25.

26.

27.

28.

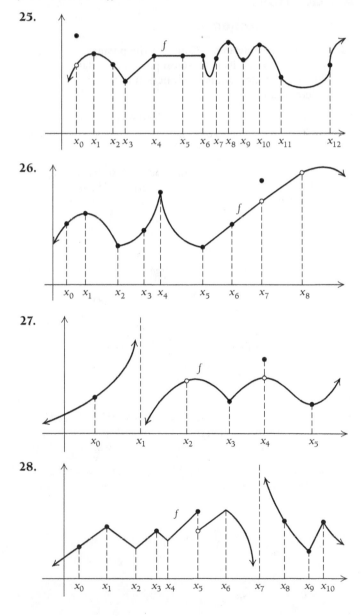

29. Draw a graph that is continuous, but not differentiable, at $x = 3$.

30. Draw a graph that is continuous, with no corners, but not differentiable, at $x = 1$.

31. Draw a graph that has a horizontal tangent line at $x = 5$.

32. Draw a graph that is differentiable and has horizontal tangent lines at $x = 0$, $x = 2$, and $x = 4$.

33. Draw a graph that has horizontal tangent lines at $x = 2$ and $x = 5$ and is continuous, but not differentiable, at $x = 3$.

34. Draw a graph that is continuous for all x, with no corners, but not differentiable at $x = -1$ and $x = 2$.

APPLICATIONS

Business and Economics

35. The postage function. Consider the postage function in Exercises 72–76 on p. 105. At what values in the domain is the function not differentiable?

36. The taxicab fare function. Consider the taxicab fare function in Exercises 69–71 on p. 105. At what values is the function not differentiable?

The end-of-day values of the Dow Jones Industrial Average for the week of December 9–13, 2013, are graphed below, where x is the day of the month.

(*Source:* Google Finance.)

37. On what day did the Dow Jones Industrial Average show the greatest rate of increase? On what day did it show the greatest rate of decrease? Give the rates.

38. Is the function in Exercise 37 differentiable at the given x-values? Why or why not?

39. Which of the lines in the following graph appear to be tangent lines? Why or why not?

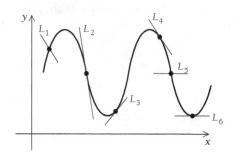

40. On the following graph, use a colored pencil to draw each secant line from point P to the points Q. Then use a different colored pencil to draw a tangent line to the curve at P. Describe what happens.

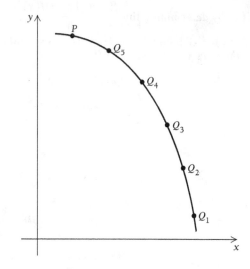

For Exercises 41–48, find $f'(x)$ for the given function.

41. $f(x) = x^4$ (See Exercise 49 in Section 1.3.)

42. $f(x) = \dfrac{1}{1 - x}$ (See Exercise 53 in Section 1.3.)

43. $f(x) = x^5$ (See Exercise 50 in Section 1.3.)

44. $f(x) = \dfrac{1}{x^2}$ (See Exercise 52 in Section 1.3.)

45. $f(x) = \sqrt{x}$ (See Example 8 in Section 1.3.)

46. $f(x) = \sqrt{2x + 1}$ (See Exercise 55 in Section 1.3.)

47. $f(x) = \dfrac{1}{\sqrt{x}}$ (See Exercise 56 in Section 1.3.)

48. $f(x) = ax^2 + bx + c$ (See Exercise 47 in Section 1.3.)

49. Consider the function f given by

$$f(x) = \frac{x^2 - 9}{x + 3}.$$

   a) For what x-value(s) is this function not differentiable?

   b) Find $f'(4)$.

50. Consider the function g given by

$$g(x) = \frac{x^2 + x}{2x}.$$

   a) For what x-value(s) is this function not differentiable?

   b) What is $g'(3)$? Describe the simplest way to determine this.

51. Consider the function k given by

$$k(x) = |x - 3| + 2.$$

   a) For what x-value(s) is the function not differentiable?

   b) Evaluate $k'(0)$, $k'(1)$, $k'(4)$, and $k'(10)$.

52. Consider the function k given by

$$k(x) = 2|x + 5|.$$

   a) For what x-value(s) is this function not differentiable?

   b) Evaluate $k'(-10)$, $k'(-7)$, $k'(-2)$, and $k'(0)$.

53. Let $f(x) = \dfrac{x^2 + 4x + 3}{x + 1}$. A student recognizes that this function can be simplified as

$$f(x) = \frac{x^2 + 4x + 3}{x + 1} = \frac{(x + 1)(x + 3)}{x + 1} = x + 3.$$

Since $y = x + 3$ is a line with slope 1, the student makes the following conclusions: $f'(-2) = 1$, $f'(-1) = 1$, $f'(0) = 1$, $f'(1) = 1$. Where did the student make an error?

54. Let $g(x) = \sqrt[3]{x}$. A student graphs this function, and the graph appears to be continuous for all real numbers x. The student concludes that g is differentiable for all x, which is false. Identify the error, and explain why the conclusion is false. What is the correct conclusion regarding the differentiability of g?

55. Let F be a function given by

$$F(x) = \begin{cases} x^2 + 1, & \text{for } x \le 2, \\ 2x + 1, & \text{for } x > 2. \end{cases}$$

   a) Verify that F is continuous at $x = 2$.

   b) Is F differentiable at $x = 2$? Why or why not?

56. Let G be a function given by

$$G(x) = \begin{cases} x^3, & \text{for } x \le 1, \\ 3x - 2, & \text{for } x > 1. \end{cases}$$

   a) Verify that G is continuous at $x = 1$.

   b) Is G differentiable at $x = 1$? Why or why not?

57. Let H be a function given by

$$H(x) = \begin{cases} 2x^2 - x, & \text{for } x \le 3, \\ mx + b, & \text{for } x > 3. \end{cases}$$

Determine the values of m and b that make H differentiable at $x = 3$.

TECHNOLOGY CONNECTION

58–63. Use a calculator to check your answers to Exercises 17–22.

64. Business: growth of an investment. A company determines that the value of an investment after t years is V, in millions of dollars, where V is given by

$$V(t) = 5t^3 - 30t^2 + 45t + 5\sqrt{t}.$$

Note: Calculators often use only the variables y and x, so you may need to change the variables.

   a) Graph V over the interval $[0, 5]$.

   b) Find the equation of the secant line passing through the points $(1, V(1))$ and $(5, V(5))$. Then graph this secant line using the same axes as in part (a).

   c) Find the average rate of change of the investment between year 1 and year 5.

   d) Repeat parts (b) and (c) for the following pairs of points: $(1, V(1))$ and $(4, V(4))$; $(1, V(1))$ and $(3, V(3))$; $(1, V(1))$ and $(1.5, V(1.5))$.

   e) What *appears* to be the slope of the tangent line to the graph at the point $(1, V(1))$?

   f) Approximate the rate at which the value of the investment is changing at $t = 1$ yr.

65. Use a calculator to determine where $f'(x)$ does not exist, if $f(x) = \sqrt[3]{x} - 5$.

Answers to Quick Checks

1. $f'(x) = 3x^2 + 2x$; $f'(-2) = 8$, $f'(4) = 56$

2. $f'(x) = \dfrac{2}{x^2}$ **3.** At $x = -6$, the graph has a corner.

- Differentiate using the Power Rule or the Sum–Difference Rule.
- Differentiate a constant or a constant times a function.
- Determine points at which a tangent line has a specified slope.

Historical Note: The German mathematician and philosopher Gottfried Wilhelm von Leibniz (1646–1716) and the English mathematician, philosopher, and physicist Sir Isaac Newton (1642–1727) are both credited with the invention of calculus, though each worked independently. Newton used the dot notation $\dot{y}$ for dy/dt, where y is a function of time; this notation is still used, though it is not as common as Leibniz notation.

Differentiation Techniques: The Power and Sum–Difference Rules

Leibniz Notation

When y is a function of x, one way to express "the derivative of y with respect to x" is the notation

$$\frac{dy}{dx}.$$

This notation was invented by the German mathematician Gottfried von Leibniz. Using this notation, if $y = f(x)$, we can write the derivative of y with respect to x as

$$\frac{dy}{dx} = f'(x).$$

We also use _prime notation_, such as y' or $f'(x)$, to represent a derivative when there is no confusion as to which variables are involved. The dy/dx notation has the same meaning.

We may also write the value of a derivative at a number, such as $f'(2)$, as

$$\frac{dy}{dx}\bigg|_{x=2}.$$

The vertical line is interpreted as "evaluated at," so the above expression is read as "the derivative of y with respect to x evaluated at $x = 2$."

We can also express $f'(x)$ as

$$\frac{d}{dx}f(x).$$

This is identical in meaning to dy/dx and is another way to denote the derivative of the function. When placed next to an expression, d/dx indicates the expression's derivative. Thus, using earlier notation, we can write

$$\frac{d}{dx}x^2 = 2x, \qquad \frac{d}{dx}x^3 = 3x^2, \qquad \frac{d}{dx}\left(\frac{1}{x}\right) = -\frac{1}{x^2}, \qquad \text{and so on.}$$

We will use all of these derivative forms often, and with practice, their use will become natural. In Chapter 2, we will attach additional meanings to dy and dx.

The Power Rule

In Section 1.4, we found the derivatives of certain power functions. Look at the following table and see if you can identify a pattern:

FUNCTION	DERIVATIVE	
x^2	$2x^1$	Example 1 in Section 1.4
x^3	$3x^2$	Example 2 in Section 1.4
x^4	$4x^3$	Exercise 41 in Section 1.4
$\dfrac{1}{x} = x^{-1}$	$-1 \cdot x^{-2} = \dfrac{-1}{x^2}$	Example 4 in Section 1.4
$\dfrac{1}{x^2} = x^{-2}$	$-2 \cdot x^{-3} = \dfrac{-2}{x^3}$	Exercise 44 in Section 1.4
$\sqrt{x} = x^{1/2}$	$\dfrac{1}{2}x^{-1/2} = \dfrac{1}{2\sqrt{x}}$	Exercise 45 in Section 1.4

The pattern can be described as follows: "To find the derivative of a power function, bring the exponent to the front of the variable as a coefficient and reduce the exponent by 1."

Write the exponent as the coefficient.

$$\frac{d}{dx}x^k = k \cdot x^{k-1}$$

Subtract 1 from the exponent.

This rule is summarized as the following theorem.

THEOREM 1   The Power Rule

For any real number k, if $y = x^k$, then

$$\frac{d}{dx}x^k = k \cdot x^{k-1}.$$

EXAMPLE 1   Differentiate each of the following:

a) $y = x^5$;   **b)** $y = x$;   **c)** $y = x^{-4}$.

Solution

a) $\dfrac{d}{dx}x^5 = 5 \cdot x^{5-1} = 5x^4$ Using the Power Rule

Quick Check 1 ✔

Differentiate:
a) $y = x^{15}$;
b) $y = x^{-7}$.

b) $\dfrac{d}{dx}x = 1 \cdot x^{1-1} = 1 \cdot x^0 = 1$

c) $\dfrac{d}{dx}x^{-4} = -4 \cdot x^{-4-1} = -4x^{-5}$,   or $-4 \cdot \dfrac{1}{x^5}$,   or $-\dfrac{4}{x^5}$

1 ✔

The Power Rule also allows us to differentiate expressions with rational exponents.

EXAMPLE 2   Differentiate:

a) $y = \sqrt[5]{x}$;   **b)** $y = x^{0.7}$.

Solution

a) $\dfrac{d}{dx}\sqrt[5]{x} = \dfrac{d}{dx}x^{1/5} = \dfrac{1}{5} \cdot x^{(1/5)-1}$

Quick Check 2 ✔

Differentiate:
a) $y = \sqrt[4]{x}$;
b) $y = x^{-1.25}$.

$$= \frac{1}{5}x^{-4/5}, \quad \text{or } \frac{1}{5} \cdot \frac{1}{x^{4/5}}, \quad \text{or } \frac{1}{5} \cdot \frac{1}{\sqrt[5]{x^4}}, \quad \text{or } \frac{1}{5\sqrt[5]{x^4}}$$

b) $\dfrac{d}{dx}x^{0.7} = 0.7x^{(0.7)-1} = 0.7x^{-0.3}$,   or $\dfrac{7}{10x^{0.3}}$

2 ✔

Numerical Differentiation and Tangent Lines

Consider $f(x) = x\sqrt{4 - x^2}$, graphed below.

To find the value of dy/dx at a point, we select dy/dx from the CALC menu and key in an x-value or use the arrow keys to move the cursor to a desired point. We then press **ENTER** to obtain the value of the derivative at the given x-value.

We can also use the TANGENT feature from the DRAW menu to draw the tangent line at any point where the derivative was found. Both the line and its equation will appear.

EXERCISES

For each function, use dy/dx to find the derivative, and then draw the tangent line at the given point. When selecting the viewing window, include the specified x-values.

1. $f(x) = x(200 - x)$;
   $x = 24, x = 138, x = 150, x = 190$

2. $f(x) = x^3 - 6x^2$;
   $x = -2, x = 0, x = 2, x = 4, x = 6.3$

3. $f(x) = -4.32 + 1.44x + 3x^2 - x^3$;
   $x = -0.5, x = 0.5, x = 2.1$

The Power Rule can be used to confirm results from Section 1.3.

● $\dfrac{d}{dx}\left(\dfrac{1}{x}\right) = \dfrac{d}{dx}(x^{-1}) = -1x^{-2} = -\dfrac{1}{x^2}$

● $\dfrac{d}{dx}\sqrt{x} = \dfrac{d}{dx}(x^{1/2}) = \dfrac{1}{2}x^{-1/2} = \dfrac{1}{2x^{1/2}} = \dfrac{1}{2\sqrt{x}}$

The Derivative of a Constant Function

Consider the constant function given by $F(x) = c$. Note that the slope of the tangent line at each point on its graph is 0.

This suggests the following theorem.

THEOREM 2

The derivative of a constant function is 0. That is, $\dfrac{d}{dx}c = 0$.

Proof: Let F be the function given by $F(x) = c$. Then

$$\frac{d}{dx}c = F'(x) = \lim_{h \to 0} \frac{F(x + h) - F(x)}{h} \qquad \text{Using the definition of derivative}$$

$$= \lim_{h \to 0} \frac{c - c}{h}$$

$$= \lim_{h \to 0} \frac{0}{h}$$

$$= 0. \qquad \text{Using Limit Property L1}$$

The difference quotient is always zero. Thus, as h approaches 0, the limit of the difference quotient is 0, so $F'(x) = 0$. ■

The Derivative of a Constant Times a Function

Now let's differentiate functions such as

$$f(x) = 5x^2 \quad \text{and} \quad g(x) = -7x^4.$$

We already know how to differentiate x^2 and x^4. Let's look for a pattern in the results of Section 1.4 and its exercise set.

FUNCTION	DERIVATIVE
$5x^2$	$10x$
$3x^{-1}$	$-3x^{-2}$
$\frac{3}{2}x^2$	$3x$
$1 \cdot x^3$	$3x^2$

Perhaps you have discovered the following theorem.

THEOREM 3

The derivative of a constant times a function is the constant times the derivative of the function. Using derivative notation, we can write this as

$$\frac{d}{dx}[c \cdot f(x)] = c \cdot \frac{d}{dx}f(x).$$

Proof: Let $F(x) = cf(x)$. Then

$$\frac{d}{dx}cf(x) = F'(x)$$

$$= \lim_{h \to 0} \frac{F(x + h) - F(x)}{h} \qquad \text{Using the definition of derivative}$$

$$= \lim_{h \to 0} \frac{cf(x + h) - cf(x)}{h} \qquad \text{Substituting}$$

$$= c \cdot \lim_{h \to 0} \left[\frac{f(x + h) - f(x)}{h} \right] \qquad \text{Factoring and using Limit Properties}$$

$$= c \cdot f'(x). \qquad \text{Using the definition of derivative} \quad ■$$

Combining this rule with the Power Rule allows us to find many derivatives.

EXAMPLE 3 Find each of the following derivatives:

a) $\dfrac{d}{dx}7x^4$;

b) $\dfrac{d}{dx}(-9x)$;

c) $\dfrac{d}{dx}\left(\dfrac{1}{5x^2}\right)$.

Solution

a) $\dfrac{d}{dx}7x^4 = 7\dfrac{d}{dx}x^4 = 7\cdot 4\cdot x^{4-1} = 28x^3$ With practice, this may be done in one step.

b) $\dfrac{d}{dx}(-9x) = -9\dfrac{d}{dx}x = -9\cdot 1 = -9$

c) $\dfrac{d}{dx}\left(\dfrac{1}{5x^2}\right) = \dfrac{d}{dx}\left(\dfrac{1}{5}x^{-2}\right) = \dfrac{1}{5}\cdot\dfrac{d}{dx}x^{-2}$

$$= \dfrac{1}{5}(-2)x^{-2-1}$$

$$= -\dfrac{2}{5}x^{-3}, \quad \text{or} \quad -\dfrac{2}{5x^3}$$

3 ✔

> **Quick Check 3** ✔
>
> Differentiate each of the following:
>
> **a)** $y = 10x^9$;
>
> **b)** $y = \pi x^3$;
>
> **c)** $y = \dfrac{2}{3x^4}$.

Recall that a function's derivative at x is also its instantaneous rate of change at x.

EXAMPLE 4 **Life Science: Volume of a Tumor.** The volume V of a spherical tumor can be approximated by

$$V(r) = \tfrac{4}{3}\pi r^3,$$

where r is the radius of the tumor, in centimeters.

a) Find the rate of change of the volume with respect to the radius.

b) Find the rate of change of the volume at $r = 1.2$ cm.

Solution

a) $\dfrac{dV}{dr} = V'(r) = 3\cdot\dfrac{4}{3}\cdot\pi r^2 = 4\pi r^2$

(This expression turns out to be equal to the tumor's surface area.)

b) $V'(1.2) = 4\pi(1.2)^2 = 5.76\pi \approx 18\,\dfrac{\text{cm}^3}{\text{cm}} = 18\text{ cm}^2$

When the radius is 1.2 cm, the volume is changing at the rate of 18 cm³ for every change of 1 cm in the radius. ∎

The Derivative of a Sum or a Difference

In Exercise 11 of Exercise Set 1.4, we found that the derivative of

$$f(x) = x^2 + x$$

is $f'(x) = 2x + 1.$

Note that the derivative of x^2 is $2x$, the derivative of x is 1, and the sum of these derivatives is $f'(x)$. This illustrates the following theorem.

TECHNOLOGY CONNECTION 📈

Exploratory

Let $y_1 = x(100 - x)$, and $y_2 = x\sqrt{100 - x^2}$. Using the Y-VARS option from the VARS menu, enter Y3 as Y1+Y2. Find the derivative of each of the three functions at $x = 8$ using the numerical differentiation feature.

    Compare your answers. How do you think you can find the derivative of a sum?

> **THEOREM 4** **The Sum–Difference Rule**
>
> *Sum.* The derivative of a sum is the sum of the derivatives:
>
> $$\dfrac{d}{dx}[f(x) + g(x)] = \dfrac{d}{dx}f(x) + \dfrac{d}{dx}g(x).$$
>
> *Difference.* The derivative of a difference is the difference of the derivatives:
>
> $$\dfrac{d}{dx}[f(x) - g(x)] = \dfrac{d}{dx}f(x) - \dfrac{d}{dx}g(x).$$

Proof: The proof of the Sum Rule relies on the fact that the limit of a sum is the sum of the limits. Let $F(x) = f(x) + g(x)$. Then

$$\lim_{h \to 0} \frac{F(x + h) - F(x)}{h} = \lim_{h \to 0} \frac{[f(x + h) + g(x + h)] - [f(x) + g(x)]}{h}$$

$$= \lim_{h \to 0} \left[\frac{f(x + h) - f(x)}{h} + \frac{g(x + h) - g(x)}{h} \right] = f'(x) + g'(x).$$

To prove the Difference Rule, we note that

$$\frac{d}{dx}(f(x) - g(x)) = \frac{d}{dx}(f(x) + (-1)g(x)) = \frac{d}{dx}f(x) + \frac{d}{dx}(-1)g(x)$$

$$= f'(x) + (-1)\frac{d}{dx}g(x) = f'(x) - g'(x). \quad \blacksquare$$

Any function that is a sum or difference of several terms can be differentiated term by term.

EXAMPLE 5 Find each of the following derivatives:

a) $\dfrac{d}{dx}(5x^3 - 7)$;

b) $\dfrac{d}{dx}\left(24x - \sqrt{x} + \dfrac{5}{x}\right)$.

Solution

a) $\dfrac{d}{dx}(5x^3 - 7) = \dfrac{d}{dx}(5x^3) - \dfrac{d}{dx}(7)$

$$= 5\frac{d}{dx}x^3 - 0$$

$$= 5 \cdot 3x^2$$

$$= 15x^2$$

b) $\dfrac{d}{dx}\left(24x - \sqrt{x} + \dfrac{5}{x}\right) = \dfrac{d}{dx}(24x) - \dfrac{d}{dx}(\sqrt{x}) + \dfrac{d}{dx}\left(\dfrac{5}{x}\right)$

$$= 24 \cdot \frac{d}{dx}x - \frac{d}{dx}x^{1/2} + 5 \cdot \frac{d}{dx}x^{-1}$$

$$= 24 \cdot 1 - \frac{1}{2}x^{(1/2)-1} + 5(-1)x^{-1-1}$$

$$= 24 - \frac{1}{2}x^{-1/2} - 5x^{-2}$$

$$= 24 - \frac{1}{2\sqrt{x}} - \frac{5}{x^2}$$

4 ✔

Quick Check 4 ✔

Differentiate:

$$y = 3x^5 + 2\sqrt[3]{x} + \frac{1}{3x^2} + \sqrt{5}.$$

A word of caution! The derivative of

$$f(x) + c,$$

a function *plus* a constant, is just the derivative of $f(x)$:

$$f'(x).$$

The derivative of

$$c \cdot f(x),$$

a function *times* a constant, is the constant times the derivative of $f(x)$:

$$c \cdot f'(x).$$

That is, the constant is retained for a product, but not for a sum or a difference.

Slopes of Tangent Lines

It is important to be able to determine points at which the tangent line to a curve has a certain slope, that is, points at which the derivative has a certain value.

EXAMPLE 6 Find any points on the graph of $f(x) = -x^3 + 6x^2$ at which **(a)** the tangent line is horizontal; **(b)** the tangent line has slope 9.

Solution

a) The derivative is used to find the slope of a tangent line. Since a horizontal tangent line has slope 0, we seek all x for which $f'(x) = 0$:

$$f'(x) = 0 \qquad \text{Setting the derivative equal to 0}$$

$$\frac{d}{dx}(-x^3 + 6x^2) = 0$$

$$-3x^2 + 12x = 0. \qquad \text{Differentiating}$$

We factor and solve:

$$-3x(x - 4) = 0$$
$$-3x = 0 \quad or \quad x - 4 = 0$$
$$x = 0 \quad or \quad x = 4. \qquad \text{Using the Principle of Zero Products}$$

We are to find points *on the graph*, so we must determine the second coordinates from the original equation, $f(x) = -x^3 + 6x^2$.

$$f(0) = -0^3 + 6 \cdot 0^2 = 0.$$
$$f(4) = -4^3 + 6 \cdot 4^2 = -64 + 96 = 32.$$

Thus, the points we are seeking are $(0, 0)$ and $(4, 32)$, as shown on the graph.

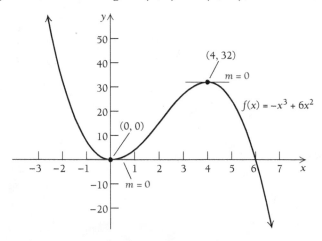

b) We want to find values of x for which $f'(x) = 9$. That is, we want to find x such that

$$-3x^2 + 12x = 9. \qquad \text{As in part (a), note that } \frac{d}{dx}(-x^3 + 6x^2) = -3x^2 + 12x.$$

To solve, we add -9 on both sides and get

$$-3x^2 + 12x - 9 = 0.$$

We then multiply both sides of the equation by $-\frac{1}{3}$, giving

$$x^2 - 4x + 3 = 0,$$

which is factored as follows:

$$(x - 3)(x - 1) = 0.$$

We have two solutions: $x = 1$ or $x = 3$. We need the actual coordinates: when $x = 1$, we have $f(1) = -(1)^3 + 6(1)^2 = 5$. Therefore, at the point $(1, 5)$ on the graph of $f(x)$, the tangent line has a slope of 9. In a similar way, we can state that the tangent line at the point $(3, 27)$ has a slope of 9 as well. All of this is illustrated in the following graph.

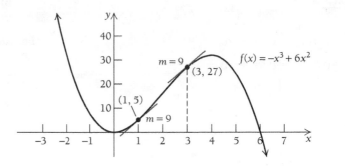

Quick Check 5 ☑

For the function in Example 6, find the points for which $f'(x) = -15$.

5 ☑

Section Summary

- Common forms of notation for the derivative of a function are y', $f'(x)$, $\dfrac{dy}{dx}$, and $\dfrac{d}{dx}f(x)$.

- The *Power Rule* for differentiation is $\dfrac{d}{dx}[x^k] = kx^{k-1}$, for all real numbers k.

- The derivative of a constant is zero: $\dfrac{d}{dx}c = 0$.

- The derivative of a constant times a function is the constant times the derivative of the function:
$$\frac{d}{dx}[c \cdot f(x)] = c \cdot \frac{d}{dx}f(x).$$

- The derivative of a sum (or difference) is the sum (or difference) of the derivatives of the terms:
$$\frac{d}{dx}[f(x) \pm g(x)] = \frac{d}{dx}f(x) \pm \frac{d}{dx}g(x).$$

1.5 | Exercise Set

Find $\dfrac{dy}{dx}$.

1. $y = x^8$

2. $y = x^7$

3. $y = -0.5x$

4. $y = -3x$

5. $y = 7$

6. $y = 12$

7. $y = 3x^{10}$

8. $y = 2x^{15}$

9. $y = x^{-8}$

10. $y = x^{-6}$

11. $y = 3x^{-5}$

12. $y = 4x^{-2}$

13. $y = x^4 - 7x$

14. $y = x^3 + 3x^2$

15. $y = 4\sqrt{x}$

16. $y = 8\sqrt{x}$

17. $y = x^{0.7}$

18. $y = x^{0.9}$

19. $y = -4.8x^{1/3}$

20. $y = \frac{1}{2}x^{4/5}$

21. $y = \dfrac{6}{x^4}$

22. $y = \dfrac{7}{x^3}$

23. $y = \dfrac{3x}{4}$

24. $y = \dfrac{4x}{5}$

Find each derivative.

25. $\dfrac{d}{dx}\left(\sqrt[4]{x} - \dfrac{3}{x}\right)$

26. $\dfrac{d}{dx}\left(\sqrt[3]{x} + \dfrac{4}{\sqrt{x}}\right)$

27. $\dfrac{d}{dx}(-2\sqrt[3]{x^5})$

28. $\dfrac{d}{dx}(-\sqrt[4]{x^3})$

29. $\dfrac{d}{dx}(5x^2 - 7x + 3)$

30. $\dfrac{d}{dx}(6x^2 - 5x + 9)$

Find $f'(x)$.

31. $f(x) = 0.3x^{1.2}$

32. $f(x) = 0.6x^{1.5}$

33. $f(x) = \dfrac{3x}{4}$

34. $f(x) = \dfrac{2x}{3}$

35. $f(x) = \dfrac{2}{5x^6}$

36. $f(x) = \dfrac{4}{7x^3}$

37. $f(x) = \dfrac{4}{x} - x^{3/5}$ **38.** $f(x) = \dfrac{5}{x} - x^{2/3}$

39. $f(x) = 7x - 14$ **40.** $f(x) = 4x - 7$

41. $f(x) = \dfrac{x^{3/2}}{3}$ **42.** $f(x) = \dfrac{x^{4/3}}{4}$

43. $f(x) = -0.01x^2 + 0.4x + 50$

44. $f(x) = -0.01x^2 - 0.5x + 70$

Find y'.

45. $y = x^{-3/4} - 3x^{2/3} + x^{5/4} + \dfrac{2}{x^4}$

46. $y = 3x^{-2/3} + x^{3/4} + x^{6/5} + \dfrac{8}{x^3}$

47. $y = \dfrac{x}{7} + \dfrac{7}{x}$ **48.** $y = \dfrac{2}{x} - \dfrac{x}{2}$

49. If $f(x) = \sqrt{x}$, find $f'(4)$.

50. If $f(x) = x^2 + 4x - 5$, find $f'(10)$.

51. If $y = x + \dfrac{2}{x^3}$, find $\dfrac{dy}{dx}\Big|_{x=1}$

52. If $y = \dfrac{4}{x^2}$, find $\dfrac{dy}{dx}\Big|_{x=-2}$

53. If $y = \sqrt[3]{x} + \sqrt{x}$, find $\dfrac{dy}{dx}\Big|_{x=64}$

54. If $y = x^3 + 2x - 5$, find $\dfrac{dy}{dx}\Big|_{x=-2}$

55. If $y = \dfrac{2}{5x^3}$, find $\dfrac{dy}{dx}\Big|_{x=4}$

56. If $y = \dfrac{1}{3x^4}$, find $\dfrac{dy}{dx}\Big|_{x=-1}$

57. Find an equation of the tangent line to the graph of $f(x) = x^2 - \sqrt{x}$
  a) at $(1, 0)$;
  b) at $(4, 14)$;
  c) at $(9, 78)$.

58. Find an equation (in $y = mx + b$ form) of the tangent line to the graph of $f(x) = x^3 - 2x + 1$
  a) at $(2, 5)$;
  b) at $(-1, 2)$;
  c) at $(0, 1)$.

59. Find the equation of the tangent line to the graph of $g(x) = \sqrt[3]{x^2}$
  a) at $(-1, 1)$;
  b) at $(1, 1)$;
  c) at $(8, 4)$.

60. Find an equation of the tangent line to the graph of $f(x) = \dfrac{1}{x^2}$
  a) at $(1, 1)$;
  b) at $(3, \frac{1}{9})$;
  c) at $(-2, \frac{1}{4})$.

For each function, find the points on the graph at which the tangent line is horizontal. If none exist, state that fact.

61. $y = -x^2 + 4$ **62.** $y = x^2 - 3$

63. $y = x^3 - 2$ **64.** $y = -x^3 + 1$

65. $y = 5x^2 - 3x + 8$ **66.** $y = 3x^2 - 5x + 4$

67. $y = -0.01x^2 + 0.4x + 50$

68. $y = -0.01x^2 - 0.5x + 70$

69. $y = -2x + 5$ **70.** $y = 2x + 4$

71. $y = -3$ **72.** $y = 4$

73. $y = -\frac{1}{3}x^3 + 6x^2 - 11x - 50$

74. $y = -x^3 + x^2 + 5x - 1$

75. $y = x^3 - 6x + 1$ **76.** $y = \frac{1}{3}x^3 - 3x + 2$

77. $f(x) = \frac{1}{3}x^3 - 3x^2 + 9x - 9$

78. $f(x) = \frac{1}{3}x^3 + \frac{1}{2}x^2 - 2$

For each function, find the points on the graph at which the tangent line has slope 1.

79. $y = 6x - x^2$ **80.** $y = 20x - x^2$

81. $y = -0.01x^2 + 2x$ **82.** $y = -0.025x^2 + 4x$

83. $y = \frac{1}{3}x^3 - x^2 - 4x + 1$ **84.** $y = \frac{1}{3}x^3 + 2x^2 + 2x$

APPLICATIONS

Life Sciences

85. Healing wound. The circumference C, in centimeters, of a healing wound is approximated by
  $$C(r) = 6.28r,$$
  where r is the wound's radius, in centimeters.
  a) Find the rate of change of the circumference with respect to the radius.
  b) Find $C'(4)$.
  c) Explain the meaning of your answer to part (b).

86. Healing wound. The circular area A, in square centimeters, of a healing wound is approximated by
  $$A(r) = 3.14r^2,$$
  where r is the wound's radius, in centimeters.
  a) Find the rate of change of the area with respect to the radius.
  b) Find $A'(3)$.
  c) Explain the meaning of your answer to part (b).

87. Growth of a baby. The median weight of a boy whose age is between 0 and 36 months is approximated by

$$w(t) = 8.15 + 1.82t - 0.0596t^2 + 0.000758t^3,$$

where t is in months and w is in pounds.

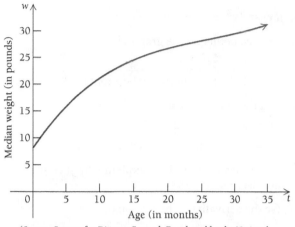

(*Source*: Centers for Disease Control. Developed by the National Center for Health Statistics in collaboration with the National Center for Chronic Disease Prevention and Health Promotion, 2000, Rechecked 2014)

Use this approximation to find the following:

a) The rate of change of weight with respect to time
b) The weight of a boy at age 10 months
c) The rate of change of a boy's weight with respect to time at age 10 months

88. Temperature during an illness. The temperature T of a person during an illness is given by

$$T(t) = -0.1t^2 + 1.2t + 98.6,$$

where T is the temperature, in degrees Fahrenheit, at time t, in days.

a) Find the rate of change of the temperature with respect to time.
b) Find the temperature at $t = 1.5$ days.
c) Find the rate of change at $t = 1.5$ days.

89. Heart rate. The equation

$$R(v) = \frac{6000}{v}$$

can be used to determine the heart rate, R, of a person whose heart pumps 6000 milliliters (mL) of blood per minute and v milliliters of blood per beat. (*Source: Mathematics Teacher*, Vol. 99, No. 4, November 2005.)

a) Find the rate of change of heart rate with respect to v, the output per beat.
b) Find the heart rate at $v = 80$ mL per beat.
c) Find the rate of change at $v = 80$ mL per beat.

90. Blood flow resistance. The equation

$$S(r) = \frac{1}{r^4}$$

can be used to determine the resistance to blood flow, S, of a blood vessel that has radius r, in millimeters (mm). (*Source: Mathematics Teacher*, Vol. 99, No. 4, November 2005.)

a) Find the rate of change of resistance with respect to r, the radius of the blood vessel.
b) Find the resistance at $r = 1.2$ mm.
c) Find the rate of change of S with respect to r when $r = 0.8$ mm.

Social Sciences

91. Population growth rate. In t years, the population of Kingsville grows from 100,000 to a size P given by

$$P(t) = 100,000 + 2000t^2.$$

a) Find the growth rate, dP/dt.
b) Find the population after 10 yr.
c) Find the growth rate at $t = 10$.
d) Explain the meaning of your answer to part (c).

92. Median age of women at first marriage. The median age of women at first marriage is approximated by

$$A(t) = 0.08t + 19.7,$$

where $A(t)$ is the median age of women marrying for the first time at t years after 1950.

a) Find the rate of change of the median age A with respect to time t.
b) Explain the meaning of your answer to part (a).

General Interest

93. View to the horizon. The view V, or distance in miles, that one can see to the horizon from a height h, in feet, is given by

$$V = 1.22\sqrt{h}.$$

a) Find the rate of change of V with respect to h.
b) How far can one see to the horizon from an airplane window at a height of 40,000 ft?

c) Find the rate of change at $h = 40,000$.
d) Explain the meaning of your answer to part (c).

94. **Super Bowl ticket prices.** The price of a ticket to the Super Bowl t years after 1967 can be estimated by

$$p(t) = 0.696t^2 - 13.290t + 61.857.$$

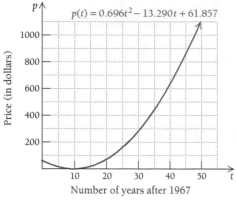

(*Source:* Based on data from extramustard.si.com.)

a) Use the function to predict the price of a Super Bowl ticket in 2014.
b) Find the rate of change of the ticket price with respect to the year, dp/dt.
c) At what rate were ticket prices changing in 2014?

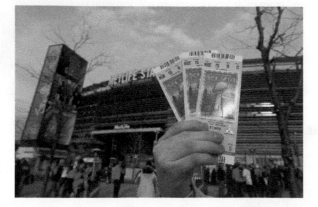

SYNTHESIS

For Exercises 95 and 96, find the interval(s) for which $f'(x)$ is positive.

95. $f(x) = x^2 - 4x + 1$

96. $f(x) = \frac{1}{3}x^3 - x^2 - 3x + 5$

97. Find the points on the graph of
$$y = x^4 - \frac{4}{3}x^2 - 4$$
at which the tangent line is horizontal.

98. Find the points on the graph of
$$y = 2x^6 - x^4 - 2$$
at which the tangent line is horizontal.

99. Use the derivative to help explain why $f(x) = x^5 + x^3$ increases for all x in $(-\infty, \infty)$.

100. Use the derivative to help explain why $g(x) = -2x - x^3$ decreases for all x in $(-\infty, \infty)$.

101. Use the derivative to help explain why $k(x) = \frac{1}{x^2}$ decreases for all x in $(0, \infty)$.

102. Use the derivative to help explain why $f(x) = x^3 + ax$ increases for all x in $(-\infty, \infty)$ when $a \geq 0$ but not when $a < 0$.

Find dy/dx. Each function can be differentiated using the rules developed in this section, but some algebra may be required beforehand.

103. $y = (x + 3)(x - 2)$ 104. $y = (x - 1)(x + 1)$

105. $y = \dfrac{x^5 - x^3}{x^2}$ 106. $y = \dfrac{x^5 + x}{x^2}$

107. $y = \sqrt{7x}$ 108. $y = \sqrt[3]{8x}$

109. $y = \left(\sqrt{x} - \dfrac{1}{\sqrt{x}}\right)^2$ 110. $y = (x + 1)^3$

111. When might Leibniz notation be more convenient than function notation?

TECHNOLOGY CONNECTION

Graph each of the following. Then estimate the x-values at which tangent lines are horizontal.

112. $f(x) = x^4 - 3x^2 + 1$

113. $f(x) = \dfrac{5x^2 + 8x - 3}{3x^2 + 2}$

For each of the following, graph f and f' and then determine $f'(1)$. For Exercises 116 and 117, use nDeriv on the TI-83.

114. $f(x) = 20x^3 - 3x^5$

115. $f(x) = x^4 - x^3$

116. $f(x) = \dfrac{4x}{x^2 + 1}$

117. $f(x) = \dfrac{5x^2 + 8x - 3}{3x^2 + 2}$

Answers to Quick Checks

1. (a) $y' = 15x^{14}$; (b) $y' = -7x^{-8} = -\dfrac{7}{x^8}$

2. (a) $y' = \frac{1}{4}x^{-3/4} = \dfrac{1}{4\sqrt[4]{x^3}}$;

   (b) $y' = -1.25x^{-2.25} = -\dfrac{1.25}{x^{2.25}}$

3. (a) $y' = 90x^8$; (b) $y' = 3\pi x^2$; (c) $y' = -\dfrac{8}{3x^5}$

4. $y' = 15x^4 + \dfrac{2}{3\sqrt[3]{x^2}} - \dfrac{2}{3x^3}$ 5. $(-1, 7)$ and $(5, 25)$

1.6

- Differentiate using the Product and Quotient Rules.
- Use the Quotient Rule to differentiate the average cost, revenue, and profit functions.

Differentiation Techniques: The Product and Quotient Rules

The Product Rule

A function can be written as the product of two other functions. For example, $F(x) = (x^2 + 3x)\sqrt{x}$ can be viewed as the product of $f(x) = x^2 + 3x$ and $g(x) = \sqrt{x}$. However, the derivative of a product of two functions is *not* the product of their derivatives.

THEOREM 5   The Product Rule

Let $F(x) = f(x) \cdot g(x)$. Then

$$F'(x) = \frac{d}{dx}[f(x) \cdot g(x)] = f(x) \cdot \left[\frac{d}{dx}g(x)\right] + g(x) \cdot \left[\frac{d}{dx}f(x)\right].$$

The derivative of a product is the first factor times the derivative of the second factor, plus the second factor times the derivative of the first factor.

The proof of the Product Rule is outlined in Exercise 75 at the end of this section.

To find the derivative of the product $f(x) \cdot g(x)$, we perform the following steps:

1. Write the first factor, $f(x)$.
2. Multiply it by the derivative of the second factor, $g'(x)$.
3. Write the second factor, $g(x)$.
4. Multiply it by the derivative of the first factor, $f'(x)$.
5. Add the result of steps (1) and (2) to the result of steps (3) and (4).

Usually we try to write the results in simplified form. In Examples 1 and 2, we do not simplify in order to better emphasize the steps being performed.

EXAMPLE 1   Find $\dfrac{d}{dx}[(x^4 - 2x^3 - 7)(3x^2 - 5x)]$. Do not simplify.

Solution   We let $f(x) = x^4 - 2x^3 - 7$ and $g(x) = 3x^2 - 5x$. We differentiate each of these, obtaining $f'(x) = 4x^3 - 6x^2$ and $g'(x) = 6x - 5$. By the Product Rule, the derivative of the given function is then

$$\frac{d}{dx}[(x^4 - 2x^3 - 7)(3x^2 - 5x)] = \overbrace{(x^4 - 2x^3 - 7)}^{f(x)} \cdot \overbrace{(6x - 5)}^{g'(x)} + \overbrace{(3x^2 - 5x)}^{g(x)} \cdot \overbrace{(4x^3 - 6x^2)}^{f'(x)}$$

In this example, we could have first multiplied the polynomials and then differentiated. Both methods give the same solution after simplification. ■

It makes no difference which factor of the given function is regarded as $f(x)$ or $g(x)$. We often regard the first function as $f(x)$ and the second function as $g(x)$, but if we switch the roles, the process still gives the same answer.

Quick Check 1 ✔

Use the Product Rule to differentiate each of the following functions. Do not simplify.

a) $y = (2x^5 + x - 1)(3x - 2)$

b) $y = (\sqrt{x} + 1)(\sqrt[5]{x} - x)$

EXAMPLE 2   For $F(x) = (x^2 + 4x - 11)(7x^3 - \sqrt{x})$, find $F'(x)$. Do not simplify.

Solution   We rewrite this as

$$F(x) = (x^2 + 4x - 11)(7x^3 - x^{1/2}).$$

Then, using the Product Rule, we have

$$F'(x) = (x^2 + 4x - 11)(21x^2 - \tfrac{1}{2}x^{-1/2}) + (7x^3 - x^{1/2})(2x + 4). \quad \textbf{1} ✔$$

The Quotient Rule

The derivative of a quotient is *not* the quotient of the derivatives. To see why, consider x^5 and x^2 and assume $x \neq 0$. The quotient x^5/x^2 is x^3, and the derivative of this quotient is $3x^2$. The derivatives of the numerator and denominator are $5x^4$ and $2x$, respectively, and the quotient of these derivatives, $5x^4/(2x)$, is $(5/2)x^3$, which is not $3x^2$.

The rule for differentiating quotients is as follows.

THEOREM 6   **The Quotient Rule**

If $Q(x) = \dfrac{N(x)}{D(x)}$,   then $Q'(x) = \dfrac{D(x) \cdot N'(x) - N(x) \cdot D'(x)}{[D(x)]^2}$.

The derivative of a quotient is the denominator times the derivative of the numerator, minus the numerator times the derivative of the denominator, all divided by the square of the denominator.

A proof of this result is outlined in Exercise 96 of Section 1.7 (on p. 166).

The Quotient Rule is illustrated below.

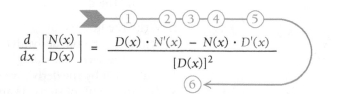

$$\frac{d}{dx}\left[\frac{N(x)}{D(x)}\right] = \frac{D(x) \cdot N'(x) - N(x) \cdot D'(x)}{[D(x)]^2}$$

There are six steps:

1. Write the denominator.
2. Multiply the denominator by the derivative of the numerator.
3. Write a minus sign.
4. Write the numerator.
5. Multiply it by the derivative of the denominator.
6. Divide the expression resulting from steps 1–5 by the square of the denominator.

EXAMPLE 3 For $Q(x) = x^5/x^2$, find $Q'(x)$.

Solution We have already seen that $x^5/x^2 = x^3$ and $\dfrac{d}{dx}x^3 = 3x^2$, but we wish to practice using the Quotient Rule. We have $D(x) = x^2$ and $N(x) = x^5$:

$$
Q'(x) = \frac{\overset{\displaystyle D(x) \cdot N'(x) - N(x) \cdot D'(x)}{}}{\underset{[D(x)]^2}{(x^2)^2}} = \frac{x^2 \cdot 5x^4 - x^5 \cdot 2x}{(x^2)^2}
$$

$$
= \frac{5x^6 - 2x^6}{x^4} = \frac{3x^6}{x^4} = 3x^2, x \neq 0. \qquad \text{This checks with the result above.}
$$

■

EXAMPLE 4 Differentiate: $f(x) = \dfrac{1 + x^2}{x^3 + 1}$.

Solution We let $N(x) = 1 + x^2$ and $D(x) = x^3 + 1$. We have

$$
f'(x) = \frac{(x^3 + 1)(2x) - (1 + x^2)(3x^2)}{(x^3 + 1)^2} \qquad \text{Using the Quotient Rule}
$$

$$
= \frac{2x^4 + 2x - 3x^2 - 3x^4}{(x^3 + 1)^2} \qquad \text{Using the distributive law}
$$

$$
= \frac{-x^4 - 3x^2 + 2x}{(x^3 + 1)^2}. \qquad \text{Simplifying}
$$

■

EXAMPLE 5 Differentiate: $f(x) = \dfrac{x^2 - 3x}{x - 1}$.

Solution We have

$$
f'(x) = \frac{(x - 1)(2x - 3) - (x^2 - 3x) \cdot 1}{(x - 1)^2} \qquad \text{Using the Quotient Rule}
$$

$$
= \frac{2x^2 - 5x + 3 - x^2 + 3x}{(x - 1)^2} \qquad \text{Using the distributive law}
$$

$$
= \frac{x^2 - 2x + 3}{(x - 1)^2}. \qquad \text{Simplifying}
$$

2 ✔

Quick Check 2 ✔

a) Differentiate: $f(x) = \dfrac{1 - 3x}{x^2 + 2}$.

Simplify your result.

b) Show that

$$
\frac{d}{dx}\left[\frac{ax + 1}{bx + 1}\right] = \frac{a - b}{(bx + 1)^2}.
$$

Application of the Quotient Rule

The total cost, total revenue, and total profit functions, discussed in Section R.4, pertain to the accumulated cost, revenue, and profit when x items are produced. Because of economies of scale and other factors, it is common for the cost, revenue (price), and profit for, say, the 10th item to differ from those for the 1000th item. For this reason, businesses often focus on *average* cost, revenue, and profit.

Checking Derivatives Graphically

To check Example 5, we first enter the function:

$$y_1 = \frac{x^2 - 3x}{x - 1}.$$

Then we enter the possible derivative:

$$y_2 = \frac{x^2 - 2x + 3}{(x - 1)^2}.$$

As a third function, we enter

$$y_3 = \text{nDeriv}(y_1, x, x).$$

Next, we deselect y_1 and graph y_2 and y_3. We use different graph styles and the **Sequential** mode to see each graph as it appears on the screen.

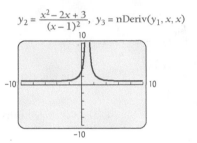

Since the graphs appear to coincide, it appears that $y_2 = y_3$ and we have a check. This is considered a partial

check, however, because the graphs might not coincide with a different viewing window.

We can also use a table to check that $y_2 = y_3$.

X	Y2	Y3
5.97	1.081	1.081
5.98	1.0806	1.0806
5.99	1.0803	1.0803
6	1.08	1.08
6.01	1.0797	1.0797
6.02	1.0794	1.0794
6.03	1.079	1.079

X = 5.97

EXERCISES

1. For the function

$$f(x) = \frac{x^2 - 4x}{x + 2},$$

use graphs and tables to determine which of the following seems to be the correct derivative.

a) $f'(x) = \dfrac{-x^2 - 4x - 8}{(x + 2)^2}$

b) $f'(x) = \dfrac{x^2 - 4x + 8}{(x + 2)^2}$

c) $f'(x) = \dfrac{x^2 + 4x - 8}{(x + 2)^2}$

2–5. Graphically check the results of Examples 1–4.

DEFINITION

If $C(x)$ is the cost of producing x items, then the **average cost** of producing x items is $\dfrac{C(x)}{x}$.

If $R(x)$ is the revenue from the sale of x items, then the **average revenue** from selling x items is $\dfrac{R(x)}{x}$.

If $P(x)$ is the profit from the sale of x items, then the **average profit** from selling x items is $\dfrac{P(x)}{x}$.

EXAMPLE 6 **Business.** Paulsen's Greenhouse finds that the cost, in dollars, of growing x hundred geraniums is modeled by

$$C(x) = 200 + 100\sqrt[4]{x}.$$

If revenue from the sale of x hundred geraniums is modeled by

$$R(x) = 120 + 90\sqrt{x},$$

find each of the following.

a) The average cost, average revenue, and average profit when x hundred geraniums are grown and sold

b) The rate at which average profit is changing when 300 geraniums have been grown and sold

Solution

a) We let A_C, A_R, and A_P represent average cost, average revenue, and average profit, respectively. Then

$$A_C(x) = \frac{C(x)}{x} = \frac{200 + 100\sqrt[4]{x}}{x};$$

$$A_R(x) = \frac{R(x)}{x} = \frac{120 + 90\sqrt{x}}{x};$$

$$A_P(x) = \frac{P(x)}{x} = \frac{R(x) - C(x)}{x} = \frac{-80 + 90\sqrt{x} - 100\sqrt[4]{x}}{x}.$$

b) To find the rate at which average profit is changing when 300 geraniums are being grown, we calculate $A_{P'}(3)$ (remember that x is in hundreds):

$$A_{P'}(x) = \frac{d}{dx}\left[\frac{-80 + 90x^{1/2} - 100x^{1/4}}{x}\right]$$

$$= \frac{x\left(\frac{1}{2} \cdot 90x^{1/2-1} - \frac{1}{4} \cdot 100x^{1/4-1}\right) - \left(-80 + 90x^{1/2} - 100x^{1/4}\right) \cdot 1}{x^2}$$

$$= \frac{45x^{1/2} - 25x^{1/4} + 80 - 90x^{1/2} + 100x^{1/4}}{x^2} = \frac{75x^{1/4} - 45x^{1/2} + 80}{x^2};$$

$$A_{P'}(3) = \frac{75\sqrt[4]{3} - 45\sqrt{3} + 80}{3^2} \approx 11.20.$$

When 300 geraniums have been grown and sold, average profit is increasing by \$11.20 per hundred plants, or about 11.2 cents per plant. ∎

TECHNOLOGY CONNECTION

Using Y-VARS

One way to save keystrokes on most calculators is to use the Y-VARS option on the VARS menu.

To check Example 6(a), we let $y_1 = 200 + 100x^{0.25}$ and $y_2 = 120 + 90x^{0.5}$. To express the profit function as y_3, we press (**Y=**) and move the cursor to enter Y3. Next we press (**VARS**) and select Y-VARS and then FUNCTION. From the FUNCTION menu we select Y2, which then appears on the (**Y=**) screen. After pressing (**−**), we repeat the procedure to get Y1 on the (**Y=**) screen.

```
Plot 1  Plot 2  Plot 3
\Y1 = 200 + 100X^0.25
\Y2 = 120 + 90X^0.5
\Y3 = Y2 − Y1
\Y4 =
\Y5 =
\Y6 =
```

EXERCISES

1. Use the Y-VARS option to enter $y_4 = y_1/x$, $y_5 = y_2/x$, and $y_6 = y_3/x$, and explain what each of the functions represents.

2. Use nDeriv from the MATH menu or dy/dx from the CALC menu to check Example 6(b).

Section Summary

- The *Product Rule* is

$$\frac{d}{dx}[f(x) \cdot g(x)] = f(x) \cdot \frac{d}{dx}[g(x)] + g(x) \cdot \frac{d}{dx}[f(x)].$$

- The *Quotient Rule* is

$$\frac{d}{dx}\left[\frac{f(x)}{g(x)}\right] = \frac{g(x) \cdot \frac{d}{dx}[f(x)] - f(x) \cdot \frac{d}{dx}[g(x)]}{[g(x)]^2}.$$

- Be careful to note the order in which the factors are written when using the Quotient Rule. Because the Quotient Rule involves subtraction, the order in which the operations are performed is important.

1.6 | Exercise Set

Differentiate two ways: first, by using the Product Rule; then, by multiplying the expressions before differentiating. Compare your results as a check. Use a graphing calculator to check your results.

1. $y = x^9 \cdot x^4$

2. $y = x^5 \cdot x^6$

3. $f(x) = (2x + 5)(3x - 4)$

4. $g(x) = (3x - 2)(4x + 1)$

5. $F(x) = 3x^4(x^2 - 4x)$

6. $G(x) = 4x^2(x^3 + 5x)$

7. $y = (3\sqrt{x} + 2)x^2$

8. $y = (4\sqrt{x} + 3)x^3$

9. $f(x) = (2x + 5)(3x^2 - 4x + 1)$

10. $g(x) = (4x - 3)(2x^2 + 3x + 5)$

11. $F(t) = (\sqrt{t} + 2)(3t - 4\sqrt{t} + 7)$

12. $G(t) = (2t + 3\sqrt{t} + 5)(\sqrt{t} + 4)$

Differentiate two ways: first, by using the Quotient Rule; then, by dividing the expressions before differentiating. Compare your results as a check. Use a graphing calculator to check your results.

13. $y = \dfrac{x^6}{x^4}$

14. $y = \dfrac{x^7}{x^3}$

15. $g(x) = \dfrac{3x^7 - x^3}{x}$

16. $f(x) = \dfrac{2x^5 + x^2}{x}$

17. $G(x) = \dfrac{8x^3 - 1}{2x - 1}$

18. $F(x) = \dfrac{x^3 + 27}{x + 3}$

19. $y = \dfrac{t^2 - 16}{t + 4}$

20. $y = \dfrac{t^2 - 25}{t - 5}$

Differentiate each function.

21. $g(x) = (5x^2 + 4x - 3)(2x^2 - 3x + 1)$

22. $f(x) = (3x^2 - 2x + 5)(4x^2 + 3x - 1)$

23. $y = \dfrac{5x^2 - 1}{2x^3 + 3}$

24. $y = \dfrac{3x^4 + 2x}{x^3 - 1}$

25. $F(x) = (-3x^2 + 4x)(7\sqrt{x} + 1)$

26. $G(x) = (8x + \sqrt{x})(5x^2 + 3)$

27. $g(t) = \dfrac{t}{3 - t} + 5t^3$

28. $f(t) = \dfrac{t}{5 + 2t} - 2t^4$

29. $G(x) = (5x - 4)^2$

30. $F(x) = (x + 3)^2$

[Hint: $(x + 3)^2 = (x + 3)(x + 3)$.]

31. $y = (x^3 - 4x)^2$

32. $y = (3x^2 - 4x + 5)^2$

33. $f(x) = 6x^{-4}(6x^3 + 10x^2 - 8x + 3)$

34. $g(x) = 5x^{-3}(x^4 - 5x^3 + 10x - 2)$

35. $F(t) = \left(t + \dfrac{2}{t}\right)(t^2 - 3)$

36. $G(t) = (3t^5 - t^2)\left(t - \dfrac{5}{t}\right)$

37. $y = \dfrac{x^3 - 1}{x^2 + 1} + 4x^3$

38. $y = \dfrac{x^2 + 1}{x^3 - 1} - 5x^2$

39. $y = \dfrac{\sqrt[3]{x} - 7}{\sqrt{x} + 3}$

40. $y = \dfrac{\sqrt{x} + 4}{\sqrt[3]{x} - 5}$

41. $f(x) = \dfrac{x^{-1}}{x + x^{-1}}$

42. $f(x) = \dfrac{x}{x^{-1} + 1}$

43. $F(t) = \dfrac{1}{t - 4}$

44. $G(t) = \dfrac{1}{t + 2}$

45. $f(x) = \dfrac{3x^2 - 5x}{x^2 - 1}$

46. $f(x) = \dfrac{3x^2 + 2x}{x^2 + 1}$

47. $g(t) = \dfrac{-t^2 + 3t + 5}{t^2 - 2t + 4}$

48. $f(t) = \dfrac{3t^2 + 2t - 1}{-t^2 + 4t + 1}$

49. Find an equation of the tangent line to the graph of $y = 8/(x^2 + 4)$ at (a) $(0, 2)$; (b) $(-2, 1)$.

50. Find an equation of the tangent line to the graph of $y = \sqrt{x}/(x + 1)$ at (a) $x = 1$; (b) $x = \frac{1}{4}$.

51. Find an equation of the tangent line to the graph of $y = x^2 + 3/(x - 1)$ at (a) $x = 2$; (b) $x = 3$.

52. Find an equation of the tangent line to the graph of $y = 4x/(1 + x^2)$ at (a) $(0, 0)$; (b) $(-1, -2)$.

APPLICATIONS

Business and Economics

53. Average cost. Preston's Leatherworks finds that the cost, in dollars, of producing x belts is given by $C(x) = 750 + 34x - 0.068x^2$. Find the rate at which average cost is changing when 175 belts have been produced.

54. Average cost. Tongue-Tied Sauces, Inc., finds that the cost, in dollars, of producing x bottles of barbecue sauce is given by $C(x) = 375 + 0.75x^{3/4}$. Find the rate at which average cost is changing when 81 bottles of barbecue sauce have been produced.

55. Average revenue. Preston's Leatherworks find that the revenue, in dollars, from the sale of x belts is given by $R(x) = 45x^{9/10}$. Find the rate at which average revenue is changing when 175 belts have been produced and sold.

56. Average revenue. Tongue-Tied Sauces, Inc., finds that the revenue, in dollars, from the sale of x bottles of barbecue sauce is given by $R(x) = 7.5x^{0.7}$. Find the rate at which average revenue is changing when 81 bottles of barbecue sauce have been produced and sold.

57. Average profit. Use the information in Exercises 53 and 55 to determine the rate at which Preston's Leatherworks' average profit per belt is changing when 175 belts have been produced and sold.

58. Average profit. Use the information in Exercises 54 and 56 to determine the rate at which Tongue-Tied Sauces' average profit per bottle of barbecue sauce is changing when 81 bottles have been produced and sold.

59. Average profit. Sparkle Pottery has determined that the cost, in dollars, of producing x vases is given by

$$C(x) = 4300 + 2.1x^{0.6}.$$

If the revenue from the sale of x vases is given by $R(x) = 65x^{0.9}$, find the rate at which average profit per vase is changing when 50 vases have been made and sold.

60. Average profit. Cruzin' Boards has found that the cost, in dollars, of producing x skateboards is given by

$$C(x) = 900 + 18x^{0.7}.$$

If the revenue from the sale of x skateboards is given by $R(x) = 75x^{0.8}$, find the rate at which average profit per skateboard is changing when 20 skateboards have been built and sold.

61. Gross domestic product. The U.S. gross domestic product (in billions of dollars) can be approximated by

$$P(t) = 567 + t(36t^{0.6} - 104),$$

where t is the number of the years since 1960. (*Source:* U.S. Bureau of Economic Analysis.)

a) Find $P'(t)$.

b) Find $P'(45)$.

c) In words, explain what $P'(45)$ represents.

Social Sciences

62. Population growth. The population P, in thousands, of the town of Coyote Wells is given by

$$P(t) = \frac{500t}{2t^2 + 9},$$

where t is the time, in years.

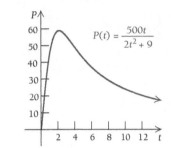

a) Find the growth rate.

b) Find the population after 12 yr.

c) Find the growth rate at $t = 12$ yr.

Life and Physical Sciences

63. Temperature during an illness. Gloria's temperature T during a recent illness is given by

$$T(t) = \frac{4t}{t^2 + 1} + 98.6,$$

where T is the temperature, in degrees Fahrenheit, at time t, in hours.

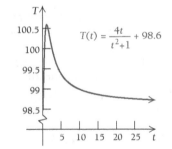

a) Find the rate of change of the temperature with respect to time.

b) Find the temperature at $t = 2$.

c) Find the rate of change of the temperature at $t = 2$.

SYNTHESIS

Differentiate each function.

64. $f(x) = \dfrac{7 - \dfrac{3}{2x}}{\dfrac{4}{x^2} + 5}$ (*Hint:* Simplify before differentiating.)

65. $y(t) = 5t(t - 1)(2t + 3)$

66. $f(x) = x(3x^3 + 6x - 2)(3x^4 + 7)$

67. $g(x) = (x^3 - 8) \cdot \dfrac{x^2 + 1}{x^2 - 1}$

68. $f(t) = (t^5 + 3) \cdot \dfrac{t^3 - 1}{t^3 + 1}$

69. $f(x) = \dfrac{(x - 1)(x^2 + x + 1)}{x^4 - 3x^3 - 5}$

70. Let $f(x) = \dfrac{x}{x + 1}$ and $g(x) = \dfrac{-1}{x + 1}$.

    a) Compute $f'(x)$.

    b) Compute $g'(x)$.

    c) What can you conclude about f and g on the basis of your results from parts (a) and (b)?

71. Let $f(x) = \dfrac{x^2}{x^2 - 1}$ and $g(x) = \dfrac{1}{x^2 - 1}$.

    a) Compute $f'(x)$.

    b) Compute $g'(x)$.

    c) What can you conclude about the graphs of f and g on the basis of your results from parts (a) and (b)?

72. Write a rule for finding the derivative of $f(x) \cdot g(x) \cdot h(x)$. Describe the rule in as few words as possible.

73. Is the derivative of the reciprocal of $f(x)$ the reciprocal of the derivative of $f(x)$? Why or why not?

74. Sensitivity. The reaction R of the body to a dose Q of medication is often represented by the general function

$$R(Q) = Q^2\left(\frac{k}{2} - \frac{Q}{3}\right),$$

where k is a constant and R is in millimeters of mercury (mmHg) if the reaction is a change in blood pressure or in degrees Fahrenheit (°F) if the reaction is a change in temperature. The rate of change dR/dQ is defined to be the body's *sensitivity* to the medication.

    a) Find a formula for the sensitivity.

    b) Explain the meaning of your answer to part (a).

75. A proof of the Product Rule appears below. Provide a justification for each step.

    a) $\dfrac{d}{dx}[f(x) \cdot g(x)] = \lim\limits_{h \to 0} \dfrac{f(x + h)g(x + h) - f(x)g(x)}{h}$

    b) $= \lim\limits_{h \to 0} \dfrac{f(x + h)g(x + h) - f(x + h)g(x) + f(x + h)g(x) - f(x)g(x)}{h}$

    c) $= \lim\limits_{h \to 0} \dfrac{f(x + h)g(x + h) - f(x + h)g(x)}{h} + \lim\limits_{h \to 0} \dfrac{f(x + h)g(x) - f(x)g(x)}{h}$

    d) $= \lim\limits_{h \to 0}\left[f(x + h) \cdot \dfrac{g(x + h) - g(x)}{h}\right] + \lim\limits_{h \to 0}\left[g(x) \cdot \dfrac{f(x + h) - f(x)}{h}\right]$

    e) $= f(x) \cdot \lim\limits_{h \to 0} \dfrac{g(x + h) - g(x)}{h} + g(x) \cdot \lim\limits_{h \to 0} \dfrac{f(x + h) - f(x)}{h}$

    f) $= f(x) \cdot g'(x) + g(x) \cdot f'(x)$

    g) $= f(x) \cdot \left[\dfrac{d}{dx}g(x)\right] + g(x) \cdot \left[\dfrac{d}{dx}f(x)\right]$

76. Business. Refer to Exercises 54, 56, and 58. At what rate is Tongue-Tied Sauces' profit changing at the break-even point? At what rate is the average profit per bottle of barbecue sauce changing at that point?

77. Business. Refer to Exercises 53, 55, and 57. At what rate is Preston's Leatherworks' profit changing at the break-even point? At what rate is the average profit per belt changing at that point?

For the function in each of Exercises 78–83, graph f and f'. Then estimate points at which the tangent line to f is horizontal. If no such point exists, state that fact.

78. $f(x) = x^2(x - 2)(x + 2)$

79. $f(x) = \left(x + \dfrac{2}{x}\right)(x^2 - 3)$

80. $f(x) = \dfrac{x^3 - 1}{x^2 + 1}$

81. $f(x) = \dfrac{0.01x^2}{x^4 + 0.0256}$

82. $f(x) = \dfrac{0.3x}{0.04 + x^2}$

83. $f(x) = \dfrac{4x}{x^2 + 1}$

84. Use a graph to decide which of the following seems to be the correct derivative of the function in Exercise 83.

$$y_1 = \frac{2}{x}$$

$$y_2 = \frac{4 - 4x}{x^2 + 1}$$

$$y_3 = \frac{4 - 4x^2}{(x^2 + 1)^2}$$

$$y_4 = \frac{4x^2 - 4}{(x^2 + 1)^2}$$

Answers to Quick Checks

1. (a) $y' = (2x^5 + x - 1)(3) + (3x - 2)(10x^4 + 1)$;

(b) $y' = (\sqrt{x} + 1)\left(\frac{1}{5\sqrt[5]{x^4}} - 1\right) + (\sqrt[5]{x} - x)\left(\frac{1}{2\sqrt{x}}\right)$

2. (a) $y' = \frac{3x^2 - 2x - 6}{(x^2 + 2)^2}$;

(b) $\frac{(bx + 1)(a) - (ax + 1)(b)}{(bx + 1)^2} = \frac{abx + a - abx - b}{(bx + 1)^2}$

$$= \frac{a - b}{(bx + 1)^2}$$

The Chain Rule

The Extended Power Rule

- Find the composition of two functions.
- Differentiate using the Extended Power Rule or the Chain Rule.

Consider the function given by $y = (1 + x^2)^3$. How do we determine its derivative? We might guess the following:

$$\frac{d}{dx}[(1 + x^2)^3] \stackrel{?}{=} 3(1 + x^2)^2. \qquad \text{Remember, this is a } \textit{guess.}$$

To check this, we first expand the function $y = (1 + x^2)^3$:

$$\begin{aligned}
y &= (1 + x^2)^3 \\
&= (1 + x^2) \cdot (1 + x^2) \cdot (1 + x^2) \\
&= (1 + 2x^2 + x^4) \cdot (1 + x^2) \qquad \text{Multiplying the first two factors} \\
&= 1 + 3x^2 + 3x^4 + x^6. \qquad \text{Multiplying by the third factor}
\end{aligned}$$

Taking the derivative of this function, we have

$$y' = 6x + 12x^3 + 6x^5.$$

Now we can factor out $6x$:

$$y' = 6x(1 + 2x^2 + x^4).$$

We rewrite $6x$ as $3 \cdot 2x$ and factor the trinomial:

$$y' = 3(1 + x^2)^2 \cdot 2x. \qquad \text{This } \textit{is} \text{ the derivative.}$$

Thus, it seems our original *guess* was close: it lacked only the extra factor, $2x$, which is the derivative of the expression inside the parentheses. This result suggests a general pattern for differentiating functions of this form, in which an expression is raised to a power k.

THEOREM 7 The Extended Power Rule

Suppose that $g(x)$ is a differentiable function of x. Then, for any real number k,

$$\frac{d}{dx}[g(x)]^k = k[g(x)]^{k-1} \cdot \frac{d}{dx}g(x).$$

A proof for the case where k is a positive integer is outlined in Exercise 95.

The Extended Power Rule allows us to differentiate functions such as $y = (1 + x^2)^{89}$ without expanding $1 + x^2$ to the 89th power (very time-consuming) and functions such as $y = (1 + x^2)^{1/3}$, for which expanding is impossible.

Let's differentiate $(1 + x^3)^5$. There are three steps to carry out.

1. Mentally block out the "inside" function, $1 + x^3$.　　$(1 + x^3)^5$
2. Differentiate the "outside" function, $(1 + x^3)^5$.　　$5(1 + x^3)^4$
3. Multiply by the derivative of the "inside" function.　　$5(1 + x^3)^4 \cdot 3x^2$

$$= 15x^2(1 + x^3)^4 \quad \text{Simplified}$$

Step (3) is commonly overlooked. Do not forget it!

EXAMPLE 1　Differentiate: **(a)** $f(x) = (1 + x^3)^{1/2}$;
(b) $y = (1 - x^2)^3 + (5 + 4x)^2$.

Solution　**a)** We have

$$\frac{d}{dx}(1 + x^3)^{1/2} = \frac{1}{2}(1 + x^3)^{1/2-1} \cdot 3x^2$$

$$= \frac{3x^2}{2}(1 + x^3)^{-1/2}$$

$$= \frac{3x^2}{2\sqrt{1 + x^3}}.$$

b) Here we combine the Sum–Difference Rule and the Extended Power Rule:

$$\frac{dy}{dx} = 3(1 - x^2)^2(-2x) + 2(5 + 4x)^1 \cdot 4 \qquad \begin{array}{l}\text{Differentiating each term using}\\ \text{the Extended Power Rule}\end{array}$$

$$= -6x(1 - x^2)^2 + 8(5 + 4x)$$
$$= -6x(1 - 2x^2 + x^4) + 40 + 32x$$
$$= -6x + 12x^3 - 6x^5 + 40 + 32x \qquad \left.\begin{array}{}\\ \\ \\ \end{array}\right\}\text{Simplifying}$$
$$= -6x^5 + 12x^3 + 26x + 40. \qquad\qquad\qquad\qquad\qquad\; \boxed{1\;☑}$$

Quick Check 1 ☑

a) Use the Extended Power Rule to differentiate $y = (x^4 + 2x^2 + 1)^3$.

b) Explain why
$$\frac{d}{dx}[(x^2 + 4x + 1)^4] = 4(x^2 + 4x + 1)^3 \cdot 2x + 4$$
is incorrect.

EXAMPLE 2　Differentiate: **(a)** $f(x) = (3x - 5)^4(7 - x)^{10}$; **(b)** $f(x) = \sqrt[4]{\dfrac{x + 3}{x - 2}}$.

Solution

a) Here we combine the Product Rule and the Extended Power Rule:

$$f'(x) = (3x - 5)^4 \cdot 10(7 - x)^9(-1) + (7 - x)^{10}\, 4(3x - 5)^3(3)$$
$$= -10(3x - 5)^4(7 - x)^9 + (7 - x)^{10}\, 12(3x - 5)^3$$
$$= 2(3x - 5)^3(7 - x)^9[-5(3x - 5) + 6(7 - x)] \quad \begin{array}{l}\text{Factoring out}\\ 2(3x - 5)^3(7 - x)^9\end{array}$$
$$= 2(3x - 5)^3(7 - x)^9(-15x + 25 + 42 - 6x)$$
$$= 2(3x - 5)^3(7 - x)^9(67 - 21x).$$

b) Here we use the Quotient Rule to differentiate the inside function:

$$\frac{d}{dx}\sqrt[4]{\frac{x + 3}{x - 2}} = \frac{d}{dx}\left(\frac{x + 3}{x - 2}\right)^{1/4} = \frac{1}{4}\left(\frac{x + 3}{x - 2}\right)^{1/4-1}\left[\frac{(x - 2)1 - 1(x + 3)}{(x - 2)^2}\right]$$

$$= \frac{1}{4}\left(\frac{x + 3}{x - 2}\right)^{-3/4}\left[\frac{x - 2 - x - 3}{(x - 2)^2}\right]$$

$$= \frac{1}{4}\left(\frac{x + 3}{x - 2}\right)^{-3/4}\left[\frac{-5}{(x - 2)^2}\right], \quad \text{or} \quad \frac{-5}{4(x + 3)^{3/4}(x - 2)^{5/4}}.$$

$$\boxed{2\;☑}$$

Quick Check 2 ☑

Differentiate:

$$f(x) = \frac{(2x^2 - 1)}{(3x^4 + 2)^2}.$$

Composition of Functions and the Chain Rule

Before discussing the Chain Rule, let's consider *composition of functions*.

One author of this text exercises three times a week at a local YMCA. When he recently bought a pair of running shoes, the box indicated equivalent men's shoe sizes in five countries.

Author Marv Bittinger and his size-$11\frac{1}{2}$ running shoes

This suggests that there are functions that convert men's shoe sizes used in one country to those used in another country. There is, indeed, a function g that gives a correspondence between men's shoe sizes in the United States and those in France:

$$g(x) = \frac{4x + 92}{3},$$

where x is the U.S. size and $g(x)$ is the French size. Thus, U.S. size $11\frac{1}{2}$ corresponds to French size

$$g\left(11\tfrac{1}{2}\right) = \frac{4 \cdot 11\frac{1}{2} + 92}{3}, \quad \text{or } 46.$$

There is also a function f that gives a correspondence between shoe sizes in France and those in Japan. The function is given by

$$f(x) = \frac{15x - 100}{2},$$

where x is the French size and $f(x)$ is the corresponding Japanese size. Thus, French size 46 corresponds to Japanese size

$$f(46) = \frac{15 \cdot 46 - 100}{2}, \quad \text{or } 295.$$

It seems reasonable to conclude that U.S. shoe size $11\frac{1}{2}$ corresponds to Japanese size 295 and that some function h describes this correspondence. Can we find a formula for h?

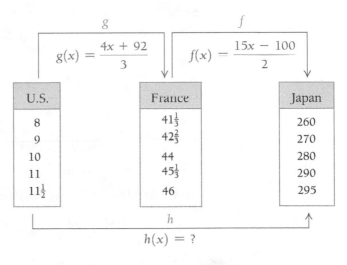

A U.S. size x corresponds to a French size $g(x) = (4x + 92)/3$. If we replace x in $f(x)$ with $(4x + 92)/3$, we can find the corresponding shoe size in Japan:

$$f(g(x)) = \frac{15[4x + 92]/3 - 100}{2}$$

$$= \frac{5(4x + 92) - 100}{2} = \frac{20x + 460 - 100}{2}$$

$$= \frac{20x + 360}{2} = 10x + 180.$$

This gives a formula for h: $h(x) = 10x + 180$. As a check, a U.S. size of $11\frac{1}{2}$ corresponds to a Japanese size $h(11\frac{1}{2}) = 10(11\frac{1}{2}) + 180 = 295$. The function h is the *composition* of f and g, symbolized by $f \circ g$ and read as "f composed with g."

> **DEFINITION**
>
> The **composed** function $f \circ g$, the **composition** of f and g, is defined as
>
> $$(f \circ g)(x) = f(g(x)).$$

We can visualize the composition of functions as shown below.

A composition machine for functions f and g

To find $(f \circ g)(x)$, we substitute $g(x)$ for x in $f(x)$. The function $g(x)$ is nested within $f(x)$.

EXAMPLE 3   For $f(x) = x^4$ and $g(x) = 2 + x^3$, find **(a)** $(f \circ g)(x)$ and **(b)** $(g \circ f)(x)$.

Solution   Consider each function separately:

$$f(x) = x^4 \qquad \text{This function raises each input to the 4th power.}$$

and

$$g(x) = 2 + x^3. \qquad \text{This function adds 2 to the cube of each input.}$$

a) We find $(f \circ g)(x) = f(g(x))$ by substituting $g(x)$ for x in $f(x)$:

$$(f \circ g)(x) = f(g(x)) = f(2 + x^3)$$
$$= (2 + x^3)^4 \qquad \text{Using } g(x) \text{ as an input}$$
$$= 16 + 32x^3 + 24x^6 + 8x^9 + x^{12}.$$

b) We find $(g \circ f)(x) = g(f(x))$ by substituting $f(x)$ for x in $g(x)$:

$$(g \circ f)(x) = g(f(x)) = g(x^4)$$
$$= 2 + (x^4)^3 = 2 + x^{12}. \qquad \text{Using } f(x) \text{ as an input}$$

Quick Check 3 ✓

Let $f(x) = x^2 + x$ and $g(x) = 3x + 2$.

Find:

a) $(f \circ g)(x)$;

b) $(g \circ f)(x)$.

EXAMPLE 4 For $f(x) = \sqrt{x}$ and $g(x) = x - 1$, find $(f \circ g)(x)$ and $(g \circ f)(x)$.

Solution

$$(f \circ g)(x) = f(g(x)) = f(x - 1) = \sqrt{x - 1}$$
$$(g \circ f)(x) = g(f(x)) = g(\sqrt{x}) = \sqrt{x} - 1$$

3 ✓

Examples 3 and 4 show that, in general, $(f \circ g)(x) \neq (g \circ f)(x)$.

How do we differentiate a composition of functions? The following theorem tells us.

THEOREM 8   The Chain Rule

The derivative of the composition $f \circ g$ is given by

$$\frac{d}{dx}[(f \circ g)(x)] = \frac{d}{dx}[f(g(x))] = f'(g(x)) \cdot g'(x).$$

As noted earlier, the Extended Power Rule is a special case of the Chain Rule. Consider $f(x) = x^k$. For any other function $g(x)$, we have $(f \circ g)(x) = [g(x)]^k$, and the derivative of the composition is

$$\frac{d}{dx}[g(x)]^k = k[g(x)]^{k-1} \cdot g'(x).$$

The Chain Rule can appear in another form. If $y = f(u)$ and $u = g(x)$, then

$$\frac{dy}{dx} = \frac{dy}{du} \cdot \frac{du}{dx}.$$

The proof of Theorem 8 is beyond the scope of this text, but is illustrated in the following example.

EXAMPLE 5 **Business: Rate of Profit.** GameBoss Video's profit, in dollars, is given by $y = f(u) = 0.1u^2 - 500$, where u is the number of units sold. Its sales are given by $u = g(x) = 125x + 40$, where x is the number of days. Find the rate at which profit is changing on the 5th day.

Solution We first find the rate of change in profit, y, on the xth day. That is, we want to find dy/dx. Thus, we form the composition of f and g, because $y = (f \circ g)(x)$ relates profit y to number of days x:

$$y = (f \circ g)(x) = f(g(x))$$
$$= 0.1(125x + 40)^2 - 500. \quad \text{Substituting}$$

Differentiating, we have

$$\frac{dy}{dx} = \frac{d}{dx}[(f \circ g)(x)] = \frac{d}{dx}[0.1(125x + 40)^2 - 500]$$

$$= 2 \cdot 0.1(125x + 40) \cdot 125 \qquad \text{Using the Extended Power Rule}$$

$$= 3125x + 1000. \qquad \text{Simplifying}$$

On the 5th day, the company's profit is changing by $3125(5) + 1000 = \$16,625$ per day.

Note that we can also find dy/dx, the rate of change in profit per day, by finding the product of dy/du, the rate of change in profit per unit, and du/dx, the rate of change in units sold per day.

We have

$$\frac{dy}{du} = \frac{d}{du}(0.1u^2 - 500) = 0.2u \frac{\text{dollars}}{\text{unit}}, \quad \text{and} \quad \frac{du}{dx} = \frac{d}{dx}(125x + 40) = 125 \frac{\text{units}}{\text{day}}.$$

Thus,

$$\frac{dy}{dx} = \frac{dy}{du} \cdot \frac{du}{dx}$$
$$= (0.2u)(125)$$
$$= 25u$$
$$= 25(125x + 40). \qquad \text{Substituting}$$

For $x = 5$, we have $dy/dx = 25(125(5) + 40) = \$16,625$ per day.

Comparing units, we have

$$\frac{dy}{dx} = \frac{dy}{du} \cdot \frac{du}{dx}$$

or

$$\frac{\text{dollars}}{\text{day}} = \frac{\text{dollars}}{\text{unit}} \cdot \frac{\text{units}}{\text{day}}.$$

In a manner of speaking, the units "simplify," leaving dollars/day.   4 ✓

Quick Check 4 ✓

If $y = u^2 + u$ and $u = x^2 + x$, find $\frac{dy}{dx}$.

EXAMPLE 6   **Business.**   A new smartwatch is placed on the market. Its quantity sold N is given as a function of time t, in weeks:

$$N(t) = \frac{250,000t^2}{(2t + 1)^2}, \qquad t > 0.$$

Find $N'(t)$. Then find $N'(52)$ and $N'(208)$, and interpret these results.

Solution   To find $N'(t)$, we use the Quotient Rule along with the Extended Power Rule:

$$N'(t) = \frac{d}{dt}\left[\frac{250,000t^2}{(2t + 1)^2}\right] = \frac{(2t + 1)^2 \cdot \frac{d}{dt}[250,000t^2] - 250,000t^2 \cdot \frac{d}{dt}[(2t + 1)^2]}{[(2t + 1)^2]^2}$$

$$= \frac{(2t + 1)^2 \cdot (500,000t) - 250,000t^2 \cdot 2(2t + 1)^1 \cdot 2}{(2t + 1)^4} \qquad \text{Using the Extended}$$

$$= \frac{(2t + 1)^2(500,000t) - 1,000,000t^2(2t + 1)}{(2t + 1)^4} \qquad \text{Power Rule}$$

$$= \frac{500,000t(2t + 1)[(2t + 1) - 2t]}{(2t + 1)^4}. \qquad \begin{array}{l}\text{Factoring} \\ 500,000t(2t + 1) \\ \text{in the numerator}\end{array}$$

Therefore,

$$N'(t) = \frac{500,000t}{(2t + 1)^3}. \qquad \text{Simplifying}$$

We evaluate $N'(t)$ at $t = 52$:

$$N'(52) = \frac{500,000(52)}{(2(52) + 1)^3} \approx 22.5.$$

Thus, after 52 weeks (1 yr), the number of smartwatches sold is increasing by about 22.5 per week.

For $t = 208$ weeks (4 yr), we get

$$N'(208) = \frac{500,000(208)}{(2(208) + 1)^3} \approx 1.4.$$

After 4 yr, the number of smartwatches sold is increasing by about 1.4 per week. What is happening here? Consider the graph of $N(t)$:

We see that the slopes of the tangent lines, representing the change in the number of smartwatches sold per week level off as t increases. Perhaps the market is becoming saturated with smartwatches; that is, although sales continue to grow, they do so at a slower and slower rate.

Section Summary

- The *Extended Power Rule* tells us that if $y = [f(x)]^k$, then

$$y' = \frac{d}{dx}[f(x)]^k = k[f(x)]^{k-1} \cdot f'(x).$$

- The *composition* of $f(x)$ with $g(x)$ is written $(f \circ g)(x)$ and is defined as $(f \circ g)(x) = f(g(x))$.
- In general, $(f \circ g)(x) \neq (g \circ f)(x)$.

- The *Chain Rule* is used to differentiate a composition of functions. If

$$F(x) = (f \circ g)(x) = f(g(x)),$$

then

$$F'(x) = \frac{d}{dx}[(f \circ g)(x)] = f'(g(x)) \cdot g'(x).$$

1.7 Exercise Set

Differentiate each function.

1. $y = (3 - 2x)^2$ ⎫
2. $y = (2x + 1)^2$ ⎬ Check by expanding and then differentiating.

3. $y = (7 - x)^{55}$ 4. $y = (8 - x)^{100}$

5. $y = \sqrt{1 - x}$ 6. $y = \sqrt{1 + 8x}$

7. $y = \sqrt{3x^2 - 4}$ 8. $y = \sqrt{4x^2 + 1}$

9. $y = (4x^2 + 1)^{-50}$ 10. $y = (8x^2 - 6)^{-40}$

11. $y = (x - 4)^8(2x + 3)^6$

12. $y = (x + 5)^7(4x - 1)^{10}$

13. $y = \dfrac{1}{(4x + 5)^2}$ 14. $y = \dfrac{1}{(3x + 8)^2}$

15. $y = \dfrac{4x^2}{(7 - 5x)^3}$ 16. $y = \dfrac{7x^3}{(4 - 9x)^5}$

17. $f(x) = (3 + x^3)^5 - (1 + x^7)^4$

18. $f(x) = (1 + x^3)^3 - (2 + x^8)^4$

19. $f(x) = x^2 + (200 - x)^2$

20. $f(x) = x^2 + (100 - x)^2$

21. $G(x) = \sqrt[3]{2x - 1} + (4 - x)^2$

22. $g(x) = \sqrt{x} + (x - 3)^3$

23. $f(x) = -5x(2x - 3)^4$

24. $f(x) = -3x(5x + 4)^6$

25. $F(x) = (5x + 2)^4(2x - 3)^8$

26. $g(x) = (3x - 1)^7(2x + 1)^5$

27. $f(x) = x^2\sqrt{4x - 1}$

28. $f(x) = x^3\sqrt{5x + 2}$

29. $F(x) = \sqrt[4]{x^2 - 5x + 2}$

30. $G(x) = \sqrt[3]{x^5 + 6x}$

31. $f(x) = \left(\dfrac{3x - 1}{5x + 2}\right)^4$ **32.** $f(x) = \left(\dfrac{2x}{x^2 + 1}\right)^3$

33. $g(x) = \sqrt{\dfrac{3 + 2x}{5 - x}}$ **34.** $g(x) = \sqrt{\dfrac{4 - x}{3 + x}}$

35. $f(x) = (2x^3 - 3x^2 + 4x + 1)^{100}$

36. $f(x) = (7x^4 + 6x^3 - x)^{204}$

37. $h(x) = \left(\dfrac{1 - 3x}{2 - 7x}\right)^{-5}$ **38.** $g(x) = \left(\dfrac{2x + 3}{5x - 1}\right)^{-4}$

39. $f(x) = \sqrt{\dfrac{x^2 + x}{x^2 - x}}$ **40.** $f(x) = \sqrt[3]{\dfrac{4 - x^3}{x - x^2}}$

41. $f(x) = \dfrac{(5x - 4)^7}{(6x + 1)^3}$ **42.** $f(x) = \dfrac{(2x + 3)^4}{(3x - 2)^5}$

43. $f(x) = 12(2x + 1)^{2/3}(3x - 4)^{5/4}$

44. $y = 6\sqrt[3]{x^2 + x}(x^4 - 6x)^3$

Find $\dfrac{dy}{du}, \dfrac{du}{dx}$, and $\dfrac{dy}{dx}$.

45. $y = \dfrac{15}{u^3}$ and $u = 2x + 1$

46. $y = \sqrt{u}$ and $u = x^2 - 1$

47. $y = u^{50}$ and $u = 4x^3 - 2x^2$

48. $y = \dfrac{u + 1}{u - 1}$ and $u = 1 + \sqrt{x}$

49. $y = (u + 1)(u - 1)$ and $u = x^3 + 1$

50. $y = u(u + 1)$ and $u = x^3 - 2x$

Find $\dfrac{dy}{dx}$ for each pair of functions.

51. $y = 5u^2 + 3u$, where $u = x^3 + 1$

52. $y = u^3 - 7u^2$, where $u = x^2 + 3$

53. $y = \sqrt{7 - 3u}$, where $u = x^2 - 9$

54. $y = \sqrt[3]{2u + 5}$, where $u = x^2 - x$

55. Find $\dfrac{dy}{dt}$ if $y = \dfrac{1}{u^2 + u}$ and $u = 5 + 3t$.

56. Find $\dfrac{dy}{dt}$ if $y = \dfrac{1}{3u^5 - 7}$ and $u = 7t^2 + 1$.

57. Find an equation for the tangent line to the graph of $y = (x^3 - 4x)^{10}$ at the point $(2, 0)$.

58. Find an equation for the tangent line to the graph of $y = \sqrt{x^2 + 3x}$ at the point $(1, 2)$.

59. Find an equation for the tangent line to the graph of $y = x\sqrt{2x + 3}$ at the point $(3, 9)$.

60. Find an equation for the tangent line to the graph of $y = \left(\dfrac{2x + 3}{x - 1}\right)^3$ at the point $(2, 343)$.

61. Consider
$$g(x) = \left(\frac{6x + 1}{2x - 5}\right)^2.$$

   a) Find $g'(x)$ using the Extended Power Rule.

   b) Note that $g(x) = \dfrac{36x^2 + 12x + 1}{4x^2 - 20x + 25}$.
   Find $g'(x)$ using the Quotient Rule.

   c) Compare your answers to parts (a) and (b). Which approach was easier, and why?

62. Consider
$$f(x) = \frac{x^2}{(1 + x)^5}.$$

   a) Find $f'(x)$ using the Quotient Rule and the Extended Power Rule.

   b) Note that $f(x) = x^2(1 + x)^{-5}$. Find $f'(x)$ using the Product Rule and the Extended Power Rule.

   c) Compare your answers to parts (a) and (b).

63. Let $f(u) = u^3$ and $g(x) = u = 2x^4 + 1$. Find $(f \circ g)'(-1)$.

64. Let $f(u) = \dfrac{u + 1}{u - 1}$ and $g(x) = u = \sqrt{x}$. Find $(f \circ g)'(4)$.

65. Let $f(u) = \sqrt[3]{u}$ and $g(x) = u = 1 + 3x^2$. Find $(f \circ g)'(2)$.

66. Let $f(u) = 2u^5$ and $g(x) = u = \dfrac{3 - x}{4 + x}$. Find $(f \circ g)'(-10)$.

For Exercises 67–70, use the Chain Rule to differentiate each function. You may need to apply the rule more than once.

67. $f(x) = (2x^3 + (4x - 5)^2)^6$

68. $f(x) = (-x^5 + 4x + \sqrt{2x + 1})^3$

69. $f(x) = \sqrt{x^2 + \sqrt{1 - 3x}}$

70. $f(x) = \sqrt[3]{2x + (x^2 + x)^4}$

APPLICATIONS

Business and Economics

71. Total revenue. A total-revenue function is given by
$$R(x) = 1000\sqrt{x^2 - 0.1x},$$
where $R(x)$ is the total revenue, in thousands of dollars, from the sale of x airplanes. Find the rate at which total revenue is changing when 20 airplanes have been sold.

72. Total cost. A total-cost function is given by

$$C(x) = 2000(x^2 + 2)^{1/3} + 700,$$

where $C(x)$ is the total cost, in thousands of dollars, of producing x airplanes. Find the rate at which total cost is changing when 20 airplanes have been produced.

73. Total profit. Use the total-cost and total-revenue functions in Exercises 71 and 72 to find the rate at which total profit is changing when x airplanes have been produced and sold.

74. Total cost. A company determines that its total cost, in thousands of dollars, for producing x chairs is

$$C(x) = \sqrt{5x^2 + 60},$$

and it plans to boost production t months from now according to the function

$$x(t) = 20t + 40.$$

How fast will costs be rising 4 months from now?

75. Consumer credit. The total outstanding consumer credit of the United States (in billions of dollars) can be modeled by the function

$$C(x) = 9.26x^4 - 85.27x^3 + 287.24x^2 - 309.12x + 2651.4,$$

where x is the number of years since 2008.

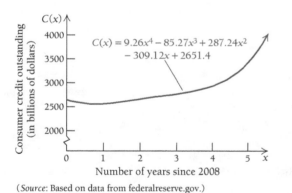

(*Source*: Based on data from federalreserve.gov.)

a) Find dC/dx.
b) Interpret the meaning of dC/dx.
c) Using this model, estimate how quickly outstanding consumer credit was rising in 2014.

76. Utility. Utility is a type of function that occurs in economics. When a consumer receives x units of a product, a certain amount of pleasure, or utility, U, is derived. Suppose the utility related to the number of tickets x sold for a ride at a county fair is

$$U(x) = 80\sqrt{\frac{2x + 1}{3x + 4}}.$$

Find the rate at which utility changes with respect to number of tickets bought.

77. Compound interest. If $1000 is invested at interest rate r, compounded quarterly, in 5 yr it will grow to an amount, A, given by (see Section R.1)

$$A = \$1000\left(1 + \frac{r}{4}\right)^{20}.$$

a) Find the rate of change, dA/dr.
b) Interpret the meaning of dA/dr.

78. Compound interest. If $1000 is invested at interest rate r, compounded annually, in 3 yr it will grow to an amount A given by (see Section R.1)

$$A = \$1000(1 + r)^3.$$

a) Find the rate of change, dA/dr.
b) Interpret the meaning of dA/dr.

79. Business profit. French's Electronics is selling laptop computers. It determines that its total profit, in dollars, is given by

$$P(x) = 0.08x^2 + 80x,$$

where x is the number of units produced and sold. Suppose that x is a function of time, in months, where $x = 5t + 1$.

a) Find the total profit as a function of time t.
b) Find the rate of change of total profit when $t = 48$ months.

80. Consumer demand. Suppose the demand function for a new autobiography is given by

$$D(p) = \frac{80,000}{p},$$

and that price p is a function of time, given by $p = 1.6t + 9$, where t is in days.

a) Find the demand as a function of time t.
b) Find the rate of change of the quantity demanded when $t = 100$ days.

Life and Physical Sciences

81. Chemotherapy. The dosage for Carboplatin chemotherapy drugs depends on several parameters for the particular drug as well as the age, weight, and sex of the patient. For female patients, the formulas giving the dosage for such drugs are

$$D = 0.85A(c + 25) \quad \text{and} \quad c = (140 - y)\frac{w}{72x},$$

where A and x depend on which drug is used, D is the dosage in milligrams (mg), c is called the creatine clearance, y is the patient's age in years, and w is the patient's weight in kilograms (kg). (*Source*: U.S. Oncology.)

a) Suppose a patient is a 45-year-old woman and the drug has parameters $A = 5$ and $x = 0.6$. Use this information to write formulas for D and c that give D as a function of c and c as a function of w.
b) Use your formulas from part (a) to compute dD/dc.
c) Use your formulas from part (a) to compute dc/dw.
d) Compute dD/dw.
e) Interpret the meaning of the derivative dD/dw.

SYNTHESIS

If $f(x)$ is a function, then $(f \circ f)(x) = f(f(x))$ is the composition of f with itself. This is called an iterated function, and the composition can be repeated many times. For example, $(f \circ f \circ f)(x) = f(f(f(x)))$. Iterated functions are very useful in many areas, including finance (compound interest is a simple case) and the sciences (in weather forecasting, for example). For each function, use the Chain Rule to find the derivative.

82. If $f(x) = x^2 + 1$, find $\dfrac{d}{dx}[(f \circ f)(x)]$.

83. If $f(x) = x + \sqrt{x}$, find $\dfrac{d}{dx}[(f \circ f)(x)]$.

84. If $f(x) = x^2 + 1$, find $\dfrac{d}{dx}[(f \circ f \circ f)(x)]$

85. If $f(x) = \sqrt{3x}$, find $\dfrac{d}{dx}[(f \circ f \circ f)(x)]$.

Do you see a shortcut?

Differentiate.

86. $y = \sqrt{(2x - 3)^2 + 1}$

87. $y = \sqrt[3]{x^3 + 6x + 1} \cdot x^5$

88. $y = \left(\dfrac{x}{\sqrt{x - 1}}\right)^3$

89. $y = (x\sqrt{1 + x^2})^3$

90. $y = \dfrac{\sqrt{1 - x^2}}{1 - x}$

91. $y = \left(\dfrac{x^2 - x - 1}{x^2 + 1}\right)^3$

92. $g(x) = \sqrt{\dfrac{x^2 - 4x}{2x + 1}}$

93. $f(t) = \sqrt{3t + \sqrt{t}}$

94. $F(x) = [6x(3 - x)^5 + 2]^4$

95. The Extended Power Rule (for positive integer powers) can be verified using the Product Rule. For example, if $y = [f(x)]^2$, then the Product Rule is applied by recognizing that $[f(x)]^2 = [f(x)] \cdot [f(x)]$. Therefore,

$$\frac{d}{dx}([f(x)] \cdot [f(x)]) = f(x) \cdot f'(x) + f'(x) \cdot f(x)$$

$$= 2f(x) \cdot f'(x).$$

a) Use the Product Rule to show that $\dfrac{d}{dx}[f(x)]^3 = 3[f(x)]^2 \cdot f'(x)$.

b) Use the Product Rule to show that $\dfrac{d}{dx}[f(x)]^4 = 4[f(x)]^3 \cdot f'(x)$.

96. The following is the beginning of an alternative proof of the Quotient Rule that uses the Product Rule and the Power Rule. Complete the proof, giving reasons for each step.

Proof: Let

$$Q(x) = \frac{N(x)}{D(x)}.$$

Then

$$Q(x) = N(x) \cdot [D(x)]^{-1}.$$

Therefore, ...

TECHNOLOGY CONNECTION

For the function in each of Exercises 97 and 98, graph f and f' over the given interval. Then estimate points at which the line tangent to f is horizontal.

97. $f(x) = 1.68x\sqrt{9.2 - x^2}$; $[-3, 3]$

98. $f(x) = \sqrt{6x^3 - 3x^2 - 48x + 45}$; $[-5, 5]$

Find the derivative of each of the following functions. Then use a calculator to check the results.

99. $f(x) = x\sqrt{4 - x^2}$

100. $f(x) = (\sqrt{2x - 1} + x^3)^5$

Answers to Quick Checks

1. **(a)** $y' = 3(x^4 + 2x^2 + 1)^2(4x^3 + 4x)$;
(b) The result lacks parentheses around $2x + 4$. It should be written: $4(x^2 + 4x + 1)^3(2x + 4)$.
2. $y' = \dfrac{-36x^5 + 24x^3 + 8x}{(3x^4 + 2)^3}$
3. **(a)** $f(g(x)) = 9x^2 + 15x + 6$;
(b) $g(f(x)) = 3x^2 + 3x + 2$
4. $\dfrac{dy}{dx} = \dfrac{dy}{du} \cdot \dfrac{du}{dx} = (2u + 1)(2x + 1) =$
$(2(x^2 + x) + 1)(2x + 1) = (2x^2 + 2x + 1)(2x + 1)$

1.8

- Find derivatives of higher order.
- Given a formula for distance, find velocity and acceleration.

Higher-Order Derivatives

Consider the function given by

$$y = f(x) = x^5 - 3x^4 + x.$$

Its derivative f' is given by

$$y' = f'(x) = 5x^4 - 12x^3 + 1.$$

The derivative, f', can also be differentiated. We can think of the derivative of f' as the rate of change of the slope of the tangent lines of f, or the rate at which $f'(x)$ is changing. We use the notation f'' to represent $(f')'$. That is,

$$f''(x) = \frac{d}{dx} f'(x).$$

We call f'' the *second derivative* of f. If $f'(x) = 5x^4 - 12x^3 + 1$, then

$$y'' = f''(x) = 20x^3 - 36x^2.$$

Continuing in this manner, we have

$$f'''(x) = 60x^2 - 72x, \qquad \text{The third derivative of } f$$
$$f''''(x) = 120x - 72, \qquad \text{The fourth derivative of } f$$
$$f'''''(x) = 120. \qquad \text{The fifth derivative of } f$$

When this type of derivative notation gets lengthy, we abbreviate it using a number in parentheses. Thus, $f^{(n)}(x)$ is the nth derivative of f. For the function above,

$$f^{(4)}(x) = 120x - 72,$$
$$f^{(5)}(x) = 120,$$
$$f^{(6)}(x) = 0, \quad \text{and}$$
$$f^{(n)}(x) = 0, \quad \text{for any integer } n \geq 6.$$

Leibniz notation for the second derivative of a function given by $y = f(x)$ is

$$\frac{d^2y}{dx^2}, \quad \text{or} \quad \frac{d}{dx}\left(\frac{dy}{dx}\right),$$

read "the second derivative of y with respect to x." The 2's in this notation are *not* exponents. If $y = x^5 - 3x^4 + x$, then

$$\frac{d^2y}{dx^2} = 20x^3 - 36x^2.$$

Leibniz notation for the third derivative is d^3y/dx^3; for the fourth derivative, d^4y/dx^4; and so on:

$$\frac{d^3y}{dx^3} = 60x^2 - 72x,$$
$$\frac{d^4y}{dx^4} = 120x - 72,$$
$$\frac{d^5y}{dx^5} = 120.$$

EXAMPLE 1 For $y = 1/x$, find d^2y/dx^2.

Solution We have $y = x^{-1}$, so

$$\frac{dy}{dx} = -1 \cdot x^{-1-1} = -x^{-2}, \quad \text{or} \quad -\frac{1}{x^2}.$$

Then

$$\frac{d^2y}{dx^2} = (-2)(-1)x^{-2-1} = 2x^{-3}, \quad \text{or} \quad \frac{2}{x^3}.$$

∎

EXAMPLE 2 For $y = (x^2 + 10x)^{20}$, find y' and y''.

Solution To find y', we use the Extended Power Rule:

$$\begin{aligned}
y' &= 20(x^2 + 10x)^{19}(2x + 10) \\
&= 20(x^2 + 10x)^{19} \cdot 2(x + 5) \quad \text{Factoring} \\
&= 40(x^2 + 10x)^{19}(x + 5).
\end{aligned}$$

To find y'', we use the Product Rule and the Extended Power Rule:

$$\begin{aligned}
y'' &= \frac{d}{dx}[40(x^2 + 10x)^{19} \cdot (x + 5)] \\
&= 40(x^2 + 10x)^{19} \cdot \frac{d}{dx}(x + 5) + (x + 5) \cdot \frac{d}{dx}[40(x^2 + 10x)^{19}] && \text{Using the Product Rule} \\
&= 40(x^2 + 10x)^{19} \cdot (1) + (x + 5) \cdot 19 \cdot 40(x^2 + 10x)^{18}(2x + 10) && \text{Using the Extended Power Rule} \\
&= 40(x^2 + 10x)^{19} + (40 \cdot 19 \cdot 2)(x + 5)^2(x^2 + 10x)^{18} \\
&= 40(x^2 + 10x)^{18}[(x^2 + 10x) + 38(x + 5)^2] && \text{Factoring} \\
&= 40(x^2 + 10x)^{18}[x^2 + 10x + 38(x^2 + 10x + 25)] \\
&= 40(x^2 + 10x)^{18}(39x^2 + 390x + 950).
\end{aligned}$$

1 ✔

Quick Check 1 ✔

a) Find y'':

(i) $y = -6x^4 + 3x^2$;

(ii) $y = \dfrac{2}{x^3}$;

(iii) $y = (3x^2 + 1)^2$.

b) Find $\dfrac{d^4}{dx^4}\left[\dfrac{1}{x}\right]$.

Velocity and Acceleration

We have already seen that a function's derivative represents its instantaneous rate of change. When the function relates distance traveled to time, the instantaneous rate of change is called *speed*, or *velocity*.* The letter v is generally used to stand for velocity.

DEFINITION

The **velocity** of an object that is $s(t)$ units from a starting point at time t is given by

$$\text{Velocity} = v(t) = s'(t) = \lim_{h \to 0} \frac{s(t + h) - s(t)}{h}.$$

Often velocity itself is a function of time. When a jet takes off or a vehicle comes to a sudden stop, the change in velocity is easily felt by passengers. The rate at which velocity changes is called *acceleration*. If Car A requires 8.4 sec to reach 65 mi/hr and Car B requires 8 sec; then B has *faster acceleration* than A. We generally use a to represent acceleration, which we regard as the rate at which velocity is changing.

---

*In this text, the words "speed" and "velocity" are used interchangeably. In physics and engineering, this is not done, since velocity requires direction and speed does not.

DEFINITION

Acceleration $= a(t) = v'(t) = s''(t)$.

EXAMPLE 3 **Free Fall.** When an object is dropped, the distance it falls in t seconds, assuming negligible air resistance, is given by

$$s(t) = 4.905t^2,$$

where $s(t)$ is in meters (m). If a stone is dropped from a cliff, find each of the following, assuming that air resistance is negligible: **(a)** how far the stone has traveled 5 sec after being dropped, **(b)** how fast it is traveling 5 sec after being dropped, and **(c)** its acceleration after it has been falling for 5 sec.

Solution

a) After 5 sec, the stone has traveled

$$s(5) = 4.905(5)^2 = 4.905(25) = 122.625 \text{ m}.$$

b) The speed at which the stone is traveling is given by

$$v(t) = s'(t) = 9.81t.$$

Thus,

$$v(5) = 9.81 \cdot 5 = 49.05 \text{ m/sec}.$$

c) The stone's acceleration after t sec is constant:

$$a(t) = v'(t) = s''(t) = 9.81 \text{ m/sec}^2.$$

Thus, $s''(5) = 9.81 \text{ m/sec}^2.$ **2** ✔

Quick Check 2 ✔

A pebble is dropped from a hot-air balloon. Find how far it has fallen, how fast it is falling, and its acceleration after 3.5 sec. Let $s(t) = 16t^2$, where t is in seconds and s is in feet.

If the graph of $y = s(t)$ represents an object's distance traveled, then the object's velocity at any time is the slope of the tangent line at that point. If the object "speeds up" (accelerates) or "slows down" (decelerates), these changes in velocity will appear as upward and downward bends, respectively, in the graph.

EXAMPLE 4 **Analyzing Velocity and Acceleration Graphically.** Kimberly leaves her home (distance $= 0$) for a 2-hr bicycle ride. The graph of her distance traveled with respect to time t is shown below.

Find the interval(s) in which Kimberly is:

a) traveling at constant velocity;

b) accelerating (speeding up);

c) decelerating (slowing down).

Solution

a) Kimberly is traveling at constant velocity when the slopes of the tangent lines do not change, that is, when the graph is linear. Thus, she is traveling at a constant velocity in the intervals $(0.2, 0.3)$, $(0.4, 0.6)$, $(0.8, 1.0)$, $(1.2, 1.5)$, and $(1.6, 1.8)$. Note that in the intervals $(0.4, 0.6)$ and $(1.2, 1.5)$, the slopes of the tangent lines are zero, indicating that she has stopped.

b) Kimberly is speeding up during the intervals $(0, 0.2)$, $(0.6, 0.8)$, and $(1.5, 1.6)$. This acceleration appears as an upward bend in the graph.

c) Kimberly is slowing down during the intervals $(0.3, 0.4)$, $(1.0, 1.2)$, and $(1.8, 2.0)$. This deceleration (or negative acceleration) appears as a downward bend in the graph. ∎

The upward and downward bends in the graph in Example 4 are examples of *concavities*, which are discussed in Chapter 2.

In Example 6 of Section 1.7, $N(t)$ represented the number of smartwatches sold after t weeks. Its first derivative was always positive (always increasing) indicating that sales were always increasing. But sales were leveling off. In the following example, we see how the second derivative can help us understand this observation.

EXAMPLE 5 **Business.** In Example 6 of Section 1.7, the function given by

$$N(t) = \frac{250{,}000t^2}{(2t + 1)^2}, t > 0,$$ represented the number of smartwatches sold after t weeks.

Its derivative is

$$N'(t) = \frac{500{,}000t}{(2t + 1)^3}.$$

Find $N''(t)$; then use it to calculate $N''(52)$ and $N''(208)$ and interpret these results.

Solution We use both the Quotient Rule and the Extended Power Rule:

$$\frac{d}{dt}[N'(t)] = \frac{(2t + 1)^3 \cdot \frac{d}{dt}[500{,}000t] - (500{,}000t) \cdot \frac{d}{dt}[(2t + 1)^3]}{[(2t + 1)^3]^2}$$

Using the Extended Power Rule

$$= \frac{(2t + 1)^3(500{,}000) - (500{,}000t)(3)(2t + 1)^2 \cdot 2}{[(2t + 1)^3]^2}$$

$$= \frac{(2t + 1)^2[(2t + 1)(500{,}000) - 6(500{,}000t)]}{(2t + 1)^6}.$$

Factoring out $(2t + 1)^2$

After simplification, we have

$$N''(t) = \frac{-2{,}000{,}000t + 500{,}000}{(2t + 1)^4}.$$

At $t = 52$, we have

$$N''(52) = \frac{-2{,}000{,}000(52) + 500{,}000}{[2(52) + 1]^4} \approx -0.851.$$

Thus, after 52 weeks (1 yr), the rate of the rate of sales is decreasing at -0.851 units per week per week. In other words, although sales are increasing during the 52nd week (remember, $N'(52) > 0$), the rate at which sales are increasing is decreasing. That is, sales are increasing but not as fast as before.

When $t = 208$,

$$N''(208) = \frac{-2{,}000{,}000(208) + 500{,}000}{[2(208) + 1]^4} \approx -0.014.$$

After 208 weeks (4 yr), sales have nearly leveled off. Remember, sales are increasing at the 208th week (recall that $N'(208) > 0$), but since the market is nearly saturated with this product, the rate at which sales are increasing has slowed to near 0.

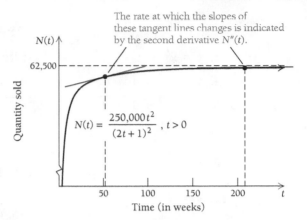

Many important real-world applications make use of the second derivative. In Chapter 2, we will examine applications in the fields of economics, health care, and the natural and physical sciences.

TECHNOLOGY CONNECTION

Exploratory

A calculator with a tangent-drawing feature can be used to explore the behavior of the second derivative. Graph $f(x) = x^2$ in the standard window, select DRAW, and then select Tangent. Choose an x-value by keying it in or using the arrow keys to trace along the graph. Press **ENTER**, and a tangent line will be drawn at the selected x-value. In the lower-left corner of the screen, the equation of the tangent line is given. The slope of the line is the coefficient of x. You can create a table of slope values at various x-values, and from this table, see how the second derivative describes the shape of a graph. (This activity can be easily adapted for Graphicus.)

EXERCISES

1. Let $f(x) = x^2$. Use the tangent-drawing feature to complete the following table:

x	−4	−2	0	2	4
Slope at x					

2. The x-values in the table are increasing. What is the corresponding behavior of the slopes (increasing or decreasing)?

3. Is the graph bending up or down? What conclusion can you make about the behavior of the slopes as x increases in value?

4. Make a table of slopes for $f(x) = -x^2$. Analyze their behavior relative to the shape of this function's graph.

5. What general conclusion can you make about the second derivative and the shape of a graph?

Section Summary

- The *second derivative* is the derivative of the first derivative of a function. In symbols, $f''(x) = [f'(x)]'$.
- The second derivative represents the rate of change of the rate of change. In other words, it represents the rate of change of the first derivative.
- A real-life example of a second derivative is *acceleration*. If $s(t)$ represents distance traveled as a function of

time for a moving object, then $v(t) = s'(t)$ represents speed (velocity). Any change in speed is the acceleration: $a(t) = v'(t) = s''(t)$.
- The common notation for the nth derivative of a function is $f^{(n)}(x)$, or $\dfrac{d^n}{dx^n} f(x)$.

1.8 | Exercise Set

Find d^2y/dx^2.

1. $y = x^4 - 7$ **2.** $y = x^5 + 9$

3. $y = 2x^4 - 5x$ **4.** $y = 5x^3 + 4x$

5. $y = 4x^2 - 5x + 7$ **6.** $y = 4x^2 + 3x - 1$

7. $y = 7x + 2$ **8.** $y = 6x - 3$

9. $y = \dfrac{1}{x^3}$ **10.** $y = \dfrac{1}{x^2}$

11. $y = \sqrt{x}$ **12.** $y = \sqrt[4]{x}$

Find $f''(x)$.

13. $f(x) = x^3 - \dfrac{5}{x}$ **14.** $f(x) = x^4 + \dfrac{3}{x}$

15. $f(x) = x^{1/5}$ **16.** $f(x) = x^{1/3}$

17. $f(x) = 2x^{-2}$ **18.** $f(x) = 4x^{-3}$

19. $f(x) = (x^2 + 3x)^7$ **20.** $f(x) = (x^3 + 2x)^6$

21. $f(x) = (3x^2 + 2x + 1)^5$

22. $f(x) = (2x^2 - 3x + 1)^{10}$

23. $f(x) = \sqrt[4]{(x^2 + 1)^3}$ **24.** $f(x) = \sqrt[3]{(x^2 - 1)^2}$

Find y''.

25. $y = x^{3/2} - 5x$ **26.** $y = x^{2/3} + 4x$

27. $y = (x^3 - x)^{3/4}$ **28.** $y = (x^4 + x)^{2/3}$

29. $y = 3x^{4/3} - x^{1/2}$ **30.** $y = 2x^{5/4} + x^{1/2}$

31. $y = \dfrac{2}{x^3} + \dfrac{1}{x^2}$ **32.** $y = \dfrac{3}{x^4} - \dfrac{1}{x}$

33. $y = (x^3 - 2)(5x + 1)$ **34.** $y = (x^2 + 3)(4x - 1)$

35. $y = \dfrac{3x + 1}{2x - 3}$ **36.** $y = \dfrac{2x + 3}{5x - 1}$

37. For $y = x^5$, find d^4y/dx^4.

38. For $y = x^4$, find d^4y/dx^4.

39. For $y = x^6 - x^3 + 2x$, find d^5y/dx^5.

40. For $y = x^7 - 8x^2 + 2$, find d^6y/dx^6.

41. For $f(x) = x^{-3} + 2x^{1/3}$, find $f^{(5)}(x)$.

42. For $f(x) = x^{-2} - x^{1/2}$, find $f^{(4)}(x)$.

43. For $g(x) = x^4 - 3x^3 - 7x^2 - 6x + 9$, find $g^{(6)}(x)$.

44. For $g(x) = 6x^5 + 2x^4 - 4x^3 + 7x^2 - 8x + 3$, find $g^{(7)}(x)$.

APPLICATIONS

Life and Physical Sciences

45. Given

$$s(t) = -10t^2 + 2t + 5,$$

where $s(t)$ is in meters and t is in seconds, find each of the following.

a) $v(t)$
b) $a(t)$
c) The velocity and acceleration when $t = 1$ sec

46. Given

$$s(t) = t^3 + t,$$

where $s(t)$ is in feet and t is in seconds, find each of the following.

a) $v(t)$
b) $a(t)$
c) The velocity and acceleration when $t = 4$ sec

47. Given

$$s(t) = 3t + 10,$$

where $s(t)$ is in miles and t is in hours, find each of the following.

a) $v(t)$
b) $a(t)$
c) The velocity and acceleration when $t = 2$ hr
d) When the distance function is given by a linear function, we have *uniform motion*. What does uniform motion mean in terms of velocity and acceleration?

48. Given

$$s(t) = t^2 - \frac{1}{2}t + 3,$$

where $s(t)$ is in meters and t is in seconds, find each of the following.

a) $v(t)$
b) $a(t)$
c) The velocity and acceleration when $t = 1$ sec

49. **Free fall.** When an object is dropped, the distance it falls in t seconds, assuming negligible air resistance, is given by

$$s(t) = 16t^2,$$

where $s(t)$ is in feet. Suppose a medic's reflex hammer falls from a hovering helicopter. Find **(a)** how far the hammer falls in 3 sec, **(b)** how fast the hammer is traveling 3 sec after being dropped, and **(c)** the hammer's acceleration after it has been falling for 3 sec.

50. Free fall. (See Exercise 49.) Suppose a worker drops a bolt from a scaffold high above a work site. Assuming negligible air resistance, find **(a)** how far the bolt falls in 2 sec, **(b)** how fast the bolt is traveling 2 sec after being dropped, and **(c)** the bolt's acceleration after it has been falling for 2 sec.

51. Free fall. Find the velocity and acceleration of the stone in Example 3 after it has been falling for 2 sec.

52. Free fall. Find the velocity and acceleration of the stone in Example 3 after it has been falling for 3 sec.

53. The following graph describes a bicycle racer's distance from a roadside television camera.

a) When is the bicyclist's velocity the greatest? How can you tell?

b) Is the bicyclist's acceleration positive or negative? How can you tell?

54. The following graph describes an airplane's distance from its last point of rest.

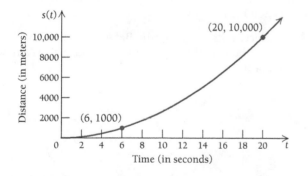

a) Is the plane's velocity greater at $t = 6$ sec or $t = 20$ sec? How can you tell?

b) Is the plane's acceleration positive or negative? How can you tell?

55. Sales. The following graph represents the sales, y, of a new video game after t weeks on the market.

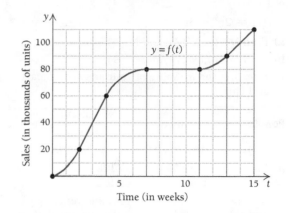

a) In what open interval(s) is $f'(t) = 0$?

b) In what open interval(s) is $f''(t) = 0$?

c) In what open interval(s) is $f''(t) > 0$?

d) In what open interval(s) is $f''(t) < 0$?

e) Describe in words and graphically the difference in meaning between "sales are increasing" and "the rate of sales is increasing."

56. Velocity and acceleration. The following graph describes the distance of Jesse's car from home as a function of time t.

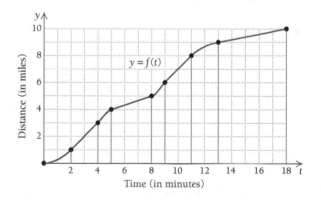

a) In what open interval(s) is Jesse's car accelerating?

b) In what open interval(s) is Jesse's car decelerating?

c) In what open interval(s) is Jesse's car maintaining a constant velocity?

57. Sales. A company determines that monthly sales $S(t)$, in thousands of dollars, after t months of marketing a product are given by

$$S(t) = 2t^3 - 40t^2 + 220t + 160.$$

a) Find $S'(1)$, $S'(2)$, and $S'(4)$.

b) Find $S''(1)$, $S''(2)$, and $S''(4)$.

c) Interpret the meaning of your answers to parts (a) and (b).

58. Sales. Nadia's fashions discovers that the number of items sold t days after launching a new sales promotion is given by

$$N(t) = 2t^3 - 3t^2 + 2t.$$

a) Find $N'(1)$, $N'(2)$, and $N'(4)$.

b) Find $N''(1)$, $N''(2)$, and $N''(4)$.

c) Interpret the meaning of your answers to parts (a) and (b).

59. Population. The function $p(t) = \dfrac{2000t}{4t + 75}$ gives the population of deer in an area after t months.

a) Find $p'(10)$, $p'(50)$, and $p'(100)$.

b) Find $p''(10)$, $p''(50)$, and $p''(100)$.

c) Interpret the meaning of your answers to parts (a) and (b). What is happening to this population of deer in the long term?

60. Medicine. A medication is injected into the bloodstream, where it is quickly metabolized. The percent concentration p of the medication after t minutes in the bloodstream is modeled by the function $p(t) = \dfrac{2.5t}{t^2 + 1}$.

a) Find $p'(0.5)$, $p'(1)$, $p'(5)$, and $p'(30)$.

b) Find $p''(0.5)$, $p''(1)$, $p''(5)$, and $p''(30)$.

c) Interpret the meaning of your answers to parts (a) and (b). What is happening to the concentration of medication in the bloodstream in the long term?

SYNTHESIS

Find y''' for each function.

61. $y = \dfrac{1}{1 - x}$

62. $y = \dfrac{1}{\sqrt{2x + 1}}$

Find y'' for each function.

63. $y = \dfrac{\sqrt{x} + 1}{\sqrt{x} - 1}$

64. $y = \dfrac{x}{\sqrt{x} - 1}$

65. For $y = x^k$, find d^5y/dx^5.

66. For $y = ax^3 + bx^2 + cx + d$, find d^3y/dx^3.

Find the first through the fourth derivatives. Be sure to simplify each derivative before continuing.

67. $f(x) = \dfrac{x - 1}{x + 2}$

68. $f(x) = \dfrac{x + 3}{x - 2}$

69. Free fall. On Earth, all free-fall distance functions are of the form $s(t) = 4.905t^2$, where t is in seconds and $s(t)$ is in meters. The second derivative always has the same value. What does that value represent?

70. Free fall. On the moon, all free-fall distance functions are of the form $s(t) = 0.81t^2$, where t is in seconds and $s(t)$ is in meters. An object is dropped from a height of 200 meters above the moon. After $t = 2$ sec,

a) How far has the object fallen?

b) How fast is it traveling?

c) What is its acceleration?

d) Explain the meaning of the second derivative of this free-fall function.

71. Hang time. On Earth, an object travels 4.905 m after 1 sec of free fall. Thus, by symmetry, an athlete would require 1 sec to jump 4.905 m high, and another second to come back down. Is it possible for a person to stay in the air for (have a "hang time" of) 2 sec? Can a person have a hang time of 1.5 sec? 1 sec? What do you think is the longest possible hang time achievable by humans jumping from level ground?

72. Free fall. Skateboarder Danny Way free-fell 28 ft from the Fender Stratocaster Guitar atop the Hard Rock Hotel & Casino in Las Vegas onto a ramp below. The distance $s(t)$, in feet, traveled by a body falling freely from rest in t seconds is approximated by $s(t) = 16t^2$. Estimate Way's velocity at the moment he touched down onto the ramp. (*Note*: Use the result from Exercise 26 in Section R.1.)

73. An object rolls 1 m in 1 min. Below are four possible graphs showing the object's distance traveled as a function of time.

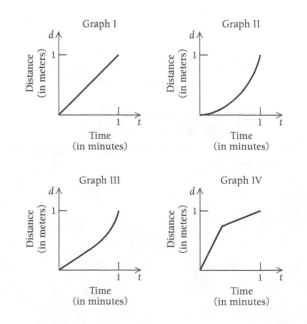

Match each graph with one of the following descriptions:

a) The object rolled unimpeded along a level table.

b) The object rolled along a level concrete walkway, then rolled along a level grassy lawn.

c) The object rolled down an incline.

d) The object rolled along a level table, then down an incline.

74. A bicyclist's distance from her starting point is given by $y = s(t)$. Suppose the graph of s has a corner. Give three situations in which a corner, rather than a smooth curve, can occur. What can you conclude about $s'(t)$ and $s''(t)$ at the corner of the graph of s?

Indeterminate forms and l'Hôpital's Rule. *Let f and g be differentiable over an open interval containing $x = a$. If*

$$\lim_{x \to a}\left(\frac{f(x)}{g(x)}\right) = \frac{0}{0} \quad or \quad \lim_{x \to a}\left(\frac{f(x)}{g(x)}\right) = \frac{\pm\infty}{\pm\infty}$$

and if $\lim_{x \to a}\left(\frac{f'(x)}{g'(x)}\right)$ exists, then

$$\lim_{x \to a}\left(\frac{f(x)}{g(x)}\right) = \lim_{x \to a}\left(\frac{f'(x)}{g'(x)}\right).$$

The forms 0/0 and $\pm\infty/\pm\infty$ are said to be indeterminate. In such cases, the limit may exist, and l'Hôpital's Rule offers a way to find the limit using differentiation. For example, in Example 1 of Section 1.1, we showed that

$$\lim_{x \to 1}\left(\frac{x^2 - 1}{x - 1}\right) = 2.$$

Since, for $x = 1$, we have $(x^2 - 1)(x - 1) = 0/0$, we differentiate the numerator and denominator separately, and reevaluate the limit:

$$\lim_{x \to 1}\left(\frac{x^2 - 1}{x - 1}\right) = \lim_{x \to 1}\left(\frac{2x}{1}\right) = 2.$$

Use this method to find the following limits. Be sure to check that the initial substitution results in an indeterminate form.

75. $\lim_{x \to 5}\left(\frac{x^2 - 25}{2x - 10}\right)$

76. $\lim_{x \to -2}\left(\frac{x^2 - 4}{x + 2}\right)$

77. $\lim_{x \to 1}\left(\frac{x^3 + 2x - 3}{x^2 - 1}\right)$

78. $\lim_{x \to 3}\left(\frac{x^3 - x - 24}{x^2 - 9}\right)$

79. $\lim_{x \to -3}\left(\frac{x^2 - 9}{x + 3}\right)$

80. $\lim_{x \to -4}\left(\frac{x^2 + x - 12}{x + 4}\right)$

81. $\lim_{x \to 2}\left(\frac{x^3 + 5x - 18}{2x^2 - 8}\right)$

82. $\lim_{x \to 10}\left(\frac{x^2 + x - 110}{x - 10}\right)$

83. $\lim_{x \to \infty}\left(\frac{4x^2 + x - 3}{2x^2 + 1}\right)$

84. $\lim_{x \to -\infty}\left(\frac{3x^3 + x + 11}{6x^3 + x + 2}\right)$

TECHNOLOGY CONNECTION

For the distance function in each of Exercises 85–88, graph s, v, and a over the given interval. Then use the graphs to determine the point(s) at which the velocity switches from increasing to decreasing or from decreasing to increasing.

85. $s(t) = 0.1t^4 - t^2 + 0.4; \quad [-5, 5]$

86. $s(t) = -t^3 + 3t; \quad [-3, 3]$

87. $s(t) = t^4 + t^3 - 4t^2 - 2t + 4; \quad [-3, 3]$

88. $s(t) = t^3 - 3t^2 + 2; [-2, 4]$

Answers to Quick Checks

1. (a) (i) $y'' = -72x^2 + 6$, (ii) $y'' = \dfrac{24}{x^5}$,

(iii) $y'' = 108x^2 + 12$; **(b)** $y^{(4)} = \dfrac{24}{x^5}$

2. Distance $= s(3.5) = 196$ ft; velocity $= s'(3.5) = 112$ ft/sec; acceleration $= s''(3.5) = 32$ ft/sec^2

CHAPTER 1 Summary

KEY TERMS AND CONCEPTS	EXAMPLES

SECTION 1.1

As x approaches (but is not equal to) a, the **limit** of $f(x)$, if it exists, is L, which is written as

$$\lim_{x \to a} f(x) = L.$$

$$\lim_{x \to 4} (2x + 3) = 11 \qquad \lim_{x \to 1} \frac{x^2 - 1}{x - 1} = 2$$

Limit Numerically   *Limit Graphically*

	x	$2x + 3$
$x < 4$	3.9	10.8
	3.99	10.98
	3.999	10.998
$x > 4$	4.1	11.2
	4.01	11.02
	4.001	11.002

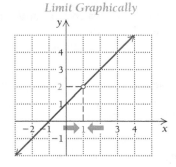

If x approaches a from the left $(x < a)$, and a **left-hand limit** exists, it is written as

$$\lim_{x \to a^-} f(x).$$

If x approaches a from the right $(x > a)$, and a **right-hand limit** exists, it is written as

$$\lim_{x \to a^+} f(x).$$

If the left-hand and right-hand limits are equal as x approaches a, then the limit as x approaches a exists.

If the left-hand and right-hand limits are *not* equal, then the limit as x approaches a does *not* exist.

Consider the function G given by

$$G(x) = \begin{cases} 4 - x, & \text{for } x < 3, \\ \sqrt{x - 2} + 1, & \text{for } x \geq 3. \end{cases}$$

Graph the function and find each limit, if it exists.

a) $\lim_{x \to 1} G(x)$ \qquad **b)** $\lim_{x \to 3} G(x)$

We check the limits from the left and from the right, both numerically and graphically.

a)   *Limit Numerically*   *Limit Graphically*

$x \to 1^-$ $(x < 1)$	$G(x)$
0.9	3.1
0.99	3.01
0.999	3.001

$x \to 1^+$ $(x > 1)$	$G(x)$
1.1	2.9
1.01	2.99
1.001	2.999

These choices
can vary.

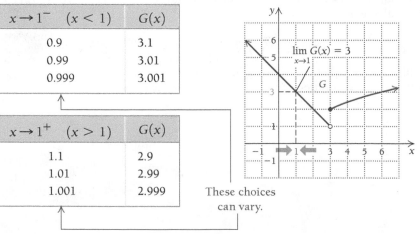

Both the tables and the graph show that as x gets closer to 1, the outputs $G(x)$ get closer to 3. Thus, $\lim_{x \to 1} G(x) = 3$.

KEY TERMS AND CONCEPTS	EXAMPLES

SECTION 1.1 (*continued*)

b)   *Limit Numerically*   *Limit Graphically*

$x \to 3^-$ $(x < 3)$	$G(x)$
2.9	1.1
2.99	1.01
2.999	1.001

$x \to 3^+$ $(x > 3)$	$G(x)$
3.1	2.0488
3.01	2.0050
3.001	2.0005

These are approaching different values, so $\lim\limits_{x\to 3} G(x)$ does not exist.

$\lim\limits_{x\to 3} G(x)$ does not exist.

Both the tables and the graph indicate that $\lim\limits_{x\to 3^-} G(x) \neq \lim\limits_{x\to 3^+} G(x)$. Since the left-hand and right-hand limits differ, $\lim\limits_{x\to 3} G(x)$ does not exist.

SECTION 1.2

For any rational function F (see Section R.5) with a in its domain, we have

$$\lim_{x\to a} F(x) = F(a).$$

For $f(x) = 2x^2 + 3x - 1$ and $a = 2$, we have

$$\lim_{x\to 2} f(x) = f(2) = 2(2)^2 + 3(2) - 1 = 13.$$

For $g(x) = \dfrac{x^2 - 16}{x + 4}$ and $a = 6$, we have

$$\lim_{x\to 6} g(x) = \frac{(6)^2 - 16}{(6) + 4} = \frac{20}{10} = 2.$$

A function f is **continuous** at $x = a$ if the following three conditions are met:

1. $f(a)$ exists. (The output at a exists.)
2. $\lim\limits_{x\to a} f(x)$ exists. (The limit as $x \to a$ exists.)
3. $\lim\limits_{x\to a} f(x) = f(a)$. (The limit is the same as the output.)

If any one of these conditions is not fulfilled, the function is **discontinuous** at $x = a$.

Is the function g given by $g(x) = \dfrac{x^2 - 3x - 4}{x + 1}$ continuous over $[-3, 3]$?

For g to be continuous over $[-3, 3]$, it must be continuous at each point in $[-3, 3]$. Note that

$$g(x) = \frac{x^2 - 3x - 4}{x + 1}$$
$$= \frac{(x + 1)(x - 4)}{x + 1}$$
$$= x - 4, \quad \text{provided } x \neq -1.$$

Since -1 is not in the domain of g, it follows that $g(-1)$ does not exist. Thus, g is not continuous over $[-3, 3]$.

$g(x) = \dfrac{x^2 - 3x - 4}{x + 1}$

SECTION 1.3

The **average rate of change** of y with respect to x between two points (x_1, y_1) and (x_2, y_2) is the slope of the line connecting the points:

$$\frac{y_2 - y_1}{x_2 - x_1}.$$

Business. At 1 P.M., a bookstore had revenue of $570 for the day, and at 4 P.M., it had revenue of $900 for the day. Therefore, the average rate of change of revenue with respect to time is

$$\frac{900 - 570}{4 - 1} = \frac{330}{3} = 110,$$

or $110 dollars per hour for the period of time between 1 P.M. and 4 P.M.

(continued)

KEY TERMS AND CONCEPTS	EXAMPLES

SECTION 1.3 (*continued*)

Let f be a function. Any line connecting two points on the graph of f is called a **secant line**. Its slope is the average rate of change of f, which is given by the **difference quotient**:

$$\frac{f(x+h) - f(x)}{h},$$

where h is the difference between the two input x-values.

Let $f(x) = 3x^2$. Then

$$f(x+h) = 3(x+h)^2 = 3x^2 + 6xh + 3h^2.$$

The difference quotient for this function simplifies to

$$\frac{f(x+h) - f(x)}{h} = \frac{3x^2 + 6xh + 3h^2 - 3x^2}{h} = 6x + 3h, \quad h \neq 0.$$

Therefore, if $x = 2$ and $h = 0.05$, the slope of the secant line is $6(2) + 3(0.05) = 12.15$.

SECTION 1.4

The **derivative** of a function f is

$$f'(x) = \lim_{h \to 0} \frac{f(x+h) - f(x)}{h}.$$

The derivative, if it exists, gives the slope of the tangent line to f at $x = a$, and that slope is the **instantaneous rate of change** at x. The process of finding a derivative is called **differentiation**.

If $f'(a)$ exists, then f is **differentiable** at $x = a$.

Let $f(x) = 3x^2$. Its simplified difference quotient is $6x + 3h$, $h \neq 0$ (see above). Therefore, the derivative is

$$f'(x) = \lim_{h \to 0} (6x + 3h) = 6x.$$

The slope of the line tangent to f at $x = 2$ is

$$f'(2) = 6(2) = 12.$$

For $f(x) = -x^2 + 5$, find $f'(x)$ and $f'(2)$.
We have

$$\frac{f(x+h) - f(x)}{h} = \frac{-(x+h)^2 + 5 - (-x^2 + 5)}{h}$$

$$= \frac{-(x^2 + 2xh + h^2) + 5 + x^2 - 5}{h}$$

$$= \frac{-2xh - h^2}{h}$$

$$= -2x - h, \quad h \neq 0.$$

Since

$$f'(x) = \lim_{h \to 0} \frac{f(x+h) - f(x)}{h} = \lim_{h \to 0} (-2x - h),$$

we have

$$f'(x) = -2x.$$

It follows that $f'(2) = -2 \cdot 2 = -4$ and f is differentiable at $x = 2$. In fact, f is differentiable for all real numbers x.

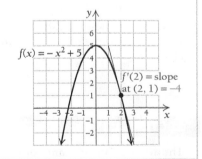

KEY TERMS AND CONCEPTS	EXAMPLES

SECTION 1.4 (continued)

Continuity (see Section 1.2):

1. If a function f is differentiable at $x = a$, then it is continuous at $x = a$. (Differentiability implies continuity.)

2. Continuity of a function f at $x = a$ does *not* necessarily mean that f is differentiable at $x = a$. Any function whose graph has a corner is continuous but not differentiable at the corner.

3. If a function f is discontinuous at $x = a$, then it is not differentiable at $x = a$.

1. Let $f(x) = 3x^2$. Since we know the derivative is $f'(x) = 6x$ and the derivative at $x = 2$ exists, we can conclude that $f(x)$ is continuous at $x = 2$.

2. The absolute-value function is continuous at $x = 0$ but not differentiable at $x = 0$, since there is a corner at $x = 0$.

3. The function $g(x) = \dfrac{x^2 - 16}{x + 4}$ is discontinuous at $x = -4$; therefore, g is not differentiable at $x = -4$. (Note that the derivative is defined at other values of x.)

SECTION 1.5

If $y = f(x)$, the derivative in Leibniz notation is written $\dfrac{dy}{dx}$ or $\dfrac{d}{dx} f(x)$. Each has the same meaning as $f'(x)$.

Let $y = x^3$. Then, in Leibniz notation, $\dfrac{dy}{dx} = 3x^2$.

The **Power Rule**:

For any real number k,

$$\frac{d}{dx} x^k = k \cdot x^{k-1}.$$

- $\dfrac{d}{dx} x^7 = 7x^6$

- $\dfrac{d}{dx} \sqrt{x} = \dfrac{d}{dx} x^{1/2} = \dfrac{1}{2} x^{-1/2} = \dfrac{1}{2\sqrt{x}}$

- $\dfrac{d}{dx} \left(\dfrac{1}{x} \right) = \dfrac{d}{dx} x^{-1} = -1 \cdot x^{-2} = -\dfrac{1}{x^2}$

The derivative of a constant is

$$\frac{d}{dx} c = 0.$$

- $\dfrac{d}{dx} 34 = 0$

- $\dfrac{d}{dx} \sqrt{2} = 0$

(continued)

KEY TERMS AND CONCEPTS	EXAMPLES

SECTION 1.5 (continued)

The derivative of a constant times a function is

$$\frac{d}{dx}[c \cdot f(x)] = c \cdot \frac{d}{dx}f(x).$$

- $\dfrac{d}{dx}3x^8 = 3 \cdot \dfrac{d}{dx}x^8 = 3 \cdot 8x^7 = 24x^7$

- $\dfrac{d}{dx}\left(\dfrac{2}{3x^2}\right) = \dfrac{2}{3} \cdot \dfrac{d}{dx}\left(\dfrac{1}{x^2}\right) = \dfrac{2}{3} \cdot (-2x^{-3}) = -\dfrac{4}{3x^3}$

The **Sum–Difference Rule:**

$$\frac{d}{dx}[f(x) \pm g(x)] = \frac{d}{dx}f(x) \pm \frac{d}{dx}g(x).$$

- $\dfrac{d}{dx}(x^7 + 3x) = 7x^6 + 3$

- $\dfrac{d}{dx}(5x - x^4) = 5 - 4x^3$

SECTION 1.6

The **Product Rule:**

$$\frac{d}{dx}[f(x) \cdot g(x)]$$
$$= f(x) \cdot g'(x) + g(x) \cdot f'(x).$$

$$\frac{d}{dx}\left[(2x + 3)\sqrt{x}\right] = (2x + 3)\frac{1}{2}x^{-1/2} + \sqrt{x} \cdot 2$$
$$= \frac{2x + 3}{2\sqrt{x}} + 2\sqrt{x}$$

The **Quotient Rule:**

$$\frac{d}{dx}\left[\frac{f(x)}{g(x)}\right] = \frac{g(x) \cdot f'(x) - f(x) \cdot g'(x)}{[g(x)]^2}.$$

$$\frac{d}{dx}\left(\frac{3x - 1}{2x + 5}\right) = \frac{(2x + 5)3 - (3x - 1)2}{(2x + 5)^2} = \frac{17}{(2x + 5)^2}$$

SECTION 1.7

The **Extended Power Rule:**

$$\frac{d}{dx}[g(x)]^k = k[g(x)]^{k-1} \cdot \frac{d}{dx}g(x).$$

$$\frac{d}{dx}(2x^5 + 4x)^7 = 7(2x^5 + 4x)^6(10x^4 + 4)$$
$$= 14(2x^5 + 4x)^6(5x^4 + 2)$$

The **Chain Rule:**

$$\frac{d}{dx}[(f \circ g)(x)] = \frac{d}{dx}[f(g(x))]$$
$$= f'(g(x)) \cdot g'(x).$$

- $\dfrac{d}{dx}\sqrt{3x^2 + 4} = \dfrac{d}{dx}(3x^2 + 4)^{1/2} = \dfrac{1}{2}(3x^2 + 4)^{-1/2}(6x) = \dfrac{3x}{\sqrt{3x^2 + 4}}$

- $\dfrac{d}{dx}\left(\dfrac{1}{8x + 1}\right) = \dfrac{d}{dx}(8x + 1)^{-1} = -1(8x + 1)^{-2}(8) = -\dfrac{8}{(8x + 1)^2}$

SECTION 1.8

The **second derivative** is the derivative of the first derivative:

$$\frac{d}{dx}[f'(x)] = [f'(x)]' = f''(x).$$

The second derivative indicates the rate of change of the derivative.

Let $f(x) = 2x^5 + 20$. Then

$$\frac{d}{dx}f(x) = f'(x) = 10x^4 + 20,$$

and therefore,

$$\frac{d^2}{dx^2}f(x) = f''(x) = 40x^3.$$

KEY TERMS AND CONCEPTS	EXAMPLES

SECTION 1.8 (*continued*)

Higher-order derivatives include second, third, fourth, and so on, derivatives of a function. The ***n*th derivative** of a function is written as $$\frac{d^n y}{dx^n} = f^{(n)}(x).$$	For $y = 5x^7 + 20x$, we have the following: $$\frac{d^3 y}{dx^3} = f^{(3)}(x) = 1050x^4,$$ $$\frac{d^4 y}{dx^4} = f^{(4)}(x) = 4200x^3,$$ $$\frac{d^5 y}{dx^5} = f^{(5)}(x) = 12{,}600x^2, \text{ and so on.}$$
A real-life application of the second derivative is **acceleration**. If $s(t)$ represents distance as a function of time, then velocity is $v(t) = s'(t)$ and acceleration is the change in velocity: $a(t) = v'(t) = s''(t)$.	**Physical Sciences.** A particle moves according to the distance function $s(t) = 5t^3$, where t is in seconds and $s(t)$ in feet. Therefore, the particle's velocity is given by $v(t) = s'(t) = 15t^2$ and its acceleration by $a(t) = v'(t) = s''(t) = 30t$. At $t = 2$ sec, the particle is $s(2) = 40$ ft from the starting point, traveling at $v(2) = 60$ ft/sec and accelerating at $a(2) = 60$ ft/sec² (it's speeding up).

CHAPTER 1
Review Exercises

These review exercises are for test preparation. They can also be used as a practice test. Answers are at the back of the book. The red bracketed section references indicate the section(s) to restudy if your answer is incorrect.

CONCEPT REINFORCEMENT

Classify each statement as either true or false.

1. If $\lim_{x \to 5} f(x)$ exists, then $f(5)$ must exist. [1.1]

2. If $\lim_{x \to 2} f(x) = L$, then $L = f(2)$. [1.1]

3. If f is continuous at $x = 3$, then $\lim_{x \to 3} f(x) = f(3)$. [1.2]

4. A function's average rate of change over the interval $[2, 8]$ is the same as its instantaneous rate of change at $x = 5$. [1.3, 1.4]

5. A function's derivative at a point, if it exists, can be found as the limit of a difference quotient. [1.4]

6. For $f'(5)$ to exist, f must be continuous at 5. [1.4]

7. If f is continuous at 5, then $f'(5)$ must exist. [1.4]

8. The acceleration function is the derivative of the velocity function. [1.8]

Match each function in column A with the most appropriate rule to use for differentiating the function. [1.5, 1.6]

Column A

9. $f(x) = x^7$

10. $g(x) = x + 9$

11. $F(x) = (5x - 3)^4$

12. $G(x) = \dfrac{2x + 1}{3x - 4}$

13. $H(x) = f(x) \cdot g(x)$

14. $f(x) = 2x - 7$

Column B

a) Extended Power Rule

b) Product Rule

c) Sum Rule

d) Difference Rule

e) Power Rule

f) Quotient Rule

For Exercises 15–17, consider

$$\lim_{x \to -7} f(x), \text{ where } f(x) = \frac{x^2 + 4x - 21}{x + 7}.$$

15. Limit numerically. [1.1]

a) Find the limit by completing the following input–output tables.

$x \to -7^-$	$f(x)$		$x \to -7^+$	$f(x)$
-7.1			-6.9	
-7.01			-6.99	
-7.001			-6.999	

b) Find $\lim_{x \to -7^-} f(x)$, $\lim_{x \to -7^+} f(x)$, and $\lim_{x \to -7} f(x)$, if each exists.

16. Limit graphically. Find the limit by graphing the function. [1.1]

17. Limit algebraically. Find the limit algebraically. Show your work. [1.2]

Find each limit, if it exists. If a limit does not exist, state that fact. [1.1, 1.2]

18. $\lim_{x \to -2} \dfrac{8}{x}$

19. $\lim_{x \to 1} (4x^3 - x^2 + 7x)$

20. $\lim_{x \to -7} \dfrac{x^2 + 2x - 35}{x + 7}$

21. $\lim_{x \to \infty} \dfrac{1}{x} + 3$

For Exercises 22–30, consider the function g graphed below.

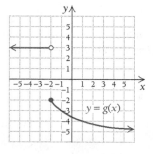

22. Find $\lim_{x \to 1} g(x)$. [1.1]

23. Find $g(1)$. [1.1]

24. Is g continuous at 1? Why or why not? [1.2]

25. Find $\lim_{x \to -2} g(x)$. [1.1]

26. Find $g(-2)$. [1.1]

27. Is g continuous at -2? Why or why not? [1.2]

28. Find the average rate of change between $x = -2$ and $x = 1$. [1.3]

29. Find $g'(-4)$. [1.4]

30. For which value(s) is $g'(x)$ not defined? Why? [1.4]

For Exercises 31–34, consider the function f graphed below.

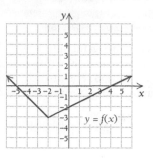

31. For which value(s) is $f'(x)$ not defined? Why? [1.4]

32. Find $\lim_{x \to 0} f(x)$. [1.1]

33. Find $\lim_{x \to -2} f(x)$. [1.1]

34. Is f continuous at $x = -2$? [1.4]

35. For $f(x) = x^3 + x^2 - 2x$, find the average rate of change as x changes from -1 to 2. [1.3]

36. Find a simplified difference quotient for $g(x) = -3x^2 + 2$. [1.3]

37. Find a simplified difference quotient for $f(x) = 2x^5 - 3$. [1.3]

38. Find an equation of the tangent line to the graph of $y = x^2 + 3x$ at the point $(-1, -2)$. [1.4]

39. Find the point(s) on the graph of $y = -x^2 + 8x - 11$ at which the tangent line is horizontal. [1.5]

40. Find the point(s) on the graph of $y = 5x^2 - 49x + 12$ at which the tangent line has slope 1. [1.5]

Find dy/dx.

41. $y = 9x^5$ [1.5]

42. $y = 8\sqrt[3]{x}$ [1.5]

43. $y = \dfrac{-3}{x^8}$ [1.5]

44. $y = 15x^{2/5}$ [1.5]

45. $y = 0.1x^7 - 3x^4 - x^3 + 6$ [1.5]

Differentiate.

46. $f(x) = \dfrac{5}{12}x^6 + 8x^4 - 2x$ [1.5]

47. $y = (x^3 - 5)(\sqrt{x} + 4x)$ [1.5, 1.6]

48. $y = \dfrac{x^2 + 8}{8 - x}$ [1.6]

49. $g(x) = (5 - x)^2(2x - 1)^5$ [1.6]

50. $f(x) = (x^5 - 3)^7$ [1.7]

51. $f(x) = x^2(4x + 2)^{3/4}$ [1.7]

52. For $y = x^3 - \dfrac{2}{x}$, find $\dfrac{d^4y}{dx^4}$. [1.8]

53. For $y = \dfrac{3}{42}x^7 - 10x^3 + 13x^2 + 28x - 2$, find y''. [1.8]

54. Social science: growth rate. The population of Lawton grows from an initial size of 10,000 to a size P, given by $P = 10,000 + 50t^2$, where t is in years. [1.5]

  a) Find the growth rate.

  b) Find the number of people in Lawton after 20 yr (at $t = 20$).

  c) Find the growth rate at $t = 20$.

For Exercises 55–58, consider the graph of $y = s(t)$, the distance a jogger has run after t minutes. [1.8]

Time (in minutes)

55. In what open interval(s) is the jogger running at a constant speed?

56. In what open interval(s) is she stopped?

57. In what open interval(s) is she accelerating?

58. In what open interval(s) is she decelerating?

59. For $s(t) = t + t^4$, with t in seconds and $s(t)$ in feet, find each of the following. [1.8]

  a) $v(t)$

  b) $a(t)$

  c) The velocity and the acceleration when $t = 2$ sec

60. Business: average revenue, cost, and profit. Given revenue and cost functions $R(x) = 40x$ and $C(x) = 5\sqrt{x} + 100$, find each of the following. Assume $R(x)$ and $C(x)$ are in dollars and x is the number of lamps produced. [1.6]

  a) The average cost, the average revenue, and the average profit when x lamps are produced and sold

  b) The rate at which average cost is changing when 9 lamps are produced

61. Find $\dfrac{d}{dx}(f \circ g)(x)$ and $\dfrac{d}{dx}(g \circ f)(x)$, given $f(x) = x^2 + 5$ and $g(x) = 1 - 2x$. [1.7]

SYNTHESIS

62. Differentiate $y = \dfrac{x\sqrt{1 + 3x}}{1 + x^3}$. [1.7]

63. Find $\dfrac{d}{dx}(f \circ f \circ f \circ f \circ f)(x)$, where $f(x) = \sqrt[3]{x}$. [1.7]

TECHNOLOGY CONNECTION

Create an input–output table to determine each of the following limits. Start with ΔTbl $= 0.1$ and then go to 0.01, 0.001, and 0.0001. When you think you know the limit, graph the functions, and use TRACE *to verify your assertion.*

64. $\displaystyle\lim_{x \to 1} \dfrac{2 - \sqrt{x + 3}}{x - 1}$ [1.1, 1.5]

65. $\displaystyle\lim_{x \to 11} \dfrac{\sqrt{x - 2} - 3}{x - 11}$ [1.1, 1.5]

66. Graph f and f' over the given interval. Then estimate points at which the tangent line to f is horizontal. [1.5]

$$f(x) = 3.8x^5 - 18.6x^3; \quad [-3, 3]$$

CHAPTER 1
Test

For Exercises 1–3, consider

$$\lim_{x \to 6} f(x), \text{ where } f(x) = \dfrac{x^2 - 36}{x - 6}.$$

1. Numerical limits.

  a) Find the limit by completing the following input–output tables.

$x \to 6^-$	$f(x)$
5.9	
5.99	
5.999	

$x \to 6^+$	$f(x)$
6.1	
6.01	
6.001	

  b) Find $\displaystyle\lim_{x \to 6^-} f(x)$, $\displaystyle\lim_{x \to 6^+} f(x)$, and $\displaystyle\lim_{x \to 6} f(x)$, if each exists.

2. Graphical limits. Find the limit by graphing the function.

3. Algebraic limits. Find the limit algebraically. Show your work.

Graphical limits. *For Exercises 4–15, consider the function f graphed below.*

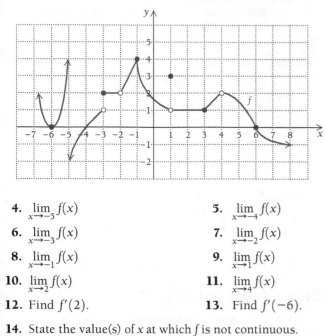

4. $\lim\limits_{x \to -5} f(x)$

5. $\lim\limits_{x \to -4} f(x)$

6. $\lim\limits_{x \to -3} f(x)$

7. $\lim\limits_{x \to -2} f(x)$

8. $\lim\limits_{x \to -1} f(x)$

9. $\lim\limits_{x \to 1} f(x)$

10. $\lim\limits_{x \to 2} f(x)$

11. $\lim\limits_{x \to 4} f(x)$

12. Find $f'(2)$.

13. Find $f'(-6)$.

14. State the value(s) of x at which f is not continuous.

15. State the value(s) of x for which $f'(x)$ is not defined.

Determine whether each function is continuous. If a function is not continuous, state why.

16.   **17.**

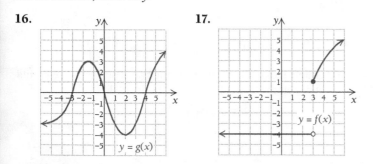

For Exercises 18 and 19, consider the function shown in Exercise 17.

18. a) Find $\lim\limits_{x \to 3} f(x)$.

b) Find $f(3)$.

c) Is f continuous at 3?

19. Find $\lim\limits_{x \to 4} f(x)$.

Find each limit, if it exists. If a limit does not exist, state why.

20. $\lim\limits_{x \to 1} (3x^4 - 2x^2 + 5)$

21. $\lim\limits_{x \to 2^+} \dfrac{x - 2}{x(x^2 - 4)}$

22. $\lim\limits_{x \to 0} \dfrac{7}{x}$

23. Find the simplified difference quotient for $f(x) = 2x^2 + 3x - 9$.

24. Find an equation of the line tangent to $y = x + (4/x)$ at the point $(4, 5)$.

25. Find the point(s) on the graph of $y = x^3 - 3x^2$ at which the tangent line is horizontal.

Find dy/dx.

26. $y = x^{23}$

27. $y = 4\sqrt[3]{x} + 5\sqrt{x}$

28. $y = \dfrac{-10}{x}$

29. $y = x^{5/4}$

30. $y = -0.5x^2 + 0.61x + 90$

Differentiate.

31. $y = \dfrac{1}{3}x^3 - x^2 + 2x + 4$

32. $y = (3\sqrt{x} + 1)(x^2 - x)$

33. $f(x) = \dfrac{x}{5 - x}$

34. $f(x) = (x + 3)^4(7 - x)^5$

35. $y = (x^5 - 4x^3 + x)^{-5}$

36. $f(x) = x\sqrt{x^2 + 5}$

37. For $y = x^4 - 3x^2$, find $\dfrac{d^3y}{dx^3}$.

38. Social sciences: memory. In a certain memory experiment, a person is able to memorize M words after t minutes, where $M = -0.001t^3 + 0.1t^2$.

a) Find the rate of change of the number of words memorized with respect to time.

b) How many words are memorized during the first 10 min (at $t = 10$)?

c) At what rate are words being memorized after 10 min (at $t = 10$)?

39. Business: average revenue, cost, and profit. Given revenue and cost functions

$$R(x) = 50x \quad \text{and} \quad C(x) = x^{2/3} + 750,$$

where x is the number of Bluetooth speakers produced and $R(x)$ and $C(x)$ are in dollars, find the following:

a) the average revenue, the average cost, and the average profit when x speakers are produced;

b) the rate at which average cost is changing when 8 speakers are produced.

For Exercises 40 and 41, let $f(x) = x^2 - x$ and $g(x) = 2x^3$.

40. Find $\dfrac{d}{dx}(f \circ g)(x)$.

41. Find $\dfrac{d}{dx}(g \circ f)(x)$.

42. A ball is placed on an inclined plane and, due to gravity alone, accelerates down the plane. Let $y = s(t)$ represent the ball's distance t seconds after starting to roll. Which graph below best represents s?

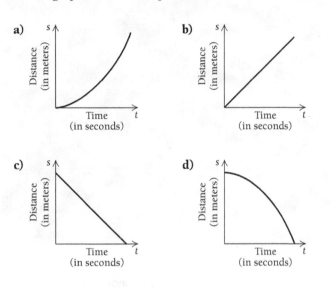

a)

b)

c)

d)

SYNTHESIS

43. Differentiate $y = \sqrt{(1 - 3x)^{2/3}(1 + 3x)^{1/3}}$.

44. Find $\lim\limits_{x \to 3} \dfrac{x^3 - 27}{x - 3}$.

TECHNOLOGY CONNECTION

45. Graph f and f' over the interval $[0, 5]$. Then estimate points at which the line tangent to f is horizontal.
$$f(x) = 5x^3 - 30x^2 + 45x + 5\sqrt{x}; \quad [0, 5]$$

46. Find the following limit by creating a table of values:
$$\lim_{x \to 0} \frac{\sqrt{5x + 25} - 5}{x}.$$

Start with ΔTbl $= 0.1$ and then go to 0.01 and 0.001. When you think you know the limit, graph
$$y = \frac{\sqrt{5x + 25} - 5}{x},$$

and use TRACE to verify your assertion.

EXTENDED TECHNOLOGY APPLICATION

Path of a Baseball: The Tale of the Tape

Have you ever watched a baseball game and seen a home run ball hit an obstruction after it has cleared the fence? Suppose a ball hits a scoreboard 60 ft above the ground and 400 ft from home plate. An announcer or a message on the scoreboard might proclaim, "According to the tale of the tape, the ball would have traveled 442 ft." How is such a calculation made? The answer is related to the curve formed by the path of a baseball.

The path of a well-hit baseball is *not* the graph of a parabola,
$$f(x) = ax^2 + bx + c.$$

A well-hit baseball follows the path of a "skewed" parabola, as shown at the lower right. One reason that the ball's flight is not parabolic is that it has backspin. This fact, combined with the frictional effect of the ball's stitches with the air, skews the path of the ball in the direction of its landing.

Let's see if we can model the path of a baseball. Consider the following data.

HORIZONTAL DISTANCE, x (In feet)	VERTICAL DISTANCE, y (In feet)
0	4.5
50	43
100	82
200	130
285	142
300	134
360	100
400	60

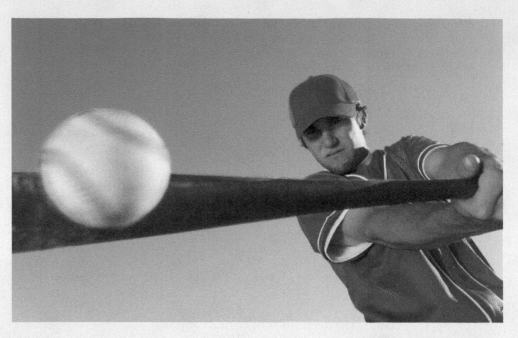

Assume for the given data that $(0, 4.5)$ is the point at home plate at which the ball is hit, roughly 4.5 ft above the ground. Also, assume the ball hits a billboard 60 ft above the ground and 400 ft from home plate.

Exercises

1. Plot the points and connect them with line segments. This can be done on many calculators by pressing STAT PLOT, turning on PLOT, and selecting the appropriate TYPE.

2. **a)** Use REGRESSION to find a cubic function

   $$y = ax^3 + bx^2 + cx + d$$

   that fits the data.
   b) Graph the function over the interval $[0, 500]$.
   c) Does the function closely model the given data?
   d) Predict the horizontal distance from home plate at which the ball would have hit the ground had it not hit the billboard.
   e) Find the rate of change of the ball's height with respect to its horizontal distance from home plate.
   f) Find the point(s) at which the graph has a horizontal tangent line. Explain the significance of the point(s).

3. **a)** Use REGRESSION to find a quartic function

   $$y = ax^4 + bx^3 + cx^2 + dx + e$$

   that fits the data.
   b) Graph the function over the interval $[0, 500]$.

c) Does the function closely model the given data?
d) Predict the horizontal distance from home plate at which the ball would have hit the ground had it not hit the billboard.
e) Find the rate of change of the ball's height with respect to its horizontal distance from home plate.
f) Find the point(s) at which the graph has a horizontal tangent line. Explain the significance of the point(s).

4. **a)** Although most calculators cannot fit such a function to the data, assume that the equation

   $$y = 0.0015x\sqrt{202{,}500 - x^2}$$

   has been found using a curve-fitting technique. Graph the function over the interval $[0, 500]$.
   b) Predict the horizontal distance from home plate at which the ball would have hit the ground had it not hit the billboard.
   c) Find the rate of change of the ball's height with respect to its horizontal distance from home plate.
   d) Find the point(s) at which the graph has a horizontal tangent line. Explain the significance of the point(s).

5. Look at the answers in Exercises 2(d), 3(d), and 4(b). Compare the merits of the quartic model in Exercise 3 to those of the model in Exercise 4.

Tale of the tape.   Actually, scoreboard operators in the major leagues use different models to predict the distance that a home run ball would have traveled. The models are linear and are related to the trajectory of the ball, that is, how high the ball is hit. See the following graph.

Suppose a ball hits an obstruction d feet horizontally from home plate at a height of H feet. Then the estimated horizontal distance D that the ball would have traveled, depending on its trajectory type, is

Low trajectory:	$D = 1.1H + d$,
Medium trajectory:	$D = 0.7H + d$,
Towering trajectory:	$D = 0.5H + d$.

Exercises

6. For a ball striking an obstacle at $d = 400$ ft and $H = 60$ ft, estimate how far the ball would have traveled if it were following a low trajectory, a medium trajectory, or a towering trajectory.

7. In 1953, Hall-of-Famer Mickey Mantle hit a towering home run in old Griffith Stadium in Washington, D.C., that hit an obstruction 60 ft high and 460 ft from home plate. Reporters asserted at the time that the ball would have traveled 565 ft. Is this estimate valid?

8. Use the appropriate formula to estimate the distance D for each of the following famous long home runs.

a) Ted Williams (Boston Red Sox, June 9, 1946): Purportedly the longest home run ball ever hit to right field at Boston's Fenway Park, Williams's ball landed in the stands 502 feet from home plate, 30 feet above the ground. Assume a medium trajectory.

b) Reggie Jackson (Oakland Athletics, July 13, 1971): Jackson's mighty blast hit an electrical transformer on top of the right-field roof at old Tiger Stadium in the 1971 All-Star Game. The transformer was 380 feet from home plate, 100 feet up. Find the distance the ball would have traveled, assuming a low trajectory and then a medium trajectory. (Jackson's home-run ball left the bat at an estimated 31.5° angle, about halfway between the low and medium range.)

c) Richie Sexson (Arizona Diamondbacks, April 26, 2004): Sexson hit a drive that caromed off the center-field scoreboard at Bank One Ballpark in Phoenix. The scoreboard is 414 feet from home plate and 75 feet high. Assume a medium trajectory.

The reported distances these balls would have traveled are 527 feet for Williams's home run, 530 feet for Jackson's, and 469 feet for Sexson's. (*Source:* www.hittrackeronline.com.) How close are your estimates?

Many thanks to Robert K. Adair, professor of physics at Yale University, for many of the ideas presented in this application.

2 Applications of Differentiation

What You'll Learn

2.1 Using First Derivatives to Classify Maximum and Minimum Values and Sketch Graphs

2.2 Using Second Derivatives to Classify Maximum and Minimum Values and Sketch Graphs

2.3 Graph Sketching: Asymptotes and Rational Functions

2.4 Using Derivatives to Find Absolute Maximum and Minimum Values

2.5 Maximum–Minimum Problems; Business, Economics, and General Applications

2.6 Marginals and Differentials

2.7 Elasticity of Demand

2.8 Implicit Differentiation and Related Rates

Why It's Important

In this chapter, we explore many applications of differentiation. We learn to find maximum and minimum values of functions, and that skill allows us to solve many kinds of problems in which we need to find the largest and/or smallest value in a real-world situation. Our differentiation skills will be applied to graphing, and we will use differentials to approximate function values. We will also use differentiation to explore elasticity of demand and related rates.

Where It's Used

Minimizing Cost: Minimizing cost is a common goal in manufacturing. For example, cylindrical food cans come in a variety of sizes. Suppose a soup can is to have a volume of 250 cm^3. The cost of material for the two circular ends is \$0.0008/cm^2, and the cost of material for the side is \$0.0015/cm^2. What dimensions minimize the cost of material for the soup can?(*This problem appears as Example 3 in Section 2.5.*)

- Find relative extrema of a continuous function using the First-Derivative Test.
- Sketch graphs of continuous functions.

Using First Derivatives to Classify Maximum and Minimum Values and Sketch Graphs

The graph below shows a typical life cycle of a retail product and is similar to graphs we will consider in this chapter. Note that the number of items sold varies with respect to time. Sales begin at a small level and increase to a point of maximum sales, after which they taper off to a low level, possibly because of new competitive products. The company then rejuvenates the product by making improvements. Think about versions of certain products: televisions can be traditional, flat-screen, or high-definition; music recordings have been produced as phonograph (vinyl) records, audiotapes, compact discs, and MP3 files. Where might each of these products be in a typical product life cycle? Is the curve below appropriate for each product?

Finding the largest and smallest values of a function—that is, the maximum and minimum values—has extensive applications. The first and second derivatives of a function can provide information for graphing functions and finding maximum and minimum values.

Increasing and Decreasing Functions

If the graph of a function rises from left to right over an interval I, the function is said to be **increasing** on, or over, I. If the graph drops from left to right, the function is said to be **decreasing** on, or over, I.

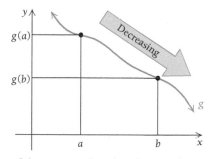

If the input a is less than the input b, then the output for a is less than the output for b.

If the input a is less than the input b, then the output for a is greater than the output for b.

Exploratory

Graph the function

$$f(x) = -\frac{1}{3}x^3 + 6x^2 - 11x - 50$$

and its derivative

$$f'(x) = -x^2 + 12x - 11$$

using the window $[-10, 25, -100, 150]$, with Xscl = 5 and Yscl = 25. Then TRACE from left to right along each graph. Moving the cursor from left to right, note that the x-coordinate always increases. If the function is increasing, the y-coordinate will increase as well. If a function is decreasing, the y-coordinate will decrease.

Over what intervals is f increasing? Over what intervals is f decreasing? Over what intervals is f' positive? Over what intervals is f' negative? What rules might relate the sign of f' to the behavior of f?

We can define these concepts as follows.

DEFINITIONS

A function f is **increasing** over I if, for every a and b in I,

   if $a < b$,   then $f(a) < f(b)$.

A function f is **decreasing** over I if, for every a and b in I,

   if $a < b$,   then $f(a) > f(b)$.

The above definitions can be restated in terms of secant lines as shown below.

Increasing: $\dfrac{f(b) - f(a)}{b - a} > 0.$ Decreasing: $\dfrac{f(b) - f(a)}{b - a} < 0.$

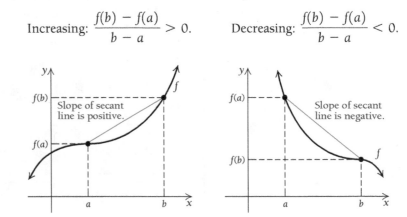

The following theorem shows how we can use the derivative (the slope of a tangent line) to determine whether a function is increasing or decreasing.

THEOREM 1

Let f be differentiable over an open interval I.
If $f'(x) > 0$ for all x in I, then f is increasing over I.
If $f'(x) < 0$ for all x in I, then f is decreasing over I.

Theorem 1 is illustrated in the following graph of $f(x) = \frac{1}{3}x^3 - x + \frac{2}{3}$.

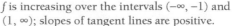

f is increasing over the intervals $(-\infty, -1)$ and $(1, \infty)$; slopes of tangent lines are positive.

f is decreasing over the interval $(-1, 1)$; slopes of tangent lines are negative.

Note in the graph above that $x = -1$ and $x = 1$ are not included in any interval over which the function is increasing or decreasing. These values are examples of *critical values*.

Critical Values

Consider the following graph of a continuous function f.

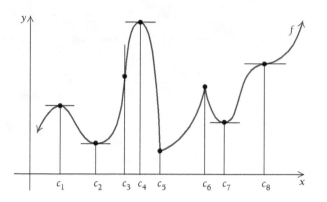

Note the following:

1. $f'(x) = 0$ at $x = c_1, c_2, c_4, c_7$, and c_8. That is, the tangent line to the graph is horizontal for these values.

2. $f'(x)$ does not exist at $x = c_3, c_5$, and c_6. The tangent line is vertical at c_3, and there are corners at both c_5 and c_6. (See also the discussion at the end of Section 1.4.)

DEFINITION

A **critical value** of a function f is any number c in the domain of f for which the tangent line at $(c, f(c))$ is horizontal or for which the derivative does not exist. That is, c is a critical value if $f(c)$ exists and

$$f'(c) = 0 \quad \text{or} \quad f'(c) \text{ does not exist.}$$

Thus, in the graph of f above:

- c_1, c_2, c_4, c_7, and c_8 are critical values because $f'(c) = 0$ for each value.
- c_3, c_5, and c_6 are critical values because $f'(c)$ does not exist for each value.

A continuous function can change from increasing to decreasing or from decreasing to increasing *only* at a critical value. In the above graph, c_1, c_2, c_4, c_5, c_6, and c_7 separate intervals over which the function f increases from those in which it decreases or intervals in which the function decreases from those in which it increases. Although c_3 and c_8 are critical values, they do not separate intervals over which the function changes from increasing to decreasing or from decreasing to increasing.

Finding Relative Maximum and Minimum Values

Now consider a graph with "peaks" and "valleys" at $x = c_1, c_2$, and c_3.

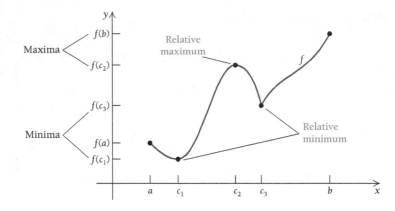

Here, $f(c_2)$ is an example of a **relative maximum** (plural: **maxima**). Each of $f(c_1)$ and $f(c_3)$ is called a **relative minimum** (plural: **minima**). Collectively, maximum and minimum values are called **extrema** (singular: **extremum**).

DEFINITIONS

Let I be the domain of f.

$f(c)$ is a **relative minimum** if there exists within I an open interval I_1 containing c such that $f(c) \le f(x)$, for all x in I_1;

and

$f(c)$ is a **relative maximum** if there exists within I an open interval I_2 containing c such that $f(c) \ge f(x)$, for all x in I_2.

Look again at the graph above. The x-values at which a continuous function has relative extrema are those values for which the derivative is 0 or for which the derivative does not exist—the critical values.

THEOREM 2

If a function f has a relative extreme value $f(c)$ on an open interval, then c is a critical value, so

$$f'(c) = 0 \quad \text{or} \quad f'(c) \text{ does not exist.}$$

A *relative extreme point,* $(c, f(c))$, is higher or lower than all other points over some open interval containing c. A relative *minimum* point will have a y-value that is *lower* than those of a neighborhood of points both to the left and to the right of it, and, similarly, a relative *maximum* point will have a y-value that is *higher* than those of a neighborhood of points to the left and right of it.

Theorem 2 is useful and important to understand. It says that to find relative extrema, we need only consider inputs for which the derivative is 0 or for which the derivative does not exist. Each critical value is a *candidate* for a value where a relative extremum *might* occur. That is, Theorem 2 does not guarantee that every critical value will yield a relative maximum or minimum. Consider, for example, the graph of

$$f(x) = (x - 1)^3 + 2,$$

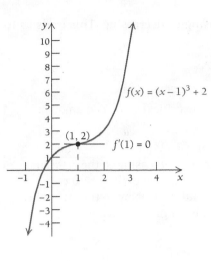

$f(x) = (x-1)^3 + 2$

$(1, 2)$

$f'(1) = 0$

shown at the left. Note that

$$f'(x) = 3(x-1)^2, \quad \text{and} \quad f'(1) = 3(1-1)^2 = 0.$$

Thus, $c = 1$ is a critical value, but f has no relative maximum or minimum at that value.

Theorem 2 does guarantee that if a relative maximum or minimum occurs, then the first coordinate of that extremum is a critical value. How can we tell when the existence of a critical value indicates a relative extremum? The following graph leads us to a test.

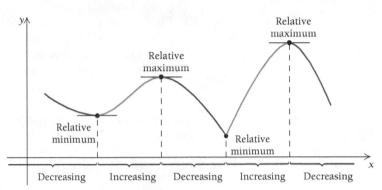

Note that at a critical value where there is a relative minimum, the function is decreasing on the left of the critical value and increasing on the right. At a critical value where there is a relative maximum, the function is increasing on the left of the critical value and decreasing on the right. In both cases, the derivative changes signs on either side of the critical value.

Graph over the interval (a, b)	$f(c)$	Sign of $f'(x)$ for x in (a, c)	Sign of $f'(x)$ for x in (c, b)	Increasing or decreasing
	Relative minimum	$-$	$+$	Decreasing on (a, c); increasing on (c, b)
	Relative maximum	$+$	$-$	Increasing on (a, c); decreasing on (c, b)
	No relative maxima or minima	$-$	$-$	Decreasing on (a, b)
	No relative maxima or minima	$+$	$+$	Increasing on (a, b)

Derivatives tell us when a function is increasing or decreasing. This leads us to the First-Derivative Test.

THEOREM 3 **The First-Derivative Test for Relative Extrema**

For any continuous function f that has exactly one critical value c in an open interval (a, b):

F1. f has a relative minimum at c if $f'(x) < 0$ on (a, c) and $f'(x) > 0$ on (c, b). That is, f is decreasing to the left of c and increasing to the right of c.

F2. f has a relative maximum at c if $f'(x) > 0$ on (a, c) and $f'(x) < 0$ on (c, b). That is, f is increasing to the left of c and decreasing to the right of c.

F3. f has neither a relative maximum nor a relative minimum at c if $f'(x)$ has the same sign on (a, c) as on (c, b).

We can use the First-Derivative Test to find relative extrema and create accurate graphs.

EXAMPLE 1 Graph the function f given by

$$f(x) = 4x^3 - 9x^2 - 30x + 25,$$

and find any relative extrema.

Solution We plot points and use them to create a rough sketch of the graph, shown as the dashed line in the figure below.

x	$f(x)$
-3	-74
-2	17
-1	42
0	25
1	-10
2	-39
3	-38
4	17

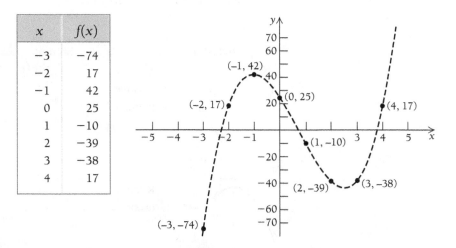

According to this sketch, it *appears* that the graph has a tangent line with slope 0 at $x = -1$ and between $x = 2$ and $x = 3$. To verify this, we use calculus to support our observations. We begin by finding the derivative:

$$f'(x) = 12x^2 - 18x - 30.$$

We next determine where $f'(x)$ does not exist or where $f'(x) = 0$. Since $f'(x)$ is defined for all real numbers, there is no value x for which $f'(x)$ does not exist.

The only possibilities for critical values are those where $f'(x) = 0$. To find such values, we solve $f'(x) = 0$:

$$12x^2 - 18x - 30 = 0$$
$$2x^2 - 3x - 5 = 0 \qquad \text{Dividing both sides by 6}$$
$$(x + 1)(2x - 5) = 0 \qquad \text{Factoring}$$
$$x + 1 = 0 \quad \text{or} \quad 2x - 5 = 0 \qquad \text{Using the Principle of Zero Products}$$
$$x = -1 \quad \text{or} \quad x = \tfrac{5}{2}.$$

The critical values are -1 and $\tfrac{5}{2}$. Since it is at these values that a relative maximum or minimum might exist, we analyze the sign of the derivative on the intervals $(-\infty, -1), (-1, \tfrac{5}{2})$, and $(\tfrac{5}{2}, \infty)$.

To do so, we choose a test value in each interval and make a substitution. Let's use the values $-2, 0$, and 4.

$(-\infty, -1)$: Test -2, $\quad f'(-2) = 12(-2)^2 - 18(-2) - 30$
$$= 48 + 36 - 30 = 54 > 0;$$

$(-1, \tfrac{5}{2})$: $\quad$ Test 0, $\quad f'(0) = 12(0)^2 - 18(0) - 30 = -30 < 0;$

$(\tfrac{5}{2}, \infty)$: $\quad$ Test 4, $\quad f'(4) = 12(4)^2 - 18(4) - 30$
$$= 192 - 72 - 30 = 90 > 0.$$

Interval			
Test Value	$x = -2$	$x = 0$	$x = 4$
Sign of $f'(x)$	$f'(-2) > 0$	$f'(0) < 0$	$f'(4) > 0$
Result	f is increasing on $(-\infty, -1)$	f is decreasing on $(-1, \tfrac{5}{2})$	f is increasing on $(\tfrac{5}{2}, \infty)$

Change indicates a relative maximum at $x = -1$. Change indicates a relative minimum at $x = \tfrac{5}{2}$.

Therefore, by the First-Derivative Test, f has a relative maximum at $x = -1$ given by

$$f(-1) = 4(-1)^3 - 9(-1)^2 - 30(-1) + 25 \qquad \text{Substituting } -1 \text{ for } x \text{ in the } \textit{original} \text{ function}$$

$$= 42 \qquad \text{This is a relative maximum.}$$

and f has a relative minimum at $x = \frac{5}{2}$ given by

$$f\left(\tfrac{5}{2}\right) = 4\left(\tfrac{5}{2}\right)^3 - 9\left(\tfrac{5}{2}\right)^2 - 30\left(\tfrac{5}{2}\right) + 25 = -\tfrac{175}{4}.$$ This is a relative minimum.

Thus, there is a relative maximum at $(-1, 42)$ and a relative minimum at $\left(\frac{5}{2}, -\frac{175}{4}\right)$, as we suspected from the original sketch of the graph.

The information obtained from the first derivative is very useful in graphing this function. We know that it is continuous and where it is increasing, where it is decreasing, and where it has relative extrema. We complete the graph by calculating additional function values. The graph of the function, shown below in red, is scaled to clearly show its important features.

Exploratory

Consider the function f given by

$$f(x) = x^3 - 3x + 2.$$

Graph both f and f' using the same set of axes. Examine the graphs using the TABLE and TRACE features. Where do you think the relative extrema of f occur? Where is the derivative equal to 0? Where does f have critical values?

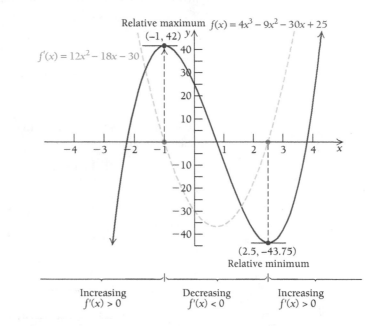

For reference, the graph of the derivative is shown in blue. Note that $f'(x) = 0$ where $f(x)$ has relative extrema. We summarize the behavior of this function by noting where it is increasing or decreasing and by characterizing its critical points:

- f is increasing over the interval $(-\infty, -1)$.
- f has a relative maximum at the point $(-1, 42)$.
- f is decreasing over the interval $\left(-1, \frac{5}{2}\right)$.
- f has a relative minimum at the point $\left(\frac{5}{2}, -\frac{175}{4}\right)$.
- f is increasing over the interval $\left(\frac{5}{2}, \infty\right)$.   **1** ✔

Quick Check 1 ✔

Graph the function g given by $g(x) = x^3 - 27x - 6$, and find any relative extrema.

To use the first derivative for graphing a function f:

1. Find all critical values by determining where $f'(x)$ is 0 and where $f'(x)$ is undefined (but $f(x)$ is defined). Find $f(x)$ for each critical value.

2. Use the critical values to divide the x-axis into intervals and choose a test value in each interval.

3. Find the sign of $f'(x)$ for each test value chosen in step 2, and use this information to determine where $f(x)$ is increasing or decreasing and to classify any extrema as relative maxima or minima.

4. Plot some additional points and sketch the graph.

> The *derivative* f' is used to find the critical values of f. The test values are substituted into the *derivative* f', and the function values are found using the *original* function f.

EXAMPLE 2 Find the relative extrema and sketch the graph of the function f given by
$$f(x) = 2x^3 - x^4.$$

Solution First, we determine the critical values. To do so, we find $f'(x)$:
$$f'(x) = 6x^2 - 4x^3.$$

Next, we find where $f'(x)$ does not exist or where $f'(x) = 0$. Note that $f'(x) = 6x^2 - 4x^3$ is defined for all real numbers x, so the only candidates for critical values are where $f'(x) = 0$:

$$
\begin{aligned}
6x^2 - 4x^3 &= 0 \quad &&\text{Setting } f'(x) \text{ equal to 0} \\
2x^2(3 - 2x) &= 0 \quad &&\text{Factoring} \\
2x^2 = 0 \quad &\text{or} \quad 3 - 2x = 0 \\
x^2 = 0 \quad &\text{or} \quad 3 = 2x \\
x = 0 \quad &\text{or} \quad x = \tfrac{3}{2}.
\end{aligned}
$$

The critical values are 0 and $\frac{3}{2}$. We use these values to divide the x-axis into three intervals: $(-\infty, 0)$, $(0, \frac{3}{2})$, and $(\frac{3}{2}, \infty)$.

We next find the sign of $f'(x)$ on each interval, using a test value.

$$
\begin{aligned}
(-\infty, 0): \quad &\text{Test } -1, \quad f'(-1) = 6(-1)^2 - 4(-1)^3 = 6 + 4 = 10 > 0; \\
\left(0, \tfrac{3}{2}\right): \quad &\text{Test } 1, \quad f'(1) = 6(1)^2 - 4(1)^3 = 6 - 4 = 2 > 0; \\
\left(\tfrac{3}{2}, \infty\right): \quad &\text{Test } 2, \quad f'(2) = 6(2)^2 - 4(2)^3 = 24 - 32 = -8 < 0.
\end{aligned}
$$

Therefore, by the First-Derivative Test, f has no extremum at $x = 0$ (since $f(x)$ is increasing on both sides of 0) and has a relative maximum at $x = \frac{3}{2}$. Thus, $f\left(\frac{3}{2}\right)$, or $\frac{27}{16}$, is a relative maximum.

We use the information obtained to sketch the graph below. Other function values are listed in the table.

x	$f(x)$, approximately
-1	-3
-0.5	-0.31
0	0
0.5	0.19
1	1
1.25	1.46
2	0

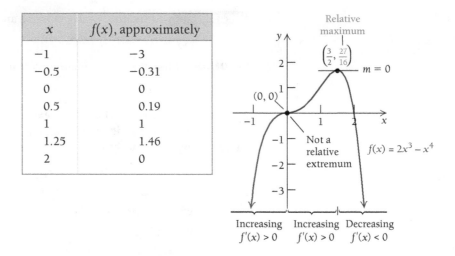

- f is increasing over the interval $(-\infty, 0)$.
- f has a critical point at $(0, 0)$, which is neither a minimum nor a maximum.
- f is increasing over the interval $\left(0, \frac{3}{2}\right)$.
- f has a relative maximum at the point $\left(\frac{3}{2}, \frac{27}{16}\right)$.
- f is decreasing over the interval $\left(\frac{3}{2}, \infty\right)$.

Since f is increasing over the intervals $(-\infty, 0)$ and $\left(0, \frac{3}{2}\right)$, we can say that f is increasing over $\left(-\infty, \frac{3}{2}\right)$ despite the fact that $f'(0) = 0$ within this interval. In this case, we observe that a secant line connecting any two points within this interval has a positive slope. **2** ✔

Quick Check 2 ✔

Find the relative extrema of the function h given by $h(x) = x^4 - \frac{8}{3}x^3$. Then sketch the graph.

EXAMPLE 3 Find the relative extrema and sketch the graph of the function f given by

$$f(x) = (x - 2)^{2/3} + 1.$$

Solution First, we determine the critical values. To do so, we find $f'(x)$:

$$f'(x) = \frac{2}{3}(x - 2)^{-1/3}$$

$$= \frac{2}{3\sqrt[3]{x - 2}}. \qquad \text{Simplifying}$$

Next, we find where $f'(x)$ does not exist or where $f'(x) = 0$. Note that $f'(x)$ does not exist at 2, although $f(x)$ does. Thus, 2 is a critical value. Since the only way for a fraction to be 0 is if its numerator is 0, we see that $f'(x) = 0$ has no solution. Thus, 2 is the only critical value. We use 2 to divide the x-axis into the intervals $(-\infty, 2)$ and $(2, \infty)$.

$$(-\infty, 2) \qquad\qquad (2, \infty)$$

$$\xleftarrow{\hspace{3cm}}\underset{2}{\mid}\xrightarrow{\hspace{3cm}} x$$

To determine the sign of $f'(x)$ we choose a test value in each interval. It is not necessary to find an exact value of the derivative; we need only determine the sign. Sometimes we can do this by just examining the formula for the derivative. We choose test values 0 and 3.

$$(-\infty, 2): \quad \text{Test } 0, \quad f'(0) = \frac{2}{3\sqrt[3]{0-2}} < 0;$$

$$(2, \infty): \quad \text{Test } 3, \quad f'(3) = \frac{2}{3\sqrt[3]{3-2}} > 0.$$

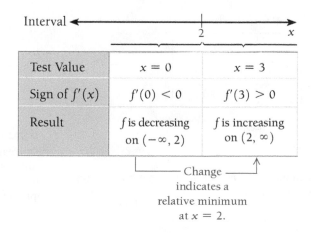

Interval	$x = 0$	$x = 3$
Test Value	$x = 0$	$x = 3$
Sign of $f'(x)$	$f'(0) < 0$	$f'(3) > 0$
Result	f is decreasing on $(-\infty, 2)$	f is increasing on $(2, \infty)$

Change indicates a relative minimum at $x = 2$.

Since we have a change from decreasing to increasing, we conclude from the First-Derivative Test that a relative minimum occurs at $(2, f(2))$, or $(2, 1)$. The graph has *no* tangent line at $(2, 1)$ since $f'(2)$ does not exist.

We use this information and some other function values to sketch the graph.

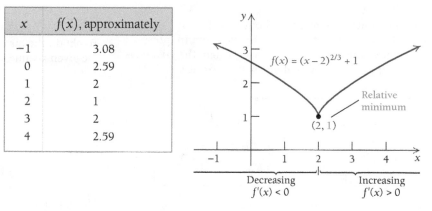

x	$f(x)$, approximately
-1	3.08
0	2.59
1	2
2	1
3	2
4	2.59

Quick Check 3 ☑

Find the relative extrema of the function g given by $g(x) = 3 - x^{1/3}$. Then sketch the graph.

- f is decreasing over the interval $(-\infty, 2)$.
- f has a relative minimum at the point $(2, 1)$.
- f is increasing over the interval $(2, \infty)$.

3 ☑

TECHNOLOGY CONNECTION

Finding Relative Extrema

To explore some methods for approximating relative extrema, let's find the relative extrema of

$$f(x) = -0.4x^3 + 6.2x^2 - 11.3x - 54.8.$$

We first graph the function, using a window that reveals the curvature.

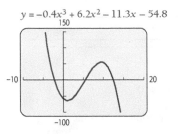

Method 1: TRACE

Using TRACE, we can move the cursor along the curve, noting where relative extrema might occur.

A relative maximum seems to be about $y = 54.5$ at $x = 9.47$. To refine the approximation, we zoom in, press TRACE, and move the cursor, again noting where the y-value is largest. The approximation is about $y = 54.61$ at $x = 9.31$.

We can repeat to refine the accuracy.

Method 2: TABLE

We can also use the TABLE feature, adjusting starting points and step values to improve accuracy:

$$\text{TblStart} = 9.3 \quad \Delta \text{Tbl} = .01$$

The relative maximum seems to be nearly $y = 54.61$ at an x-value between 9.32 and 9.33. We could next set up a new table showing function values between $f(9.32)$ and $f(9.33)$ to refine the approximation.

Method 3: MAXIMUM, MINIMUM

Using the MAXIMUM option from the CALC menu, we find that a relative maximum of about 54.61 occurs at $x \approx 9.32$.

Method 4: fMax or fMin

This feature calculates a relative maximum or minimum value over any closed interval. We see from the initial graph that a relative maximum occurs in $[-10, 20]$. Using the fMax option from the MATH menu, we see that a relative maximum occurs on $[-10, 20]$ when $x \approx 9.32$.

To obtain the maximum value, we evaluate the function at the given x-value, obtaining the following.

The approximation is about $y = 54.61$ at $x = 9.32$.

Using any of these methods, we find the relative minimum $y \approx -60.30$ at $x \approx 1.01$.

EXERCISE

1. Using one of the methods described above, approximate the relative extrema of the function in Example 1.

Section Summary

- A function f is *increasing* over an interval I if, for all a and b in I such that $a < b$, we have $f(a) < f(b)$. Equivalently, the slope of the secant line connecting a and b is positive:

$$\frac{f(b) - f(a)}{b - a} > 0.$$

- A function f is *decreasing* over an interval I if, for all a and b in I such that $a < b$, we have $f(a) > f(b)$. Equivalently, the slope of the secant line connecting a and b is negative:

$$\frac{f(b) - f(a)}{b - a} < 0.$$

- A function f is *increasing* over an open interval I if, for all x in I, the slope of the tangent line at x is positive; that is, $f'(x) > 0$. Similarly, a function f is *decreasing*

over an open interval I if, for all x in I, the slope of the tangent line is negative; that is, $f'(x) < 0$.

- A *critical value* is a number c in the domain of f such that $f'(c) = 0$ or $f'(c)$ does not exist. The point $(c, f(c))$ is called a *critical point*.
- A relative maximum point is higher than all other points in some interval containing it. Similarly, a relative minimum point is lower than all other points in some interval containing it. The y-value of such a point is called a relative maximum (or minimum) *value* of the function.
- Minimum and maximum points are collectively called *extrema*.
- Critical values are candidates for possible relative extrema. The *First-Derivative Test* is used to classify a critical value as a relative minimum, a relative maximum, or neither.

2.1   Exercise Set

Find any relative extrema of each function. List each extremum along with the x-value at which it occurs. Then sketch a graph of the function.

1. $f(x) = x^2 + 6x - 3$

2. $f(x) = x^2 + 4x + 5$

3. $f(x) = 2 - 3x - 2x^2$

4. $f(x) = 5 - x - x^2$

5. $F(x) = 0.5x^2 + 2x - 11$

6. $g(x) = 1 + 6x + 3x^2$

7. $g(x) = x^3 + \frac{1}{2}x^2 - 2x + 5$

8. $G(x) = x^3 - x^2 - x + 2$

9. $f(x) = x^3 - 3x^2$

10. $f(x) = x^3 - 3x + 6$

11. $f(x) = x^3 + 3x$

12. $f(x) = 3x^2 + 2x^3$

13. $F(x) = 1 - x^3$

14. $g(x) = 2x^3 - 16$

15. $G(x) = x^3 - 6x^2 + 10$

16. $f(x) = 12 + 9x - 3x^2 - x^3$

17. $g(x) = x^3 - x^4$

18. $f(x) = x^4 - 2x^3$

19. $f(x) = \frac{1}{3}x^3 - 2x^2 + 4x - 1$

20. $F(x) = -\frac{1}{3}x^3 + 3x^2 - 9x + 2$

21. $f(x) = 3x^4 - 15x^2 + 12$

22. $g(x) = 2x^4 - 20x^2 + 18$

23. $G(x) = \sqrt[3]{x + 2}$

24. $F(x) = \sqrt[3]{x - 1}$

25. $f(x) = 1 - x^{2/3}$

26. $f(x) = (x + 3)^{2/3} - 5$

27. $G(x) = \dfrac{-8}{x^2 + 1}$

28. $F(x) = \dfrac{5}{x^2 + 1}$

29. $g(x) = \dfrac{4x}{x^2 + 1}$

30. $g(x) = \dfrac{x^2}{x^2 + 1}$

31. $f(x) = \sqrt[3]{x}$

32. $f(x) = (x + 1)^{1/3}$

33. $g(x) = \sqrt{x^2 + 2x + 5}$

34. $F(x) = \dfrac{1}{\sqrt{x^2 + 1}}$

35–68. Check the results of Exercises 1–34 using a calculator.

For Exercises 69–84, draw a graph to match the description given. Answers will vary.

69. $f(x)$ is increasing over $(-\infty, 2)$ and decreasing over $(2, \infty)$.

70. $g(x)$ is decreasing over $(-\infty, -3)$ and increasing over $(-3, \infty)$.

71. $G(x)$ is decreasing over $(-\infty, 4)$ and $(9, \infty)$ and increasing over $(4, 9)$.

72. $F(x)$ is increasing over $(-\infty, 5)$ and $(12, \infty)$ and decreasing over $(5, 12)$.

73. $g(x)$ has a positive derivative over $(-\infty, -3)$ and a negative derivative over $(-3, \infty)$.

74. $f(x)$ has a negative derivative over $(-\infty, 1)$ and a positive derivative over $(1, \infty)$.

75. $F(x)$ has a negative derivative over $(-\infty, 2)$ and $(5, 9)$ and a positive derivative over $(2, 5)$ and $(9, \infty)$.

76. $G(x)$ has a positive derivative over $(-\infty, -2)$ and $(4, 7)$ and a negative derivative over $(-2, 4)$ and $(7, \infty)$.

77. $f(x)$ has a positive derivative over $(-\infty, 3)$ and $(3, 9)$, a negative derivative over $(9, \infty)$, and a derivative equal to 0 at $x = 3$.

78. $g(x)$ has a negative derivative over $(-\infty, 5)$ and $(5, 8)$, a positive derivative over $(8, \infty)$, and a derivative equal to 0 at $x = 5$.

79. $F(x)$ has a negative derivative over $(-\infty, -1)$ and a positive derivative over $(-1, \infty)$, and $F'(-1)$ does not exist.

80. $G(x)$ has a positive derivative over $(-\infty, 0)$ and $(3, \infty)$ and a negative derivative over $(0, 3)$, but neither $G'(0)$ nor $G'(3)$ exists.

81. $f(x)$ has a negative derivative over $(-\infty, -2)$ and $(1, \infty)$ and a positive derivative over $(-2, 1)$, and $f'(-2) = 0$, but $f'(1)$ does not exist.

82. $g(x)$ has a positive derivative over $(-\infty, -3)$ and $(0, 3)$, a negative derivative over $(-3, 0)$ and $(3, \infty)$, and a derivative equal to 0 at $x = -3$ and $x = 3$, but $g'(0)$ does not exist.

83. $H(x)$ is increasing over $(-\infty, \infty)$, but the derivative does not exist at $x = 1$.

84. $K(x)$ is decreasing over $(-\infty, \infty)$, but the derivative does not exist at $x = 0$ and $x = 2$.

85. Consider this graph.

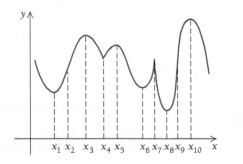

What makes an x-value a critical value? Which x-values above are critical values, and why?

86. Consider this graph.

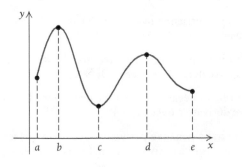

Using the graph and the intervals noted, explain how a function being increasing or decreasing relates to the first derivative.

APPLICATIONS

Business and Economics

87. Employment. According to the U.S. Bureau of Labor Statistics, the number of managerial and professional employees since 2006 is modeled by

$$E(t) = 107.833t^3 - 971.369t^2 + 2657.917t + 50,347.833,$$

where t is the number of years since 2006 and E is thousands of employees. (*Source*: data.bls.gov.) Find the relative extrema of this function, and sketch the graph. Interpret the meaning of the relative extrema.

88. Advertising. Brody Electronics estimates that it will sell N units of a new toy after spending a thousands of dollars on advertising, where

$$N(a) = -a^2 + 300a + 6, \quad 0 \le a \le 300.$$

Find the relative extrema and sketch a graph of the function.

Life and Physical Sciences

89. Solar eclipse. On July 2, 2019, a total solar eclipse will occur over the South Pacific Ocean and parts of South America. (*Source*: eclipse.gsfc.nasa.gov.) The path of the eclipse is modeled by

$$f(t) = 0.00259t^2 - 0.457t + 36.237,$$

where $f(t)$ is the latitude in degrees south of the equator at t minutes after the start of the total eclipse. What is the latitude closest to the equator, in degrees, at which the total eclipse will be visible?

90. Temperature during an illness. The temperature of a person during an intestinal illness is given by

$$T(t) = -0.1t^2 + 1.2t + 98.6, \quad 0 \le t \le 12,$$

where T is the temperature (°F) at t days. Find the relative extrema and sketch a graph of the function.

SYNTHESIS

In Exercises 91–96, the graph of a derivative f' is shown. Use the information in each graph to determine where f is increasing or decreasing and the x-values of any extrema. Then sketch a possible graph of f.

91.

92.

93.

94.

95.

96.

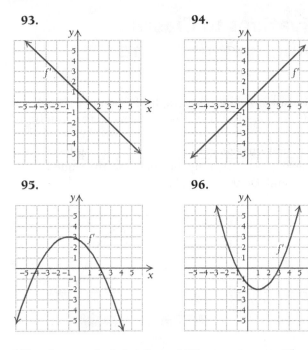

Graph each function. Then estimate any relative extrema.

97. $f(x) = -x^6 - 4x^5 + 54x^4 + 160x^3 - 641x^2 - 828x + 1200$

98. $f(x) = x^4 + 4x^3 - 36x^2 - 160x + 400$

99. $f(x) = \sqrt[3]{|4 - x^2|} + 1$

100. $f(x) = x\sqrt{9 - x^2}$

Use a calculator's absolute-value feature to graph each function and determine relative extrema and intervals over which the function is increasing or decreasing. State any x-values at which the derivative does not exist.

101. $f(x) = |x - 2|$ **102.** $f(x) = |2x - 5|$

103. $f(x) = |x^2 - 1|$ **104.** $f(x) = |x^2 - 3x + 2|$

105. $f(x) = |9 - x^2|$ **106.** $f(x) = |-x^2 + 4x - 4|$

107. $f(x) = |x^3 - 1|$ **108.** $f(x) = |x^4 - 2x^2|$

Life science: caloric intake and life expectancy.   *The data in the following table give, for various countries for the period 2007–2011, daily caloric intake, projected life expectancy, and under-five mortality. Use the data for Exercises 109 and 110.*

COUNTRY	DAILY CALORIC INTAKE	LIFE EXPECTANCY AT BIRTH (in years)	UNDER-FIVE MORTALITY (number of deaths before age 5 per 1000 births)
Argentina	3030	76	14
Australia	3220	82	5
Bolivia	2100	66	51
Canada	3530	81	6
Dominican Republic	2270	73	25
Germany	3540	80	4
Haiti	1850	62	70
Mexico	3260	77	17
United States	3750	78	8
Venezuela	2650	74	16

(Source: U.N. FAO Statistical Yearbook, 2013.)

109. Life expectancy and daily caloric intake.
   a) Use the regression procedures of Section R.6 to fit a cubic function $y = f(x)$ to the data in the table, where x is daily caloric intake and y is life expectancy. Then fit a quartic function and decide which fits best.
   b) What is the domain of the function?
   c) Does the function have any relative extrema?

110. Under-five mortality and daily caloric intake.
   a) Use the regression procedures of Section R.6 to fit a cubic function $y = f(x)$ to the data in the table, where x is daily caloric intake and y is under-five mortality. Then fit a quartic function and decide which fits best.
   b) What is the domain of the function?
   c) Does the function have any relative extrema?

111. Describe a procedure that can be used to select an appropriate viewing window for the functions given in (a) Exercises 1–34 and (b) Exercises 97–100.

Answers to Quick Checks

1. Relative maximum at $(-3, 48)$, relative minimum at $(3, -60)$

2. Relative minimum at $(2, -\frac{16}{3})$

3. There are no extrema.

2.2

● Classify the relative extrema of a function using the Second-Derivative Test.

● Graph a continuous function in a manner that shows concavity.

Using Second Derivatives to Classify Maximum and Minimum Values and Sketch Graphs

The graphs of two functions are shown below. The graph of f bends upward and the graph of g bends downward. Let's relate these observations to the functions' derivatives.

Using a straightedge, draw tangent lines as you move along the graph of f from left to right. What happens to the slopes of the tangent lines? Do the same for the graph of g. Look at how the graphs bend. Do you see a pattern?

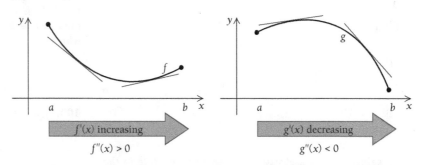

Concavity: Increasing and Decreasing Derivatives

For the graph of f, the slopes of the tangent lines are increasing. That is, f' is increasing over the interval. This can be determined by noting that $f''(x)$ is positive, since the relationship between f' and f'' is like the relationship between f and f'. For the graph of g, the slopes are decreasing. This can be determined by noting that g' is decreasing whenever $g''(x)$ is negative. The bending of each curve is called the graph's *concavity*.

DEFINITION

Suppose that f is a function whose derivative f' exists at every point in an open interval I. Then

f is **concave up** on I if f' is increasing over I.

f is **concave down** on I if f' is decreasing over I.

The following theorem states how the concavity of a function's graph and the second derivative of the function are related.

THEOREM 4   A Test for Concavity

1. If $f''(x) > 0$ on an interval I, then the graph of f is concave up on I.
2. If $f''(x) < 0$ on an interval I, then the graph of f is concave down on I.

TECHNOLOGY CONNECTION

Exploratory

Graph

$$f(x) = -\frac{1}{3}x^3 + 6x^2 - 11x - 50$$

and its second derivative,

$$f''(x) = -2x + 12,$$

using the viewing window $[-10, 25, -100, 150]$, with $Xscl = 5$ and $Yscl = 25$.

Over what intervals is the graph of f concave up? Over what intervals is the graph of f concave down? Over what intervals is the graph of f'' positive? Over what intervals is the graph of f'' negative? How do you think the sign of $f''(x)$ relates to the concavity of f?

Now graph the first derivative,

$$f'(x) = -x^2 + 12x - 11,$$

and the second derivative,

$$f''(x) = -2x + 12,$$

using the window $[-10, 25, -200, 50]$, with $Xscl = 5$ and $Yscl = 25$.

Over what intervals is the first derivative f' increasing? Over what intervals is the first derivative f' decreasing? Over what intervals is the graph of f'' positive? Over what intervals is the graph of f'' negative? How do you think the sign of $f''(x)$ relates to the concavity of f?

A function can be decreasing and concave up, decreasing and concave down, increasing and concave up, or increasing and concave down. That is, *concavity* and *increasing/decreasing* are separate concepts. It is the increasing or decreasing aspect of the *derivative* that tells us about the function's concavity.

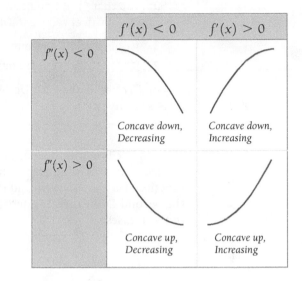

Classifying Relative Extrema Using Second Derivatives

Let's see how we can use second derivatives to determine whether a function has a relative extremum on an open interval.

The following graphs show both types of concavity at a critical value, where $f'(c) = 0$. When the second derivative is positive (graph is concave up) at the critical value, the critical point is a relative minimum point, and when the second derivative is negative (graph is concave down), the critical point is a relative maximum point.

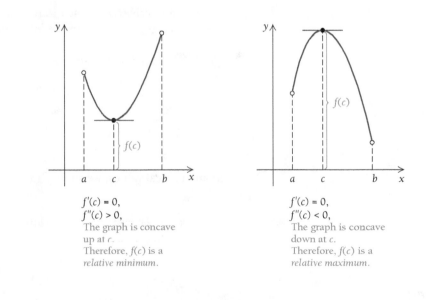

$f'(c) = 0$,
$f''(c) > 0$,
The graph is concave up at c.
Therefore, $f(c)$ is a *relative minimum*.

$f'(c) = 0$,
$f''(c) < 0$,
The graph is concave down at c.
Therefore, $f(c)$ is a *relative maximum*.

This analysis is summarized in Theorem 5:

> **THEOREM 5** **The Second-Derivative Test for Relative Extrema**
>
> Suppose that f is differentiable for every x in an open interval (a, b) and that there is a critical value c in (a, b) for which $f'(c) = 0$. Then:
>
> 1. $f(c)$ is a relative minimum if $f''(c) > 0$.
> 2. $f(c)$ is a relative maximum if $f''(c) < 0$.
>
> For $f''(c) = 0$, the First-Derivative Test can be used to determine whether $f(x)$ is a relative extremum.

When c is a critical value and $f''(c) = 0$, an extremum may or may not exist at c. Consider the following graphs. In each one, f' and f'' are both 0 at $c = 2$, but the first function has an extremum and the second function does not. An approach other than the Second-Derivative Test must be used to determine whether $f(c)$ is an extremum in these cases.

$f(x) = (x - 2)^4 + 1$
$f'(x) = 4(x - 2)^3$
$f''(x) = 12(x - 2)^2$
$f'(2) = 0$
$f''(2) = 0$
Relative minimum at $c = 2$

$f(x) = (x - 2)^3 + 1$
$f'(x) = 3(x - 2)^2$
$f''(x) = 6(x - 2)$
$f'(2) = 0$
$f''(2) = 0$
No relative extremum

The second derivative is used to help identify extrema and determine the overall behavior of a graph, as we see in the following examples.

EXAMPLE 1 Find any relative extrema and graph the function f given by
$$f(x) = x^3 + 3x^2 - 9x - 13.$$

Solution We find both the first and second derivatives:
$$f'(x) = 3x^2 + 6x - 9,$$
$$f''(x) = 6x + 6.$$

To find any critical values, we solve $f'(x) = 0$:

$$3x^2 + 6x - 9 = 0$$
$$x^2 + 2x - 3 = 0 \quad \text{Dividing both sides by 3}$$
$$(x + 3)(x - 1) = 0 \quad \text{Factoring}$$
$$x + 3 = 0 \quad \text{or} \quad x - 1 = 0 \quad \text{Using the Principle of Zero Products}$$
$$x = -3 \quad \text{or} \quad x = 1.$$

We next find second coordinates by substituting the critical values in the original function:

$$f(-3) = (-3)^3 + 3(-3)^2 - 9(-3) - 13 = 14;$$
$$f(1) = (1)^3 + 3(1)^2 - 9(1) - 13 = -18.$$

We now use the Second-Derivative Test with the critical values -3 and 1:

$$f''(-3) = 6(-3) + 6 = -12 < 0; \rightarrow \text{Relative maximum at } x = -3$$

$$f''(1) = 6(1) + 6 = 12 > 0. \longrightarrow \text{Relative minimum at } x = 1$$

Thus, $f(-3) = 14$ is a relative maximum and $f(1) = -18$ is a relative minimum. We plot both $(-3, 14)$ and $(1, -18)$, including short arcs at each point to indicate the concavity. By plotting more points, we can make a sketch, as shown below.

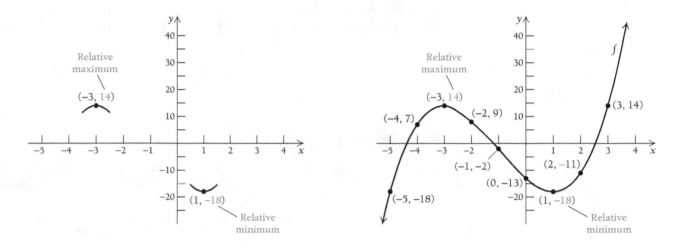

EXAMPLE 2   Find any relative extrema and graph the function f given by

$$f(x) = 3x^5 - 20x^3.$$

Solution   We find both the first and second derivatives:

$$f'(x) = 15x^4 - 60x^2,$$
$$f''(x) = 60x^3 - 120x.$$

Then we solve $f'(x) = 0$ to find any critical values:

$$15x^4 - 60x^2 = 0$$
$$15x^2(x^2 - 4) = 0$$
$$15x^2(x + 2)(x - 2) = 0 \qquad\qquad \text{Factoring}$$
$$15x^2 = 0 \quad \text{or} \quad x + 2 = 0 \quad \text{or} \quad x - 2 = 0 \qquad \text{Using the Principle of Zero Products}$$
$$x = 0 \quad \text{or} \qquad x = -2 \quad \text{or} \qquad x = 2.$$

We next find second coordinates by substituting in the original function:

$$f(-2) = 3(-2)^5 - 20(-2)^3 = 64;$$
$$f(0) = 3(0)^5 - 20(0)^3 = 0.$$
$$f(2) = 3(2)^5 - 20(2)^3 = -64;$$

All three of these y-values are candidates for relative extrema.

We now use the Second-Derivative Test with the values $-2, 0$, and 2:

$$f''(-2) = 60(-2)^3 - 120(-2) = -240 < 0; \rightarrow \text{Relative maximum at } x = -2$$

$$f''(0) = 60(0)^3 - 120(0) = 0. \longrightarrow \text{The Second-Derivative Test fails. Use the First-Derivative Test.}$$

$$f''(2) = 60(2)^3 - 120(2) = 240 > 0; \longrightarrow \text{Relative minimum at } x = 2$$

Thus, $f(-2) = 64$ is a relative maximum, and $f(2) = -64$ is a relative minimum. Since $f'(-1) < 0$ and $f'(1) < 0$, we know that f is decreasing on $(-2, 0)$ and $(0, 2)$. Thus, by the First-Derivative Test, f has no relative extremum at $(0, 0)$. We complete the graph, plotting other points as needed. The extrema are shown in the graph at right.

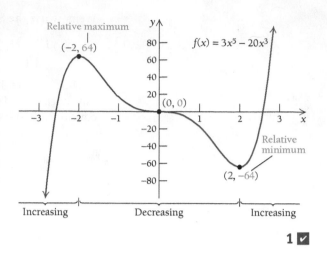

Quick Check 1 ✔

Find any relative extrema and graph the function g given by $g(x) = 10x^3 - 6x^5$.

1 ✔

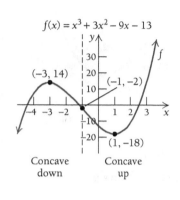

Points of Inflection

Concavity changes from down to up at $(-1, -2)$ in the graph in Example 1 (repeated at the left) and from up to down at $(0, 0)$ in the graph in Example 2 (above). Such points are called **points of inflection**, or **inflection points**. At each such point, the direction of concavity changes. In the figures below, point P is an inflection point. The figures display the sign of $f''(x)$ to indicate the concavity on either side of P.

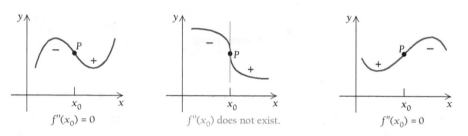

As we move to the right along each curve, the concavity changes at P. Since, as we move through P, the sign of $f''(x)$ changes, either the value of $f''(x_0)$ at P must be 0 or $f''(x_0)$ must not exist.

THEOREM 6   Finding Points of Inflection

If f has a point of inflection, it must occur at a value x_0, in the domain of f, where

$$f''(x_0) = 0 \quad \text{or} \quad f''(x_0) \text{ does not exist.}$$

The converse of Theorem 6 is not necessarily true. That is, if $f''(x_0)$ is 0 or does not exist, then there is not necessarily a point of inflection at x_0. There must be a change in the direction of concavity on either side of x_0 for $(x_0, f(x_0))$ to be a point of inflection. For example, for $f(x) = (x - 2)^4 + 1$ (see the graph on p. 206), we have $f''(2) = 0$, but $(2, f(2))$ is not a point of inflection since the graph of f is concave up on both sides of $x = 2$.

To find *candidates* for points of inflection, we look for x-values at which $f''(x) = 0$ or $f''(x)$ does not exist. If $f''(x)$ changes sign on either side of the x-value, we have a point of inflection.

Theorem 6 is analogous to Theorem 2. Whereas Theorem 2 tells us that candidates for extrema occur when $f'(x) = 0$ or $f'(x)$ does not exist, Theorem 6 tells us that candidates for points of inflection occur when $f''(x) = 0$ or $f''(x)$ does not exist.

EXAMPLE 3 Use the second derivative to determine any point(s) of inflection for the function in Example 2.

Solution The function is given by $f(x) = 3x^5 - 20x^3$, and its second derivative is $f''(x) = 60x^3 - 120x$. We set $f''(x)$ equal to 0 and solve for x:

$$60x^3 - 120x = 0$$
$$60x(x^2 - 2) = 0 \qquad \text{Factoring out } 60x$$
$$60x(x + \sqrt{2})(x - \sqrt{2}) = 0 \qquad \text{Factoring } x^2 - 2 \text{ as a difference of squares}$$
$$x = 0 \quad \text{or} \quad x = -\sqrt{2} \quad \text{or} \quad x = \sqrt{2}. \qquad \text{Using the Principle of Zero Products}$$

Next, we check the sign of $f''(x)$ over the intervals bounded by these three x-values. We are looking for a change in sign from one interval to the next:

Interval				
	$-\sqrt{2}$	0	$\sqrt{2}$	
Test Value	$x = -2$	$x = -1$	$x = 1$	$x = 2$
Sign of $f''(x)$	$f''(-2) < 0$	$f''(-1) > 0$	$f''(1) < 0$	$f''(2) > 0$
Result	Concave down on $(-\infty, -\sqrt{2})$	Concave up on $(-\sqrt{2}, 0)$	Concave down on $(0, \sqrt{2})$	Concave up on $(\sqrt{2}, \infty)$

The graph changes from concave down to concave up at $x = -\sqrt{2}$, from concave up to concave down at $x = 0$, and from concave down to concave up at $x = \sqrt{2}$. Therefore, $(-\sqrt{2}, f(-\sqrt{2}))$, $(0, f(0))$, and $(\sqrt{2}, f(\sqrt{2}))$ are points of inflection. Since

$$f(-\sqrt{2}) = 3(-\sqrt{2})^5 - 20(-\sqrt{2})^3 = 28\sqrt{2},$$
$$f(0) = 3(0)^5 - 20(0)^3 = 0,$$
$$\text{and} \qquad f(\sqrt{2}) = 3(\sqrt{2})^5 - 20(\sqrt{2})^3 = -28\sqrt{2},$$

these points are $(-\sqrt{2}, 28\sqrt{2})$, $(0, 0)$, and $(\sqrt{2}, -28\sqrt{2})$, as shown below.

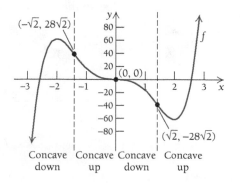

Quick Check 2 ✔

Determine the points of inflection for the function given by $g(x) = 10x^3 - 6x^5$.

2 ✔

Curve Sketching

The first and second derivatives enhance our ability to sketch curves. We use the following strategy:

Strategy for Sketching Graphs*

a) *Derivatives and domain.* Find $f'(x)$ and $f''(x)$. Note the domain of f.

b) *Critical values of f.* Find the critical values by solving $f'(x) = 0$ and finding where $f'(x)$ does not exist. These numbers yield candidates for relative maxima or minima. Find the function values at these points.

c) *Increasing and/or decreasing; relative extrema.* Substitute each critical value, x_0, from step (b) into $f''(x)$. If $f''(x_0) < 0$, then $f(x_0)$ is a relative maximum and f is increasing on the left of x_0 and decreasing on the right. If $f''(x_0) > 0$, then $f(x_0)$ is a relative minimum and f is decreasing on the left of x_0 and increasing on the right.

d) *Inflection points.* Determine candidates for inflection points by finding where $f''(x) = 0$ or where $f''(x)$ does not exist. Find the function values at these points.

e) *Concavity.* Use the candidates for inflection points from step (d) to define intervals. Substitute test values into $f''(x)$ to determine where the graph is concave up ($f''(x) > 0$) and where it is concave down ($f''(x) < 0$).

f) *Sketch the graph.* Sketch the graph using the information from steps (a)–(e), plotting extra points as needed.

The examples that follow apply this step-by-step strategy.

EXAMPLE 4   Find any relative extrema and graph the function f given by

$$f(x) = x^3 - 3x + 2.$$

Solution

a) *Derivatives and domain.* Find $f'(x)$ and $f''(x)$:

$$f'(x) = 3x^2 - 3,$$
$$f''(x) = 6x.$$

Like any polynomial function, f, f', and f'' have as their domain $(-\infty, \infty)$, or $\mathbb{R}$.

b) *Critical values of f.* Find the critical values by determining where $f'(x)$ does not exist and by solving $f'(x) = 0$. We know that $f'(x) = 3x^2 - 3$ exists for all values of x, so the only critical values are where $f'(x)$ is 0:

$$3x^2 - 3 = 0 \qquad \text{Setting } f'(x) \text{ equal to } 0$$
$$3x^2 = 3$$
$$x^2 = 1$$
$$x = \pm 1. \qquad \text{Using the Principle of Square Roots}$$

We have $f(-1) = 4$ and $f(1) = 0$, so we plot $(-1, 4)$ and $(1, 0)$.

---

*This strategy is refined further, for rational functions, in Section 2.3.

c) *Increasing and/or decreasing; relative extrema.* Substitute the critical values into $f''(x)$:

$$f''(-1) = 6(-1) = -6 < 0,$$

so $f(-1) = 4$ is a relative maximum, with f increasing on $(-\infty, -1)$ and decreasing on $(-1, 1)$.

$$f''(1) = 6 \cdot 1 = 6 > 0,$$

so $f(1) = 0$ is a relative minimum, with f decreasing on $(-1, 1)$ and increasing on $(1, \infty)$.

d) *Inflection points.* Find possible inflection points by finding where $f''(x)$ does not exist and by solving $f''(x) = 0$. We know that $f''(x) = 6x$ exists for all values of x, so we solve $f''(x) = 0$:

$$6x = 0 \qquad \text{Setting } f''(x) \text{ equal to } 0$$
$$x = 0. \qquad \text{Dividing both sides by } 6$$

We have $f(0) = 2$, which gives us another point, $(0, 2)$, on the graph.

e) *Concavity.* Find the intervals on which f is concave up or concave down. From step (c), we can conclude that f is concave down over the interval $(-\infty, 0)$ and concave up over $(0, \infty)$.

Interval	$x = -1$	$x = 1$
Test Value	$x = -1$	$x = 1$
Sign of $f''(x)$	$f''(-1) < 0$	$f''(1) > 0$
Result	f' is decreasing; f is concave down on $(-\infty, 0)$	f' is increasing; f is concave up on $(0, \infty)$

Change indicates a
point of inflection
at $x = 0$.

f) *Sketch the graph.* Sketch the graph using the information in steps (a)–(e), plotting some extra values if desired. The graph follows.

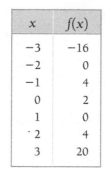

x	$f(x)$
-3	-16
-2	0
-1	4
0	2
1	0
2	4
3	20

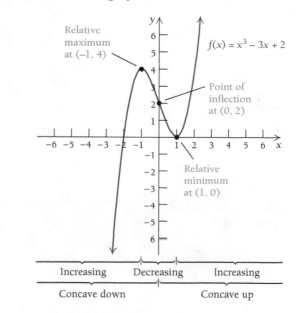

Relative maximum at $(-1, 4)$

$f(x) = x^3 - 3x + 2$

Point of inflection at $(0, 2)$

Relative minimum at $(1, 0)$

Increasing   Decreasing   Increasing

Concave down   Concave up

EXAMPLE 5 Find any relative extrema and graph the function f given by

$$f(x) = x^4 - 2x^2.$$

Solution

a) *Derivatives and domain.* Find $f'(x)$ and $f''(x)$:

$$f'(x) = 4x^3 - 4x,$$
$$f''(x) = 12x^2 - 4.$$

The domain of f, f', and f'' is $\mathbb{R}$.

b) *Critical values.* Since the domain of f' is $\mathbb{R}$, the only critical values are where $f'(x) = 0$:

$$\begin{aligned} 4x^3 - 4x &= 0 \qquad \text{Setting } f'(x) \text{ equal to } 0 \\ 4x(x^2 - 1) &= 0 \\ 4x = 0 \quad &\text{or} \quad x^2 - 1 = 0 \\ x = 0 \quad &\text{or} \quad x^2 = 1 \\ &\qquad\;\; x = \pm 1. \qquad \text{Using the Principle of Square Roots} \end{aligned}$$

We have $f(0) = 0, f(-1) = -1$, and $f(1) = -1$, so $(0, 0)$, $(-1, -1)$, and $(1, -1)$ are on the graph.

c) *Increasing and/or decreasing; relative extrema.* Substitute the critical values into $f''(x)$. For $x = -1$, we have

$$f''(-1) = 12(-1)^2 - 4 = 8 > 0,$$

so $f(-1) = -1$ is a relative minimum, with f decreasing on $(-\infty, -1)$ and increasing on $(-1, 0)$. For $x = 0$, we have

$$f''(0) = 12 \cdot 0^2 - 4 = -4 < 0,$$

so $f(0) = 0$ is a relative maximum, with f increasing on $(-1, 0)$ and decreasing on $(0, 1)$. For $x = 1$, we have

$$f''(1) = 12 \cdot 1^2 - 4 = 8 > 0,$$

so $f(1) = -1$ is also a relative minimum, with f decreasing on $(0, 1)$ and increasing on $(1, \infty)$.

d) *Inflection points.* Find where $f''(x)$ does not exist and where $f''(x) = 0$. Since the domain of f'' is $\mathbb{R}$, we solve $f''(x) = 0$:

$$\begin{aligned} 12x^2 - 4 &= 0 \qquad \text{Setting } f''(x) \text{ equal to } 0 \\ 4(3x^2 - 1) &= 0 \\ 3x^2 - 1 &= 0 \qquad \text{Dividing both sides by 4} \\ 3x^2 &= 1 \\ x^2 &= \frac{1}{3} \\ x &= \pm\frac{1}{\sqrt{3}}. \qquad \text{Using the Principle of Square Roots} \end{aligned}$$

We have

$$f\!\left(\frac{1}{\sqrt{3}}\right) = \left(\frac{1}{\sqrt{3}}\right)^4 - 2\left(\frac{1}{\sqrt{3}}\right)^2$$

$$= \frac{1}{9} - \frac{2}{3} = -\frac{5}{9}$$

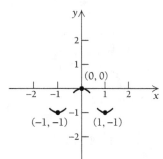

TECHNOLOGY CONNECTION

EXERCISE

1. Consider

$$f(x) = x^3(x - 2)^3.$$

How many relative extrema do you anticipate finding? Where do you think they will be?

Graph f, f', and f'' using $[-1, 3, -2, 6]$ as a viewing window. Estimate any relative extrema and any inflection points of f. Then check your work using the method of Examples 4 and 5.

and

$$f\left(-\frac{1}{\sqrt{3}}\right) = -\frac{5}{9}.$$

Thus, $\left(-\frac{1}{\sqrt{3}}, -\frac{5}{9}\right)$ and $\left(\frac{1}{\sqrt{3}}, -\frac{5}{9}\right)$ are possible inflection points.

e) *Concavity.* Find the intervals on which f is concave up or concave down. From step (c), we can conclude that f is concave up over the intervals $\left(-\infty, -1/\sqrt{3}\right)$ and $\left(1/\sqrt{3}, \infty\right)$ and concave down over the interval $\left(-1/\sqrt{3}, 1/\sqrt{3}\right)$.

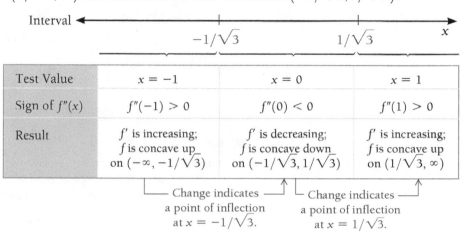

Interval	$-1/\sqrt{3}$		$1/\sqrt{3}$	
Test Value	$x = -1$	$x = 0$	$x = 1$
Sign of $f''(x)$	$f''(-1) > 0$	$f''(0) < 0$	$f''(1) > 0$
Result	f' is increasing; f is concave up on $(-\infty, -1/\sqrt{3})$	f' is decreasing; f is concave down on $(-1/\sqrt{3}, 1/\sqrt{3})$	f' is increasing; f is concave up on $(1/\sqrt{3}, \infty)$

Change indicates a point of inflection at $x = -1/\sqrt{3}$.

Change indicates a point of inflection at $x = 1/\sqrt{3}$.

f) *Sketch the graph.* Sketch the graph using the information in steps (a)–(e). By solving $x^4 - 2x^2 = 0$, we can find the x-intercepts easily. They are $\left(-\sqrt{2}, 0\right)$, $(0, 0)$, and $\left(\sqrt{2}, 0\right)$. Other function values can also be calculated.

Quick Check 3

Find the relative maxima and minima of the function f given by $f(x) = 1 + 8x^2 - x^4$, and sketch the graph.

3 ✔

EXAMPLE 6 Graph the function f given by

$$f(x) = (2x - 5)^{1/3} + 1.$$

List the coordinates of any extrema and points of inflection. State where the function is increasing or decreasing, as well as where it is concave up or concave down.

Solution
a) *Derivatives and domain.* Find $f'(x)$ and $f''(x)$:

$$f'(x) = \tfrac{1}{3}(2x - 5)^{-2/3} \cdot 2 = \tfrac{2}{3}(2x - 5)^{-2/3}, \text{ or } \frac{2}{3(2x - 5)^{2/3}};$$

$$f''(x) = -\tfrac{4}{9}(2x - 5)^{-5/3} \cdot 2 = -\tfrac{8}{9}(2x - 5)^{-5/3}, \text{ or } \frac{-8}{9(2x - 5)^{5/3}}.$$

The domain of f is $\mathbb{R}$. However, the domain of f' and f'' is $\left(-\infty, \frac{5}{2}\right) \cup \left(\frac{5}{2}, \infty\right)$ since their denominators equal zero when $x = \frac{5}{2}$.

b) *Critical values.* Since

$$f'(x) = \frac{2}{3(2x - 5)^{2/3}}$$

is never 0 (a rational expression equals 0 only when its numerator is 0), the only critical value is when $f'(x)$ does not exist. The only instance where $f'(x)$ does not exist is when its denominator is 0:

$$
\begin{array}{ll}
3(2x - 5)^{2/3} = 0 & \text{Setting the denominator equal to zero} \\
(2x - 5)^{2/3} = 0 & \text{Dividing both sides by 3} \\
(2x - 5)^2 = 0 & \text{Cubing both sides} \\
2x - 5 = 0 & \text{Using the Principle of Square Roots} \\
2x = 5 & \\
x = \frac{5}{2} &
\end{array}
$$

We now have $f\left(\frac{5}{2}\right) = \left(2 \cdot \frac{5}{2} - 5\right)^{1/3} + 1 = 0 + 1 = 1$, so we plot the point $\left(\frac{5}{2}, 1\right)$.

c) *Increasing and/or decreasing; relative extrema.* Since $f''\left(\frac{5}{2}\right)$ does not exist, the Second-Derivative Test cannot be used at $x = \frac{5}{2}$. Instead, we use the First-Derivative Test, selecting 2 and 3 as test values on either side of $\frac{5}{2}$:

$$f'(2) = \frac{2}{3(2 \cdot 2 - 5)^{2/3}} = \frac{2}{3(-1)^{2/3}} = \frac{2}{3 \cdot 1} = \frac{2}{3} > 0,$$

and $f'(3) = \dfrac{2}{3(2 \cdot 3 - 5)^{2/3}} = \dfrac{2}{3 \cdot 1^{2/3}} = \dfrac{2}{3 \cdot 1} = \dfrac{2}{3} > 0.$

Since $f'(x) > 0$ on each side of $x = \frac{5}{2}$, we know that f is increasing on both $\left(-\infty, \frac{5}{2}\right)$ and $\left(\frac{5}{2}, \infty\right)$; thus, $f\left(\frac{5}{2}\right) = 1$ is *not* an extremum.

d) *Inflection points.* Find where $f''(x)$ does not exist and where $f''(x) = 0$. Since $f''(x)$ is never 0 (why?), we only need to find where $f''(x)$ does not exist. Since $f''(x)$ cannot exist for $2x - 5 = 0$, there is a possible inflection point at $\left(\frac{5}{2}, 1\right)$.

e) *Concavity.* We check the concavity on each side of $x = \frac{5}{2}$. We choose $x = 2$ and $x = 3$ as our test values:

$$f''(2) = \frac{-8}{9(2 \cdot 2 - 5)^{5/3}} = \frac{-8}{9(-1)} > 0,$$

so f is concave up on $\left(-\infty, \frac{5}{2}\right)$. And

$$f''(3) = \frac{-8}{9(2 \cdot 3 - 5)^{5/3}} = \frac{-8}{9 \cdot 1} < 0,$$

so f is concave down on $\left(\frac{5}{2}, \infty\right)$.

Interval		
Test Value	$x = 2$	$x = 3$
Sign of $f''(x)$	$f''(2) > 0$	$f''(3) < 0$
Result	f' is increasing; f is concave up on $\left(-\infty, \dfrac{5}{2}\right)$	f' is decreasing; f is concave down on $\left(\dfrac{5}{2}, \infty\right)$

Change indicates a point of inflection at $x = 5/2$.

f) *Sketch the graph.* Sketch the graph using the information in steps (a)–(e). By solving $(2x - 5)^{1/3} + 1 = 0$, we can find the *x*-intercept, $(2, 0)$. Other function values can also be calculated.

x	$f(x)$, approximately
0	−0.71
1	−0.44
2	0
$\frac{5}{2}$	1
3	2
4	2.44
5	2.71

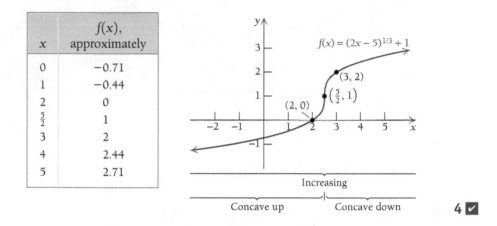

Quick Check 4 ✔

Find any relative extrema and graph the function f given by

$$f(x) = 1 - (x - 2)^{1/3}.$$

4 ✔

The following figures illustrate some information concerning a function f that can be found from its first and second derivatives. Note that the *x*-coordinates of the *x*-intercepts of f' are the critical values of f. Note that the intervals over which f is increasing or decreasing are those intervals for which f' is positive or negative, respectively.

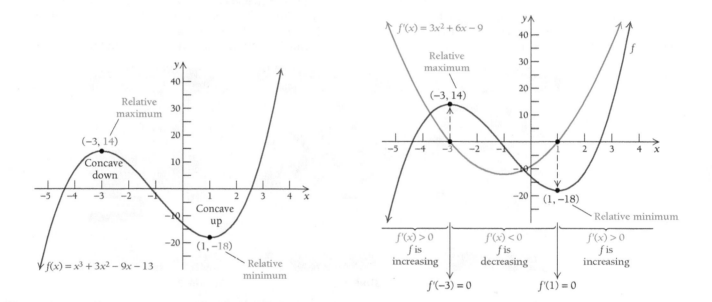

In the figures below, note that the intervals over which f' is increasing or decreasing are, respectively, those intervals over which f'' is positive or negative. And finally, note that when $f''(x) < 0$, the graph of f is concave down, and when $f''(x) > 0$, the graph of f is concave up.

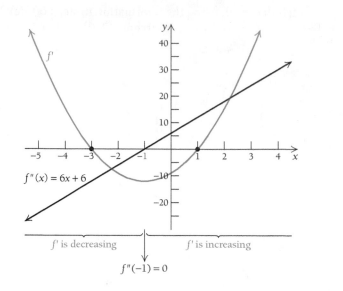

$$f''(x) = 6x + 6$$

f' is decreasing | f' is increasing

$$f''(-1) = 0$$

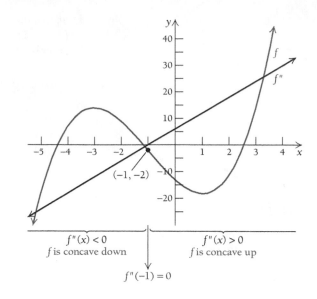

$(-1, -2)$

$f''(x) < 0$
f is concave down

$f''(x) > 0$
f is concave up

$$f''(-1) = 0$$

TECHNOLOGY CONNECTION

Using Graphicus to Find Roots, Extrema, and Inflection Points and to Graph Derivatives

Graphicus has the capability of finding roots, relative extrema, and points of inflection. Let's consider $f(x) = x^4 - 2x^2$, from Example 5.

After opening Graphicus, touch the blank rectangle at the top of the screen and enter y(x)=x^4-2x^2. Press $\boxed{+}$ in the upper right. You will see the graph (Fig. 1). Then touch the fourth icon from the left at the bottom, and you will see the roots highlighted on the graph (Fig. 2). Touch the left-hand root

FIGURE 1   FIGURE 2   FIGURE 3

FIGURE 4   FIGURE 5   FIGURE 6   FIGURE 7

(continued)

symbol, and a value for one root, in this case, an approximation, -1.414214, is displayed (Fig. 3).

To find the relative extrema, touch the fifth icon from the left; the relative extrema will be highlighted on the graph in a different color. Touch each point to identify the relative minima at $(-1, -1)$ and $(1, -1)$ and a relative maximum at $(0, 0)$ (Fig. 4).

To find points of inflection, touch the sixth icon from the left, and the points of inflection will be highlighted as shown in Fig. 5. Touch these points and the approximations $(-0.577, -0.556)$ and $(0.577, -0.556)$ are displayed.

Graphicus can graph derivatives. Go back to the original graph of f (Fig. 1). Touch $\boxed{+}$; then press Add derivative, and you will see the original graph and the graph of the first derivative as a dashed line of a different color (Fig. 6). Touch $\boxed{+}$ and Add derivative again, and you will see the graph of the original function, with dashed graphs of the first and second derivatives in different colors (Fig. 7). You can toggle between the derivatives by pressing the colored squares above the graphs.

EXERCISES

Use Graphicus to graph each function and its first and second derivatives. Then find approximations for roots, relative extrema, and points of inflection.

1. $f(x) = 2x^3 - x^4$ **2.** $f(x) = x(200 - x)$

3. $f(x) = x^3 - 6x^2$

4. $f(x) = -4.32 + 1.44x + 3x^2 - x^3$

5. $g(x) = x\sqrt{4 - x^2}$

6. $g(x) = \dfrac{4x}{x^2 + 1}$ **7.** $f(x) = \dfrac{x^2 - 3x}{x - 1}$

8. $f(x) = |x + 2| - 3$ **9.** $f(x) = 3x^5 - 5x^3$

Section Summary

- The second derivative f'' is used to determine the *concavity* of the graph of f.
- If $f''(x) > 0$ for all x in an open interval I, then the graph of f is *concave up* over I.
- If $f''(x) < 0$ for all x in an open interval I, then the graph of f is *concave down* over I.
- If c is a critical value and $f''(c) > 0$, then $f(c)$ is a relative minimum.
- If c is a critical value and $f''(c) < 0$, then $f(c)$ is a relative maximum.

- If c is a critical value and $f''(c) = 0$, the First-Derivative Test must be used to determine if $f(c)$ is a relative extremum.
- If $f''(x_0) = 0$ or $f''(x_0)$ does not exist, and there is a change in concavity on the left and on the right of x_0, then the point $(x_0, f(x_0))$ is called a *point of inflection*.
- Finding relative extrema, intervals over which a function is increasing or decreasing, intervals of upward or downward concavity, and points of inflection form a strategy for accurate curve sketching.

2.2 Exercise Set

For each function, find all relative extrema and classify each as a maximum or minimum. Use the Second-Derivative Test where possible.

1. $f(x) = 4 - x^2$ **2.** $f(x) = 5 - x^2$

3. $f(x) = x^2 + x - 1$ **4.** $f(x) = x^2 - x$

5. $f(x) = -4x^2 + 3x - 1$ **6.** $f(x) = -5x^2 + 8x - 7$

7. $f(x) = x^3 - 12x - 1$

8. $f(x) = 8x^3 - 6x + 1$

Sketch the graph of each function. List the coordinates of any extrema or points of inflection. State where the function is increasing or decreasing and where its graph is concave up or concave down.

9. $f(x) = x^3 - 27x$ **10.** $f(x) = x^3 - 12x$

11. $f(x) = 2x^3 - 3x^2 - 36x + 28$

12. $f(x) = 3x^3 - 36x - 3$ **13.** $f(x) = 80 - 9x^2 - x^3$

14. $f(x) = \frac{8}{3}x^3 - 2x + \frac{1}{3}$ **15.** $f(x) = -x^3 + 3x - 2$

16. $f(x) = -x^3 + 3x^2 - 4$

17. $f(x) = 3x^4 - 16x^3 + 18x^2$
(Round results to three decimal places.)

18. $f(x) = 3x^4 + 4x^3 - 12x^2 + 5$
(Round results to three decimal places.)

19. $f(x) = x^4 - 6x^2$ **20.** $f(x) = 2x^2 - x^4$

21. $f(x) = x^3 - 6x^2 + 9x + 1$

22. $f(x) = x^3 - 2x^2 - 4x + 3$

23. $f(x) = x^4 - 2x^3$ **24.** $f(x) = 3x^4 + 4x^3$

25. $f(x) = x^3 - 6x^2 - 135x$

26. $f(x) = x^3 - 3x^2 - 144x - 140$

27. $f(x) = x^4 - 4x^3 + 10$ **28.** $f(x) = \frac{4}{3}x^3 - 2x^2 + x$

29. $f(x) = x^3 - 6x^2 + 12x - 6$

30. $f(x) = x^3 + 3x + 1$ **31.** $f(x) = 5x^3 - 3x^5$

32. $f(x) = 20x^3 - 3x^5$
(Round results to three decimal places.)

33. $f(x) = x^2(1 - x)^2$
(Round results to three decimal places.)

34. $f(x) = x^2(3 - x)^2$
(Round results to three decimal places.)

35. $f(x) = (x - 1)^{2/3}$ **36.** $f(x) = (x + 1)^{2/3}$

37. $f(x) = (x - 3)^{1/3} - 1$ **38.** $f(x) = (x - 2)^{1/3} + 3$

39. $f(x) = -2(x - 4)^{2/3} + 5$

40. $f(x) = -3(x - 2)^{2/3} + 3$

41. $f(x) = -x\sqrt{1 - x^2}$ **42.** $f(x) = x\sqrt{4 - x^2}$

43. $f(x) = \dfrac{8x}{x^2 + 1}$ **44.** $f(x) = \dfrac{x}{x^2 + 1}$

45. $f(x) = \dfrac{-4}{x^2 + 1}$ **46.** $f(x) = \dfrac{3}{x^2 + 1}$

For Exercises 47–56, sketch a graph that possesses the characteristics listed. Answers may vary.

47. f is decreasing and concave up on $(-\infty, 2)$,
f is decreasing and concave down on $(2, \infty)$.

48. f is increasing and concave up on $(-\infty, 4)$,
f is increasing and concave down on $(4, \infty)$.

49. f is decreasing and concave down on $(-\infty, 3)$,
f is decreasing and concave up on $(3, \infty)$.

50. f is increasing and concave down on $(-\infty, 1)$,
f is increasing and concave up on $(1, \infty)$.

51. f is concave up at $(1, -3)$, concave down at $(8, 7)$, and has an inflection point at $(5, 4)$.

52. f is concave down at $(1, 5)$, concave up at $(7, -2)$, and has an inflection point at $(4, 1)$.

53. $f'(-3) = 0, f''(-3) < 0, f(-3) = 8; f'(9) = 0$,
$f''(9) > 0, f(9) = -6; f''(2) = 0$, and $f(2) = 1$

54. $f'(-1) = 0, f''(-1) > 0, f(-1) = -5; f'(7) = 0$,
$f''(7) < 0, f(7) = 10; f''(3) = 0$, and $f(3) = 2$

55. $f'(0) = 0, f''(0) < 0, f(0) = 5; f'(2) = 0, f''(2) > 0$,
$f(2) = 2; f'(4) = 0, f''(4) < 0$, and $f(4) = 3$

56. $f'(-1) = 0, f''(-1) > 0, f(-1) = -2; f'(1) = 0$,
$f''(1) > 0, f(1) = -2; f'(0) = 0, f''(0) < 0$,
and $f(0) = 0$

APPLICATIONS

Business and Economics

Total revenue, cost, and profit.   Using the same set of axes, graph R, C, and P, the total-revenue, total-cost, and total-profit functions.

57. $R(x) = 50x - 0.5x^2$, $C(x) = 4x + 10$

58. $R(x) = 50x - 0.5x^2$, $C(x) = 10x + 3$

59. Small business.   The percentage of the U.S. national income generated by nonfarm proprietors between 1970 and 2000 can be modeled by the function f given by

$$p(x) = \frac{13x^3 - 240x^2 - 2460x + 585{,}000}{75{,}000},$$

where x is the number of years since 1970. (*Source*: Based on data from www.bls.gov.) Sketch the graph of this function for $0 \le x \le 40$.

60. Labor force.   The percentage of the U.S. civilian labor force aged 45–54 between 1970 and 2000 can be modeled by the function f given by

$$f(x) = 0.025x^2 - 0.71x + 20.44,$$

where x is the number of years after 1970. (*Source*: Based on data from www.bls.gov.) Sketch the graph of this function for $0 \le x \le 30$.

Life and Physical Sciences

61. Rainfall in Reno.   The average monthly rainfall in Reno, Nevada, is approximated by

$$R(t) = -0.006t^4 + 0.213t^3 - 1.702t^2 + 0.615t + 27.745,$$

where $R(t)$ is the amount of rainfall in millimeters at t months since December. (*Source*: Based on data from weather.com.)

Find the point(s) of inflection for R. What is the significance of these point(s)?

62. Coughing velocity. A person coughs when a foreign object is in the windpipe. The velocity of the cough depends on the size of the object. Suppose a person has a windpipe with a 20-mm radius. If a foreign object has a radius r, in millimeters, then the velocity V, in millimeters per second, needed to remove the object by a cough is given by

$$V(r) = k(20r^2 - r^3), \quad 0 \le r \le 20,$$

where k is some positive constant. For what size object is the maximum velocity required to remove the object?

SYNTHESIS

In each of Exercises 63 and 64, determine which graph is the derivative of the other and explain why.

63.   **64.**

65. Use calculus to prove that the relative minimum or maximum for any function f for which

$$f(x) = ax^2 + bx + c, \quad a \ne 0,$$

occurs at $x = -b/(2a)$.

66. Use calculus to prove that the point of inflection for any function g given by

$$g(x) = ax^3 + bx^2 + cx + d, \quad a \ne 0,$$

occurs at $x = -b/(3a)$.

For Exercises 67–73, assume that f is differentiable over $(-\infty, \infty)$. Classify each of the following statements as either true or false. If a statement is false, explain why.

67. If f has exactly two critical values at $x = a$ and $x = b$, where $a < b$, then there must exist exactly one point of inflection at $x = c$ such that $a < c < b$. In other words, exactly one point of inflection must exist between any two critical points.

68. If f has exactly two critical values at $x = a$ and $x = b$, where $a < b$, then there must exist at least one point of inflection at $x = c$ such that $a < c < b$. In other words, at least one point of inflection must exist between any two critical points.

69. A function f can have no extrema but still have at least one point of inflection.

70. If f has two points of inflection, then there is a critical value located between those points of inflection.

71. The function f can have a point of inflection at a critical value.

72. The function f can have a point of inflection at an extreme value.

73. A function f can have exactly one extreme value but no points of inflection.

74. Hours of daylight. The number of hours of daylight in Chicago is represented in the graph below. On what dates is the number of hours of daylight changing most rapidly? How can you tell?

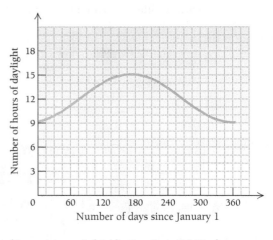

(*Source:* Astronomical Applications Dept., U.S. Naval Observatory.)

TECHNOLOGY CONNECTION

Graph each function. Then estimate any relative extrema. Where appropriate, round to three decimal places.

75. $f(x) = 4x - 6x^{2/3}$

76. $f(x) = 3x^{2/3} - 2x$

77. $f(x) = x^2(1 - x)^3$

78. $f(x) = x^2(x - 2)^3$

79. $f(x) = (x - 1)^{2/3} - (x + 1)^{2/3}$

80. $f(x) = x - \sqrt{x}$

81. Head of household education. The data in the following table relate the percentage of households headed by someone with a bachelor's degree or higher to the number of years since 2000.

NUMBER OF YEARS SINCE 2000	PERCENTAGE OF HOUSEHOLDS
0	66.0
1	75.2
3	78.3
7	84.0
9	88.5
10	89.2
11	89.9

(*Source:* www.census.gov/prod/2013pubs/ p20-569.pdf.)

a) Use regression (see Section R.6) to fit linear, cubic, and quartic functions $y = f(x)$ to the data, where x is the number of years since 2000 and y is the percentage of households headed by someone with a bachelor's degree or higher. Which function f best fits the data?
b) What is the domain of f?
c) Does f have any relative extrema? How can you tell?

Answers to Quick Checks

1. Relative minimum: -4 at $x = -1$; relative maximum: 4 at $x = 1$

2. $(0, 0)$, $\left(\frac{\sqrt{2}}{2}, 2.475\right)$, and $\left(-\frac{\sqrt{2}}{2}, -2.475\right)$
3. Relative maxima: 17 at $x = -2$ and $x = 2$; relative minimum: 1 at $x = 0$

4. No relative extrema

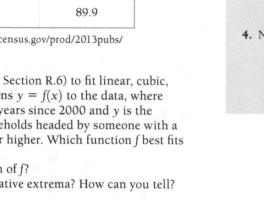

2.3

- Find limits involving infinity.
- Determine the asymptotes of a function's graph.
- Graph rational functions.

Graph Sketching: Asymptotes and Rational Functions

Thus far we have developed a strategy for graphing continuous functions. We now consider discontinuous functions, most of which are rational functions. Our graphing skills must allow for discontinuities and certain lines called *asymptotes*.

Recall the definition of a rational function:

> **DEFINITION**
>
> A **rational function** is a function f that can be described by
>
> $$f(x) = \frac{P(x)}{Q(x)},$$
>
> where $P(x)$ and $Q(x)$ are polynomials, with $Q(x)$ not the zero polynomial. The domain of f consists of all x for which $Q(x) \neq 0$.

We wish to graph rational functions in which the denominator is not a constant. Before doing so, we need to reconsider limits.

Vertical and Horizontal Asymptotes

Consider the rational function

$$f(x) = \frac{x^2 - 1}{x^2 + x - 6} = \frac{(x-1)(x+1)}{(x-2)(x+3)},$$

whose graph is shown below.

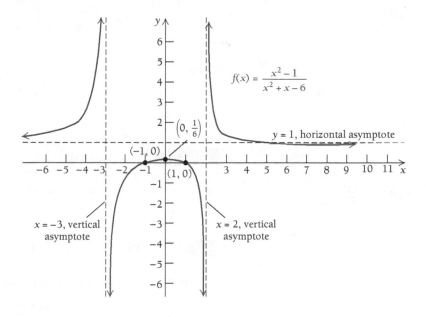

$$f(x) = \frac{x^2-1}{x^2+x-6}$$

$y = 1$, horizontal asymptote

$\left(0, \frac{1}{6}\right)$

$(-1, 0)$

$(1, 0)$

$x = -3$, vertical asymptote

$x = 2$, vertical asymptote

Note that as x gets closer to 2 from the left, the function values approach $-\infty$. As x gets closer to 2 from the right, the function values approach ∞. Thus,

$$\lim_{x \to 2^-} f(x) = -\infty \quad \text{and} \quad \lim_{x \to 2^+} f(x) = \infty.$$

For this graph, we can regard the line $x = 2$ as a "limiting line" called a *vertical asymptote*. The line $x = -3$ is another vertical asymptote.

> **DEFINITION**
>
> The line $x = a$ is a **vertical asymptote** if any of these limit statements is true:
>
> $$\lim_{x \to a^-} f(x) = \infty, \quad \lim_{x \to a^-} f(x) = -\infty, \quad \lim_{x \to a^+} f(x) = \infty, \quad \text{or} \quad \lim_{x \to a^+} f(x) = -\infty.$$

If a rational function f is simplified, meaning that the numerator and denominator have no common factor other than -1 or 1, then if a makes the denominator 0, the line $x = a$ is a vertical asymptote. For example,

$$f(x) = \frac{x^2 - 9}{x - 3} = \frac{(x-3)(x+3)}{x-3}$$

does not have a vertical asymptote at $x = 3$ because $(x - 3)$ is a common factor of the numerator and the denominator. In contrast,

$$g(x) = \frac{x^2 - 4}{x^2 + x - 12} = \frac{(x+2)(x-2)}{(x-3)(x+4)}$$

has $x = 3$ and $x = -4$ as vertical asymptotes since neither $(x - 3)$ nor $(x + 4)$ is a factor of the numerator.

The figures below show four ways in which a vertical asymptote can occur. The dashed lines represent the asymptotes. They are shown for visual assistance only; they are not part of the graphs of the functions.

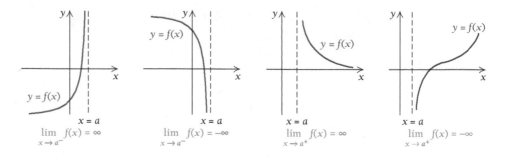

Quick Check 1 ☑

Determine the vertical asymptotes of

$$f(x) = \frac{1}{x(x^2 - 16)}.$$

EXAMPLE 1   Determine the vertical asymptotes of $f(x) = \dfrac{3x - 2}{x(x - 5)(x + 3)}$.

Solution   The expression is simplified. Thus, the vertical asymptotes are the lines $x = 0$, $x = 5$, and $x = -3$.   **1** ☑

EXAMPLE 2   Determine the vertical asymptotes of $f(x) = \dfrac{x^2 - 2x}{x^3 - x}$.

Solution   We first simplify the expression:

$$f(x) = \frac{x^2 - 2x}{x^3 - x} = \frac{x(x - 2)}{x(x - 1)(x + 1)}$$

$$= \frac{x - 2}{(x - 1)(x + 1)}, \quad x \neq 0.$$

We now see that the vertical asymptotes are the lines $x = -1$ and $x = 1$.   **2** ☑

Quick Check 2 ☑

Determine the vertical asymptotes of

$$g(x) = \frac{x - 2}{x^3 - x^2 - 2x}.$$

Look again at the graph on p. 221. Note that function values approach 1 as x approaches $-\infty$, meaning that $f(x) \to 1$ as $x \to -\infty$. Also, function values approach 1 as x approaches ∞, meaning that $f(x) \to 1$ as $x \to \infty$. Thus,

$$\lim_{x \to -\infty} f(x) = 1 \quad \text{and} \quad \lim_{x \to \infty} f(x) = 1.$$

The line $y = 1$ is called a *horizontal asymptote*.

DEFINITION

The line $y = b$ is a **horizontal asymptote** if either or both of the following limit statements is true:

$$\lim_{x \to -\infty} f(x) = b \quad \text{or} \quad \lim_{x \to \infty} f(x) = b.$$

Horizontal asymptotes occur when the degree of the numerator is less than or equal to the degree of the denominator. (The degree of a polynomial in one variable is the highest power of that variable.) The following figures show three ways in which horizontal asymptotes can occur.

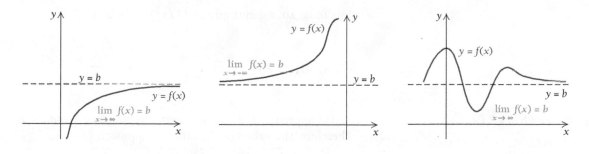

A horizontal asymptote is the limit of a rational function as inputs approach $-\infty$ or ∞.

EXAMPLE 3 Determine the horizontal asymptote of $f(x) = \dfrac{3x - 4}{x}$.

Solution To find the horizontal asymptote, we consider

$$\lim_{x \to \infty} f(x) = \lim_{x \to \infty} \frac{3x - 4}{x}.$$

As the inputs approach ∞, the outputs approach 3. Thus,

$$\lim_{x \to \infty} \frac{3x - 4}{x} = 3.$$

Another way to find this limit is to use the fact that

$$\text{as } x \to \infty, \text{ we have } \frac{1}{x} \to 0, \text{ and more generally, } \frac{b}{ax^n} \to 0,$$

for any positive integer n and any constants a and b, $a \neq 0$. We multiply by 1, using $(1/x) \div (1/x)$:

$$\lim_{x \to \infty} \frac{3x - 4}{x} = \lim_{x \to \infty} \frac{3x - 4}{x} \cdot \frac{(1/x)}{(1/x)}$$

$$= \lim_{x \to \infty} \frac{\dfrac{3x}{x} - \dfrac{4}{x}}{\dfrac{x}{x}}$$

$$= \lim_{x \to \infty} \frac{3 - \dfrac{4}{x}}{1} \quad \text{Simplifying, we assume } x \neq 0.$$

$$= \lim_{x \to \infty} \left(3 - \frac{4}{x} \right)$$

$$= 3 - 0 = 3.$$

In a similar manner, it can be shown that

$$\lim_{x \to -\infty} f(x) = 3.$$

The horizontal asymptote is the line $y = 3$.

EXAMPLE 4 Determine the horizontal asymptote of $f(x) = \dfrac{3x^2 + 2x - 4}{2x^2 - x + 1}$.

Solution As in Example 3, the degree of the numerator is the same as the degree of the denominator. Let's adapt the algebraic approach used in that example.

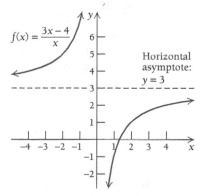

$f(x) = \dfrac{3x - 4}{x}$

Horizontal asymptote: $y = 3$

A visualization of Example 3

Horizontal asymptote: $y = \dfrac{3}{2}$

$f(x) = \dfrac{3x^2 + 2x - 4}{2x^2 - x + 1}$

A visualization of Example 4

To do so, we multiply by $(1/x^2) \div (1/x^2)$:

$$f(x) = \frac{3x^2 + 2x - 4}{2x^2 - x + 1} \cdot \frac{\dfrac{1}{x^2}}{\dfrac{1}{x^2}} = \frac{3 + \dfrac{2}{x} - \dfrac{4}{x^2}}{2 - \dfrac{1}{x} + \dfrac{1}{x^2}}.$$

Quick Check 3 ✔

Determine the horizontal asymptote of

$$f(x) = \frac{(2x - 1)(x + 1)}{(3x + 2)(5x + 6)}.$$

As $|x|$ approaches ∞, the numerator approaches 3 and the denominator approaches 2. Therefore, the values of the function approach $\frac{3}{2}$. Thus,

$$\lim_{x \to -\infty} f(x) = \frac{3}{2} \quad \text{and} \quad \lim_{x \to \infty} f(x) = \frac{3}{2}.$$

The line $y = \frac{3}{2}$ is a horizontal asymptote.   **3** ✔

Examples 3 and 4 lead to the following result.

> When the degree of the numerator is the same as the degree of the denominator, the line $y = a/b$ is a horizontal asymptote, where a is the leading coefficient of the numerator and b is the leading coefficient of the denominator.

A visualization of Example 5

EXAMPLE 5   Determine the horizontal asymptote of $f(x) = \dfrac{2x + 3}{x^3 - 2x^2 + 4}$.

Solution   Since the degree of the numerator is less than the degree of the denominator, there is a horizontal asymptote. To identify that asymptote, we divide both the numerator and denominator by the highest power of x in the denominator, as in Examples 3 and 4, and find the limits as $|x| \to \infty$:

$$f(x) = \frac{2x + 3}{x^3 - 2x^2 + 4} \cdot \frac{\dfrac{1}{x^3}}{\dfrac{1}{x^3}} = \frac{\dfrac{2}{x^2} + \dfrac{3}{x^3}}{1 - \dfrac{2}{x} + \dfrac{4}{x^3}}.$$

As $|x|$ approaches ∞, the expressions with a denominator that is a power of x approach 0. Thus, the numerator of $f(x)$ approaches 0 as its denominator approaches 1; hence, the entire expression approaches 0. That is, for $x \to -\infty$ or $x \to \infty$,

$$f(x) \approx \frac{0 + 0}{1 - 0 + 0},$$

so $\lim\limits_{x \to -\infty} f(x) = 0$ and $\lim\limits_{x \to \infty} f(x) = 0$,

and the x-axis, the line $y = 0$, is a horizontal asymptote.   ∎

> When the degree of the numerator is less than the degree of the denominator, the x-axis, or the line $y = 0$, is a horizontal asymptote.

Slant Asymptotes

Some asymptotes are neither vertical nor horizontal. For example, in the graph of

$$f(x) = \frac{x^2 - 4}{x - 1},$$

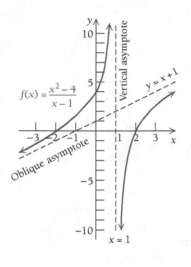

$$f(x) = \frac{x^2 - 4}{x - 1}$$

Oblique asymptote

Vertical asymptote

$y = x + 1$

$x = 1$

shown at left, as $|x|$ approaches ∞, the curve approaches the line $y = x + 1$. The line $y = x + 1$ is called a *slant asymptote*, or *oblique asymptote*. In Example 6, we will see how the line $y = x + 1$ is determined.

> **DEFINITION**
>
> A linear asymptote that is neither vertical nor horizontal is called a **slant asymptote**, or an **oblique asymptote**. For any rational function of the form $f(x) = P(x)/Q(x)$, a slant asymptote occurs when the degree of $P(x)$ is exactly 1 more than the degree of $Q(x)$.

We find a slant asymptote by division.

EXAMPLE 6   Find the slant asymptote of $f(x) = \dfrac{x^2 - 4}{x - 1}$.

Solution   When we divide the numerator by the denominator, we obtain a quotient of $x + 1$ and a remainder of -3:

$$
\begin{array}{r}
x + 1 \\
x - 1 \overline{)\, x^2 \quad\;\; - 4} \\
\underline{x^2 - x} \\
x - 4 \\
\underline{x - 1} \\
-3
\end{array}
\qquad
f(x) = \frac{x^2 - 4}{x - 1} = (x + 1) + \frac{-3}{x - 1}.
$$

Quick Check 4 ✔

Find the slant asymptote of

$$g(x) = \frac{2x^2 + x - 1}{x - 3}.$$

Note that as $|x|$ approaches ∞, $-3/(x - 1)$ approaches 0. Thus, $y = x + 1$ is the slant asymptote.

4 ✔

Intercepts

If they exist, **x-intercepts** occur at values of x for which $y = f(x) = 0$ and are points at which the graph crosses (or touches) the x-axis. If it exists, the **y-intercept** occurs at the value of y for which $x = 0$ and is the point at which the graph crosses (or touches) the y-axis.

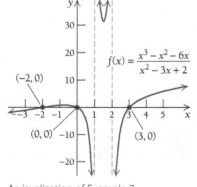

$$f(x) = \frac{x^3 - x^2 - 6x}{x^2 - 3x + 2}$$

$(-2, 0)$

$(0, 0)$

$(3, 0)$

A visualization of Example 7

EXAMPLE 7   Find the intercepts of the function given by

$$f(x) = \frac{x^3 - x^2 - 6x}{x^2 - 3x + 2}.$$

Solution   We factor the numerator and the denominator:

$$f(x) = \frac{x(x + 2)(x - 3)}{(x - 1)(x - 2)}.$$

To find the x-intercepts, we solve $f(x) = 0$. Such values occur when the numerator is 0 and the denominator is not. Thus, we solve

$$x(x + 2)(x - 3) = 0.$$

The x-values that make the numerator 0 are 0, -2, and 3. Since none of these make the denominator 0, they yield the x-intercepts $(0, 0)$, $(-2, 0)$, and $(3, 0)$.

To find the y-intercept, we let $x = 0$:

$$f(0) = \frac{0^3 - 0^2 - 6(0)}{0^2 - 3(0) + 2} = 0.$$

Quick Check 5 ✔

Find the intercepts of the function given by

$$h(x) = \frac{x^3 - x}{x^2 - 4}.$$

In this case, the y-intercept is also an x-intercept, $(0, 0)$.

5 ✔

Sketching Graphs

We can now refine our strategy for graphing.

Strategy for Sketching Graphs

a) *Intercepts.* Find any x- and y-intercepts.

b) *Asymptotes.* Find any vertical, horizontal, or slant asymptotes.

c) *Derivatives and domain.* Find $f'(x)$ and $f''(x)$. Find the domain of f.

d) *Critical values of f.* Find any inputs for which $f'(x)$ is not defined or for which $f'(x) = 0$.

e) *Increasing and/or decreasing; relative extrema.* Substitute each critical value, x_0, from step (d) into $f''(x)$. If $f''(x_0) < 0$, then x_0 yields a relative maximum and f is increasing on the left of x_0 and decreasing on the right. If $f''(x_0) > 0$, then x_0 yields a relative minimum and f is decreasing on the left of x_0 and increasing on the right. On intervals where no critical value exists, use f' and test values to find where f is increasing or decreasing.

f) *Inflection points.* Determine candidates for inflection points by finding x-values for which $f''(x)$ does not exist or for which $f''(x) = 0$. Find the function values at these points. If a function value $f(x)$ does not exist, then the function does not have an inflection point at x.

g) *Concavity.* Use the values from step (f) as endpoints of intervals. Determine the concavity over each interval by checking to see where f' is increasing— that is, where $f''(x) > 0$—and where f' is decreasing—that is, where $f''(x) < 0$. Do this by substituting a test value from each interval into $f''(x)$. Use the results of step (d).

h) *Sketch the graph.* Use the information from steps (a)–(g) to sketch the graph, plotting extra points as needed.

EXAMPLE 8 Sketch the graph of $f(x) = \dfrac{8}{x^2 - 4}$.

Solution

a) *Intercepts.* The x-intercepts occur at values for which the numerator is 0 but the denominator is not. Here, the numerator is a constant, so there are no x-intercepts. To find the y-intercept, we compute $f(0)$:

$$f(0) = \frac{8}{0^2 - 4} = \frac{8}{-4} = -2.$$

This gives us one point on the graph, $(0, -2)$.

b) *Asymptotes.*

Vertical: The denominator, $x^2 - 4 = (x + 2)(x - 2)$, is 0 for x-values of -2 and 2. Thus, the graph has the lines $x = -2$ and $x = 2$ as vertical asymptotes. We draw them as dashed lines (they are guidelines, *not* part of the actual graph).

Horizontal: The degree of the numerator is less than the degree of the denominator, so the x-axis, $y = 0$, is the horizontal asymptote.

Slant: There is no slant asymptote since the degree of the numerator is not 1 more than the degree of the denominator.

c) *Derivatives and domain.* We find $f'(x)$ and $f''(x)$ using the Quotient Rule:

$$f'(x) = \frac{-16x}{(x^2 - 4)^2} \quad \text{and} \quad f''(x) = \frac{16(3x^2 + 4)}{(x^2 - 4)^3}.$$

The domain of f, f', and f'' is $(-\infty, -2) \cup (-2, 2) \cup (2, \infty)$, as determined in step (b).

d) *Critical values of f.* We look for values of x for which $f'(x) = 0$ or for which $f'(x)$ does not exist. From step (c), we see that $f'(x) = 0$ for values of x for which $-16x = 0$, but the denominator is not 0. The only such number is 0 itself. The derivative $f'(x)$ does not exist at -2 and 2, but neither value is in the domain of f. Thus, the only critical value is 0.

e) *Increasing and/or decreasing; relative extrema.* We use the undefined values and the critical values to determine the intervals over which f is increasing and the intervals over which f is decreasing. The values to consider are $-2, 0$, and 2.

Since $\quad f''(0) = \dfrac{16(3 \cdot 0^2 + 4)}{(0^2 - 4)^3} = \dfrac{64}{-64} < 0,$

we know that a relative maximum exists at $(0, f(0))$, or $(0, -2)$. Thus, f is increasing over the interval $(-2, 0)$ and decreasing over $(0, 2)$.

Since $f''(x)$ does not exist for the x-values -2 and 2, we use $f'(x)$ and test values to see if f is increasing or decreasing on $(-\infty, -2)$ and $(2, \infty)$.

Test -3: $\quad f'(-3) = \dfrac{-16(-3)}{[(-3)^2 - 4]^2} = \dfrac{48}{25} > 0$, so f is increasing on $(-\infty, -2)$.

Test 3: $\quad f'(3) = \dfrac{-16(3)}{[(3)^2 - 4]^2} = \dfrac{-48}{25} < 0$, so f is decreasing on $(2, \infty)$.

f) *Inflection points.* We determine candidates for inflection points by finding where $f''(x)$ does not exist and where $f''(x) = 0$. The only values for which $f''(x)$ does not exist are where $x^2 - 4 = 0$, or -2 and 2. Neither value is in the domain of f, so we focus solely on where $f''(x) = 0$, or

$16(3x^2 + 4) = 0.$

Since $16(3x^2 + 4) > 0$ for all real numbers x, there are no points of inflection.

g) *Concavity.* Since no values were found in step (f), the only place where concavity could change is on either side of the vertical asymptotes, $x = -2$ and $x = 2$. To check, we see where $f''(x)$ is positive or negative. The numbers -2 and 2 divide the x-axis into three intervals. We choose a test value in each interval and substitute into $f''(x)$.

Test -3: $\quad f''(-3) = \dfrac{16[3(-3)^2 + 4]}{[(-3)^2 - 4]^3} > 0.$

Test 0: $\quad f''(0) = \dfrac{16[3(0)^2 + 4]}{[(0)^2 - 4]^3} < 0.$ We already knew this from step (e).

Test 3: $\quad f''(3) = \dfrac{16[3(3)^2 + 4]}{[(3)^2 - 4]^3} > 0.$

Interval			
Test Value	$x = -3$	$x = 0$	$x = 3$
Sign of $f''(x)$	$f''(-3) > 0$	$f''(0) < 0$	$f''(3) > 0$
Result	f' is increasing; f is concave up on $(-\infty, -2)$	f' is decreasing; f is concave down on $(-2, 2)$	f' is increasing; f is concave up on $(2, \infty)$

Change does not indicate a point of inflection since $f(-2)$ does not exist.

Change does not indicate a point of inflection since $f(2)$ does not exist.

The function is concave up over the intervals $(-\infty, -2)$ and $(2, \infty)$. The function is concave down over $(-2, 2)$.

h) *Sketch the graph.* We sketch the graph using the information in the following table, plotting extra points as needed. The graph is shown below.

x	$f(x)$
-4	$\frac{2}{3}$
-3	1.6
-1	$-2\frac{2}{3}$
0	-2
1	$-2\frac{2}{3}$
3	1.6
4	$\frac{2}{3}$

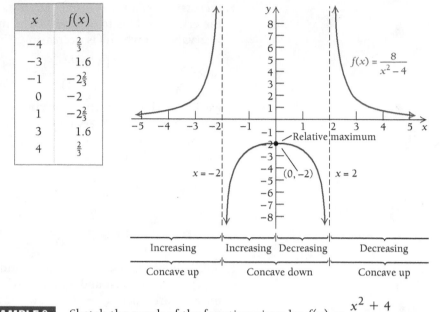

EXAMPLE 9 Sketch the graph of the function given by $f(x) = \dfrac{x^2 + 4}{x}$.

Solution

a) *Intercepts.* The equation $f(x) = 0$ has no solution, so there is no x-intercept. Since 0 is not in the domain, there is no y-intercept either.

b) *Asymptotes.*

Vertical: Since replacing x with 0 makes the denominator 0, the line $x = 0$ (the y-axis) is a vertical asymptote.

Horizontal: The degree of the numerator is greater than the degree of the denominator, so there is no horizontal asymptote.

Slant: The degree of the numerator is 1 greater than the degree of the denominator, so there is a slant asymptote. Note that

$$\frac{x^2 + 4}{x} = \frac{x^2}{x} + \frac{4}{x} = x + \frac{4}{x}.$$

As $|x|$ approaches ∞, $4/x$ approaches 0, so the line $y = x$ is a slant asymptote.

c) *Derivatives and domain.* We find $f'(x)$ and $f''(x)$:

$$f'(x) = 1 - 4x^{-2} = 1 - \frac{4}{x^2};$$

$$f''(x) = 8x^{-3} = \frac{8}{x^3}.$$

The domain of f, f', and f'' is $(-\infty, 0) \cup (0, \infty)$, or all real numbers except 0.

d) *Critical values of f.* We see from step (c) that $f'(x)$ is undefined at $x = 0$, but 0 is not in the domain of f. Thus, to find critical values, we solve $f'(x) = 0$, looking for solutions other than 0:

$$1 - \frac{4}{x^2} = 0 \qquad \text{Setting } f'(x) \text{ equal to 0}$$

$$1 = \frac{4}{x^2}$$

$$x^2 = 4 \qquad \text{Multiplying both sides by } x^2$$

$$x = \pm 2.$$

Thus, -2 and 2 are critical values.

e) *Increasing and/or decreasing; relative extrema.* We use the values found in step (d) to determine where f is increasing or decreasing. The points to consider are $-2, 0$, and 2.

Since

$$f''(-2) = \frac{8}{(-2)^3} = -1 < 0,$$

we know that a relative maximum exists at $(-2, f(-2))$, or $(-2, -4)$. Thus, f is increasing over $(-\infty, -2)$ and decreasing over $(-2, 0)$.

Since

$$f''(2) = \frac{8}{(2)^3} = 1 > 0,$$

we know that a relative minimum exists at $(2, f(2))$, or $(2, 4)$. Thus, f is decreasing over $(0, 2)$ and increasing over $(2, \infty)$.

f) *Inflection points.* We determine candidates for inflection points by finding where $f''(x)$ does not exist or where $f''(x) = 0$. The only value for which $f''(x)$ does not exist is 0, but 0 is not in the domain of f. Thus, the only place an inflection point could occur is where $f''(x) = 0$:

$$\frac{8}{x^3} = 0.$$

But this equation has no solution. Thus, there are no points of inflection.

g) *Concavity.* Since no values were found in step (f), the only place where concavity could change would be on either side of the vertical asymptote, $x = 0$. In step (e), we used the Second-Derivative Test to determine relative extrema. From that work, we know that f is concave down over $(-\infty, 0)$ and concave up over $(0, \infty)$.

Test Value	$x = -2$	$x = 2$
Sign of $f''(x)$	$f''(-2) < 0$	$f''(2) > 0$
Result	f' is decreasing; f is concave down on $(-\infty, 0)$	f' is increasing; f is concave up on $(0, \infty)$

Interval ← ———— | ———— → x
                  0

Change does not indicate a point of inflection since $f(0)$ does not exist.

h) *Sketch the graph.* We sketch the graph, shown below, using the preceding information and additional computed values of f.

x	$f(x)$
-4	-5
-2	-4
-1	-5
1	5
2	4
4	5

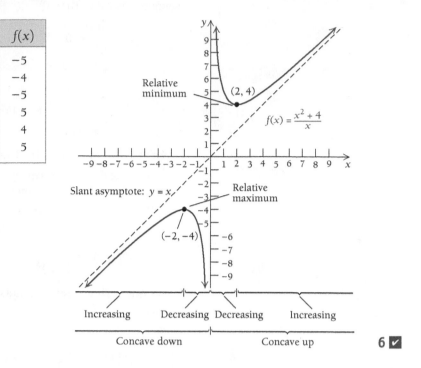

Quick Check 6 ✔

Sketch the graph of the function given by

$$f(x) = \frac{x^2 - 9}{x - 1}.$$

Section Summary

- A line $x = a$ is a *vertical asymptote* if $\lim_{x \to a^-} f(x) = \pm\infty$ or $\lim_{x \to a^+} f(x) = \pm\infty$.
- A line $y = b$ is a *horizontal asymptote* if $\lim_{x \to \infty} f(x) = b$ or $\lim_{x \to -\infty} f(x) = b$.
- A *slant asymptote* occurs when the degree of the numerator is 1 greater than the degree of the denominator.

Division of polynomials can be used to determine the equation of the slant asymptote.

- Vertical, horizontal, and slant asymptotes can be used as guides for accurate curve sketching. Asymptotes are not a part of a graph but are visual guides only.

2.3 Exercise Set

Determine the vertical asymptote(s) of each function. If none exists, state that fact.

1. $f(x) = \dfrac{x + 4}{x - 2}$

2. $f(x) = \dfrac{2x - 3}{x - 5}$

3. $f(x) = \dfrac{5x}{x^2 - 25}$

4. $f(x) = \dfrac{3x}{x^2 - 9}$

5. $f(x) = \dfrac{x + 3}{x^3 - x}$

6. $f(x) = \dfrac{x + 2}{x^3 - 6x^2 + 8x}$

7. $f(x) = \dfrac{x + 2}{x^2 + 6x + 8}$

8. $f(x) = \dfrac{x + 6}{x^2 + 7x + 6}$

9. $f(x) = \dfrac{7}{x^2 + 49}$

10. $f(x) = \dfrac{6}{x^2 + 36}$

Determine the horizontal asymptote of each function. If none exists, state that fact.

11. $f(x) = \dfrac{6x}{8x + 3}$

12. $f(x) = \dfrac{3x^2}{6x^2 + x}$

13. $f(x) = \dfrac{4x}{x^2 - 3x}$

14. $f(x) = \dfrac{2x}{3x^3 - x^2}$

15. $f(x) = 4 + \dfrac{2}{x}$

16. $f(x) = 5 - \dfrac{3}{x}$

17. $f(x) = \dfrac{6x^3 + 4x}{3x^2 - x}$ **18.** $f(x) = \dfrac{8x^4 - 5x^2}{2x^3 + x^2}$

19. $f(x) = \dfrac{4x^3 - 3x + 2}{x^3 + 2x - 4}$ **20.** $f(x) = \dfrac{6x^4 + 4x^2 - 7}{2x^5 - x + 3}$

21. $f(x) = \dfrac{2x^3 - 4x + 1}{4x^3 + 2x - 3}$ **22.** $f(x) = \dfrac{5x^4 - 2x^3 + x}{x^5 - x^3 + 8}$

Sketch the graph of each function. Indicate where each function is increasing or decreasing, where any relative extrema occur, where asymptotes occur, where the graph is concave up or concave down, where any points of inflection occur, and where any intercepts occur.

23. $f(x) = \dfrac{4}{x}$ **24.** $f(x) = -\dfrac{5}{x}$

25. $f(x) = \dfrac{-2}{x - 5}$ **26.** $f(x) = \dfrac{1}{x - 5}$

27. $f(x) = \dfrac{1}{x - 3}$ **28.** $f(x) = \dfrac{1}{x + 2}$

29. $f(x) = \dfrac{-2}{x + 5}$ **30.** $f(x) = \dfrac{-3}{x - 3}$

31. $f(x) = \dfrac{2x + 1}{x}$ **32.** $f(x) = \dfrac{3x - 1}{x}$

33. $f(x) = x + \dfrac{2}{x}$ **34.** $f(x) = x + \dfrac{9}{x}$

35. $f(x) = \dfrac{-1}{x^2}$ **36.** $f(x) = \dfrac{2}{x^2}$

37. $f(x) = \dfrac{x}{x - 3}$ **38.** $f(x) = \dfrac{x}{x + 2}$

39. $f(x) = \dfrac{1}{x^2 + 3}$ **40.** $f(x) = \dfrac{-1}{x^2 + 2}$

41. $f(x) = \dfrac{x + 3}{x^2 - 9}$ (*Hint:* Simplify.)

42. $f(x) = \dfrac{x - 1}{x^2 - 1}$

43. $f(x) = \dfrac{x - 1}{x + 2}$ **44.** $f(x) = \dfrac{x - 2}{x + 1}$

45. $f(x) = \dfrac{x^2 - 9}{x + 1}$ **46.** $f(x) = \dfrac{x^2 - 4}{x + 3}$

47. $f(x) = \dfrac{x - 3}{x^2 + 2x - 15}$ **48.** $f(x) = \dfrac{x + 1}{x^2 - 2x - 3}$

49. $f(x) = \dfrac{2x^2}{x^2 - 16}$ **50.** $f(x) = \dfrac{x^2 + x - 2}{2x^2 - 2}$

51. $f(x) = \dfrac{10}{x^2 + 4}$ **52.** $f(x) = \dfrac{1}{x^2 - 1}$

53. $f(x) = \dfrac{x^2 + 1}{x}$ **54.** $f(x) = \dfrac{x^3}{x^2 - 1}$

55. $f(x) = \dfrac{x^2 - 16}{x + 4}$ **56.** $f(x) = \dfrac{x^2 - 9}{x - 3}$

APPLICATIONS

Business and Economics

57. Average cost. The total cost, in thousands of dollars, for Acme, Inc., to produce x pairs of rocket skates is given by

$$C(x) = 3x^2 + 80.$$

a) The *average cost* is given by $A(x) = C(x)/x$. Find $A(x)$.
b) Graph the average cost.
c) Find the slant asymptote for the graph of $y = A(x)$, and interpret its significance.

58. Depreciation. Suppose that the value V of the inventory at Fido's Pet Supply, in hundreds of dollars, decreases (depreciates) after t months, where

$$V(t) = 50 - \dfrac{25t^2}{(t + 2)^2}.$$

a) Find $V(0)$, $V(5)$, $V(10)$, and $V(70)$.
b) Find the maximum value of the inventory over the interval $[0, \infty)$.
c) Draw a graph of V.
d) Does there seem to be a value below which $V(t)$ will never fall? Explain.

59. Total cost and revenue. The total cost and total revenue, in dollars, from producing x couches are given by

$$C(x) = 5000 + 600x \quad \text{and} \quad R(x) = -\tfrac{1}{2}x^2 + 1000x.$$

a) Find the total-profit function, $P(x)$.
b) The *average profit* is given by $A(x) = P(x)/x$. Find $A(x)$.
c) Find the slant asymptote for the graph of $y = A(x)$.
d) Graph the average profit.

60. Cost of pollution control. Cities and companies find that the cost of pollution control increases along with the percentage of pollutants being removed. Suppose the cost C, in dollars, of removing $p\%$ of the pollutants from a chemical spill is given by

$$C(p) = \dfrac{48{,}000}{100 - p}.$$

a) Find $C(0)$, $C(20)$, $C(80)$, and $C(90)$.
b) Find the domain of C.
c) Draw a graph of C.
d) Can the company or city afford to remove 100% of the pollutants due to this spill? Explain.

61. Purchasing power. The purchasing power of the U.S. dollar t years after 1990 can be modeled by the function

$$P(x) = \frac{1}{1 + 0.0362x}.$$

(*Source*: Based on data from the Consumer Price Index.)

a) Find $P(5)$, $P(10)$, and $P(25)$.
b) When was the purchasing power $0.50?
c) Find $\lim\limits_{x \to \infty} P(x)$.

Life and Physical Sciences

62. Medication in the bloodstream. After an injection, the amount of a medication A, in cubic centimeters (cc), in the bloodstream decreases with time t, in hours. Suppose that under certain conditions A is given by

$$A(t) = \frac{A_0}{t^2 + 1},$$

where A_0 is the initial amount of the medication. Assume that an initial amount of 100 cc is injected.

a) Find $A(0)$, $A(1)$, $A(2)$, $A(7)$, and $A(10)$.
b) Find the maximum amount of medication in the bloodstream over the interval $[0, \infty)$.
c) Graph the function.
d) According to this function, does the medication ever completely leave the bloodstream? Explain your answer.

General Interest

63. Baseball: earned-run average. A pitcher's *earned-run average* (the average number of runs given up in every 9 innings, or 1 complete game) is given by

$$E = 9 \cdot \frac{r}{n},$$

where r is the number of earned runs allowed in n innings. If we set the number of earned runs allowed at 4 and let n vary, we get a function given by

$$E(n) = 9 \cdot \frac{4}{n}.$$

While pitching for the St. Louis Cardinals in 1968, Bob Gibson had an earned-run average of 1.12, a record low.

a) Complete the following table, rounding to two decimal places:

Innings Pitched, n	9	6	3	1	$\frac{2}{3}$	$\frac{1}{3}$
Earned-Run Average, E						

b) The number of innings pitched n is equivalent to the number of outs that a pitcher is able to get while pitching, divided by 3. For example, a pitcher who gets just 1 out is credited with pitching $\frac{1}{3}$ of an inning. Find $\lim\limits_{n \to 0} E(n)$. Under what circumstances might this limit be plausible?

SYNTHESIS

64. Explain why a vertical asymptote is only a guide and is not part of the graph of a function.

65. Using graphs and limits, explain how three types of asymptotes are used when graphing rational functions.

Find each limit, if it exists.

66. $\lim\limits_{x \to -\infty} \dfrac{-3x^2 + 5}{2 - x}$

67. $\lim\limits_{x \to 0} \dfrac{|x|}{x}$

68. $\lim\limits_{x \to -2} \dfrac{x^3 + 8}{x^2 - 4}$

69. $\lim\limits_{x \to -\infty} \dfrac{-6x^3 + 7x}{2x^2 - 3x - 10}$

70. $\lim\limits_{x \to 1} \dfrac{x^3 - 1}{x^2 - 1}$

TECHNOLOGY CONNECTION

Graph each function using a graphing utility.

71. $f(x) = x^2 + \dfrac{1}{x^2}$

72. $f(x) = \dfrac{x}{\sqrt{x^2 + 1}}$

73. $f(x) = \dfrac{x^3 + 4x^2 + x - 6}{x^2 - x - 2}$

74. $f(x) = \dfrac{x^3 + 2x^2 - 15x}{x^2 - 5x - 14}$

75. $f(x) = \dfrac{x^3 + 2x^2 - 3x}{x^2 - 25}$

76. $f(x) = \left| \dfrac{1}{x} - 2 \right|$

77. Graph the function given by

$$f(x) = \frac{x^2 - 3}{2x - 4}.$$

a) Find any x-intercepts.
b) Find the y-intercept if it exists.
c) Find any asymptotes.

78. Graph the function given by

$$f(x) = \frac{\sqrt{x^2 + 3x + 2}}{x - 3}.$$

a) Estimate $\lim\limits_{x\to\infty} f(x)$ and $\lim\limits_{x\to-\infty} f(x)$ using the graph and input–output tables as needed to refine your estimates.
b) What appears to be the domain of the function? Explain.
c) Find $\lim\limits_{x\to-2^-} f(x)$ and $\lim\limits_{x\to-1^+} f(x)$.

79. Not all asymptotes are linear. Use long division to find an equation for the nonlinear asymptote that is approached by the graph of

$$f(x) = \frac{x^5 + x - 9}{x^3 + 6x}.$$

Then graph the function and its asymptote.

80. Refer to the graph on p. 221. The function is given by

$$f(x) = \frac{x^2 - 1}{x^2 + x - 6}.$$

a) Inspect the graph and estimate the coordinates of any extrema.
b) Find f' and use it to determine the critical values. (*Hint*: you will need the quadratic formula.) Round the x-values to the nearest hundredth.
c) Graph f in the window $[0, 0.2, 0.16, 0.17]$. Use TRACE or MAXIMUM to confirm your results from part (b).
d) Graph f in the window $[9.8, 10, 0.9519, 0.95195]$. Use TRACE or MINIMUM to confirm your results from part (b).

e) How close were your estimates of part (a)? Would you have been able to identify the relative minimum point without calculus?

In Exercises 81–86, determine a rational function that meets the given conditions, and sketch its graph.

81. The function f has a vertical asymptote at $x = 2$, a horizontal asymptote at $y = -2$, and $f(0) = 0$.

82. The function f has a vertical asymptote at $x = 0$, a horizontal asymptote at $y = 3$, and $f(1) = 2$.

83. The function g has vertical asymptotes at $x = -1$ and $x = 1$, a horizontal asymptote at $y = 1$, and $g(0) = 2$.

84. The function g has vertical asymptotes at $x = -2$ and $x = 0$, a horizontal asymptote at $y = -3$, and $g(1) = 4$.

85. The function h has vertical asymptotes at $x = -3$ and $x = 2$, a horizontal asymptote at $y = 0$, and $h(1) = 2$.

86. The function h has vertical asymptotes at $x = -\frac{1}{2}$ and $x = \frac{1}{2}$, a horizontal asymptote at $y = 0$, and $h(0) = -3$.

Answers to Quick Checks

1. The lines $x = 0$, $x = 4$, and $x = -4$ are vertical asymptotes. **2.** The lines $x = -1$ and $x = 0$ are vertical asymptotes. **3.** The line $y = \frac{2}{15}$ is a horizontal asymptote. **4.** The line $y = 2x + 7$ is a slant asymptote. **5.** x-intercepts: $(1, 0), (-1, 0), (0, 0)$; y-intercept: $(0, 0)$
6.

Using Derivatives to Find Absolute Maximum and Minimum Values

2.4

● Find absolute extrema using Maximum–Minimum Principle 1.
● Find absolute extrema using Maximum–Minimum Principle 2.

If an extremum is the highest or lowest value over a function's entire domain, it is called an *absolute extremum*. For example, the parabola given by $f(x) = x^2 + 1$ has a relative minimum at $(0, 1)$. This is also the lowest point for the *entire* graph of f, so it is also the absolute minimum. In applications, we are often interested in absolute extrema.

Absolute Maximum and Minimum Values

A relative minimum may or may not be an absolute minimum, meaning the smallest value of the function over its entire domain. Similarly, a relative maximum may or may not be an absolute maximum, meaning the greatest value of a function over its entire domain.

The function in the following graph has relative minima at c_1 and c_3.

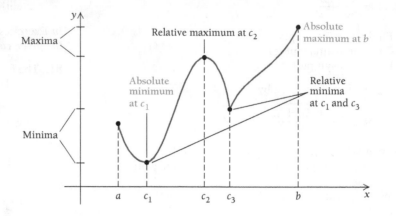

The relative minimum at c_1 is also the absolute minimum. On the other hand, the relative maximum at c_2 is *not* the absolute maximum. The absolute maximum occurs at b.

DEFINITION

Suppose that f is a function with domain I.

$f(c)$ is an **absolute minimum** if $f(c) \leq f(x)$ for all x in I.

$f(c)$ is an **absolute maximum** if $f(c) \geq f(x)$ for all x in I.

Finding Absolute Maximum and Minimum Values over Closed Intervals

Let's consider continuous functions for which the domain is a closed interval. Look at the graphs of f and g below, and try to determine where the absolute maxima and minima (extrema) occur for each function.

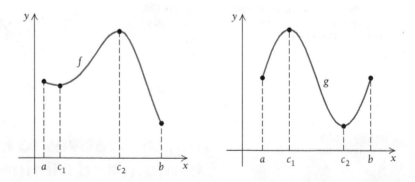

Note that each function does indeed have an absolute maximum value and an absolute minimum value. This leads us to the following theorem.

THEOREM 7   The Extreme-Value Theorem

A continuous function f defined over a closed interval $[a, b]$ must have an absolute maximum value and an absolute minimum value over $[a, b]$.

Look again at f and g on the previous page and consider the critical values and the endpoints. The graph of f starts at $f(a)$, falls to $f(c_1)$, rises from $f(c_1)$ to $f(c_2)$, and falls to $f(b)$. The graph of g starts at $g(a)$, rises to $g(c_1)$, falls from $g(c_1)$ to $g(c_2)$, and rises to $g(b)$. It seems reasonable that whatever the maximum and minimum values are, they occur at a critical value or endpoint.

THEOREM 8   Maximum–Minimum Principle 1

Suppose f is a continuous function defined over a closed interval $[a, b]$. To find the absolute maximum and minimum values over $[a, b]$:

a) First find $f'(x)$.

b) Then determine all critical values in $[a, b]$. That is, find all c in $[a, b]$ for which

$$f'(c) = 0 \quad \text{or} \quad f'(c) \text{ does not exist.}$$

c) List the values from step (b) and the endpoints of the interval:

$$a, c_1, c_2, \ldots, c_n, b.$$

d) Evaluate $f(x)$ for each value in step (c):

$$f(a), f(c_1), f(c_2), \ldots, f(c_n), f(b).$$

The largest of these is the **absolute maximum of f over $[a, b]$.** The smallest of these is the **absolute minimum of f over $[a, b]$.**

EXAMPLE 1   Find the absolute maximum and minimum values of

$$f(x) = x^3 - 3x + 2$$

over the interval $\left[-2, \frac{3}{2}\right]$.

Solution   Keep in mind that we are considering only the interval $\left[-2, \frac{3}{2}\right]$.

a) Find $f'(x)$: $f'(x) = 3x^2 - 3$.

b) Find the critical values. The derivative exists for all real numbers. Thus, we solve $f'(x) = 0$:

$$3x^2 - 3 = 0$$
$$3x^2 = 3$$
$$x^2 = 1$$
$$x = \pm 1.$$

c) List the critical values and the endpoints: $-2, -1, 1,$ and $\frac{3}{2}$.

d) Evaluate $f(x)$ at each value in step (c):

$$f(-2) = (-2)^3 - 3(-2) + 2 = -8 + 6 + 2 = 0;$$
$$f(-1) = (-1)^3 - 3(-1) + 2 = -1 + 3 + 2 = 4;$$
$$f(1) = (1)^3 - 3(1) + 2 = 1 - 3 + 2 = 0;$$
$$f(\tfrac{3}{2}) = (\tfrac{3}{2})^3 - 3(\tfrac{3}{2}) + 2 = \tfrac{27}{8} - \tfrac{9}{2} + 2 = \tfrac{7}{8}$$

The largest of these values, 4, is the maximum. It occurs at $x = -1$. The smallest of these values is 0. It occurs twice: at $x = -2$ and $x = 1$. Thus, over the interval $\left[-2, \frac{3}{2}\right]$, the

$$\text{absolute maximum} = 4 \text{ at } x = -1$$

and the

$$\text{absolute minimum} = 0 \text{ at } x = -2 \text{ and } x = 1.$$

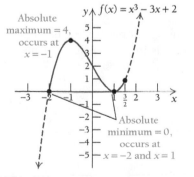

Absolute maximum = 4, occurs at $x = -1$

y, $f(x) = x^3 - 3x + 2$

Absolute minimum = 0, occurs at $x = -2$ and $x = 1$

A visualization of Example 1

As we see in Example 1, an absolute maximum or minimum value can occur at more than one point.

TECHNOLOGY CONNECTION

Finding Absolute Extrema

To find the absolute extrema in Example 1, we can use any of the methods described in the Technology Connection on p. 200. In this case, we adapt Methods 3 and 4.

Method 3

Method 3 is selected because there are relative extrema in the interval $\left[-2, \frac{3}{2}\right]$. This method gives approximations of these relative extrema.

$y = x^3 - 3x + 2$ $y = x^3 - 3x + 2$

Maximum
X = −1.000002 Y = 4

Minimum
X = .99999689 Y = 2.9E−11

Next, we check function values at these x-values and at the endpoints, using Maximum–Minimum Principle 1 to determine the absolute maximum and minimum values over $\left[-2, \frac{3}{2}\right]$.

X	Y1	
-2	0	Min
-1	4	Max
1	0	Min
1.5	.875	

X =

Method 4

Example 2 considers the same function as in Example 1, but over a different interval. Because there are no relative extrema, we can use fMax and fMin from the MATH menu. The minimum and maximum values occur at the endpoints, as the following graphs show.

fMin(Y1,X,−3,−1.5)
−2.999994692
Y1(Ans)
−15.99987261

fMax(Y1,X,−3,−1.5)
−1.500005458
Y1(Ans)
3.124979532

EXERCISE

1. Use a graph to estimate the absolute extrema of $f(x) = x^3 - x^2 - x + 2$, first over the interval $[-2, 1]$ and then over $[-1, 2]$. Then check your work using the methods of Examples 1 and 2.

Maximum = $3\frac{1}{8}$, occurs at $x = -\frac{3}{2}$

$f(x) = x^3 - 3x + 2$

Minimum = −16, occurs at $x = -3$

A visualization of Example 2

Quick Check 1 ✔

Find the absolute maximum and minimum values of the function given in Example 2 over the interval $[0, 3]$.

EXAMPLE 2 Find the absolute maximum and minimum values of

$$f(x) = x^3 - 3x + 2$$

over $\left[-3, -\frac{3}{2}\right]$.

Solution As in Example 1, the derivative is 0 at −1 and 1. But neither −1 nor 1 is in the interval $\left[-3, -\frac{3}{2}\right]$, so there are no critical values in this interval. Thus, the maximum and minimum values occur at the endpoints:

$$f(-3) = (-3)^3 - 3(-3) + 2$$
$$= -27 + 9 + 2 = -16;$$
$$f\left(-\frac{3}{2}\right) = \left(-\frac{3}{2}\right)^3 - 3\left(-\frac{3}{2}\right) + 2$$
$$= -\frac{27}{8} + \frac{9}{2} + 2 = \frac{25}{8} = 3\frac{1}{8}.$$

Thus, the absolute maximum over $\left[-3, -\frac{3}{2}\right]$, is $3\frac{1}{8}$, which occurs at $x = -\frac{3}{2}$, and the absolute minimum is −16, which occurs at $x = -3$.   **1** ✔

Finding Absolute Maximum and Minimum Values over Other Intervals

When there is only one critical value c in I, we may not need to check endpoint values to determine whether the function has an absolute maximum or minimum value at that point.

THEOREM 9   Maximum–Minimum Principle 2

Suppose f is a function such that $f'(x)$ exists for every x in an interval I and there is *exactly one* (critical) value c in I, for which $f'(c) = 0$. Then

$$f(c) \text{ is the absolute maximum value over } I \text{ if } f''(c) < 0$$

or

$$f(c) \text{ is the absolute minimum value over } I \text{ if } f''(c) > 0.$$

Theorem 9 holds no matter what the interval I is—whether open, closed, or infinite in length. If $f''(c) = 0$, either we must use Maximum–Minimum Principle 1 or we must know more about the behavior of the function over the given interval.

EXAMPLE 3   Find the absolute extrema of $f(x) = 4x - x^2$.

Solution   When no interval is specified, we consider the entire domain of the function. In this case, the domain is the set of all real numbers.

a) Find $f'(x)$:

$$f'(x) = 4 - 2x.$$

b) Find the critical values. The derivative exists for all real numbers. Thus, we need only solve $f'(x) = 0$:

$$4 - 2x = 0$$
$$-2x = -4$$
$$x = 2.$$

c) Since there is only one critical value, we apply Maximum–Minimum Principle 2 using the second derivative:

$$f''(x) = -2.$$

The second derivative is constant. Thus, $f''(2) = -2$, and since this is negative, we have the absolute maximum:

$$f(2) = 4 \cdot 2 - 2^2,$$
$$= 8 - 4 = 4.$$

The function has no minimum, as the graph, shown below, indicates.

EXAMPLE 4   Find the absolute extrema of $f(x) = 4x - x^2$ over the interval $[1, 4]$.

Solution   From Example 3, we know that the absolute maximum of f on $(-\infty, \infty)$ is $f(2)$, or 4. Since 2 is in $[1, 4]$, we know that the absolute maximum of f over $[1, 4]$ will occur at 2. To find the absolute minimum, we need to check the endpoints:

$$f(1) = 4 \cdot 1 - 1^2 = 3$$

and

$$f(4) = 4 \cdot 4 - 4^2 = 0.$$

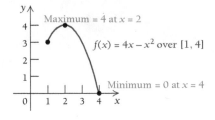

We also see from the graph that the minimum is 0. It occurs at $x = 4$. Thus, the

$$\text{absolute maximum} = 4 \text{ at } x = 2,$$

and the

$$\text{absolute minimum} = 0 \text{ at } x = 4.$$ **2 ✔**

Quick Check 2 ✔

Find the absolute extrema of $f(x) = x^2 - 10x$ over each interval:

a) $[0, 6]$;   **b)** $[4, 10]$.

A Strategy for Finding Absolute Maximum and Minimum Values

The following general strategy can be used when finding absolute maximum and minimum values of continuous functions.

> **A Strategy for Finding Absolute Maximum and Minimum Values**
>
> To find the absolute extrema of a continuous function over an interval:
>
> **a)** Find $f'(x)$.
> **b)** Find the critical values.
> **c)** If the interval is closed and there is more than one critical value, use Maximum–Minimum Principle 1.
> **d)** If the interval is closed and there is exactly one critical value, use either Maximum–Minimum Principle 1 or Maximum–Minimum Principle 2. If it is easy to find $f''(x)$, use Maximum–Minimum Principle 2.
> **e)** If the interval is not closed, such as $(-\infty, \infty)$, $(0, \infty)$, or (a, b), and the function has only one critical value, use Maximum–Minimum Principle 2. In such a case, if the function has a maximum, it will have no minimum; and if it has a minimum, it will have no maximum.

Finding absolute maximum and minimum values when more than one critical value occurs in an interval that is not closed, such as any of those listed in step (e) above, requires a detailed graph or techniques beyond the scope of this book.

EXAMPLE 5   Find the absolute maximum and minimum values of

$$f(x) = (x - 2)^3 + 1.$$

Solution

a) Find $f'(x)$.

$$f'(x) = 3(x - 2)^2.$$

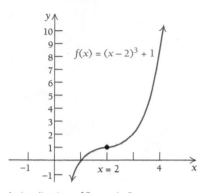

A visualization of Example 5

Quick Check 3 ✔

Let $f(x) = x^n$, where n is a positive odd integer. Explain why functions of this form never have an absolute minimum or maximum.

Finding Absolute Extrema

Let's do Example 6 using MAXIMUM and MINIMUM from the CALC menu. The shape of the graph leads us to see that there is no absolute maximum, but there is an absolute minimum.

[0, 10, 0, 50]

Since

$$\sqrt{7} \approx 2.6458,$$

the results in the window confirm the solution found in Example 6.

EXERCISE

1. Use a graph to estimate the absolute extrema of $f(x) = 10x + 1/x$ over $(0, \infty)$. Then check your work using the method of Example 6.

---

b) Find the critical values. The derivative exists for all real numbers. Thus, we solve $f'(x) = 0$:

$$3(x - 2)^2 = 0$$
$$(x - 2)^2 = 0$$
$$x - 2 = 0$$
$$x = 2.$$

c) Since there is only one critical value and there are no endpoints, we can try to apply Maximum–Minimum Principle 2 using the second derivative:

$$f''(x) = 6(x - 2).$$

We have

$$f''(2) = 6(2 - 2) = 0,$$

so Maximum–Minimum Principle 2 does not apply. We cannot use Maximum–Minimum Principle 1 because there are no endpoints. But note that $f'(x) = 3(x - 2)^2$ is never negative. Thus, $f(x)$ is increasing everywhere except at $x = 2$, so there is no maximum and no minimum. For $x < 2$, say $x = 1$, we have $f''(1) = -6 < 0$. For $x > 2$, say $x = 3$, we have $f''(3) = 6 > 0$. Thus, at $x = 2$, the function has a *point of inflection*.　　　　**3** ✔

EXAMPLE 6　Find the absolute maximum and minimum values of

$$f(x) = 5x + \frac{35}{x}$$

over the interval $(0, \infty)$.

Solution

a) Find $f'(x)$. Since $f(x) = 5x + 35x^{-1}$, we have

$$f'(x) = 5 - 35x^{-2}$$
$$= 5 - \frac{35}{x^2}.$$

b) Find the critical values. Since $f'(x)$ exists for all values of x in $(0, \infty)$, the only critical values are those for which $f'(x) = 0$:

$$5 - \frac{35}{x^2} = 0 \qquad \text{Setting } f'(x) \text{ equal to } 0$$

$$5 = \frac{35}{x^2}$$

$$5x^2 = 35 \qquad \text{Multiplying both sides by } x^2, \text{ since } x \neq 0$$

$$x^2 = 7$$

$$x = \sqrt{7}. \qquad \text{Taking the positive root only, since the negative root is not in } (0, \infty)$$

c) Since $(0, \infty)$ is not closed and there is only one critical value, we can apply Maximum–Minimum Principle 2 using the second derivative,

$$f''(x) = 70x^{-3} = \frac{70}{x^3}.$$

Since

$$f''(\sqrt{7}) = \frac{70}{(\sqrt{7})^3} > 0,$$

an absolute minimum occurs at $x = \sqrt{7}$:

$$\text{Absolute minimum} = f(\sqrt{7})$$

$$= 5 \cdot \sqrt{7} + \frac{35}{\sqrt{7}}$$

$$= 5\sqrt{7} + \frac{35}{\sqrt{7}} \cdot \frac{\sqrt{7}}{\sqrt{7}}$$

$$= 5\sqrt{7} + \frac{35\sqrt{7}}{7}$$

$$= 5\sqrt{7} + 5\sqrt{7}$$

$$= 10\sqrt{7} \approx 26.458 \quad \text{at } x = \sqrt{7}.$$

The function has no maximum value, which can happen since the interval $(0, \infty)$ is *not* closed.

Quick Check 4 ✔

Find the absolute maximum and minimum values of

$$g(x) = \frac{2x^2 + 18}{x}$$

over the interval $(0, \infty)$.

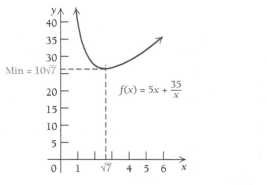

4 ✔

Section Summary

- An *absolute minimum* of f is a value $f(c)$ such that $f(c) \le f(x)$ for all x in the domain of f.
- An *absolute maximum* of f is a value $f(c)$ such that $f(c) \ge f(x)$ for all x in the domain of f.
- If the domain of f is a closed interval and f is continuous over that domain, then the *Extreme–Value Theorem* guarantees the existence of both an absolute minimum and an absolute maximum.

- Endpoints of a closed interval may be absolute extrema, but not relative extrema.
- If there is exactly one critical value c in the domain of f such that $f'(c) = 0$, then *Maximum–Minimum Principle 2* may be used to find the absolute extrema. Otherwise, *Maximum–Minimum Principle 1* has to be used.

2.4 | Exercise Set

1. **Fuel economy.** According to the U.S. Department of Energy, a vehicle's fuel economy, in miles per gallon (mpg), decreases rapidly for speeds over 60 mph.

   a) Estimate the speed at which the absolute maximum gasoline mileage is obtained.

   b) Estimate the speed at which the absolute minimum gasoline mileage is obtained.

   c) What is the mileage obtained at 70 mph?

2. **Fuel economy.** Using the graph in Exercise 1, estimate the absolute maximum and the absolute minimum fuel economy over the interval $[30, 70]$.

(*Sources:* U.S. Dept. of Energy; a study by West, B.H., McGill, R.N., Hodgson, J.W., Sluder, S.S., and Smith, D.E., Oak Ridge National Laboratory, 1999; www.mpgforspeed.com, 2014.)

Find the absolute maximum and minimum values of each function over the indicated interval, and indicate the x-values at which they occur.

3. $f(x) = 5 + x - x^2$; $[0, 2]$

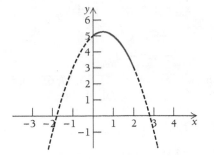

4. $f(x) = 4 + x - x^2$; $[0, 2]$

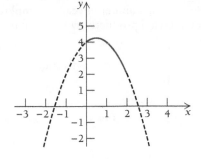

5. $f(x) = x^3 - \frac{1}{2}x^2 - 2x + 5$; $[-2, 1]$

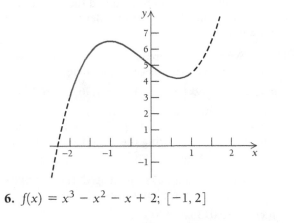

6. $f(x) = x^3 - x^2 - x + 2$; $[-1, 2]$

7. $f(x) = x^3 + \frac{1}{2}x^2 - 2x + 4$; $[-2, 0]$

8. $f(x) = x^3 - x^2 - x + 3$; $[-1, 0]$

9. $f(x) = 2x + 4$; $[-1, 1]$

10. $f(x) = 5x - 7$; $[-2, 3]$

11. $f(x) = 7 - 4x$; $[-2, 5]$

12. $f(x) = -2 - 3x$; $[-10, 10]$

13. $f(x) = -5$; $[-1, 1]$

14. $f(x) = x^2 - 6x - 3$; $[-1, 5]$

15. $g(x) = 24$; $[4, 13]$

16. $f(x) = 3 - 2x - 5x^2$; $[-3, 3]$

17. $f(x) = x^2 - 4x + 5$; $[-1, 3]$

18. $f(x) = x^3 - 3x^2$; $[0, 5]$

19. $f(x) = 1 + 6x - 3x^2$; $[0, 4]$

20. $f(x) = x^3 - 3x + 6$; $[-1, 3]$

21. $f(x) = x^3 - 3x$; $[-5, 1]$

22. $f(x) = 3x^2 - 2x^3$; $[-5, 1]$

23. $f(x) = 1 - x^3$; $[-8, 8]$

24. $f(x) = 2x^3$; $[-10, 10]$

25. $f(x) = x^3 - 6x^2 + 10$; $[0, 4]$

26. $f(x) = 12 + 9x - 3x^2 - x^3$; $[-3, 1]$

27. $f(x) = x^3 - x^4$; $[-1, 1]$

28. $f(x) = x^4 - 2x^3$; $[-2, 2]$

29. $f(x) = x^4 - 2x^2 + 5$; $[-2, 2]$

30. $f(x) = x^4 - 8x^2 + 3$; $[-3, 3]$

31. $f(x) = 1 - x^{2/3}$; $[-8, 8]$

32. $f(x) = (x + 3)^{2/3} - 5$; $[-4, 5]$

33. $f(x) = x + \dfrac{4}{x}$; $[-8, -1]$

34. $f(x) = x + \dfrac{1}{x}$; $[1, 20]$

35. $f(x) = \dfrac{x^2}{x^2 + 1}$; $[-2, 2]$

36. $f(x) = \dfrac{4x}{x^2 + 1}$; $[-3, 3]$

37. $f(x) = (x + 1)^{1/3}$; $[-2, 26]$

38. $f(x) = \sqrt[3]{x}$; $[8, 64]$

39–48. Check Exercises 3, 5, 9, 13, 19, 23, 33, 35, 37, and 38 with a graphing calculator.

Find the absolute extrema of each function, if they exist, over the indicated interval. Also indicate the x-value at which each extremum occurs. When no interval is specified, use the real numbers, $(-\infty, \infty)$.

49. $f(x) = 30x - x^2$

50. $f(x) = 12x - x^2$

51. $f(x) = 2x^2 - 40x + 270$

52. $f(x) = 2x^2 - 20x + 340$

53. $f(x) = 16x - \frac{4}{3}x^3$; $(0, \infty)$

54. $f(x) = x - \frac{4}{3}x^3$; $(0, \infty)$

55. $f(x) = x(60 - x)$

56. $f(x) = x(25 - x)$

57. $f(x) = \frac{1}{3}x^3 - 5x$; $[-3, 3]$

58. $f(x) = \frac{1}{3}x^3 - 3x$; $[-2, 2]$

59. $f(x) = -0.001x^2 + 4.8x - 60$

60. $f(x) = -0.01x^2 + 1.4x - 30$

61. $f(x) = -x^3 + x^2 + 5x - 1$; $(0, \infty)$

62. $f(x) = -\frac{1}{3}x^3 + 6x^2 - 11x - 50$; $(0, 3)$

63. $f(x) = 15x^2 - \frac{1}{2}x^3$; $[0, 30]$

64. $f(x) = 4x^2 - \frac{1}{2}x^3$; $[0, 8]$

65. $f(x) = 2x + \frac{72}{x}$; $(0, \infty)$

66. $f(x) = x + \frac{3600}{x}$; $(0, \infty)$

67. $f(x) = x^2 + \frac{432}{x}$; $(0, \infty)$

68. $f(x) = x^2 + \frac{250}{x}$; $(0, \infty)$

69. $f(x) = 2x^4 + x$; $[-1, 1]$

70. $f(x) = 2x^4 - x$; $[-1, 1]$

71. $f(x) = \sqrt[3]{x}$; $[0, 8]$

72. $f(x) = \sqrt{x}$; $[0, 4]$

73. $f(x) = (x - 1)^3$

74. $f(x) = (x + 1)^3$

75. $f(x) = 2x - 3$; $[-1, 1]$

76. $f(x) = 9 - 5x$; $[-10, 10]$

77. $f(x) = 2x - 3$; $[-1, 5)$

78. $f(x) = x^{2/3}$; $[-1, 1]$

79. $f(x) = 9 - 5x$; $[-2, 3)$

80. $f(x) = \frac{1}{3}x^3 - x + \frac{2}{3}$

81. $g(x) = x^{2/3}$

82. $f(x) = \frac{1}{3}x^3 - 2x^2 + x$; $[0, 4]$

83. $f(x) = \frac{1}{3}x^3 - \frac{1}{2}x^2 - 2x + 1$

84. $g(x) = \frac{1}{3}x^3 + 2x^2 + x$; $[-4, 0]$

85. $t(x) = x^4 - 2x^2$

86. $f(x) = 2x^4 - 4x^2 + 2$

87–96. Check Exercises 49, 51, 53, 57, 61, 65, 67, 69, 73, and 85 with a graphing calculator.

APPLICATIONS

Business and Economics

97. Monthly productivity. An employee's monthly productivity M, in number of units produced, is found to be a function of t, the number of years of employment. For a certain product, a productivity function is given by

$$M(t) = -2t^2 + 100t + 180, \quad 0 \le t \le 40.$$

Find the maximum productivity and the year in which it is achieved.

98. Advertising. Sound Software estimates that it will sell N units of a program after spending a dollars on advertising, where

$$N(a) = -a^2 + 300a + 6, \quad 0 \le a \le 300,$$

and a is in thousands of dollars. Find the maximum number of units that can be sold and the amount that must be spent on advertising in order to achieve that maximum.

99. Unemployment. The percentage of unemployed workers in service occupations can be modeled by

$$p(x) = -0.039x^3 + 0.594x^2 - 1.967x + 7.555,$$

where x is the number of years since 2003. (*Source: Based on data from www.bls.gov.*) According to this model, in what year during the period 2003–2013 was this percentage a maximum?

100. Labor. The percentage of women aged 21–54 in the U.S. civilian labor force can be modeled by

$$f(x) = -0.0135x^2 + 0.265x + 74.6,$$

where x is the number of years since 1992. (*Source: based on data from www.bls.gov.*) According to this model, in what year during the period 1992–2012 was this percentage a maximum?

101. Worldwide oil production. One model of worldwide oil production is

$$P(t) = 2.69t^4 - 63.941t^3 + 459.895t^2 - 688.692t + 24{,}150.217,$$

where $P(t)$ is the number of barrels, in thousands, produced t years after 2000. (*Source: Based on data from the U.S. Energy Information Administration.*) According to this model, in what year did worldwide oil production achieve an absolute minimum? What was that minimum?

102. Maximizing profit. Corner Stone Electronics determines that its weekly profit, in dollars, from the production and sale of x amplifiers is

$$P(x) = \frac{1500}{x^2 - 6x + 10}.$$

Find the number of amplifiers, x, for which the total weekly profit is a maximum.

Maximizing profit. *The total-cost and total-revenue functions for producing x items are*

$$C(x) = 5000 + 600x \quad \text{and} \quad R(x) = -\frac{1}{2}x^2 + 1000x,$$

where $0 \leq x \leq 600$. Use these functions for Exercises 103 and 104.

103. a) Find the total-profit function $P(x)$.
  b) Find the number of items, x, for which total profit is a maximum.

104. a) *Average profit* is given by $A(x) = P(x)/x$. Find $A(x)$.
  b) Find the number of items, x, for which average profit is a maximum.

Life and Physical Sciences

105. Blood pressure. For a dosage of x cubic centimeters (cc) of a certain drug, the resulting blood pressure B is approximated by

$$B(x) = 305x^2 - 1830x^3, \quad 0 \leq x \leq 0.16.$$

Find the maximum blood pressure and the dosage at which it occurs.

SYNTHESIS

106. How is the second derivative useful in finding the absolute extrema of a function?

For Exercises 107–110, find the absolute maximum and minimum values of each function, and sketch the graph.

107. $f(x) = \begin{cases} 2x + 1 & \text{for } -3 \leq x \leq 1, \\ 4 - x^2, & \text{for } 1 < x \leq 2 \end{cases}$

108. $g(x) = \begin{cases} x^2, & \text{for } -2 \leq x \leq 0, \\ 5x, & \text{for } 0 < x \leq 2 \end{cases}$

109. $h(x) = \begin{cases} 1 - x^2, & \text{for } -4 \leq x < 0, \\ 1 - x, & \text{for } 0 \leq x < 1, \\ x - 1, & \text{for } 1 \leq x \leq 2 \end{cases}$

110. $F(x) = \begin{cases} x^2 + 4, & \text{for } -2 \leq x < 0, \\ 4 - x, & \text{for } 0 \leq x < 3, \\ \sqrt{x - 2}, & \text{for } 3 \leq x \leq 67 \end{cases}$

111. Consider the piecewise-defined function f defined by:

$$f(x) = \begin{cases} x^2 + 2, & \text{for } -2 \leq x \leq 0, \\ 2, & \text{for } 0 < x < 4, \\ x - 2, & \text{for } 4 \leq x \leq 6. \end{cases}$$

  a) Sketch its graph.
  b) Identify the absolute maximum.
  c) What is the absolute minimum?

112. Physical science: dry lake elevation. Dry lakes are common in the Western deserts of the United States. These beds of ancient lakes are notable for having perfectly flat terrain. Rogers Dry Lake in California has been used as a landing site for space shuttle missions in recent years. The graph shows the elevation E, in feet, as a function of the distance x, in miles, from a point near one side ($x = 0$) of Rogers Dry Lake to a point near the other side. (*Source:* www.mytopo.com.)

  a) What is the maximum elevation?
  b) What is the minimum elevation?

Find the absolute maximum and minimum values of the function, if they exist, over the indicated interval.

113. $g(x) = x\sqrt{x + 3}; \quad [-3, 3]$

114. $h(x) = x\sqrt{1 - x}; \quad [0, 1]$

115. Business: total cost. Certain costs in business can be separated into two components: those that increase with volume and those that decrease with volume. For example, customer service becomes more expensive as its quality increases, but part of the increased cost is offset by fewer customer complaints. Katie's Clocks determines that its cost of service, $C(x)$, in thousands of dollars, is modeled by

$$C(x) = (2x + 4) + \left(\frac{2}{x - 6}\right), \quad x > 6,$$

where x represents the number of "quality units." Find the number of "quality units" that the firm should use in order to minimize its total cost of service.

116. Let
$$y = (x - a)^2 + (x - b)^2.$$
For what value of x is y a minimum?

117. Business: worldwide oil production. Refer to Exercise 101. In what year(s) during the period 2000–2008 was worldwide oil production increasing most rapidly, and at what rate was it increasing?

118. How is the first derivative useful in finding the absolute extrema of a function?

119. Business: U.S. oil production. One model of oil production in the United States is given by
$$P(t) = 0.0000000219t^4 - 0.0000167t^3 + 0.00155t^2$$
$$+ 0.002t + 0.22, \quad 0 \le t \le 110,$$
where $P(t)$ is the number of barrels of oil, in billions, produced in a year, t years after 1910. (*Source: Beyond Oil*, by Kenneth S. Deffeyes, p. 41, Hill and Wang, New York, 2005.)

a) According to this model, what is the absolute maximum amount of oil produced in the United States and in what year did that production occur?

b) According to this model, at what rate was United States oil production declining in 2010 and in 2015?

Graph each function over the given interval. Visually estimate where any absolute extrema occur. Then use the TABLE feature to refine each estimate.

120. $f(x) = x^{2/3}(x - 5); \quad [1, 4]$

121. $f(x) = \dfrac{3}{4}(x^2 - 1)^{2/3}; \quad [\frac{1}{2}, \infty)$

122. $f(x) = x\left(\dfrac{x}{2} - 5\right)^4; \quad \mathbb{R}$

123. Life and physical sciences: contractions during pregnancy. The following table gives the pressure of a pregnant woman's contractions as a function of time.

TIME, T (in minutes)	PRESSURE (in millimeters of mercury)
0	10
1	8
2	9.5
3	15
4	12
5	14
6	14.5

Use a calculator that has the REGRESSION option.

a) Fit a linear equation to the data. Predict the pressure of the contractions after 7 min.

b) Fit a quartic polynomial to the data. Predict the pressure of the contractions after 7 min. Find the smallest contraction over the interval $[0, 10]$.

Answers to Quick Checks

1. Absolute maximum is 20 at $x = 3$; absolute minimum is 0 at $x = 1$. **2.** (a) Absolute maximum is 0 at $x = 0$; absolute minimum is -25 at $x = 5$. (b) Absolute maximum is 0 at $x = 10$; absolute minimum is -25 at $x = 5$. **3.** The derivative is $f'(x) = nx^{n-1}$. If n is odd, $n - 1$ is even. Thus, nx^{n-1} is always positive or zero, never negative. **4.** No absolute maximum; absolute minimum is 12 at $x = 3$.

2.5

● Solve maximum–minimum problems using calculus.

Maximum–Minimum Problems; Business, Economics, and General Applications

An important use of calculus is solving maximum–minimum problems, that is, finding the absolute maximum or minimum value of some variable.

EXAMPLE 1 **Maximizing Area.** A hobby store has 20 ft of fencing to fence off a rectangular area for an electric train in one corner of its display room. The two sides up against the wall require no fence. What dimensions of the rectangle will maximize the area? What is the maximum area?

Solution   Let's first make a drawing and express the area using one variable. If we let x = the length, in feet, of one side and y = the length, in feet, of the other, then, since the sum of the lengths must be 20 ft, we have

$$x + y = 20 \quad \text{and} \quad y = 20 - x.$$

Thus, the area is given by

$$
\begin{aligned}
A &= xy \\
&= x(20 - x) \\
&= 20x - x^2.
\end{aligned}
$$

$y = 20 - x$

We are trying to find the maximum value of

$$A(x) = 20x - x^2$$

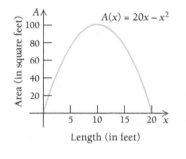

Length (in feet)

over the interval $(0, 20)$. We consider the interval $(0, 20)$ because x is a length and cannot be negative or 0. Since there is only 20 ft of fencing, x cannot be greater than 20. Also, x cannot be 20 because then the length of y would be 0.

a) We first find $A'(x)$: $A'(x) = 20 - 2x.$

b) This derivative exists for all values of x in $(0, 20)$. Thus, the only critical values are where

$$
\begin{aligned}
A'(x) = 20 - 2x &= 0 \\
-2x &= -20 \\
x &= 10.
\end{aligned}
$$

Since there is only one critical value, we can use the second derivative to determine whether we have a maximum. Note that

$$A''(x) = -2,$$

Since $A''(10)$ is negative, $A(10)$ is a maximum. Now

$$
\begin{aligned}
A(10) &= 10(20 - 10) \\
&= 10 \cdot 10 \\
&= 100.
\end{aligned}
$$

Quick Check 1 ✔

Repeat Example 1 starting first with 50 ft of fencing, and then with 100 ft of fencing. Do you detect a pattern? If you had n feet of fencing, what would be the dimensions of the maximum area (in terms of n)?

Thus, the maximum area of 100 ft^2 is obtained using 10 ft for the length of one side and $20 - 10$, or 10 ft for the other.   **1** ✔

Here is a general strategy for solving maximum–minimum problems.

A Strategy for Solving Maximum–Minimum Problems

1. Read the problem carefully. If relevant, make a drawing.

2. Make a list of appropriate variables and constants, noting what varies, what stays fixed, and what units are used. Label the measurements on your drawing, if one exists.

3. Translate the problem to an equation involving a quantity Q to be maximized or minimized. Try to represent Q in terms of the variables of step 2.

4. Try to express Q as a function of one variable. Use the procedures developed in Sections 2.1–2.4 to determine the maximum or minimum values and the points at which they occur.

EXAMPLE 2   **Maximizing Volume.**   From a thin piece of cardboard 8 in. by 8 in., square corners are cut out so that the sides can be folded up to make a box. What dimensions will yield a box of maximum volume? What is the maximum volume?

Solution   We make a drawing in which x is the length, in inches, of each square to be cut. It is important to note that since the original square is 8 in. by 8 in., after the smaller squares are removed, the lengths of the sides of the box will be $(8 - 2x)$ in. by $(8 - 2x)$ in.

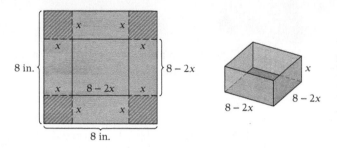

After the four small squares are removed and the sides are folded up, the volume V of the resulting box is

$$V = l \cdot w \cdot h = (8 - 2x) \cdot (8 - 2x) \cdot x,$$

or $V(x) = 4x^3 - 32x^2 + 64x.$

Since $8 - 2x > 0$, this means that $x < 4$. Thus, we need to maximize

$$V(x) = 4x^3 - 32x^2 + 64x \quad \text{over the interval } (0, 4).$$

To do so, we first find $V'(x)$:

$$V'(x) = 12x^2 - 64x + 64.$$

Since $V'(x)$ exists for all x in the interval $(0, 4)$, we can set it equal to zero to find the critical values:

$$12x^2 - 64x + 64 = 0$$
$$4(3x^2 - 16x + 16) = 0$$
$$4(3x - 4)(x - 4) = 0$$
$$3x - 4 = 0 \quad \text{or} \quad x - 4 = 0$$
$$3x = 4 \quad \text{or} \qquad x = 4$$
$$x = \tfrac{4}{3} \quad \text{or} \qquad x = 4.$$

The only critical value in $(0, 4)$ is $\tfrac{4}{3}$. Thus, we can use the second derivative,

$$V''(x) = 24x - 64,$$

to determine whether we have a maximum. Since

$$V''(\tfrac{4}{3}) = 24 \cdot \tfrac{4}{3} - 64 = 32 - 64 < 0,$$

we know that $V(\tfrac{4}{3})$ is a maximum.

Thus, to maximize the box's volume, small squares with edges measuring $\tfrac{4}{3}$ in., or $1\tfrac{1}{3}$ in., should be cut from each corner of the original 8 in. by 8 in. piece of cardboard. When the sides are folded up, the resulting box will have sides of length

$$8 - 2x = 8 - 2 \cdot \frac{4}{3} = \frac{24}{3} - \frac{8}{3} = \frac{16}{3} = 5\frac{1}{3} \text{ in.}$$

and a height of $1\tfrac{1}{3}$ in. The maximum volume is

$$V\left(\frac{4}{3}\right) = 4\left(\frac{4}{3}\right)^3 - 32\left(\frac{4}{3}\right)^2 + 64\left(\frac{4}{3}\right) = \frac{1024}{27} = 37\frac{25}{27} \text{ in}^3.$$

Quick Check 2 ☑

Repeat Example 2 starting with a sheet of cardboard measuring 8.5 in. by 11 in. (the size of a typical sheet of paper). Will this box hold 1 liter (L) of liquid? (*Hint:* 1 L = 1000 cm^3 and 1 in^3 = 16.38 cm^3.)

2 ☑

In manufacturing, minimizing the amount of material used is always preferred, both from a cost standpoint and in terms of efficiency.

EXAMPLE 3   Minimizing Cost of Material.   Mendoza Manufacturers specializes in food-storage containers and makes a cylindrical soup can with a volume of 250 cm³. The cost of material for the two circular ends is \$0.0008/cm², and the cost of material for the side is \$0.0015/cm². What dimensions minimize the cost of material for the soup can? What is the minimum cost?

Solution   Recall from Section R.1 that we estimated the dimensions that give the lowest cost using a spreadsheet.

	A	B	C
1			
2	Radius	Height	Cost
3	r	h	C
4	4.1	4.733322705	0.267434061
5	4.2	4.510609676	0.267251237
6	4.3	4.303253363	0.267371533

←— Possible minimum cost

The spreadsheet shows that a radius of about 4.2 cm gives a minimal cost of \$0.267251237 per can.

We can use calculus to find exact values for the radius and height that will minimize the cost per can. We let h = height of the can and r = radius, both measured in centimeters. The formula for volume of a cylinder is

$$V = \pi r^2 h.$$

Since we know the volume is 250 cm³, this formula allows us to relate h and r, expressing one in terms of the other. We solve for h in terms of r:

$$\pi r^2 h = 250$$

$$h = \frac{250}{\pi r^2}.$$

The can has two circular ends, each with an area of πr^2. Thus, the cost of material for the two circular ends is $2(0.0008)\pi r^2 = 0.0016\pi r^2$.

The side of the can, when disassembled, is a rectangle of area $2\pi rh$, as shown at left. The cost of material for the side is

$$2(0.0015)\pi rh = 0.003\pi rh$$

$$= 0.003\pi r\left(\frac{250}{\pi r^2}\right) \qquad \text{Substituting}$$

$$= \frac{0.75}{r}. \qquad \text{Simplifying}$$

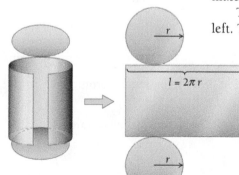

Each of the circular ends of the disassembled can has an area of πr^2, and the side has an area of $2\pi rh$.

Thus, the total cost of material for one can is given by

$$C(r) = 0.0016\pi r^2 + \frac{0.75}{r}, \text{where } r > 0.$$

Differentiating, we have

$$C'(r) = 0.0032\pi r - \frac{0.75}{r^2}.$$

We set the derivative equal to zero and solve to find the critical value(s):

$$0.0032\pi r - \frac{0.75}{r^2} = 0$$

$$0.0032\pi r = \frac{0.75}{r^2}$$

$$0.0032\pi r^3 = 0.75 \qquad \text{Multiplying both sides by } r^2$$

$$r^3 = \frac{0.75}{0.0032\pi}$$

$$r = \sqrt[3]{\frac{0.75}{0.0032\pi}}$$

$$r \approx 4.21 \qquad \text{Using a calculator}$$

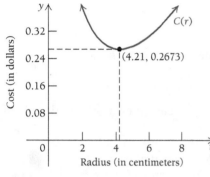

Note that the critical value $r \approx 4.21$ is the only critical value in the interval $(0, \infty)$. To determine whether this critical value results in a minimum or maximum value of C, we use the Second-Derivative Test:

$$C''(r) = 0.0032\pi + \frac{1.5}{r^3}$$

$$C''(4.21) = 0.0032\pi + \frac{1.5}{(4.21)^3} > 0.$$

The second derivative is positive, so the critical value indicates a minimum point. Thus, the cost of material for one can is minimized when $r = 4.21$ cm. The can will have a height of $h = 250/\pi(4.21)^2 \approx 4.49$ cm, and the cost of material will be $0.2673 per can.

We rounded our answer above. If we do not, we find that a radius of 4.209725752. . . cm will give a minimal cost of $0.26723831. . . per can. A manufacturer who produces millions of cans may be interested in carrying the precision of the calculations to six or seven decimal places.   3 ✔

Quick Check 3 ✔

Repeat Example 3, assuming that the can has an open top. That is, it consists of one circular end and the side.

EXAMPLE 4   **Business: Maximizing Revenue.**   Cruzing Tunes determines that in order to sell x units of a new car stereo, the price per unit, in dollars, must be

$$p(x) = 1000 - x.$$

It also determines that the total cost of producing x units is given by

$$C(x) = 3000 + 20x.$$

a) Find the total revenue, $R(x)$.

b) Find the total profit, $P(x)$.

c) How many units must be made and sold in order to maximize profit?

d) What is the maximum profit?

e) What price per unit must be charged in order to make this maximum profit?

Solution

a) $R(x) =$ Total revenue

$\qquad = (\text{Number of units}) \cdot (\text{Price per unit})$

$\qquad = \qquad x \qquad \cdot \qquad p$

$\qquad = \qquad x \qquad \cdot (1000 - x) \qquad \text{Substituting}$

$\qquad = 1000x - x^2.$

b) $P(x) =$ Total revenue $-$ Total cost

$\qquad = R(x) - C(x)$

$\qquad = (1000x - x^2) - (3000 + 20x)$

$\qquad = -x^2 + 980x - 3000$

c) To find the maximum value of $P(x)$, we first find $P'(x)$:

$$P'(x) = -2x + 980.$$

Note that $x \geq 0$. The critical value(s) are found by solving $P'(x) = 0$:

$$P'(x) = -2x + 980 = 0$$
$$-2x = -980$$
$$x = 490.$$

There is only one critical value. We can therefore try to use the second derivative to determine whether we have an absolute maximum. Note that

$$P''(x) = -2, \text{ a constant.}$$

Quick Check 4 ✔

Repeat Example 4 with the price function

$$p(x) = 1750 - 2x$$

and the cost function

$$C(x) = 2250 + 15x.$$

Round your answers when necessary.

Since, $P''(490)$ is negative, profit is maximized when 490 units are produced and sold.

d) The maximum profit is given by

$$P(490) = -(490)^2 + 980 \cdot 490 - 3000$$
$$= \$237,100.$$

Thus, Cruzing Tunes make a maximum profit of \$237,100 by producing and selling 490 stereos.

e) The price per unit needed to maximize profit is

$$p = 1000 - 490 = \$510. \qquad\qquad \textbf{4} ✔$$

FIGURE 1

FIGURE 2

Let's take a general look at the profit, cost, and revenue.

Figure 1 shows an example of total-cost and total-revenue functions. We can estimate what the maximum profit is by looking for the widest gap between $R(x)$ and $C(x)$, when $R(x) > C(x)$. Points B_0 and B_2 are break-even points.

Figure 2 shows the related total-profit function. Note that when production is too low ($< x_0$), there is a loss, perhaps due to high fixed or initial costs and low revenue. When production is too high ($> x_2$), there is also a loss, perhaps due to the increased cost of overtime pay or expansion.

The business operates at a profit everywhere between x_0 and x_2. Note that maximum profit occurs at a critical value x_1. Assuming that $P'(x)$ exists for all x in some interval, usually $[0, \infty)$, the critical value x_1 occurs at some number x such that

$$P'(x) = 0 \quad \text{and} \quad P''(x) < 0.$$

Since $P(x) = R(x) - C(x)$, it follows that

$$P'(x) = R'(x) - C'(x) \quad \text{and} \quad P''(x) = R''(x) - C''(x).$$

Thus, maximum profit occurs at some number x such that

$$P'(x) = R'(x) - C'(x) = 0 \quad \text{and} \quad P''(x) = R''(x) - C''(x) < 0,$$

or $\qquad R'(x) = C'(x) \quad \text{and} \quad R''(x) < C''(x).$

In summary, we have the following theorem.

THEOREM 10

Maximum profit occurs at those x-values for which

$$R'(x) = C'(x) \quad \text{and} \quad R''(x) < C''(x).*$$

---

*In Section 2.6, the concepts of *marginal revenue* and *marginal cost* are introduced, allowing $R'(x) = C'(x)$ to be regarded as Marginal revenue = Marginal cost.

You can check that the results in parts (c) and (d) of Example 4 can be easily found using Theorem 10.

EXAMPLE 5 **Business: Determining Ticket Price.** By keeping records, a theater determines that at a ticket price of $26, it averages 1000 people in attendance. For every drop in price of $1, it gains 50 customers. Each customer spends an average of $4 on concessions. What ticket price should the theater charge in order to maximize total revenue?

Solution Let x be the number of dollars by which the ticket price of $26 should be decreased. (If x is negative, the price is increased.) We first express the total revenue R as a function of x. Note that the increase in ticket sales is $50x$ when the price drops x dollars:

$$R(x) = \text{(Revenue from tickets)} + \text{(Revenue from concessions)}$$
$$= \text{(Number of people)} \cdot \text{(Ticket price)} + \text{(Number of people)} \cdot 4$$
$$= (1000 + 50x)(26 - x) + (1000 + 50x) \cdot 4$$
$$= -50x^2 + 500x + 30{,}000.$$

To find x such that $R(x)$ is a maximum, we first find $R'(x)$:

$$R'(x) = -100x + 500.$$

This derivative exists for all real numbers x. Thus, the only critical values are where $R'(x) = 0$; so we solve that equation:

$$-100x + 500 = 0$$
$$-100x = -500$$
$$x = 5 \qquad \text{This corresponds to lowering the price by \$5.}$$

Since this is the only critical value, we can use the second derivative,

$$R''(x) = -100,$$

to determine whether we have a maximum. Since $R''(5)$ is negative, $R(5)$ is a maximum. Therefore, in order to maximize revenue, the theater should charge

$$\$26 - \$5, \quad \text{or} \quad \$21 \text{ per ticket.} \qquad \text{5} ☑$$

Quick Check 5 ☑

A baseball team charges $30 per ticket and averages 20,000 people in attendance per game. Each person spends an average of $8 on concessions. For every drop of $1 in the ticket price, the attendance rises by 800 people. What ticket price should the team charge to maximize total revenue?

Minimizing Inventory Costs

A retail business outlet needs to be concerned about inventory costs. Suppose, for example, that a home electronics store sells 2500 television sets per year. It *could* operate by ordering all the sets at once. But then the owners would face the carrying costs (insurance, building space, and so on) of storing them all. Thus, they might make several smaller orders, so that the largest number they would ever have to store is 500. However, each time they reorder, there are costs for paperwork, delivery charges, labor, and so on. It seems, therefore, that there must be some balance between carrying costs and reorder costs. Let's see how calculus can help determine what that balance might be. We are trying to minimize the following function:

Total inventory costs = (Yearly carrying costs) + (Yearly reorder costs).

The *lot size* x is the largest number ordered each reordering period. If x units are ordered each period, then during that time somewhere between 0 and x units are in stock. To have a representative expression for the amount in stock at any one time in the period, we can use the average, $x/2$. This represents the average amount held in stock over the course of each time period.

Refer to the graphs shown on the next page. If the lot size is 2500, then during the period between orders, there are somewhere between 0 and 2500 units in stock.

On average, there are 2500/2, or 1250 units in stock. If the lot size is 1250, then during the period between orders, there are somewhere between 0 and 1250 units in stock. On average, there are 1250/2, or 625 units in stock. In general, if the lot size is x, the average inventory is $x/2$.

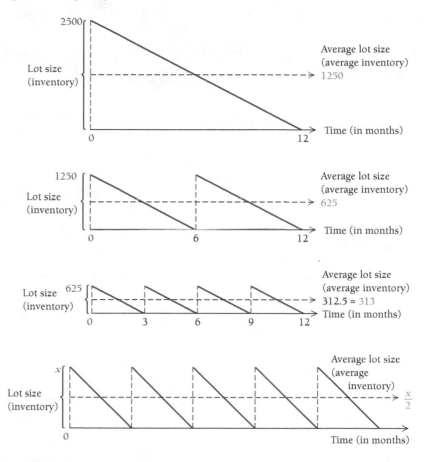

EXAMPLE 6 **Business: Minimizing Inventory Costs.** Fred's Electronics sells 2500 television sets per year. It costs $20 to store one set for a year. To reorder, there is a fixed cost of $20, plus a fee of $9 per set. How many times per year should the store reorder, and in what lot size, to minimize inventory costs?

Solution Let $x =$ the lot size. Inventory costs are given by

$$C(x) = (\text{Yearly carrying costs}) + (\text{Yearly reorder costs}).$$

We consider each component of inventory costs separately.

a) *Yearly carrying costs.* The average amount held in stock is $x/2$, and it costs $20 per set for storage. Thus,

$$\text{Yearly carrying costs} = \begin{pmatrix} \text{Yearly cost} \\ \text{per item} \end{pmatrix} \cdot \begin{pmatrix} \text{Average number} \\ \text{of items} \end{pmatrix}$$

$$= 20 \cdot \frac{x}{2}.$$

b) *Yearly reorder costs.* We know that x is the lot size, and we let N be the number of reorders each year. Then $Nx = 2500$, and $N = 2500/x$. Thus,

$$\text{Yearly reorder costs} = \begin{pmatrix} \text{Cost of each} \\ \text{order} \end{pmatrix} \cdot \begin{pmatrix} \text{Number of} \\ \text{reorders} \end{pmatrix}$$

$$= (20 + 9x)\frac{2500}{x}.$$

c) Thus, we have

$$C(x) = 20 \cdot \frac{x}{2} + (20 + 9x)\frac{2500}{x}$$

$$= 10x + \frac{50,000}{x} + 22,500 = 10x + 50,000x^{-1} + 22,500.$$

d) To find a minimum value of C over $[1, 2500]$, we first find $C'(x)$:

$$C'(x) = 10 - \frac{50,000}{x^2}.$$

e) Note that $C'(x)$ exists for all x in $[1, 2500]$, so the only critical values are those x-values such that $C'(x) = 0$. We solve $C'(x) = 0$:

$$10 - \frac{50,000}{x^2} = 0$$

$$10 = \frac{50,000}{x^2}$$

$$10x^2 = 50,000$$

$$x^2 = 5000$$

$$x = \sqrt{5000} \approx 70.7.$$

Since there is only one critical value in $[1, 2500]$, that is, $x \approx 70.7$, we can use the second derivative to see whether that value yields a maximum or a minimum:

$$C''(x) = \frac{100,000}{x^3}.$$

$C''(x)$ is positive for all x in $[1, 2500]$, so we have a minimum at $x \approx 70.7$.

However, it is impossible to reorder 70.7 sets each time, so we consider the two whole numbers closest to 70.7, which are 70 and 71. Since

$$C(70) \approx \$23,914.29 \quad \text{and} \quad C(71) \approx \$23,914.23,$$

it follows that the lot size that will minimize cost is 71, although the difference, $0.06, is not much. (*Note:* Such a procedure will not work for all functions but will work for the type we are considering here.) The number of times an order should be placed is 2500/71 with a remainder of 15, indicating that 35 orders should be placed. Of those, $35 - 15 = 20$ will be for 71 items and 15 will be for 72 items.   **6** ✔

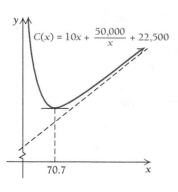

$$C(x) = 10x + \frac{50,000}{x} + 22,500$$

Quick Check 6 ✔

Repeat Example 6 with a storage cost of $30 per set and assuming that the store sells 3000 sets per year.

The lot size that minimizes total inventory costs is often referred to as the *economic ordering quantity*. Three assumptions are made in using the preceding method to determine the economic ordering quantity. First, the demand for the product is the same year round. For television sets, this may be reasonable, but for seasonal items such as clothing or skis, this assumption is unrealistic. Second, the time between placing an order and receiving the product remains consistent year-round. Finally, the costs involved, such as storage, shipping charges, and so on, do not vary. This assumption may not be reasonable in a time of inflation, although variation in these costs can be allowed for by anticipating what they might be and using average costs. Regardless, the model described above is useful, allowing us to analyze a seemingly difficult problem using calculus.

Using Excel Spreadsheets to Numerically Estimate Minimum and Maximum Values

An Excel spreadsheet can numerically estimate absolute extrema. For example, to estimate the values for Example 2, we open a blank spreadsheet and enter text in the cells as shown below:

	A	B	C	D
1	Starting value			
2	Step size:			
3				
4	Height	Length	Width	Volume
5	H=x	L=8–2x	W=8–2x	V=H*L*W

In cell A6, we enter =B1; in cells B6 and C6, we enter =8-2*A6; and in cell D6, we enter =A6*B6*C6. In cell A7, we enter =A6+B2. We copy cells B6, C6, and D6 and paste them into cells B7, C7, and D7, then copy cells A7 through D7 and paste them into cells A8 through D14. This creates nine active rows. More rows can be added if necessary.

In cell B1, we enter a starting x-value, and in cell B2, a step size. For example, if we enter 0 into cell B1 and 0.25 into cell B2, the values in cells A6–A14 will be x = 0, 0.25, 0.5, 0.75, 1, and so on. The result is the following table:

	A	B	C	
1	Starting value	0		
2	Step size:	0.25		
3				
4	Height	Length	Width	Volume
5	H=x	L=8–2x	W=8–2x	V=H*L*W
6	0	8	8	0
7	0.25	7.5	7.5	14.0625
8	0.5	7	7	24.5
9	0.75	6.5	6.5	31.6875
10	1	6	6	36
11	1.25	5.5	5.5	37.8125	← Possible largest volume
12	1.5	5	5	37.5	
13	1.75	4.5	4.5	35.4375	
14	2	4	4	32	

We see that a possible maximum volume of 37.8125 in^2 occurs when x = 1.25 in.

To refine our estimate, we enter 1 into cell B1 and 0.1 into cell B2, giving the following table:

	A	B	C	
1	Starting value	1		
2	Step size:	0.1		
3				
4	Height	Length	Width	Volume
5	H=x	L=8–2x	W=8–2x	V=H*L*W
6	1	6	6	36
7	1.1	5.8	5.8	37.004
8	1.2	5.6	5.6	37.632
9	1.3	5.4	5.4	37.908	← Possible largest volume
10	1.4	5.2	5.2	37.856	
11	1.5	5	5	37.5	
12	1.6	4.8	4.8	36.864	

By reducing the step size, we obtain a new possible maximum volume of 37.908 in^3 when x = 1.3 in. Although we could further reduce the step size, we now have an estimate of the maximum volume and the x-value at which it occurs. We use calculus to determine these values exactly.

EXERCISES

1. Use a spreadsheet to verify the results of Example 1.

2. Use a spreadsheet to verify the results of Example 4.

3. Use a spreadsheet to verify the results of Example 3.

4. Use a spreadsheet to verify the results of Example 6.

Section Summary

- In many real-life applications, we need to determine the minimum or maximum value of a function modeling a situation.

- Maximum profit occurs at those x-values for which $R'(x) = C'(x)$ and $R''(x) < C''(x)$.

2.5 | Exercise Set

1. Of all numbers whose sum is 70, find the two that have the maximum product. That is, maximize $Q = xy$, where $x + y = 70$.

2. Of all numbers whose sum is 50, find the two that have the maximum product. That is, maximize $Q = xy$, where $x + y = 50$.

3. Of all numbers whose difference is 6, find the two that have the minimum product.

4. Of all numbers whose difference is 4, find the two that have the minimum product.

5. Maximize $Q = xy^2$, where x and y are positive numbers such that $x + y^2 = 4$.

6. Maximize $Q = xy^2$, where x and y are positive numbers such that $x + y^2 = 1$.

7. Minimize $Q = x^2 + 2y^2$, where $x + y = 3$.

8. Minimize $Q = 2x^2 + 3y^2$, where $x + y = 5$.

9. Maximize $Q = xy$, where x and y are positive numbers such that $x + \frac{4}{3}y^2 = 1$.

10. Maximize $Q = xy$, where x and y are positive numbers such that $\frac{4}{3}x^2 + y = 16$.

11. **Maximizing area.** A rancher wants to enclose two rectangular areas near a river, one for sheep and one for cattle. There are 240 yd of fencing available. What is the largest total area that can be enclosed?

12. **Maximizing area.** A lifeguard needs to rope off a rectangular swimming area in front of Long Lake Beach, using 180 yd of rope and floats. What dimensions of the rectangle will maximize the area? What is the maximum area? (Note that the shoreline is one side of the rectangle.)

13. **Maximizing area.** Hentz Industries plans to enclose three parallel rectangular areas for sorting returned goods. The three areas are within one large rectangular area and 1200 yd of fencing is available. What is the largest total area that can be enclosed?

14. **Maximizing area.** Grayson Farms plans to enclose three parallel rectangular livestock pens within one large rectangular area using 600 ft of fencing. One side of the enclosure is a pre-existing stone wall.

   a) If the three rectangular pens have their longer sides parallel to the stone wall, find the largest possible total area that can be enclosed.

b) If the three rectangular pens have their shorter sides perpendicular to the stone wall, find the largest possible total area that can be enclosed.

15. Maximizing area. Of all rectangles that have a perimeter of 42 ft, find the dimensions of the one with the largest area. What is its area?

16. Maximizing area. A carpenter is building a rectangular shed with a fixed perimeter of 54 ft. What are the dimensions of the largest shed that can be built? What is its area?

17. Maximizing volume. From a thin piece of cardboard 20 in. by 20 in., square corners are cut out so that the sides can be folded up to make a box. What dimensions will yield a box of maximum volume? What is the maximum volume?

18. Maximizing volume. From a 50-cm-by-50-cm sheet of aluminum, square corners are cut out so that the sides can be folded up to make a box. What dimensions will yield a box of maximum volume? What is the maximum volume?

19. Minimizing surface area. Mendoza Soup Company is constructing an open-top, square-based, rectangular metal tank that will have a volume of 32 ft^3. What dimensions will minimize surface area? What is the minimum surface area?

20. Minimizing surface area. Drum Tight Containers is designing an open-top, square-based, rectangular box that will have a volume of 62.5 in^3. What dimensions will minimize surface area? What is the minimum surface area?

21. Minimizing surface area. Open Air Waste Management is designing a rectangular construction dumpster that will be twice as long as it is wide and must hold 12 yd^3 of debris. Find the dimensions of the dumpster that will minimize its surface area.

22. Minimizing surface area. Ever Green Gardening is designing a rectangular compost container that will be twice as tall as it is wide and must hold 18 ft^3 of composted food scraps. Find the dimensions of the compost container with minimal surface area (include the bottom and top).

APPLICATIONS

Business and Economics

Maximizing profit.   *For Exercises 23–28, find the maximum profit and the number of units that must be produced and sold in order to yield the maximum profit. Assume that revenue, R(x), and cost, C(x), are in dollars for Exercises 23–26.*

23. $R(x) = 50x - 0.5x^2, \quad C(x) = 4x + 10$

24. $R(x) = 50x - 0.5x^2, \quad C(x) = 10x + 3$

25. $R(x) = 2x, \quad C(x) = 0.01x^2 + 0.6x + 30$

26. $R(x) = 5x, \quad C(x) = 0.001x^2 + 1.2x + 60$

27. $R(x) = 9x - 2x^2, \quad C(x) = x^3 - 3x^2 + 4x + 1$; assume that $R(x)$ and $C(x)$ are in thousands of dollars, and x is in thousands of units.

28. $R(x) = 100x - x^2, C(x) = \frac{1}{3}x^3 - 6x^2 + 89x + 100$; assume that $R(x)$ and $C(x)$ are in thousands of dollars, and x is in thousands of units.

29. Maximizing profit. Riverside Appliances is marketing a new refrigerator. It determines that in order to sell x refrigerators, the price per refrigerator must be

$$p = 280 - 0.4x.$$

It also determines that the total cost of producing x refrigerators is given by

$$C(x) = 5000 + 0.6x^2.$$

a) Find the total revenue, $R(x)$.
b) Find the total profit, $P(x)$.
c) How many refrigerators must the company produce and sell in order to maximize profit?
d) What is the maximum profit?
e) What price per refrigerator must be charged in order to maximize profit?

30. Maximizing profit. Raggs, Ltd., a clothing firm, determines that in order to sell x suits, the price per suit must be

$$p = 150 - 0.5x.$$

It also determines that the total cost of producing x suits is given by

$$C(x) = 4000 + 0.25x^2.$$

a) Find the total revenue, $R(x)$.
b) Find the total profit, $P(x)$.
c) How many suits must the company produce and sell in order to maximize profit?
d) What is the maximum profit?
e) What price per suit must be charged in order to maximize profit?

31. Maximizing profit. Gritz-Charlston is a 300-unit luxury hotel. All rooms are occupied when the hotel charges $80 per day for a room. For every increase of x dollars in the daily room rate, there are x rooms vacant. Each occupied room costs $22 per day to service and maintain. What should the hotel charge per day in order to maximize profit?

32. Maximizing revenue.   Edwards University wants to determine what price to charge for tickets to football games. At a price of $18 per ticket, attendance averages 40,000 people per game. Every decrease of $3 to the ticket price adds 10,000 people to the average attendance. Every person at a game spends an average of $4.50 on concessions. What price per ticket should be charged to maximize revenue? How many people will attend at that price?

33. Maximizing parking tickets.   Oak Glen currently employs 8 patrol officers who each write an average of 24 parking tickets per day. For every additional officer placed on patrol, the average number of parking tickets per day written by each officer decreases by 4. How many additional officers should be placed on patrol in order to maximize the number of parking tickets written per day?

34. Maximizing yield.   Hood Apple Farm yields an average of 30 bushels of apples per tree when 20 trees are planted on an acre of ground. If 1 more tree is planted per acre, the yield decreases by 1 bushel (bu) per tree as a result of crowding. How many trees should be planted on an acre in order to get the highest yield?

35. Nitrogen prices.   During 2001, nitrogen prices fell by 41%. Over the same year, nitrogen demand went up by 12%. (*Source: Chemical Week.*)

a) Assuming a linear change in demand, find the demand function, $q(x)$, by finding the equation of the line that passes through the points $(1, 1)$ and $(0.59, 1.12)$. Here x is the price as a fraction of the January 2001 price, and $q(x)$ is the demand as a fraction of the demand in January.

b) As a percentage of the January 2001 price, what should the price of nitrogen be to maximize revenue?

36. Vanity license plates.   According to a pricing model, increasing the fee for vanity license plates by $1 decreases the percentage of a state's population that will request them by 0.04%. (*Source:* E. D. Craft, "The demand for vanity (plates): Elasticities, net revenue maximization, and deadweight loss," *Contemporary Economic Policy*, Vol. 20, 133–144 (2002).)

a) Recently, the fee for vanity license plates in Maryland was $25, and the percentage of the state's population that had vanity plates was 2.13%. Use this information to construct the demand function, $q(x)$, for the percentage of Maryland's population that will request vanity license plates for a fee of x dollars.

b) Find the fee, x, that will maximize revenue from vanity plates.

37. Maximizing revenue.   When the Marchant Theater charges $5 for admission, there is an average

attendance of 180 people. For every $0.10 increase in admission, there is a loss of 1 customer from the average number. What admission should be charged in order to maximize revenue?

38. Minimizing costs.   A rectangular box with a volume of 320 ft^3 is to be constructed with a square base and top. The cost per square foot for the bottom is 15¢, for the top is 10¢, and for the sides is 2.5¢. What dimensions will minimize the cost?

39. Minimizing cost.   A rectangular parking area measuring 5000 ft^2 is to be enclosed on three sides using chain-link fencing that costs $4.50 per foot. The fourth side will be a wooden fence that costs $7 per foot. What dimensions will minimize the total cost to enclose this area, and what is the minimum cost (rounded to the nearest dollar)?

40. Minimizing cost.   A rectangular garden measuring 1200 yd^2 is to be enclosed on two parallel sides by stone wall that costs $35 per yd and the other two sides by wooden fencing that costs $28 per yd. What dimensions will minimize the total cost of enclosing this garden, and what is the minimum cost (rounded to the nearest dollar)?

41. Maximizing area.   Bradley Publishing decides that each page in a new book must have an area of 73.125 in^2, a 0.75-in. margin at the top and at the bottom of each page, and a 0.5-in. margin on each of the sides. What should the outside dimensions of each page be so that the printed area is a maximum?

42. Minimizing inventory costs.   A sporting goods store sells 100 pool tables per year. It costs $20 to store one pool table for a year. To reorder, there is a fixed cost of $40 per shipment plus $16 for each pool table. How many times per year should the store order pool tables, and in what lot size, in order to minimize inventory costs?

43. Minimizing inventory costs.   A pro shop in a bowling center sells 200 bowling balls per year. It costs $4 to store one bowling ball for a year. To reorder, there is a fixed cost of $1, plus $0.50 for each bowling ball. How many times per year should the shop order bowling balls, and in what lot size, in order to minimize inventory costs?

44. Minimizing inventory costs. A retail outlet for Boxowitz Calculators sells 720 calculators per year. It costs
$2 to store one calculator for a year. To reorder, there is
a fixed cost of $5, plus $2.50 for each calculator. How
many times per year should the store order calculators,
and in what lot size, in order to minimize inventory
costs?

45. Minimizing inventory costs. Bon Temps Surf and
Scuba Shop sells 360 surfboards per year. It costs $8 to
store one surfboard for a year. Each reorder costs $10,
plus an additional $5 for each surfboard ordered. How
many times per year should the store order surfboards,
and in what lot size, in order to minimize inventory
costs?

46. Minimizing inventory costs. Repeat Exercise 44
using the same data, but assume yearly sales of
256 calculators with the fixed cost of each reorder
set at $4.

47. Minimizing inventory costs. Repeat Exercise 45
using the same data, but change the reorder costs
from an additional $5 per surfboard to $6 per surfboard.

48. Minimizing surface area. A closed-top cylindrical
container is to have a volume of 250 in^2. What dimensions (radius and height) will minimize the surface
area?

49. Minimizing surface area. An open-top cylindrical
container is to have a volume of 400 cm^2. What
dimensions (radius and height) will minimize the
surface area?

50. Minimizing cost. Assume that the costs of the materials for making the cylindrical container described in
Exercise 48 are $0.005/in^2 for the circular base and
top and $0.003/in^2 for the wall. What dimensions will
minimize the cost of materials?

51. Minimizing cost. Assume that the costs of the materials for making the cylindrical container described
in Exercise 49 are $0.0015/cm^2 for the base and
$0.008/cm^2 for the wall. What dimensions will mini-
mize the cost of materials?

General Interest

52. Maximizing volume. The postal service places a limit
of 84 in. on the combined length and girth of (distance
around) a package to be sent parcel post. What dimensions of a rectangular box with square cross-section will
contain the largest volume that can be mailed? (*Hint:*
There are two different girths.)

53. Minimizing cost. A rectangular play area of 48 yd^2
is to be fenced off in a person's yard. The next-door
neighbor agrees to pay half the cost of the fence on the
side of the play area that lies along the property line.
What dimensions will minimize the cost of the fence?

54. Maximizing light. A Norman window is a rectangle
with a semicircle on top. Suppose that the perimeter of a particular Norman window is to be 24 ft.
What should its dimensions be in order to allow
the maximum amount of light to enter through the
window?

55. Maximizing light. Repeat Exercise 54, but assume
that the semicircle is to be stained glass, which trans-
mits only half as much light as clear glass does.

56–110. Use a spreadsheet to numerically verify the result
of Exercises 1–55.

SYNTHESIS

111. For what positive number is the sum of its reciprocal
and five times its square a minimum?

112. For what positive number is the sum of its reciprocal
and four times its square a minimum?

113. Business: maximizing profit. The amount of money
that customers deposit in a bank in savings accounts is
directly proportional to the interest rate that the bank
pays on that money. Suppose a bank is able to loan out
all the money deposited in its savings accounts at an
interest rate of 18%. What interest rate should it pay on
its savings accounts in order to maximize profit?

114. A 24-in. piece of wire is cut in two pieces. One piece is used to form a circle and the other to form a square. How should the wire be cut so that the sum of the areas is a minimum? A maximum?

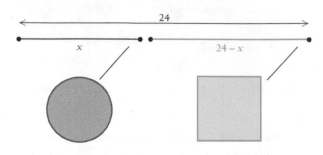

115. Business: minimizing costs. A power line is to be constructed from a power station at point A to an island at point C, which is 1 mi directly out in the water from a point B on the shore. Point B is 4 mi downshore from the power station at A. It costs \$5000 per mile to lay the power line under water and \$3000 per mile to lay the line under ground. At what point S downshore from A should the line come to the shore in order to minimize cost? Note that S could very well be B or A. (*Hint*: The length of CS is $\sqrt{1 + x^2}$.)

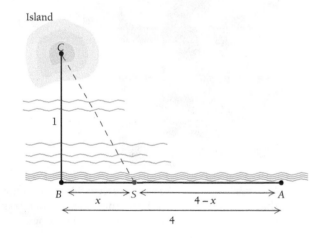

116. Life science: flights of homing pigeons. It is known that homing pigeons tend to avoid flying over water in the daytime, perhaps because downdrafts of air over water make flying difficult. Suppose a homing pigeon is released on an island at point C, which is 3 mi directly out in the water from a point B on shore. Point B is 8 mi downshore from the pigeon's home loft at point A. Assume that a pigeon flying over water uses energy at a rate 1.28 times the rate over land. Toward what point S downshore from A should the pigeon fly in order to minimize the total energy required to get to the home loft at A? Assume that

    Total energy =
    (Energy rate over water) · (Distance over water)
    +(Energy rate over land) · (Distance over land).

117. A rectangular field is to be divided into two parallel rectangular areas, as shown in the figure below. If the total fencing available is k units, show that the length of each of the three parallel fences will be $k/6$ units.

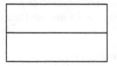

118. Business: minimizing distance. A road is to be built between two cities C_1 and C_2, which are on opposite sides of a river of uniform width r. C_1 is a units from the river, and C_2 is b units from the river, with $a \le b$. A bridge will carry the traffic across the river. Where should the bridge be located in order to minimize the total distance between the cities? Give a general solution using the constants a, b, p, and r as shown in the figure.

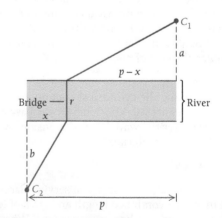

119. Business: minimizing cost. The total cost, in dollars, of producing x units of a certain product is given by

$$C(x) = 8x + 20 + \frac{x^3}{100}.$$

a) Find the average cost, $A(x) = C(x)/x$.
b) Find $C'(x)$ and $A'(x)$.
c) Find the minimum of $A(x)$ and the value x_0 at which it occurs. Find $C'(x_0)$.
d) Compare $A(x_0)$ and $C'(x_0)$.

120. Business: minimizing cost. Consider

$$A(x) = C(x)/x.$$

a) Find $A'(x)$ in terms of $C'(x)$ and $C(x)$.
b) Show that if $A(x)$ has a minimum, then it will occur at that value of x_0 for which

$$C'(x_0) = A(x_0)$$
$$= \frac{C(x_0)}{x_0}.$$

This result shows that if average cost can be minimized, such a minimum will occur when marginal cost equals average cost.

121. Minimize $Q = x^3 + 2y^3$, where x and y are positive numbers, such that $x + y = 1$.

122. Minimize $Q = 3x + y^3$, where $x^2 + y^2 = 2$.

123. Business: minimizing inventory costs—a general solution. A store sells Q units of a product per year. It costs a dollars to store one unit for a year. To reorder, there is a fixed cost of b dollars, plus c dollars for each unit. How many times per year should the store reorder, and in what lot size, in order to minimize inventory costs?

124. Business: minimizing inventory costs. Use the general solution found in Exercise 123 to find how many times per year a store should reorder, and in what lot size, when $Q = 2500$, $a = \$10$, $b = \$20$, and $c = \$9$.

Answers to Quick Checks

1. With 50 ft of fencing, the dimensions are 25 ft by 25 ft (625 ft^2 area); with 100 ft of fencing, they are 50 ft by 50 ft (2500 ft^2 area); in general, n feet of fencing gives $n/2$ ft by $n/2$ ft ($n^2/4$ ft^2 area). **2.** The dimensions are approximately 1.585 in. by 5.33 in. by 7.83 in.; the volume is 66.15 in^3, or 1083.5 cm^3, slightly more than 1 L. **3.** $r \approx 5.3$ cm, $h \approx 2.83$ cm, $c \approx \$0.212/$can **4. (a)** $R(x) = 1750x - 2x^2$; **(b)** $P(x) = -2x^2 + 1735x - 2250$; **(c)** $x = 434$ units; **(d)** maximum profit $= \$374,028$; **(e)** price per unit $= \$882.00$ **5.** $\$23.50$ **6.** $x \approx 63$; the store should place 8 orders for 63 sets and 39 orders for 64 sets.

Marginals and Differentials

In this section, we consider ways of using calculus to make linear approximations. Suppose, for example, that a company is considering an increase in production. Usually the company wants at least an approximation of what the resulting changes in *cost*, *revenue*, and *profit* will be.

- Find marginal cost, revenue, and profit.
- Find Δy and dy.
- Use differentials for approximations.

Marginal Cost, Revenue, and Profit

Suppose an animal rescue organization that produces its own public service announcements (PSAs) is considering an increase in monthly production from 12 PSAs to 13. To estimate the resulting increase in cost, it would be reasonable to find the rate at which cost is increasing when 12 PSAs are produced and add that to the cost of producing 12 PSAs. That is,

$$C(13) \approx C(12) + C'(12).$$

The number $C'(12)$ is called the *marginal cost at 12*. Remember that $C'(12)$ is the slope of the tangent line at the point $(12, C(12))$. If, for example, this slope is $\frac{3}{4}$, we can regard it as a vertical change of 3 with a horizontal change of 4, or a vertical change of $\frac{3}{4}$ with a horizontal change of 1. It is this latter interpretation that we use for estimating. Graphically, this interpretation can be viewed as shown in the following graph. Note in the figure that $C'(12)$ is slightly more than the difference between $C(13)$ and $C(12)$, or $C(13) - C(12)$. For other curves, $C'(12)$ may be slightly less than $C(13) - C(12)$. Almost always, however, it is simpler to compute $C'(12)$ than it is to compute $C(13) - C(12)$.

Generalizing, we have the following.

DEFINITIONS

Let $C(x)$, $R(x)$, and $P(x)$ represent, respectively, the total cost, revenue, and profit from the production and sale of x items.

The **marginal cost** at x, given by $C'(x)$, is the approximate cost of the $(x + 1)$st item:

$$C'(x) \approx C(x + 1) - C(x), \text{ or } C(x + 1) \approx C(x) + C'(x).$$

The **marginal revenue** at x, given by $R'(x)$, is the approximate revenue from the $(x + 1)$st item:

$$R'(x) \approx R(x + 1) - R(x), \text{ or } R(x + 1) \approx R(x) + R'(x).$$

The **marginal profit** at x, given by $P'(x)$, is the approximate profit from the $(x + 1)$st item:

$$P'(x) \approx P(x + 1) - P(x), \text{ or } P(x + 1) \approx P(x) + P'(x).$$

The student can confirm that $P'(x) = R'(x) - C'(x)$.

EXAMPLE 1   **Business: Marginal Cost, Revenue, and Profit.**   Given

$$C(x) = 62x^2 + 27,500$$

and $R(x) = x^3 - 12x^2 + 40x + 10,$

find each of the following.

a) Total profit, $P(x)$

b) Total cost, revenue, and profit from the production and sale of 50 units of the product

c) The marginal cost, revenue, and profit when 50 units are produced and sold

Solution

a)   Total profit $= P(x) = R(x) - C(x)$

$$= x^3 - 12x^2 + 40x + 10 - (62x^2 + 27,500)$$

$$= x^3 - 74x^2 + 40x - 27,490$$

b) We have

$$C(50) = 62 \cdot 50^2 + 27{,}500 = \$182{,}500 \qquad \text{The total cost of producing the first 50 units}$$

$$R(50) = 50^3 - 12 \cdot 50^2 + 40 \cdot 50 + 10 = \$97{,}010 \qquad \text{The total revenue from the sale of the first 50 units}$$

$$P(50) = R(50) - C(50)$$
$$= \$97{,}010 - \$182{,}500 \qquad \text{We could also use } P(x) \text{ from part (a).}$$
$$= -\$85{,}490 \qquad \text{There is a } \textit{loss} \text{ of } \$85{,}490 \text{ when 50 units are produced and sold.}$$

c) We have

$$C'(x) = 124x,$$
$$C'(50) = 124 \cdot 50 = \$6200 \qquad \text{Once 50 units have been made, the approximate cost of the 51st unit (marginal cost) is \$6200.}$$

$$R'(x) = 3x^2 - 24x + 40,$$
$$R'(50) = 3 \cdot 50^2 - 24 \cdot 50 + 40 = \$6340 \qquad \text{Once 50 units have been sold, the approximate revenue from the 51st unit (marginal revenue) is \$6340.}$$

$$P'(x) = 3x^2 - 148x + 40,$$
$$P'(50) = 3 \cdot 50^2 - 148 \cdot 50 + 40 = \$140 \qquad \text{Once 50 units have been produced and sold, the approximate profit from the sale of the 51st item (marginal profit) is \$140}$$

1 ✔

Quick Check 1 ✔

Given

$$C(x) = 10x + 3$$
$$\text{and} \quad R(x) = 50x - 0.5x^2,$$

find each of the following
a) $P(x)$
b) Total cost, revenue, and profit from the production and sale of 40 units
c) The marginal cost, revenue, and profit when 40 units are produced and sold

---

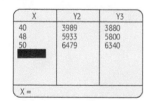

Often, in business, formulas for $C(x)$, $R(x)$, and $P(x)$ are not known, but information may exist about the cost, revenue, and profit trends at a particular value $x = a$. For example, $C(a)$ and $C'(a)$ may be known, allowing a reasonable prediction to be made about $C(a + 1)$. In a similar manner, predictions can be made for $R(a + 1)$ and $P(a + 1)$. In Example 1, formulas *do* exist, so it is possible to see how accurate our predictions were. We check $C(51) - C(50)$ and leave the checks of $R(51) - R(50)$ and $P(51) - P(50)$ to the student (see the Technology Connection in the margin):

$$C(51) - C(50) = 62 \cdot 51^2 + 27{,}500 - (62 \cdot 50^2 + 27{,}500)$$
$$= 6262,$$

whereas $\qquad C'(50) = 6200.$

In this case, $C'(50)$ provides an approximation of $C(51) - C(50)$ that is within 1% of the actual value.

Note that marginal cost is different from *average* cost:

$$\text{Average cost per unit for 50 units} = \frac{C(50)}{50} \begin{array}{l} \longleftarrow \text{Total cost of 50 units} \\ \longleftarrow \text{The number of units, 50} \end{array}$$

$$= \frac{182{,}500}{50} = \$3650,$$

whereas

$$\text{Marginal cost when 50 units are produced} = \$6200$$

$$\approx \text{cost of the 51st unit.}$$

Differentials and Delta Notation

Just as marginal cost $C'(x_0)$ is used to estimate $C(x_0 + 1)$, the value of $f'(x_0)$, can be used to estimate values of $f(x)$ for x-values near x_0. To do so, we need to develop some notation.
Recall that the difference quotient,

$$\frac{f(x + h) - f(x)}{h},$$

represents the slope of a secant line, as shown in the graph. The number h is regarded as the *change* in x. Another notation for such a change is Δx (read "delta x"), called **delta notation**. The expression Δx is *not* the product of Δ and x, but rather a new type of variable that represents the *change* in the value of x from a *first* value to a *second*. Thus,

$$\Delta x = (x + h) - x = h.$$

If subscripts are used for the first and second values of x, we have

$$\Delta x = x_2 - x_1, \quad \text{or} \quad x_2 = x_1 + \Delta x.$$

Note that the value of Δx can be positive or negative. For example,

$$\text{if } x_1 = 4 \text{ and } \Delta x = 0.7, \text{ then } x_2 = 4.7,$$

and $\quad$ if $x_1 = 4$ and $\Delta x = -0.7$, then $x_2 = 3.3$.

We generally omit the subscripts and use x and $x + \Delta x$. Now suppose we have a function given by $y = f(x)$. A change in x from x to $x + \Delta x$ yields a change in y from $f(x)$ to $f(x + \Delta x)$. The change in y is given by

$$\Delta y = f(x + \Delta x) - f(x).$$

EXAMPLE 2 Find Δy in each case.

a) $y = x^2, x = 4$, and $\Delta x = 0.1$

b) $y = x^3, x = 2$, and $\Delta x = -0.1$

Solution

a) We have

$$\Delta y = (4 + 0.1)^2 - 4^2$$
$$= (4.1)^2 - 4^2 = 16.81 - 16 = 0.81.$$

b) We have

$$\Delta y = [2 + (-0.1)]^3 - 2^3$$
$$= (1.9)^3 - 2^3 = 6.859 - 8 = -1.141. \qquad 2 ✔$$

Quick Check 2 ✔

For $y = 2x^4 + x, x = 2$, and $\Delta x = -0.05$, find Δy.

Let's now use calculus to predict function values. If delta notation is used, the difference quotient

$$\frac{f(x + h) - f(x)}{h}$$

becomes

$$\frac{f(x + \Delta x) - f(x)}{\Delta x} = \frac{\Delta y}{\Delta x}.$$

We can then express the derivative as

$$\frac{dy}{dx} = \lim_{\Delta x \to 0} \frac{\Delta y}{\Delta x}.$$

For values of Δx close to 0, we have the approximation

$$\frac{dy}{dx} \approx \frac{\Delta y}{\Delta x}, \quad \text{or} \quad f'(x) \approx \frac{\Delta y}{\Delta x}.$$

Multiplying both sides by Δx, we have

$$\Delta y \approx f'(x) \, \Delta x.$$

We can see this in the graph at the left.

From this graph, it seems reasonable to assume that, for small values of Δx, the y-values on the tangent line can be used to estimate function values on the curve.

For f, a continuous, differentiable function, and small Δx,

$$f'(x) \approx \frac{\Delta y}{\Delta x} \quad \text{and} \quad \Delta y \approx f'(x) \cdot \Delta x.$$

Up to now, we have treated dy/dx as one symbol. We now define dy and dx as separate entities. These symbols are called **differentials.**

DEFINITION

For $y = f(x)$, we define

$\qquad dx$, called the **differential of x**, by $dx = \Delta x$

and $\quad dy$, called the **differential of y**, by $dy = f'(x)\, dx.$

We can illustrate dx and dy as shown at the right. Note that $dx = \Delta x$, but, in general, $dy \neq \Delta y$, though $dy \approx \Delta y$, for small values of dx.

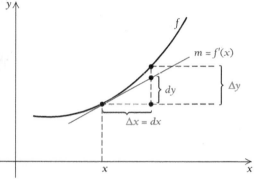

EXAMPLE 3 Consider the function given by $y = f(x) = \sqrt{x}$.

a) Find dy when $x = 9$ and $dx = 1$.

b) Compare dy to Δy.

c) Use the results of parts (a) and (b) to estimate $\sqrt{10}$.

Solution

a) We find dy/dx, then dy:

$$\frac{dy}{dx} = \frac{1}{2\sqrt{x}} \qquad \text{Differentiating } y = x^{1/2} \text{ with respect to } x$$

$$dy = \frac{1}{2\sqrt{x}}\,dx.$$

To find dy when $x = 9$ and $dx = 1$, we substitute:

$$dy = \frac{1}{2\sqrt{9}}(1) = \frac{1}{6} = 0.1666\ldots .$$

b) The value Δy is the actual change in y between $x = 9$ and $x = 10$:

$$\Delta y = \sqrt{10} - \sqrt{9}$$

$$= 3.16227767\ldots - 3 \qquad \text{Using a calculator}$$

$$= 0.16227767.$$

We see that $\Delta y = 0.16227767$ and $dy = 0.1666\ldots$ do not differ by much.

Quick Check 3 ☑

For $y = \sqrt{x}$, find dy when $x = 100$ and $dx = -2$. Compare dy to Δy, and estimate the value of $\sqrt{98}$.

c) Note that $\sqrt{10} \approx \sqrt{9} + dy$, so $\sqrt{10} \approx 3 + 0.1666\ldots = 3.1666\ldots$ is a close approximation of $\sqrt{10}$.   **3** ☑

We see that the approximation dy and the actual change Δy are reasonably close. It is easier to calculate the approximation since that involves fewer steps, but the trade-off is some loss in accuracy. As long as dx is small, this loss in accuracy is often acceptable, as the following example illustrates.

EXAMPLE 4   **Business: Cost and Tolerance.**   In preparation for laying new tile, Michelle measures the floor of a banquet hall and finds it to be square, measuring 100 ft by 100 ft. Suppose these measurements are accurate to ± 6 in. (the tolerance).

a) Use a differential to estimate the difference in area (dA) due to the tolerance.

b) Compare the result from part (a) with the actual difference in area (ΔA).

c) If each tile covers 1 ft^2 and a box of 12 tiles costs \$24, how many extra boxes of tiles should Michelle buy for covering the floor? What is the extra cost?

Solution

a) The floor is a square, with a presumed measurement of 100 ft per side and a tolerance of ± 6 in. $= \pm 0.5$ ft. The area A in square feet (ft^2) for a square of side length x ft is

$$A(x) = x^2.$$

The derivative is $dA/dx = 2x$, and solving for dA gives the differential of A:

$$dA = 2x\, dx.$$

To find dA, we substitute $x = 100$ and $dx = \pm 0.5$:

$$dA = 2(100)(\pm 0.5) = \pm 100.$$

The value of dA is the approximate difference in area due to the inexactness in measuring. Therefore, if Michelle's measurements are off by half a foot, the total area can differ by approximately ± 100 ft^2. A small "error" in measurement can lead to a significant difference in the resulting area.

b) The actual difference in area, ΔA, is calculated. We set $x_1 = 100$ ft, and let x_2 represent the length plus or minus the tolerance.

   If the true length is at the low end, we have $x_2 = 99.5$ ft. The floor's area is then $99.5^2 = 9900.25$ ft^2. The actual difference in area is

$$\begin{aligned}
\Delta A &= A(x_2) - A(x_1) \\
&= A(99.5) - A(100) \\
&= 99.5^2 - 100^2 \\
&= 9900.25 - 10{,}000 \\
&= -99.75 \text{ ft}^2.
\end{aligned}$$

   If the true length is at the high end, we have $x_2 = 100.5$ ft. The floor's area is then $100.5^2 = 10{,}100.25$ ft^2. The actual difference in area is

$$\begin{aligned}
\Delta A &= A(x_2) - A(x_1) \\
&= A(100.5) - A(100) \\
&= 100.5^2 - 100^2 \\
&= 10{,}100.25 - 10{,}000 \\
&= 100.25 \text{ ft}^2.
\end{aligned}$$

Quick Check 4 ☑

The four walls of a room measure 10 ft by 10 ft each, with a tolerance of ±0.25 ft.

a) Calculate the approximate difference in area, dA, for the four walls.

b) Workers will texture the four walls using "knockdown" spray. Each bottle of knockdown spray costs $9 and covers 12 ft^2. How many extra bottles should the workers buy to allow for overage in wall area? What will the extra cost be?

We see that ΔA, the actual difference in area, can range from -99.75 ft^2 to 100.25 ft^2. Both values compare well with the approximate value of $dA = \pm100$ ft^2.

c) The tiles (each measuring 1 ft^2) come 12 to a box. Thus, if the room were exactly 100 ft by 100 ft (an area of 10,000 ft^2), Michelle would need $10,000/12 = 833.33\ldots$, or 834 boxes to cover the floor. To take into account the possibility that the room is larger by 100 ft^2, she needs a total of $10,100/12 = 841.67\ldots$, or 842 boxes of tiles. Therefore, she should buy $842 - 834$, or 8 extra boxes of tiles, for an extra cost of $(8)(24) = \$192$.   **4** ☑

Historically, differentials were quite valuable when used to make approximations. However, with the advent of computers and graphing calculators, such use has diminished considerably. The use of marginals remains important in the study of business and economics.

Section Summary

- If $C(x)$ represents the cost of producing x items, then *marginal cost* $C'(x)$ is its derivative, and $C'(x) \approx C(x + 1) - C(x)$. Thus, the cost to produce the $(x + 1)$st item can be approximated by $C(x + 1) \approx C(x) + C'(x)$.
- If $R(x)$ represents the revenue from selling x items, then *marginal revenue* $R'(x)$ is its derivative, and $R'(x) \approx R(x + 1) - R(x)$. Thus, the revenue from the $(x + 1)$st item can be approximated by $R(x + 1) \approx R(x) + R'(x)$.
- If $P(x)$ represents profit from selling x items, then *marginal profit* $P'(x)$ is its derivative, and $P'(x) \approx P(x + 1) - P(x)$. Thus, the profit

from the $(x + 1)$st item can be approximated by $P(x + 1) \approx P(x) + P'(x)$.
- In *delta notation*, $\Delta x = (x + h) - x = h$, and $\Delta y = f(x + h) - f(x)$. For small values of Δx, we have $\dfrac{\Delta y}{\Delta x} \approx f'(x)$, which is equivalent to $\Delta y \approx f'(x)\,\Delta x$.
- The *differential* of x is $dx = \Delta x$. Since $\dfrac{dy}{dx} = f'(x)$, we have $dy = f'(x)\,dx$. In general, $dy \approx \Delta y$, and the approximation is often very close for sufficiently small dx.

2.6 | Exercise Set

APPLICATIONS

Business and Economics

1. Marginal revenue, cost, and profit. Let $R(x), C(x)$, and $P(x)$ be, respectively, the revenue, cost, and profit, in dollars, from the production and sale of x items. If

$$R(x) = 50x - 0.5x^2 \quad \text{and} \quad C(x) = 4x + 10,$$

find each of the following.

a) $P(x)$
b) $R(20), C(20)$, and $P(20)$
c) $R'(x), C'(x)$, and $P'(x)$
d) $R'(20), C'(20)$, and $P'(20)$

2. Marginal revenue, cost, and profit. Let $R(x), C(x)$, and $P(x)$ be, respectively, the revenue, cost, and profit, in dollars, from the production and sale of x items. If

$$R(x) = 5x \quad \text{and} \quad C(x) = 0.001x^2 + 1.2x + 60,$$

find each of the following.

a) $P(x)$
b) $R(100), C(100)$, and $P(100)$
c) $R'(x), C'(x)$, and $P'(x)$
d) $R'(100), C'(100)$, and $P'(100)$
e) Describe what each quantity in parts (b) and (d) represents.

3. Marginal cost. Suppose the daily cost, in hundreds of dollars, of producing x security systems is

$$C(x) = 0.002x^3 + 0.1x^2 + 42x + 300,$$

and currently 40 security systems are produced daily.

a) What is the current daily cost?
b) What would be the additional daily cost of increasing production to 41 security systems daily?
c) What is the marginal cost when $x = 40$?
d) Use marginal cost to estimate the daily cost of increasing production to 42 security systems daily.

4. Marginal cost. Suppose the monthly cost, in dollars, of producing x daypacks is

$$C(x) = 0.001x^3 + 0.07x^2 + 19x + 700,$$

and currently 25 daypacks are produced monthly.

a) What is the current monthly cost?
b) What would be the additional cost of increasing production to 26 daypacks monthly?
c) What is the marginal cost when $x = 25$?
d) Use marginal cost to estimate the difference in cost between producing 25 and 27 daypacks per month.
e) Use the answer from part (d) to predict $C(27)$.

5. Marginal revenue. Pierce Manufacturing determines that the daily revenue, in dollars, from the sale of x lawn chairs is

$$R(x) = 0.005x^3 + 0.01x^2 + 0.5x.$$

Currently, Pierce sells 70 lawn chairs daily.

a) What is the current daily revenue?
b) How much would revenue increase if 73 lawn chairs were sold each day?
c) What is the marginal revenue when 70 lawn chairs are sold daily?
d) Use the answer from part (c) to estimate $R(71)$, $R(72)$, and $R(73)$.

6. Marginal profit. For Sunshine Motors, the weekly profit, in dollars, from selling x cars is

$$P(x) = -0.006x^3 - 0.2x^2 + 900x - 1200,$$

and currently 60 cars are sold weekly.

a) What is the current weekly profit?
b) How much profit would be lost if the dealership were able to sell only 59 cars weekly?
c) What is the marginal profit when $x = 60$?
d) Use marginal profit to estimate the weekly profit if sales increase to 61 cars weekly.

7. Marginal revenue. Solano Carriers finds that its monthly revenue, in dollars, from the sale of x carry-on suitcases is

$$R(x) = 0.007x^3 - 0.5x^2 + 150x.$$

Currently Solano is selling 26 carry-on suitcases monthly.

a) What is the current monthly revenue?
b) How much would revenue increase if sales increased from 26 to 28 suitcases?
c) What is the marginal revenue when 26 suitcases are sold?
d) Use the answers from parts (a)–(c) to estimate the revenue resulting from selling 27 suitcases per month.

8. Marginal profit. Crawford Computing finds that its weekly profit, in dollars, from the production and sale of x laptop computers is

$$P(x) = -0.004x^3 - 0.3x^2 + 600x - 800.$$

Currently Crawford builds and sells 9 laptops weekly.

a) What is the current weekly profit?
b) How much profit would be lost if production and sales dropped to 8 laptops weekly?

c) What is the marginal profit when $x = 9$?
d) Use the answers from parts (a)–(c) to estimate the profit resulting from the production and sale of 10 laptops weekly.

9. Sales. Let $N(x)$ be the number of computers sold annually when the price is x dollars per computer. Explain in words what occurs if $N(1000) = 500{,}000$ and $N'(1000) = -100$.

10. Sales. Estimate the number of computers sold in Exercise 9 if the price is raised to $1025.

For Exercises 11–16, assume that $C(x)$ and $R(x)$ are in dollars and x is the number of units produced and sold.

11. For the total-cost function

$$C(x) = 0.01x^2 + 1.6x + 100,$$

find ΔC and $C'(x)$ when $x = 80$ and $\Delta x = 1$.

12. For the total-cost function

$$C(x) = 0.01x^2 + 0.6x + 30,$$

find ΔC and $C'(x)$ when $x = 70$ and $\Delta x = 1$.

13. For the total-revenue function

$$R(x) = 2x,$$

find ΔR and $R'(x)$ when $x = 70$ and $\Delta x = 1$.

14. For the total-revenue function

$$R(x) = 3x,$$

find ΔR and $R'(x)$ when $x = 80$ and $\Delta x = 1$.

15. a) Using $C(x)$ from Exercise 11 and $R(x)$ from Exercise 14, find the total profit, $P(x)$.
b) Find ΔP and $P'(x)$ when $x = 80$ and $\Delta x = 1$.

16. a) Using $C(x)$ from Exercise 12 and $R(x)$ from Exercise 13, find the total profit, $P(x)$.
b) Find ΔP and $P'(x)$ when $x = 70$ and $\Delta x = 1$.

17. Marginal supply. The supply S, of a new rollerball pen is given by

$$S = 0.007p^3 - 0.5p^2 + 150p,$$

where p is the price in dollars.

a) Find the rate of change of quantity with respect to price, dS/dp.
b) How many units will producers want to supply when the price is $25 per unit?
c) Find the rate of change at $p = 25$, and interpret this result.
d) Would you expect dS/dp to be positive or negative? Why?

18. Average cost. The average cost for Turtlehead, Inc., to produce x units of its thermal outerwear is given by the function

$$A(x) = \frac{13x + 100}{x}.$$

Use $A'(x)$ to estimate the change in average cost as production goes from 100 units to 101 units.

19. Marginal productivity. An employee's monthly productivity, M, in number of units produced, is found to be a function of the number of years of service, t. For a certain product, the productivity function is given by

$$M(t) = -2t^2 + 100t + 180.$$

a) Find the productivity of an employee after 5 yr, 10 yr, 25 yr, and 45 yr of service.

b) Find the marginal productivity.

c) Find the marginal productivity at $t = 5$, $t = 10$, $t = 25$, $t = 45$; and interpret the results.

d) Explain how an employee's marginal productivity might be related to experience and to age.

20. Supply. A supply function for a certain product is given by

$$S(p) = 0.08p^3 + 2p^2 + 10p + 11,$$

where $S(p)$ is the number of items produced when the price is p dollars. Use $S'(p)$ to estimate how many more units a producer will supply when the price changes from $18.00 per unit to $18.20 per unit.

21. Gross domestic product. The U.S. gross domestic product, in billions of current dollars, may be modeled by the function

$$P(x) = 567 + x(36x^{0.6} - 104),$$

where x is the number of years since 1960. (*Source:* U.S. Bureau for Economic Analysis.) Use $P'(x)$ to estimate how much the gross domestic product increased from 2014 to 2015.

22. Advertising. Norris Inc. finds that it sells N units of a product after spending x thousands of dollars on advertising, where

$$N(x) = -x^2 + 300x + 6.$$

Use $N'(x)$ to estimate how many more units Norris will sell by increasing its advertising expenditure from $100,000 to $101,000.

Marginal tax rate. *Businesses and individuals are frequently concerned about their marginal tax rate, or the rate at which the next dollar earned is taxed. In progressive taxation, the 80,001st dollar earned is taxed at a higher rate than the 25,001st dollar earned and at a lower rate than the 140,001st dollar earned. Use the following graph, showing the marginal tax rate for 2014 for single filers, to answer Exercises 23–26.*

SINGLE FILERS INCOME BRACKET	RATE
0–9075	10%
9076–36900	15%
36901–89350	25%
89351–186350	28%
186351–405100	33%
405101–406750	35%
406751+	39.6

(*Source:* irs.gov, 2014.)

23. Was the taxation in 2014 progressive? Why or why not?

24. Marcy and Tyrone work for the same marketing agency. Because she is not yet a partner, Marcy's year-end income is approximately $95,000; Tyrone's year-end income is approximately $185,000. Suppose one of them is to receive another $5000 in income for the year. Which one would keep more of that $5000 after taxes? Why?

25. Alan earns $85,000 per year and is considering a second job that would earn him another $10,000 annually. At what rate will his tax liability (the amount he must pay in taxes) change if he takes the extra job? Express your answer in tax dollars paid per dollar earned.

26. Iris earns $50,000 per year and is considering extra work that would earn her an extra $3000 annually. At what rate will her tax liability grow if she takes the extra work (see Exercise 25)?

Find Δy and $f'(x)\Delta x$. Round to four and two decimal places, respectively.

27. For $y = f(x) = x^3, x = 2$, and $\Delta x = 0.01$

28. For $y = f(x) = x^2, x = 2$, and $\Delta x = 0.01$

29. For $y = f(x) = x + x^2, x = 3$, and $\Delta x = 0.04$

30. For $y = f(x) = x - x^2, x = 3$, and $\Delta x = 0.02$

31. For $y = f(x) = 1/x, x = 1$, and $\Delta x = 0.2$

32. For $y = f(x) = 1/x^2, x = 1$, and $\Delta x = 0.5$

33. For $y = f(x) = 3x - 1, x = 4$, and $\Delta x = 2$

34. For $y = f(x) = 2x - 3, x = 8$, and $\Delta x = 0.5$

Use $\Delta y \approx f'(x)\Delta x$ to find a decimal approximation of each radical expression. Round to three decimal places.

35. $\sqrt{26}$ **36.** $\sqrt{8}$

37. $\sqrt{102}$ **38.** $\sqrt{103}$

39. $\sqrt[3]{1005}$ **40.** $\sqrt[3]{28}$

Find dy.

41. $y = \sqrt{3x - 2}$ **42.** $y = \sqrt{x + 1}$

43. $y = (2x^3 + 1)^{3/2}$ **44.** $y = x^3(2x + 5)^2$

45. $y = \dfrac{x^3 + x + 2}{x^2 + 3}$

46. $y = \sqrt[5]{x + 27}$

47. $y = x^4 - 2x^3 + 5x^2 + 3x - 4$

48. $y = (7 - x)^8$

49. In Exercise 48, find dy when $x = 1$ and $dx = 0.01$.

50. In Exercise 47, find dy when $x = 2$ and $dx = 0.1$.

51. For $y = (3x - 10)^5$, find dy when $x = 4$ and $dx = 0.03$.

52. For $y = x^5 - 2x^3 - 7x$, find dy when $x = 3$ and $dx = 0.02$.

53. For $f(x) = x^4 - x^2 + 8$, use a differential to approximate $f(5.1)$.

54. For $f(x) = x^3 - 5x + 9$, use a differential to approximate $f(3.2)$.

SYNTHESIS

Life and Physical Sciences

55. Body surface area. Certain chemotherapy dosages depend on a patient's surface area. According to the Gehan and George model,

$$S = 0.02235h^{0.42246}w^{0.51456},$$

where h is the patient's height in centimeters, w is his or her weight in kilograms, and S is the approximation to his or her surface area in square meters. (*Source:* www.halls. md.) Joanne is 160 cm tall and weighs 60 kg. Use a differential to estimate how much her surface area changes after her weight decreases by 1 kg.

56. Medical dosage. The function

$$N(t) = \frac{0.8t + 1000}{5t + 4}$$

gives the bodily concentration $N(t)$, in parts per million, of a dosage of medication after t hours. Use differentials to determine whether the concentration changes more from 1.0 hr to 1.1 hr or from 2.8 hr to 2.9 hr.

General Interest

57. Major League ticket prices. The average ticket price of a major league baseball game can be modeled by the function

$$p(x) = 0.06x^3 - 0.5x^2 + 1.64x + 24.76,$$

where x is the number of years after 2008. (*Source:* Major League Baseball.) Use differentials to predict whether ticket price will increase more between 2010 and 2012 or between 2014 and 2016.

58. Suppose a rope surrounds the earth at the equator. The rope is lengthened by 10 ft. By about how much is the rope raised above the earth?

Business and Economics

59. Marginal average cost. In Section 1.6, we defined the average cost of producing x units of a product in terms of the total cost $C(x)$ by $A(x) = C(x)/x$. Find a general expression for *marginal average cost*, $A'(x)$.

60. Cost and tolerance. A firm contracts to paint the exterior of a large water tank in the shape of a half-dome (a hemisphere). The radius of the tank is measured to be 100 ft with a tolerance of ± 6 in. (± 0.5 ft). (The formula for the surface area of a hemisphere is $A = 2\pi r^2$; use 3.14 as an approximation for π.) Each can of paint costs \$30 and covers 300 ft^2.

   a) Calculate dA, the approximate difference in the surface area due to the tolerance.

   b) Assuming the painters cannot bring partial cans of paint to the job, how many extra cans should they bring to cover the extra area they may encounter?

   c) How much extra should the painters plan to spend on paint to account for the possible extra area?

61. Strategic oil supply. The U.S. Strategic Petroleum Reserve (SPR) stores petroleum in large spherical caverns built into salt deposits along the Gulf of Mexico. (*Source:* U.S. Department of Energy.) These caverns can be enlarged by filling the void with water, which dissolves the surrounding salt, and then pumping brine out. Suppose a cavern has a radius of 400 ft, which engineers want to enlarge by 2 ft. Use a differential to estimate how much volume will be added to form the enlarged cavern. (The formula for the volume of a sphere is $V = \frac{4}{3}\pi r^3$; use 3.14 as an approximation for π.)

Marginal revenue. *In each of Exercises 62–66, a demand function, $p = D(x)$, expresses price, in dollars, as a function of the number of items produced and sold. Find the marginal revenue.*

62. $p = 100 - \sqrt{x}$

63. $p = 400 - x$

64. $p = 500 - x$

65. $p = \dfrac{4000}{x} + 3$

66. $p = \dfrac{3000}{x} + 5$

67. Look up "differential" in a book or Web site devoted to math history. In a short paragraph, describe your findings.

68. Explain the uses of the differential.

Elasticity of Demand

- Find the elasticity of a demand function.
- Find the maximum of a total-revenue function.
- Characterize demand in terms of elasticity.

Retailers and manufacturers often need to know how a small change in price will affect the demand for a product. If a small increase in price produces no change in demand, a price increase may make sense; if a small increase in price creates a large drop in demand, the increase is probably ill advised. To measure the sensitivity of demand to a small percent increase in price, economists calculate the *elasticity of demand*.

Suppose that Klix Video has found that demand for rentals of its DVDs is given by

$$q = D(x) = 120 - 2x,$$

where q is the number of DVDs rented per day at x dollars per rental. Klix Video wants to determine what effect a small increase in the price per rental will have on revenue.

If the price per rental is currently \$2, the demand is $q = D(2) = 120 - 20(2) = 80$ DVDs per day. If the price per rental is raised by a small amount, such as 10%, to \$2.20, the demand will be $q = D(2.2) = 120 - 20(2.2) = 76$ DVDs per day, a 5% decrease. The percent decrease in demand is smaller than the percent increase in price. In this case, the total revenue grows from (\$2 per rental)(80 rentals), or \$160, to (\$2.20 per rental)(76 rentals), or \$167.20.

If the price per rental is currently \$4, the demand is $q = D(4) = 120 - 20(4) = 40$ DVDs per day. If the price per rental is raised by 10% to \$4.40, the demand will be $q = D(4.4) = 120 - 20(4.4) = 32$ DVDs per day, a 20% decrease. Here, the percent decrease in demand is larger thant the percent increase in price. In this case, the total revenue decreases from (\$4 per rental)(40 rentals), or \$160, to (\$4.40 rentals)(32 rentals), or \$140.80.

Let's develop a general formula for elasticity of demand. Suppose q represents a quantity of goods purchased and x is the price per unit of the goods. Recall that q and x are related by the demand function, D, where

$$q = D(x).$$

For any change, Δx, in the price per unit, the percent change in price is

$$\frac{\Delta x}{x} = \frac{\Delta x}{x} \cdot \frac{100}{100} = \frac{\Delta x \cdot 100}{x}\%.$$

A change in price produces a change, Δq, in the quantity demanded, and the percent change in this quantity is

$$\frac{\Delta q}{q} = \frac{\Delta q \cdot 100}{q}\%.$$

The ratio of percent change in quantity sold to percent change in price is

$$\frac{\Delta q / q}{\Delta x / x},$$

which can be expressed as

$$\frac{x}{q} \cdot \frac{\Delta q}{\Delta x}.$$

Since, for differentiable functions,

$$\lim_{\Delta x \to 0} \frac{\Delta q}{\Delta x} = \frac{dq}{dx},$$

we have

$$\lim_{\Delta x \to 0} \frac{x}{q} \cdot \frac{\Delta q}{\Delta x} = \frac{x}{q} \cdot \frac{dq}{dx} = \frac{x}{q} \cdot D'(x) = \frac{x}{D(x)} \cdot D'(x).$$

This result is the basis of the following definition.

DEFINITION

The **elasticity of demand** E is given as a function of price x by

$$E(x) = -\frac{x \cdot D'(x)}{D(x)}.$$

To understand the purpose of the negative sign in the preceding definition, note that the price, x, and the demand, $D(x)$, are both nonnegative. Since $D(x)$ is normally decreasing, $D'(x)$ is usually negative. By inserting a negative sign in the definition, economists make $E(x)$ nonnegative and easier to work with.

EXAMPLE 1   **Economics: Elasticity of Demand for DVD Rentals.**   The demand for DVD rentals at Klix Video is given by

$$q = D(x) = 120 - 20x,$$

where q is the number of DVDs rented per day at x dollars per rental. Find each of the following.

a) The elasticity as a function of x

b) The elasticity at $x = 2$ and at $x = 4$. Interpret the meaning of these values of the elasticity.

c) The value of x for which $E(x) = 1$. Interpret the meaning of this price.

d) The total-revenue function, $R(x) = x \cdot D(x)$

e) The price x at which total revenue is a maximum

Solution

a) To find the elasticity, we first find the derivative $D'(x)$:

$$D'(x) = -20.$$

Then we substitute -20 for $D'(x)$ and $120 - 20x$ for $D(x)$ in the expression for elasticity:

$$E(x) = -\frac{x \cdot D'(x)}{D(x)} = -\frac{x \cdot (-20)}{120 - 20x} = \frac{20x}{120 - 20x} = \frac{x}{6 - x}.$$

b) $E(2) = \dfrac{2}{6 - 2} = \dfrac{1}{2}$

At $x = 2$, the elasticity is $\frac{1}{2}$, which is less than 1. Thus, the ratio of percent change in quantity to percent change in price is less than 1. A small percentage increase in price will cause an even smaller percentage decrease in the quantity demanded.

$$E(4) = \frac{4}{6 - 4} = 2$$

At $x = 4$, the elasticity is 2, which is greater than 1. Thus, the ratio of percent change in quantity to percent change in price is greater than 1. A small percentage increase in price will cause a larger percentage decrease in the quantity demanded.

c) We set $E(x) = 1$ and solve for x:

$$\frac{x}{6 - x} = 1$$

$$x = 6 - x \qquad \text{We multiply both sides by } 6 - x, \text{ assuming that } x \neq 6.$$

$$2x = 6$$

$$x = 3.$$

Quick Check 1 ✔

Economics: Demand for DVD Rentals. Internet rentals affect Klix Video in such a way that the demand for rentals of its DVDs changes to

$$q = D(x) = 30 - 5x.$$

a) Find the quantity demanded when the price is $2 per rental, $3 per rental, and $5 per rental.

b) Find the elasticity of demand as a function of x.

c) Find the elasticity at $x = 2$, $x = 3$, and $x = 5$. Interpret the meaning of these values.

d) Find the value of x for which $E(x) = 1$. Interpret the meaning of this price.

e) Find the total-revenue function, $R(x) = x \cdot D(x)$.

f) Find the price x at which total revenue is a maximum.

Thus, when the price is $3 per rental, the ratio of the percent change in quantity to the percent change in price is 1.

d) Recall that total revenue $R(x)$ is given by $x \cdot D(x)$. Then

$$R(x) = x \cdot D(x) = x(120 - 20x) = 120x - 20x^2.$$

e) To find the price x that maximizes total revenue, we find $R'(x)$:

$$R'(x) = 120 - 40x.$$

We see that $R'(x)$ exists for all x in the interval $[0, \infty)$. Thus, we solve:

$$R'(x) = 120 - 40x = 0$$
$$-40x = -120$$
$$x = 3.$$

Since there is only one critical value, we use the second derivative to see if it yields a maximum:

$$R''(x) = -40 < 0.$$

Thus, $R''(3)$ is negative, so $R(3)$ is a maximum. That is, total revenue is a maximum at $3 per rental.   1 ✔

   Note in parts (c) and (e) of Example 1 that the value of x for which $E(x) = 1$ is the same as the value of x for which total revenue is a maximum. The following theorem states that this is always the case.

THEOREM 11

Total revenue is increasing at those x-values for which $E(x) < 1$.

Total revenue is decreasing at those x-values for which $E(x) > 1$.

Total revenue is maximized at the value(s) of x for which $E(x) = 1$.

Proof: We know that

$$R(x) = x \cdot D(x),$$

so
$$R'(x) = x \cdot D'(x) + D(x) \cdot 1 \qquad \text{Using the Product Rule}$$

$$= D(x)\left[\frac{x \cdot D'(x)}{D(x)} + 1\right] \qquad \text{Factoring; check this by multiplying.}$$

$$= D(x)[-E(x) + 1]$$

$$= D(x)[1 - E(x)].$$

Since we can assume that $D(x) > 0$, it follows that $R'(x)$ is positive for $E(x) < 1$, is negative for $E(x) > 1$, and is 0 when $E(x) = 1$. Thus, total revenue is increasing for $E(x) < 1$, is decreasing for $E(x) > 1$, and is maximized when $E(x) = 1$. ∎

   In summary, suppose Klix Video in Example 1 raises the price per rental and the total revenue increases. Then we say the demand is *inelastic*. If the total revenue decreases, we say the demand is *elastic*.

   In a typical economy, goods with inelastic demands tend to be items people purchase regularly, such as food, clothing, and fuel. These goods tend to be purchased in set amounts, regardless of small fluctuations in price. Goods with elastic demands tend to be larger items purchased occasionally, such as a vehicle or furniture. Purchases of such items can be delayed until the price falls.

Elasticity and Revenue

For a particular value of the price x:

1. The demand is *inelastic* if $E(x) < 1$. An increase in price will bring an increase in revenue. If demand is inelastic, then revenue is increasing.
2. The demand has *unit elasticity* if $E(x) = 1$. The demand has unit elasticity when revenue is at a maximum.
3. The demand is *elastic* if $E(x) > 1$. An increase in price will bring a decrease in revenue. If demand is elastic, then revenue is decreasing.

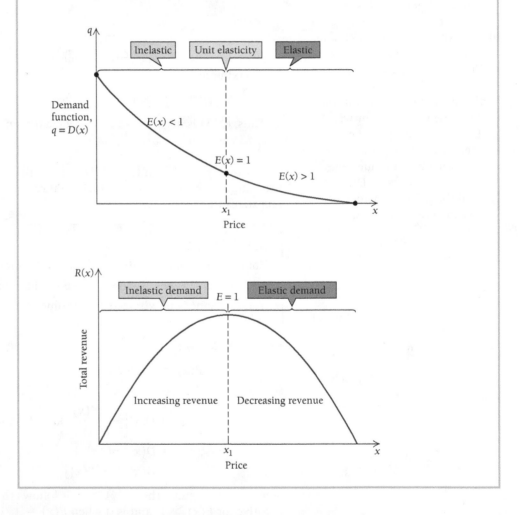

Section Summary

- For a demand function $q = D(x)$, where x is in dollars, the **elasticity of demand** is

$$E(x) = -\frac{xD'(x)}{D(x)}.$$

- Demand is **inelastic** when $E(x) < 1$. If demand is inelastic, then revenue is increasing.

- Demand is **elastic** when $E(x) > 1$. If demand is elastic, then revenue is decreasing.
- Demand has **unit elasticity** when $E(x) = 1$. If demand has unit elasticity at price x, then revenue is maximized.

2.7 Exercise Set

For the demand function given in each of Exercises 1–10, find the following.

    a) *The elasticity*
    b) *The elasticity at the given price, stating whether the demand is elastic or inelastic*
    c) *The value(s) of x for which total revenue is a maximum (assume that x is in dollars)*

1. $q = D(x) = 400 - x;\quad x = 125$

2. $q = D(x) = 500 - x;\quad x = 38$

3. $q = D(x) = 200 - 4x;\quad x = 46$

4. $q = D(x) = 500 - 2x;\quad x = 57$

5. $q = D(x) = \dfrac{400}{x};\quad x = 50$

6. $q = D(x) = \dfrac{3000}{x};\quad x = 60$

7. $q = D(x) = \sqrt{600 - x};\quad x = 100$

8. $q = D(x) = \sqrt{300 - x};\quad x = 250$

9. $q = D(x) = \dfrac{100}{(x + 3)^2};\quad x = 1$

10. $q = D(x) = \dfrac{500}{(2x + 12)^2};\quad x = 8$

APPLICATIONS

Business and Economics

11. Demand for oil. Suppose you have been hired as an economic consultant concerning the world demand for oil. The demand function is

$$q = D(x) = 50{,}000 + 300x - 3x^2, \quad \text{for } 0 \le x \le 180,$$

where q is measured in millions of barrels of oil per day at a price of x dollars per barrel.

    a) Find the elasticity.
    b) Find the elasticity at a price of \$75 per barrel, stating whether demand is elastic or inelastic at that price.
    c) Find the elasticity at a price of \$100 per barrel, stating whether demand is elastic or inelastic at that price.
    d) Find the elasticity at a price of \$25 per barrel, stating whether demand is elastic or inelastic at that price.
    e) At what price is revenue a maximum?
    f) What quantity of oil will be sold at the price that maximizes revenue? Compare the current world price to your answer.
    g) At a price of \$110 per barrel, will a small increase in price cause total revenue to increase or decrease?

12. Demand for chocolate chip cookies. Good Times Bakers determines that the demand function for its chocolate chip cookies is

$$q = D(x) = 967 - 25x,$$

where q is the quantity of cookies sold when the price is x cents per cookie.

    a) Find the elasticity.
    b) At what price is elasticity of demand equal to 1?
    c) At what prices is elasticity of demand elastic?
    d) At what prices is elasticity of demand inelastic?
    e) At what price is the revenue a maximum?
    f) At a price of 20¢ per cookie, will a small increase in price cause total revenue to increase or decrease?

13. Demand for computer games. High Wire Electronics determines the following demand function for a new game:

$$q = D(x) = \sqrt{200 - x^3},$$

where q is the number of games sold per day when the price is x dollars per game.

    a) Find the elasticity.
    b) Find the elasticity when $x = 3$.
    c) At $x = 3$, will a small increase in price cause total revenue to increase or decrease?

14. Demand for tomato plants. Sunshine Gardens determines the following demand function during early summer for tomato plants:

$$q = D(x) = \dfrac{2x + 300}{10x + 11},$$

where q is the number of plants sold per day when the price is x dollars per plant.

a) Find the elasticity.

b) Find the elasticity when $x = 3$.

c) At $3 per plant, will a small increase in price cause total revenue to increase or decrease?

SYNTHESIS

15. **Business.** Tipton Industries determines that the demand function for its sunglass cases is

$$q = D(x) = 180 - 10x,$$

where q is the quantity of sunglass cases sold when the price is x dollars per case.

a) Find the elasticity of demand.

b) Find the elasticity when $x = 8$.

c) At what price is revenue a maximum?

d) If the price is $8 and Tipton Industries raises the price by 20%, will revenue increase or decrease? Does this contradict the answers to parts (b) and (c)? Why or why not?

16. **Economics: constant elasticity curve.**

a) Find the elasticity of the demand function

$$q = D(x) = \frac{k}{x^n},$$

where k is a positive constant and n is an integer greater than 0.

b) Is the value of the elasticity dependent on the price per unit?

c) For what value of n does total revenue have a maximum?

17. Explain in your own words the concept of elasticity and its usefulness to economists. Do research or consult an economist to determine when and how this concept was first developed.

18. Explain how the elasticity of demand for a product can be affected by the availability of substitutes for the product.

Answers to Quick Check

1. **(a)** $20, 15, 5$; **(b)** $E(x) = \dfrac{x}{6 - x}$; **(c)** $0.5, 1, 5$

(see Example 1 for the interpretations);

(d) $3; **(e)** $R(x) = 30x - 5x^2$; **(f)** $3

2.8

- Differentiate implicitly.
- Solve related-rate problems.

Implicit Differentiation and Related Rates*

We often write a function with the output variable (such as y) isolated on one side of the equation. For example, if we write $y = x^3$, we have expressed y as an *explicit* function of x. With an equation like $y^3 + x^2y^5 - x^4 = -11$, it may be difficult to isolate the output variable. In such a case, we have an *implicit* relationship between the variables x and y and can find the derivative of y with respect to x using *implicit differentiation*.

Implicit Differentiation

Consider the equation

$$y^3 = x.$$

This equation *implies* that y is a function of x, for if we solve for y, we get

$$y = \sqrt[3]{x}$$
$$= x^{1/3}.$$

We know from our earlier work that

$$\frac{dy}{dx} = \frac{1}{3}x^{-2/3}. \tag{1}$$

---

*This section can be omitted without loss of continuity.

A method known as **implicit differentiation** allows us to find dy/dx *without* solving for y. To do so, we use the Chain Rule, treating y as a function of x, and differentiate both sides of

$$y^3 = x$$

with respect to x:

$$\frac{d}{dx}y^3 = \frac{d}{dx}x.$$

The derivative on the left side is found using the Extended Power Rule:

$$3y^2\frac{dy}{dx} = 1. \qquad \text{Remembering that the derivative of } y \text{ with respect to } x \text{ is written } dy/dx$$

Finally, we solve for dy/dx by dividing both sides by $3y^2$:

$$\frac{dy}{dx} = \frac{1}{3y^2}, \quad \text{or} \quad \frac{1}{3}y^{-2}.$$

We can show that this indeed gives us the same answer as equation (1) by replacing y with $x^{1/3}$:

$$\frac{dy}{dx} = \frac{1}{3}y^{-2} = \frac{1}{3}(x^{1/3})^{-2} = \frac{1}{3}x^{-2/3}.$$

Equations like

$$y^3 + x^2y^5 - x^4 = -11$$

determine y as a function of x, but are difficult to solve for y. We can nevertheless find a formula for the derivative of y *without* solving for y. To do so usually involves the Extended Power Rule in the form

$$\frac{d}{dx}y^n = ny^{n-1}\cdot\frac{dy}{dx}.$$

EXAMPLE 1 For $y^3 + x^2y^5 - x^4 = -11$:

a) Find dy/dx using implicit differentiation.

b) Find the slope of the tangent line to the curve at the point $(2, 1)$.

Solution

a) We differentiate the term x^2y^5 using the Product Rule. Because y is a function of x, it is critical that dy/dx is included as a factor in the result any time a term involving y is differentiated. When an expression involving just x is differentiated, there is no factor dy/dx.

$$\frac{d}{dx}(y^3 + x^2y^5 - x^4) = \frac{d}{dx}(-11) \qquad \text{Differentiating both sides with respect to } x$$

$$\frac{d}{dx}y^3 + \frac{d}{dx}x^2y^5 - \frac{d}{dx}x^4 = 0$$

$$3y^2\cdot\frac{dy}{dx} + x^2\cdot 5y^4\cdot\frac{dy}{dx} + y^5\cdot 2x - 4x^3 = 0. \qquad \text{Using the Extended Power Rule and the Product Rule}$$

We next isolate those terms with dy/dx as a factor on one side:

$$3y^2 \cdot \frac{dy}{dx} + 5x^2y^4 \cdot \frac{dy}{dx} = 4x^3 - 2xy^5 \qquad \text{Adding } 4x^3 - 2xy^5 \text{ to both sides}$$

$$(3y^2 + 5x^2y^4)\frac{dy}{dx} = 4x^3 - 2xy^5 \qquad \text{Factoring } dy/dx$$

$$\frac{dy}{dx} = \frac{4x^3 - 2xy^5}{3y^2 + 5x^2y^4}. \qquad \begin{array}{l}\text{Solving for } dy/dx \text{ and leaving the}\\ \text{answer in terms of } x \text{ and } y\end{array}$$

b) To find the slope of the tangent line to the curve at $(2, 1)$, we replace x with 2 and y with 1:

$$\frac{dy}{dx} = \frac{4 \cdot 2^3 - 2 \cdot 2 \cdot 1^5}{3 \cdot 1^2 + 5 \cdot 2^2 \cdot 1^4} = \frac{28}{23}.$$

Quick Check 1 ✔

For $y^2x + 2x^3y^3 = y + 1$, find dy/dx using implicit differentiation.

1 ✔

It is common for the expression for dy/dx to contain *both* variables x and y. When this occurs, we calculate a slope by evaluating the derivative at both the x-value and the y-value of the point of tangency.

The steps in Example 1 are typical of those used when differentiating implicitly.

To differentiate implicitly:

a) Differentiate both sides of the equation with respect to x (or whatever variable you are differentiating with respect to).

b) Apply the rules for differentiation (the Power, Product, Quotient, and Chain Rules) as necessary. Any time an expression involving y is differentiated, dy/dx will be a factor in the result.

c) Isolate all terms with dy/dx as a factor on one side of the equation.

d) If necessary, factor out dy/dx.

e) If necessary, divide both sides of the equation to isolate dy/dx.

The demand function for a product (see Section R.5) is often given implicitly.

EXAMPLE 2   Differentiate the demand equation $x = \sqrt{200 - p^3}$, implicitly to find dp/dx.

Quick Check 2 ✔

Differentiate the equation

$$y = 2\sqrt{1 + p^2}$$

implicitly to find $\dfrac{dp}{dy}$.

Solution

$$\frac{d}{dx}x = \frac{d}{dx}\sqrt{200 - p^3}$$

$$1 = \frac{1}{2}(200 - p^3)^{-1/2} \cdot (-3p^2) \cdot \frac{dp}{dx} \qquad \begin{array}{l}\text{Using the Extended Power}\\ \text{Rule twice}\end{array}$$

$$1 = \frac{-3p^2}{2\sqrt{200 - p^3}} \cdot \frac{dp}{dx}$$

$$\frac{2\sqrt{200 - p^3}}{-3p^2} = \frac{dp}{dx}$$

2 ✔

Related Rates

Suppose y is a function of x,

$$y = f(x),$$

and x is a function of time, t. Since y depends on x and x depends on t, it follows that y depends on t. The Chain Rule gives the following:

$$\frac{dy}{dt} = \frac{dy}{dx} \cdot \frac{dx}{dt}.$$

Thus, the rate of change of y is *related* to the rate of change of x. When this comes up in problems, it helps to keep in mind that any variable can be thought of as a function of time t. If no expression in terms of t is given, the variable's rate of change with respect to t will be 0.

EXAMPLE 3 **Business: Service Area.** A restaurant supplier services the restaurants in a circular area in such a way that the radius r is increasing at the rate of 2 mi per year at the moment when $r = 5$ mi. At that moment, how fast is the area increasing?

Solution The area A and radius r are related by

$$A = \pi r^2.$$

We take the derivative of both sides with respect to t, and then evaluate, using $dr/dt = 2$ mi/yr and $r = 5$ mi:

$$\frac{dA}{dt} = 2\pi r \cdot \frac{dr}{dt}.$$
The factor dr/dt results from the Chain Rule and the fact that r is assumed to be a function of t.

$$\frac{dA}{dt} = 2\pi(5 \text{ mi})\left(2\,\frac{\text{mi}}{\text{yr}}\right)$$ Substituting

$$= 20\pi\,\frac{\text{mi}^2}{\text{yr}} \approx 63 \text{ mi}^2/\text{yr}.$$

The supplier's service area is growing at a rate of about 63 square miles per year when $r = 5$ mi and $dr/dt = 2$ mi/yr. **3** ☑

Quick Check 3 ☑

A spherical balloon is leaking, losing 20 cm^3 of air per minute. At the moment when the radius of the balloon is 8 cm, how fast is the radius decreasing? (*Hint:* $V = \frac{4}{3}\pi r^3$.)

EXAMPLE 4   Business: Rates of Change of Revenue, Cost, and Profit.   For Luce Landscaping, the total revenue and the total cost for yard maintenance of x homes are given by

$$R(x) = 1000x - x^2, \quad \text{and} \quad C(x) = 3000 + 20x.$$

Suppose that Luce is adding 10 homes per day at the moment when the 400th customer is signed. At that moment, what is the rate of change of (a) total revenue, (b) total cost, and (c) total profit?

Solution

a) We regard $R(x) = 1000x - x^2$ as $R = 1000x - x^2$. Implicitly differentiating with respect to time t, we have

$$\frac{dR}{dt} = 1000 \cdot \frac{dx}{dt} - 2x \cdot \frac{dx}{dt} \qquad \text{Differentiating both sides with respect to time}$$

$$= 1000 \cdot 10 - 2(400)10 \qquad \text{Substituting 10 for } dx/dt \text{ and 400 for } x$$

$$= \$2000 \text{ per day.}$$

b) We regard $C(x) = 3000 + 20x$ as $C = 3000 + 20x$. Implicitly differentiating with respect to time t, we have

$$\frac{dC}{dt} = 20 \cdot \frac{dx}{dt} \qquad \text{Differentiating both sides with respect to time}$$

$$= 20(10)$$

$$= \$200 \text{ per day.}$$

c) Since $P(x) = R(x) - C(x)$, we have

$$\frac{dP}{dt} = \frac{dR}{dt} - \frac{dC}{dt}$$

$$= \$2000 \text{ per day} - \$200 \text{ per day}$$

$$= \$1800 \text{ per day.}$$

Section Summary

- If variables x and y are related to one another by an equation but neither variable is isolated on one side of the equation, we say that x and y have an implicit relationship. To find dy/dx without solving such an equation for y, we use *implicit differentiation*.
- Whenever we implicitly differentiate y with respect to x, the factor dy/dx will appear as a result of the Chain Rule.

- To determine the slope of a tangent line at a point on the graph of an implicit relationship, we may need to evaluate the derivative by inserting both the x-value and the y-value of the point of tangency.
- If two or more variables are related to one another by an equation, then we may implicity differentiate with respect to time t. The result is a *related rate*.

2.8 Exercise Set

Differentiate implicitly to find dy/dx. Then find the slope of the curve at the given point.

1. $3x^3 - y^2 = 8$; $(2, 4)$

2. $x^3 + 2y^3 = 6$; $(2, -1)$

3. $2x^3 + 4y^2 = -12$; $(-2, -1)$

4. $2x^2 - 3y^3 = 5$; $(-2, 1)$

5. $x^2 + y^2 = 1$; $\left(\dfrac{1}{2}, \dfrac{\sqrt{3}}{2}\right)$

6. $x^2 - y^2 = 1$; $(\sqrt{3}, \sqrt{2})$

7. $2x^3y^2 = -18$; $(-1, 3)$

8. $3x^2y^4 = 12$; $(2, -1)$

9. $x^4 - x^2y^3 = 12$; $(-2, 1)$

10. $x^3 - x^2y^2 = -9$; $(3, -2)$

11. $xy + y^2 - 2x = 0$; $(1, -2)$

12. $xy - x + 2y = 3$; $\left(-5, \dfrac{2}{3}\right)$

13. $4x^3 - y^4 - 3y + 5x + 1 = 0$; $(1, -2)$

14. $x^2y - 2x^3 - y^3 + 1 = 0$; $(2, -3)$

Differentiate implicitly to find dy/dx.

15. $x^2 + 2xy = 3y^2$

16. $2xy + 3 = 0$

17. $x^2 - y^2 = 16$

18. $x^2 + y^2 = 25$

19. $y^3 = x^5$

20. $y^5 = x^3$

21. $x^2y^3 + x^3y^4 = 11$

22. $x^3y^2 + x^5y^3 = -19$

For each demand equation in Exercises 23–30, differentiate implicitly to find dp/dx.

23. $p^2 + p + 2x = 40$

24. $p^3 + p - 3x = 50$

25. $xp^3 = 24$

26. $x^3p^2 = 108$

27. $\dfrac{x^2p + xp + 1}{2x + p} = 1$ (*Hint:* Clear the fraction first.)

28. $\dfrac{xp}{x + p} = 2$ (*Hint:* Clear the fraction first.)

29. $(p + 4)(x + 3) = 48$

30. $1000 - 300p + 25p^2 = x$

31. Nonnegative variable quantities G and H are related by the equation

$$G^2 + H^2 = 25.$$

What is the rate of change dH/dt when $dG/dt = 3$ and $G = 0$? $G = 1$? $G = 3$?

32. Variable quantities A and B are related by the equation

$$A^3 + B^3 = 9.$$

What is the rate of change dA/dt at the moment when $A = 2$ and $dB/dt = 3$?

APPLICATIONS

Business and Economics

Rates of change of total revenue, cost, and profit.   *In Exercises 33–36, find the rates of change of total revenue, cost, and profit with respect to time. Assume that R(x) and C(x) are in dollars.*

33. $R(x) = 50x - 0.5x^2$,

$C(x) = 10x + 3$,

when $x = 10$ and $dx/dt = 5$ units per day

34. $R(x) = 50x - 0.5x^2$,

$C(x) = 4x + 10$,

when $x = 30$ and $dx/dt = 20$ units per day

35. $R(x) = 280x - 0.4x^2$,

$C(x) = 5000 + 0.6x^2$,

when $x = 200$ and $dx/dt = 300$ units per day

36. $R(x) = 2x$,

$C(x) = 0.01x^2 + 0.6x + 30$,

when $x = 20$ and $dx/dt = 8$ units per day

37. **Change of sales.** Suppose that the price p, in dollars, and number of sales, x, of a mechanical pencil are related by

$$5p + 4x + 2px = 60.$$

If p and x are both functions of time, measured in days, find the rate at which x is changing when

$$x = 3, p = 5, \text{ and } \frac{dp}{dt} = 1.5.$$

38. **Change of revenue.** For x and p as described in Exercise 37, find the rate at which total revenue $R = xp$ is changing when

$$x = 3, p = 5, \text{ and } \frac{dp}{dt} = 1.5.$$

Life and Natural Sciences

39. Rate of change of the Arctic ice cap. In a trend that scientists attribute, at least in part, to global warming, the floating cap of sea ice on the Arctic Ocean has been shrinking since 1980. The ice cap always shrinks in summer and grows in winter. Average minimum size of the ice cap, in square miles, can be approximated by

$$A = \pi r^2.$$

In 2013, the radius of the ice cap was approximately 792 mi and was shrinking at a rate of approximately 4.7 mi/yr. (*Source*: Based on data from nsidc.org.) How fast was the area changing at that time?

40. Rate of change of a healing wound. The area of a healing wound is given by

$$A = \pi r^2.$$

The radius is decreasing at the rate of 1 millimeter per day (-1 mm/day) at the moment when $r = 25$ mm. How fast is the area decreasing at that moment?

41. Body surface area. Certain chemotherapy dosages depend on a patient's surface area. According to the Mosteller model,

$$S = \frac{\sqrt{hw}}{60},$$

where h is the patient's height in centimeters, w is the patient's weight in kilograms, and S is the approximation of the patient's surface area in square meters. (*Source*: www.halls.md.) Assume that Kim's height is a constant 165 cm, but she is losing weight. If she loses 2 kg per month, how fast is her surface area decreasing at the instant she weighs 70 kg?

Poiseuille's Law. *The flow of blood in a blood vessel is faster toward the center of the vessel and slower toward the outside. The speed of the blood, V, in millimeters per second (mm/sec), is given by*

$$V = \frac{p}{4Lv}(R^2 - r^2),$$

where R is the radius of the blood vessel, r is the distance of the blood from the center of the vessel, and p, L, and v are physical constants related to blood pressure, length of the

blood vessel, and viscosity of the blood, respectively. Assume that dV/dt is measured in millimeters per second squared (mm/sec²). Use this formula for Exercises 42 and 43.

42. Assume that r is a constant as well as p, L, and v.

a) Find the rate of change dV/dt in terms of R and dR/dt when $L = 80$ mm, $p = 500$, and $v = 0.003$.

b) A person goes out into the cold to shovel snow. Cold air has the effect of contracting blood vessels far from the heart. Suppose a blood vessel contracts at a rate of

$$\frac{dR}{dt} = -0.0002 \text{ mm/sec}$$

at a place where the radius of the vessel is $R = 0.075$ mm. Find the rate of change, dV/dt, at that location.

The flow of blood in a blood vessel can be modeled by Poiseuille's Law.

43. Assume that r is a constant as well as p, L, and v.

a) Find the rate of change dV/dt in terms of R and dR/dt when $L = 70$ mm, $p = 400$, and $v = 0.003$.

b) When shoveling snow in cold air, a person with a history of heart trouble can develop angina (chest pains) due to contracting blood vessels. To counteract this, he or she may take a nitroglycerin tablet, which dilates the blood vessels. Suppose, after a nitroglycerin tablet is taken, a blood vessel dilates at a rate of

$$\frac{dR}{dt} = 0.00015 \text{ mm/sec}$$

at a place where the radius of the vessel is $R = 0.1$ mm. Find the rate of change, dV/dt.

General Interest

44. Two cars start from the same point at the same time. One travels north at 25 mph, and the other travels east at 60 mph. How fast is the distance between them increasing at the end of 1 hr? (*Hint:* $D^2 = x^2 + y^2$. To find D after 1 hr, solve $D^2 = 25^2 + 60^2$.)

45. A ladder 26 ft long leans against a vertical wall. If the lower end is being moved away from the wall at the rate of 5 ft/sec, how fast is the height of the top changing (this will be a negative rate) when the lower end is 10 ft from the wall?

46. An inner city revitalization zone is a rectangle that is twice as long as it is wide. A diagonal through the region is growing at a rate of 90 m per year at a time when the region is 440 m wide. How fast is the area changing at that point in time?

47. The volume of a cantaloupe is approximated by

$$V = \tfrac{4}{3}\pi r^3.$$

The radius is growing at the rate of 0.7 cm/week, at a time when the radius is 7.5 cm. How fast is the volume changing at that moment?

SYNTHESIS

Differentiate implicitly to find dy/dx.

48. $\sqrt{x} + \sqrt{y} = 1$ **49.** $\dfrac{1}{x^2} + \dfrac{1}{y^2} = 5$

50. $y^3 = \dfrac{x-1}{x+1}$ **51.** $y^2 = \dfrac{x^2-1}{x^2+1}$

52. $x^{3/2} + y^{2/3} = 1$

53. $(x-y)^3 + (x+y)^3 = x^5 + y^5$

Differentiate implicitly to find d²y/dx².

54. $xy + x - 2y = 4$ **55.** $y^2 - xy + x^2 = 5$

56. $x^2 - y^2 = 5$ **57.** $x^3 - y^3 = 8$

58. Explain the usefulness of implicit differentiation.

59. Look up the word "implicit" in a dictionary. Explain how that definition can be related to the concept of a function that is defined "implicitly."

TECHNOLOGY CONNECTION

Graph each of the following equations. Equations must be solved for y before they can be entered into most calculators. Graphicus does not require that equations be solved for y.

60. $x^2 + y^2 = 4$
Note: You will probably need to sketch the graph in two parts: $y = \sqrt{4 - x^2}$ and $y = -\sqrt{4 - x^2}$. Then graph the tangent line to the graph at the point $(-1, \sqrt{3})$.

61. $x^4 = y^2 + x^6$
Then graph the tangent line to the graph at the point $(-0.8, 0.384)$.

62. $y^4 = y^2 - x^2$

63. $x^3 = y^2(2 - x)$

64. $y^2 = x^3$

Answers to Quick Checks
1. $\dfrac{dy}{dx} = \dfrac{y^2 + 6x^2y^3}{1 - 2xy - 6x^3y^2}$ 2. $\dfrac{dp}{dy} = \dfrac{\sqrt{1 + p^2}}{2p}$
3. Approximately -0.025 cm/min

A function is **increasing** over an open interval I if, for all x in I, $f'(x) > 0$. A function is **decreasing** over an open interval I if, for all x in I, $f'(x) < 0$.	 f is increasing over the interval (x_0, x_3) and decreasing over (x_3, x_6).

If f is a continuous function, then a **critical value** is any number c in the domain of f for which $f'(c) = 0$ or $f'(c)$ does not exist.

If $f'(c)$ does not exist, then the graph of f may have a corner or a vertical tangent at $(c, f(c))$.

In both cases, the ordered pair $(c, f(c))$ is called a **critical point**.

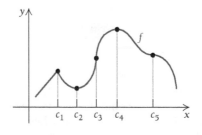

The values c_1, c_2, c_3, c_4, and c_5 are critical values of f.

- $f'(c_1)$ does not exist (corner).
- $f'(c_2) = 0$.
- $f'(c_3)$ does not exist (vertical tangent).
- $f'(c_4) = 0$.
- $f'(c_5) = 0$.

If f is a continuous function, then any **relative extremum** (**maximum** or **minimum**) occurs at a critical value.

The converse is not true: a critical value may not correspond to an extremum.

- The critical point $(c_1, f(c_1))$ is a relative maximum.
- The critical point $(c_2, f(c_2))$ is a relative minimum.
- The critical point $(c_3, f(c_3))$ is neither a relative maximum nor a relative minimum.
- The critical point $(c_4, f(c_4))$ is a relative maximum.
- The critical point $(c_5, f(c_5))$ is neither a relative maximum nor a relative minimum.

KEY TERMS AND CONCEPTS	EXAMPLES

SECTION 2.1 (continued)

The **First-Derivative Test** allows us to classify a critical value as a relative maximum, a relative minimum, or neither.

Find the relative extrema of the function given by
$$f(x) = \tfrac{1}{3}x^3 - \tfrac{1}{2}x^2 - 20x + 7.$$

Critical values occur where $f'(x) = 0$ or $f'(x)$ does not exist. The derivative $f'(x) = x^2 - x - 20$ exists for all real numbers, so the only critical values occur when $f'(x) = 0$. Setting $x^2 - x - 20 = 0$ and solving, we have $x = -4$ and $x = 5$ as the critical values.

To apply the First-Derivative Test, we check the sign of $f'(x)$ to the left and right of each critical value, using test values:

Test Value	$x = -5$	$x = 0$	$x = 6$
Sign of $f'(x)$	$f'(-5) > 0$	$f'(0) < 0$	$f'(6) > 0$
Result	f increasing on $(-\infty, -4)$	f decreasing on $(-4, 5)$	f increasing on $(5, \infty)$

Therefore, there is a relative maximum at $x = -4$: $f(-4) = 57\tfrac{2}{3}$. There is a relative minimum at $x = 5$: $f(5) = -63\tfrac{5}{6}$.

SECTION 2.2

The **second derivative**, $f''(x)$, can be used to determine the **concavity** of a graph.

If $f''(x) > 0$ for all x in an open interval I, then the graph of f is **concave up** over I.

If $f''(x) < 0$ for all x in an open interval I, then the graph of f is **concave down** over I.

A **point of inflection** occurs at $(x_0, f(x_0))$ if $f''(x_0) = 0$ and there is a change in concavity on either side of x_0.

The function given by
$$f(x) = \tfrac{1}{3}x^3 - \tfrac{1}{2}x^2 - 20x + 7$$
has the second derivative $f''(x) = 2x - 1$. Setting the second derivative equal to 0, we have $x_0 = \tfrac{1}{2}$. Using test values, we can check the concavity on either side of $x_0 = \tfrac{1}{2}$:

Test Value	$x = 0$	$x = 1$
Sign of $f''(x)$	$f''(0) < 0$	$f''(1) > 0$
Result	f is concave down on $\left(-\infty, \tfrac{1}{2}\right)$	f is concave up on $\left(\tfrac{1}{2}, \infty\right)$

Therefore, the graph of f is concave down over the interval $\left(-\infty, \tfrac{1}{2}\right)$ and concave up over the interval $\left(\tfrac{1}{2}, \infty\right)$. Since there is a change in concavity on either side of $x_0 = \tfrac{1}{2}$, we also conclude that the point $\left(\tfrac{1}{2}, -3\tfrac{1}{12}\right)$ is a point of inflection, where $f\left(\tfrac{1}{2}\right) = -3\tfrac{1}{12}$.

The **Second-Derivative Test** can also be used to classify relative extrema:

If $f'(c) = 0$ and $f''(c) > 0$, then $f(c)$ is a relative minimum.

If $f'(c) = 0$ and $f''(c) < 0$, then $f(c)$ is a relative maximum.

If $f'(c) = 0$ and $f''(c) = 0$, then the First-Derivative Test must be used to classify $f(c)$.

For the function
$$f(x) = \tfrac{1}{3}x^3 - \tfrac{1}{2}x^2 - 20x + 7,$$
evaluating the second derivative, $f''(x) = 2x - 1$, at the critical values yields the following conclusions:

- At $x = -4$, we have $f''(-4) < 0$. Since $f'(-4) = 0$ and the graph is concave down, we conclude that there is a relative maximum at $x = -4$.
- At $x = 5$, we have $f''(5) > 0$. Since $f'(5) = 0$ and the graph is concave up, we conclude that there is a relative minimum at $x = 5$.

(continued)

KEY TERMS AND CONCEPTS	EXAMPLES

SECTION 2.3

A line $x = a$ is a **vertical asymptote** if

$$\lim_{x \to a^-} f(x) = \infty,$$

$$\lim_{x \to a^-} f(x) = -\infty,$$

$$\lim_{x \to a^+} f(x) = \infty,$$

or

$$\lim_{x \to a^+} f(x) = -\infty.$$

Consider the function given by

$$f(x) = \frac{x^2 - 1}{x^2 + x - 6}.$$

Factoring, we have

$$f(x) = \frac{(x + 1)(x - 1)}{(x + 3)(x - 2)}.$$

This expression is simplified. Therefore, $x = -3$ and $x = 2$ are vertical asymptotes since

$$\lim_{x \to -3^-} f(x) = \infty \quad \text{and} \quad \lim_{x \to -3^+} f(x) = -\infty$$

and

$$\lim_{x \to 2^-} f(x) = -\infty \quad \text{and} \quad \lim_{x \to 2^+} f(x) = \infty.$$

An asymptote is usually represented as a dashed line; it is not part of the graph itself.

A line $y = b$ is a **horizontal asymptote** if

$$\lim_{x \to -\infty} f(x) = b$$

or

$$\lim_{x \to \infty} f(x) = b.$$

For the function given by

$$f(x) = \frac{x^2 - 1}{x^2 + x - 6},$$

we have

$$\lim_{x \to -\infty} f(x) = 1 \quad \text{and} \quad \lim_{x \to \infty} f(x) = 1.$$

Thus, the line $y = 1$ is a horizontal asymptote.

For a rational function of the form $f(x) = P(x)/Q(x)$, a **slant asymptote** occurs if the degree of the numerator is 1 greater than the degree of the denominator.

Let $f(x) = \dfrac{x^2 + 1}{x + 3}$. Division yields

$$f(x) = x - 3 + \frac{10}{x + 3}.$$

As $x \to \infty$ or $x \to -\infty$,

the remainder $\dfrac{10}{x + 3} \to 0$.

Therefore, the slant asymptote is $y = x - 3$.

Asymptotes, extrema, x- and y-intercepts, points of inflection, concavity, and intervals over which the function is increasing or decreasing are all used in the strategy for accurate graph sketching.

Consider the function given by
$f(x) = \frac{1}{3}x^3 - \frac{1}{2}x^2 - 20x + 7.$

- f has a relative maximum point at $(-4, 57\frac{2}{3})$ and a relative minimum point at $(5, -63\frac{5}{6})$.
- f has a point of inflection at $(\frac{1}{2}, -3\frac{1}{12})$.
- f is increasing over the intervals $(-\infty, -4)$ and $(5, \infty)$, decreasing over the interval $(-4, 5)$, concave down over the interval $(-\infty, \frac{1}{2})$, and concave up over the interval $(\frac{1}{2}, \infty)$.
- f has a y-intercept at $(0, 7)$.

KEY TERMS AND CONCEPTS	EXAMPLES

SECTION 2.3 (continued)

Consider the function given by

$$f(x) = \frac{x^2 - 1}{x^2 + x - 6}.$$

- f has vertical asymptotes $x = -3$ and $x = 2$.
- f has a horizontal asymptote given by $y = 1$.
- f has a y-intercept at $(0, \frac{1}{6})$.
- f has x-intercepts at $(-1, 0)$ and $(1, 0)$.
- f has a relative maximum at $(0.101, 0.168)$ and a relative minimum at $(9.899, 0.952)$.
- f is concave up on $(-\infty, -3)$ and $(2, 14.929)$, and concave down on $(-3, 2)$ and $(14.929, \infty)$.

SECTION 2.4

If f is continuous over $[a, b]$, then the **Extreme-Value Theorem** tells us that f will have both an absolute maximum value and an absolute minimum value over this interval. One or both absolute extrema may occur at an endpoint of this interval.

Maximum–Minimum Principle 1 can be used to determine these absolute extrema: we find all critical values $c_1, c_2, c_3, \ldots, c_n$, in $[a, b]$, then evaluate

$$f(a), f(c_1), f(c_2), f(c_3), \ldots, f(c_n), f(b).$$

The largest of these is the **absolute maximum**, and the smallest is the **absolute minimum**.

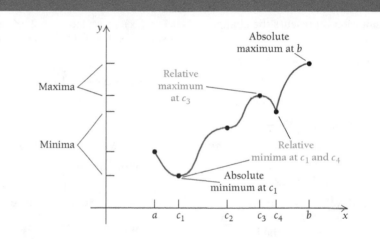

If f is differentiable for all x in an interval I, and there is exactly one critical value c in I such that $f'(c) = 0$, then, according to **Maximum–Minimum Principle 2**, $f(c)$ is an absolute extremum over I.

Let $f(x) = x + \dfrac{2}{x}$, for $x > 0$. The derivative is $f'(x) = 1 - \dfrac{2}{x^2}$. We solve for the critical value:

$$1 - \frac{2}{x^2} = 0$$
$$x^2 = 2$$
$$x = \pm\sqrt{2}.$$

The only critical value over the interval where $x > 0$ is $x = \sqrt{2}$. The second derivative is $f''(x) = \dfrac{4}{x^3}$. We see that

$$f''(\sqrt{2}) = \frac{4}{(\sqrt{2})^3} > 0. \text{ Therefore,}$$

$(\sqrt{2}, f(\sqrt{2}))$ is an absolute minimum.

(continued)

KEY TERMS AND CONCEPTS	EXAMPLES

SECTION 2.5

Many real-world applications involve maximum–minimum problems.

See Examples 1–6 in Section 2.5 and the problem-solving strategy on p. 245.

SECTION 2.6

Marginal cost, marginal revenue, and marginal profit are estimates of the cost, revenue, and profit for the $(x + 1)$st item produced:

- $C'(x) \approx C(x + 1) - C(x)$,
  so $C(x + 1) \approx C(x) + C'(x)$.
- $R'(x) \approx R(x + 1) - R(x)$,
  so $R(x + 1) \approx R(x) + R'(x)$.
- $P'(x) \approx P(x + 1) - P(x)$,
  so $P(x + 1) \approx P(x) + P'(x)$.

Delta notation represents the change in a variable:

$$\Delta x = x_2 - x_1$$

and

$$\Delta y = f(x_2) - f(x_1).$$

If $x_2 = x_1 + h$, then $\Delta x = h$.

If Δx is small, then the derivative can be used to approximate Δy:

$$\Delta y \approx f'(x) \cdot \Delta x.$$

For $f(x) = x^2$, let $x_1 = 2$ and $x_2 = 2.1$. Then, $\Delta x = 2.1 - 2 = 0.1$. Since $f(x_1) = f(2) = 4$ and $f(x_2) = f(2.1) = 4.41$, we have

$$\Delta y = f(x_2) - f(x_1) = 4.41 - 4 = 0.41.$$

Since $\Delta x = 0.1$ is small, we can approximate Δy by

$$\Delta y \approx f'(x)\,\Delta x.$$

The derivative is $f'(x) = 2x$. Therefore,

$$\Delta y \approx f'(2) \cdot (0.1) = 2(2) \cdot (0.1) = 0.4.$$

This approximation, 0.4, is very close to the actual difference, 0.41.

Differentials allow us to approximate changes in the output variable y given a change in the input variable x:

$$dx = \Delta x$$

and

$$dy = f'(x)\,dx.$$

If Δx is small, then $dy \approx \Delta y$.

In practice, it is often simpler to calculate dy, and it provides a close approximation for Δy.

For $y = \sqrt[3]{x}$, find dy when $x = 27$ and $dx = 2$.
Note that $\dfrac{dy}{dx} = \dfrac{1}{3\sqrt[3]{x^2}}$. Thus, $dy = \dfrac{1}{3\sqrt[3]{x^2}}\,dx$. Evaluating, we have

$$dy = \frac{1}{3\sqrt[3]{(27)^2}}\,(2) = \frac{2}{27}.$$

This result can be used to approximate the value of $\sqrt[3]{29}$, using the fact that $\sqrt[3]{29} \approx \sqrt[3]{27} + dy$:

$$\sqrt[3]{29} \approx \sqrt[3]{27} + dy = 3 + \frac{2}{27} \approx 3.074.$$

Thus, the approximation $\sqrt[3]{29} \approx 3.074$ is very close to the actual value, $\sqrt[3]{29} = 3.07231\ldots$, found with a calculator.

SECTION 2.7

The **elasticity of demand** E is a function of x, the price:

$$E(x) = -\frac{x \cdot D'(x)}{D(x)}.$$

Business. The Leslie Davis Band finds that demand for its CD at performances is given by

$$q = D(x) = 50 - 2x,$$

where x is the price, in dollars, of each CD sold and q is the number of CDs sold at a performance. Find the elasticity when the price is $10 per CD, and interpret the result. Then, find the price at which revenue is maximized.

KEY TERMS AND CONCEPTS	**EXAMPLES**

SECTION 2.7 (*continued*)

When $E(x) > 1$, total revenue is decreasing;
when $E(x) < 1$, total revenue is increasing;
and
when $E(x) = 1$, total revenue is maximized.

Elasticity at x is given by

$$E(x) = -\frac{x \cdot D'(x)}{D(x)}$$

$$= -\frac{x(-2)}{50 - 2x}$$

$$= -\frac{-2x}{50 - 2x} = \frac{x}{25 - x}.$$

Thus, $E(10) = \dfrac{10}{25 - 10} = \dfrac{2}{3}.$

Since $E(10)$ is less than 1, the demand for the CD is *inelastic*, and a modest increase in price will increase revenue.
    Revenue is maximized when $E(x) = 1$:

$$\frac{x}{25 - x} = 1$$

$$x = 25 - x$$

$$2x = 25$$

$$x = 12.5.$$

At a price of $12.50 per CD, revenue will be maximized.

SECTION 2.8

If an equation has variables x and y and y is not isolated on one side of the equation, the derivative dy/dx can be found without solving for y using **implicit differentiation**.

Find $\dfrac{dy}{dx}$ if $y^5 = x^3 + 7$.

We differentiate both sides with respect to x, and then solve for $\dfrac{dy}{dx}$.

$$\frac{d}{dx}y^5 = \frac{d}{dx}x^3 + \frac{d}{dx}7$$

$$5y^4 \frac{dy}{dx} = 3x^2$$

$$\frac{dy}{dx} = \frac{3x^2}{5y^4}.$$

A **related rate** occurs when the rate of change of one variable (with respect to time) can be calculated in terms of the rate of change (with respect to time) of another variable of which it is a function.

A large cube of ice is melting, losing 30 cm^3 of its volume, V, per minute. When the length of a side is 20 cm, how fast is that length decreasing?

    Since $V = x^3$ and both V and x are changing with time, we differentiate each variable with respect to time:

$$\frac{dV}{dt} = 3x^2 \frac{dx}{dt}.$$

We have $x = 20$ and $\dfrac{dV}{dt} = -30$. Evaluating gives

$$-30 = 3(20)^2 \frac{dx}{dt}$$

or $\dfrac{dx}{dt} = \dfrac{30}{3(20)^2} = -0.025$ cm/min.

CHAPTER 2
Review Exercises

These review exercises are for test preparation. They can also be used as a practice test. Answers are at the back of the book. The red bracketed section references tell you what part(s) of the chapter to restudy if your answer is incorrect.

CONCEPT REINFORCEMENT

Match each description in column A with the most appropriate graph in column B. [2.1–2.4]

Column A   Column B

1. A function with a relative maximum but no absolute extrema

a)

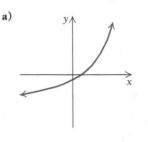

2. A function with both a vertical asymptote and a horizontal asymptote

b)

3. A function that is concave up and decreasing

c)

4. A function that is concave up and increasing

d)

5. A function with three critical values

e)

6. A function with one critical value and a second derivative that is always positive

f)

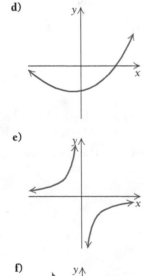

7. A function with a first derivative that is always positive

g)

In Exercises 8–16, classify each statement as either true or false.

8. Every continuous function has at least one critical value. [2.1]

9. If a continuous function $y = f(x)$ has extrema, they will always occur where $f'(x) = 0$. [2.1]

10. If $f'(c) = 0$ and $f''(c) > 0$, then $f(c)$ is a relative minimum. [2.2]

11. If $f'(c) = 0$ and $f''(c) = 0$, then $f(c)$ cannot be a relative minimum. [2.2]

12. If the graph of $f(x) = P(x)/Q(x)$ has a horizontal asymptote, then the degree of the polynomial $P(x)$ is less than or equal to that of the polynomial $Q(x)$. [2.3]

13. Absolute extrema of a continuous function f always occur at the endpoints of a closed interval. [2.4]

14. In general, if f is a continuous function, then $\Delta x = dx$ and $\Delta y \geq dy$. [2.6]

15. If the elasticity of demand at a certain price x is 1, then revenue is maximized at this price. [2.7]

16. In a related-rate problem, the variables are commonly differentiated implicitly with respect to time, t. [2.8]

REVIEW EXERCISES

For each function given, find any extrema, along with the x-value at which they occur. Then sketch a graph of the function. [2.1]

17. $f(x) = 4 - 3x - x^2$ 18. $f(x) = x^4 - 2x^2 + 3$

19. $f(x) = \dfrac{-8x}{x^2 + 1}$ 20. $f(x) = 4 + (x - 1)^3$

21. $f(x) = x^3 + x^2 - x + 3$ 22. $f(x) = 3x^{2/3}$

23. $f(x) = 2x^3 - 3x^2 - 12x + 10$

24. $f(x) = x^3 - 3x + 2$

Sketch the graph of each function. List any minimum or maximum values, where they occur, and any points of inflection. State where the function is increasing or decreasing and where it is concave up or concave down. [2.2]

25. $f(x) = \frac{1}{3}x^3 + 3x^2 + 9x + 2$

26. $f(x) = x^2 - 10x + 8$

27. $f(x) = 4x^3 - 6x^2 - 24x + 5$

28. $f(x) = x^4 - 2x^2$

29. $f(x) = 3x^4 + 2x^3 - 3x^2 + 1$ (Round to three decimal places where appropriate.)

30. $f(x) = \frac{1}{5}x^5 + \frac{3}{4}x^4 - \frac{4}{3}x^3 + 8$ (Round to three decimal places where appropriate.)

Sketch the graph of each function. Indicate where each function is increasing or decreasing, the coordinates at which any relative extrema occur, where any asymptotes occur, where the graph is concave up or concave down, and where any intercepts occur. [2.3]

31. $f(x) = \dfrac{2x + 5}{x + 1}$

32. $f(x) = \dfrac{x}{x - 2}$

33. $f(x) = \dfrac{5}{x^2 - 16}$

34. $f(x) = -\dfrac{x + 1}{x^2 - x - 2}$

35. $f(x) = \dfrac{x^2 - 2x + 2}{x - 1}$

36. $f(x) = \dfrac{x^2 + 3}{x}$

For each function, find any absolute extrema over the indicated interval. Indicate the x-value at which each extremum occurs. Where no interval is specified, use the real line. [2.4]

37. $f(x) = x^4 - 2x^2 + 3; \; [0, 3]$

38. $f(x) = 8x^2 - x^3; \; [-1, 8]$

39. $f(x) = x + \dfrac{50}{x}; \; (0, \infty)$

40. $f(x) = x^4 - 2x^2 + 1$

41. Maximize $Q = xy$, where $3x + 4y = 24$. [2.5]

42. Find the minimum value of $Q = x^2 - 2y^2$, where $x - 2y = 1$. [2.5]

43. Business: maximizing profit. If $R(x) = 52x - 0.5x^2$ and $C(x) = 22x - 1$, find the maximum profit and the number of units that must be produced and sold in order to yield this maximum profit. Assume that $R(x)$ and $C(x)$ are in dollars. [2.5]

44. Business: minimizing cost. A rectangular box with a square base and a cover is to have a volume of 2500 ft^3. If the cost of material is $2/ft^2 for the bottom, $3/ft^2 for the top, and $1/ft^2 for the sides, what should the dimensions of the box be in order to minimize the cost? [2.5]

45. Business: minimizing inventory cost. Venice Cyclery sells 360 hybrid bicycles per year. It costs $8 to store

one bicycle for a year. To reorder, there is a fixed cost of $10, plus $2 for each bicycle. How many times per year should the shop order bicycles, and in what lot size, in order to minimize inventory costs? [2.5]

46. Business: marginal revenue. Crane Foods determines that its daily revenue, $R(x)$, in dollars, from the sale of x frozen dinners is

$$R(x) = 4x^{3/4}. \; [2.6]$$

a) What is Crane's daily revenue when 81 frozen dinners are sold?

b) What is Crane's marginal revenue when 81 frozen dinners are sold?

c) Use the answers from parts (a) and (b) to estimate $R(82)$.

For Exercises 47 and 48, $y = f(x) = 2x^3 + x$. [2.6]

47. Find Δy and dy, given that $x = 1$ and $\Delta x = -0.05$.

48. a) Find dy.

  b) Find dy when $x = -2$ and $dx = 0.01$.

49. Approximate $\sqrt{83}$ using $\Delta y \approx f'(x)\,\Delta x$. [2.6]

50. Physical science: waste storage. The Waste Isolation Pilot Plant (WIPP) in New Mexico consists of large rooms carved into a salt deposit and is used for long-term storage of radioactive waste. (*Source:* www.wipp .energy.gov.) A new storage room in the shape of a cube with an edge length of 200 ft is to be carved into the salt. Use a differential to estimate the potential difference in the volume of this room if the edge measurements have a tolerance of ± 2 ft. [2.6]

51. Economics: elasticity of demand. Consider the demand function given by

$$q = D(x) = 400 - 5x. \; [2.7]$$

a) Find the elasticity.

b) Find the elasticity at $x = 10$, and state whether the demand is elastic or inelastic.

c) Find the elasticity at $x = 50$, and state whether the demand is elastic or inelastic.

d) At a price of $25, will a small increase in price cause total revenue to increase or decrease?

e) Find the price at which total revenue is a maximum.

52. Differentiate the following implicitly to find dy/dx. Then find the slope of the curve at the given point.

$$2x^3 + 2y^3 = -9xy; \quad (-1, -2) \; [2.8]$$

53. A ladder 25 ft long leans against a vertical wall. If the bottom moves away from the wall at the rate of 6 ft/sec, how fast is the height of the top changing when the lower end is 7 ft from the wall? [2.8]

54. Business: total revenue, cost, and profit. Find the rates of change, with respect to time, of total revenue, cost, and profit for

$$R(x) = 120x - 0.5x^2 \quad \text{and} \quad C(x) = 15x + 6,$$

when $x = 100$ and $dx/dt = 30$ units per day. Assume that $R(x)$ and $C(x)$ are in dollars. [2.8]

SYNTHESIS

55. Find the absolute maximum and minimum values, if they exist, over the indicated interval.

$f(x) = (x - 3)^{2/5};\quad (-\infty, \infty)$ [2.4]

56. Find the absolute maximum and minimum values of the piecewise-defined function given by

$$f(x) = \begin{cases} 2 - x^2, & \text{for } -2 \leq x \leq 1, \\ 3x - 2, & \text{for } 1 < x < 2, \\ (x - 4)^2, & \text{for } 2 \leq x \leq 6. \end{cases}$$ [2.4]

57. Differentiate implicitly to find dy/dx:

$(x - y)^4 + (x + y)^4 = x^6 + y^6$. [2.8]

58. Find any relative maxima and minima of

$y = x^4 - 8x^3 - 270x^2$. [2.1, 2.2]

59. Determine a rational function f whose graph has a vertical asymptote at $x = -2$ and a horizontal asymptote at $y = 3$ and includes the point $(1, 2)$. [2.3]

TECHNOLOGY CONNECTION

Use a calculator to estimate the relative extrema of each function. [2.1, 2.2]

60. $f(x) = 3.8x^5 - 18.6x^3$

61. $f(x) = \sqrt[3]{|9 - x^2|} - 1$

62. **Life and physical sciences: incidence of breast cancer.** The following table provides data relating the incidence of breast cancer per 100,000 women of various ages.

  a) Use REGRESSION to fit linear, quadratic, cubic, and quartic functions to the data. (The function used in Exercise 28 of Section R.1 was found in this manner.)

AGE	INCIDENCE PER 100,000
0	0
27	10
32	25
37	60
42	125
47	187
52	224
57	270
62	340
67	408
72	437
77	475
82	460
87	420

(*Source:* National Cancer Institute.)

  b) Which function best fits the data?

  c) Determine the domain of the function on the basis of the function and the problem situation.

  d) Determine the maximum value of the function over the domain. At what age is the incidence of breast cancer the greatest? [2.1, 2.2]

CHAPTER 2
Test

Find all relative minimum or maximum values as well as the x-values at which they occur. State where each function is increasing or decreasing. Then sketch a graph of the function.

1. $f(x) = x^2 - 4x - 5$ **2.** $f(x) = 4 + 3x - x^3$

3. $f(x) = (x - 2)^{2/3} - 4$ **4.** $f(x) = \dfrac{16}{x^2 + 4}$

Sketch a graph of each function. List any extrema, and indicate any asymptotes or points of inflection.

5. $f(x) = x^3 + x^2 - x + 1$ **6.** $f(x) = 2x^4 - 4x^2 + 1$

7. $f(x) = (x - 2)^3 + 3$ **8.** $f(x) = x\sqrt{9 - x^2}$

9. $f(x) = \dfrac{2}{x - 1}$ **10.** $f(x) = \dfrac{-8}{x^2 - 4}$

11. $f(x) = \dfrac{x^2 - 1}{x}$ **12.** $f(x) = \dfrac{x - 3}{x + 2}$

Find the absolute maximum and minimum values, if they exist, of each function over the indicated interval. Where no interval is specified, use the real line.

13. $f(x) = x(6 - x)$

14. $f(x) = x^3 + x^2 - x + 1;\quad \left[-2, \tfrac{1}{2}\right]$

15. $f(x) = -x^2 + 8.6x + 10$

16. $f(x) = -2x + 5;\quad [-1, 1]$

17. $f(x) = -2x + 5$

18. $f(x) = 3x^2 - x - 1$

19. $f(x) = x^2 + \dfrac{128}{x};\quad (0, \infty)$

20. Maximize $Q = xy^2$, where $x + 2y = 50$.

21. Minimize $Q = x^2 + y^2$, where $x - y = 10$.

22. Business: maximum profit. Find the maximum profit and the number of units, x, of a leather briefcase that must be produced and sold in order to yield the maximum profit. Assume that $R(x)$ and $C(x)$ are the revenue and cost, in dollars, when x units are produced:

$$R(x) = x^2 + 110x + 60,$$
$$C(x) = 1.1x^2 + 10x + 80.$$

23. Business: minimizing cost. From a thin piece of cardboard 60 in. by 60 in., square corners are cut out so that the sides can be folded up to make an open box. What dimensions will yield a box of maximum volume? What is the maximum volume?

24. Business: minimizing inventory costs. Ironside Sports sells 1225 tennis rackets per year. It costs $2 to store one tennis racket for a year. To reorder, there is a fixed cost of $1, plus $0.50 for each tennis racket. How many times per year should Ironside order tennis rackets, and in what lot size, in order to minimize inventory costs?

25. For $y = f(x) = x^2 - 3, x = 5$, and $\Delta x = 0.1$, find Δy and $f'(x)\,\Delta x$.

26. Approximate $\sqrt{50}$ using $\Delta y \approx f'(x)\,\Delta x$.

27. For $y = \sqrt{x^2 + 3}$:

a) Find dy.

b) Find dy when $x = 2$ and $dx = 0.01$.

28. Economics: elasticity of demand. Consider the demand function given by

$$q = D(x) = \frac{600}{(x + 4)^2}.$$

a) Find the elasticity.

b) Find the elasticity at $x = 1$, stating whether demand is elastic or inelastic.

c) Find the elasticity at $x = 12$, stating whether demand is elastic or inelastic.

d) At a price of $12, will a small increase in price cause total revenue to increase or decrease?

e) Find the price at which total revenue is a maximum.

29. Differentiate the following implicitly to find dy/dx. Then find the slope of the curve at $(1, 2)$:

$$x^3 + y^3 = 9.$$

30. A spherical balloon has a radius of 15 cm. Use a differential to find the approximate change in the volume of the balloon if the radius is increased or decreased by 0.5 cm. (The volume of a sphere is $V = \frac{4}{3}\pi r^3$. Use 3.14 for π.)

31. A pole 13 ft long leans against a vertical wall. If the lower end moves away from the wall at the rate of 0.4 ft/sec, how fast is the upper end sliding down when the lower end is 12 ft from the wall?

SYNTHESIS

32. Find the absolute maximum and minimum values of the following function, if they exist, over $[0, \infty)$:

$$f(x) = \frac{x^2}{1 + x^3}.$$

33. Business: minimizing average cost. The total cost in dollars of producing x units of a visor is given by

$$C(x) = 100x + 100\sqrt{x} + \frac{\sqrt{x^3}}{100}.$$

How many units should be produced to minimize average cost?

TECHNOLOGY CONNECTION

34. Estimate any extrema of the function given by
$$f(x) = 5x^3 - 30x^2 + 45x + 5\sqrt{x}.$$

35. Estimate any extrema of the function given by
$$g(x) = x^5 - x^3.$$

36. Maximize $Q = x^2y^2$, where $x^2 + y = 20$ and x and y are positive.

37. Business: advertising. The business of manufacturing and selling bowling balls is one of frequent changes. Companies introduce new models to the market about every 3 to 4 months. Typically, a new model is created because of advances in technology such as new surface stock or a new way to place weight blocks in a ball. To decide how to best use advertising dollars, companies track sales in relation to amount spent on advertising. Suppose a company has the following data from past sales.

AMOUNT SPENT ON ADVERTISING (in thousands)	NUMBER OF BOWLING BALLS SOLD, N
$ 0	8
50	13,115
100	19,780
150	22,612
200	20,083
250	12,430
300	4

a) Use REGRESSION to fit linear, quadratic, cubic, and quartic functions to the data.

b) Determine the domain of the function in part (a) that best fits the data and the problem situation. How did you arrive at your answer?

c) Determine the maximum value of the function over the domain. How much should the company spend on advertising a new model in order to maximize the number of bowling balls sold?

Maximum Sustainable Harvest

In certain situations, biologists are able to determine what is called a **reproduction curve**. This is a function

$$y = f(P)$$

such that if P is the population at a given point in time, then $f(P)$ is the population a year later. Such a curve is shown below.

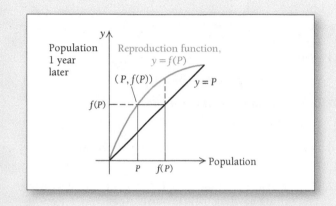

The line $y = P$ is significant because if it coincides with the curve $y = f(P)$, then we know that the population stays the same from year to year. Here the graph of f lies mostly above the line, indicating that the population is increasing.

Too many deer in a forest can deplete the food supply and cause the population to decrease. In such cases, hunters are often allowed to "harvest" some of the deer. Then with a greater food supply, the remaining deer population may prosper and increase.

We know that a population P will grow to a population $f(P)$ in a year. If the population were increasing, then hunters could "harvest" the amount

$$f(P) - P$$

each year without shrinking the initial population P. If the population were remaining the same or decreasing, then such a harvest would deplete the population.

Suppose we want to know the value of P_0 that will allow the harvest to be the largest. If we could determine that P_0, we could let the population grow until it reached that level and then begin harvesting year after year the amount $f(P_0) - P_0$.

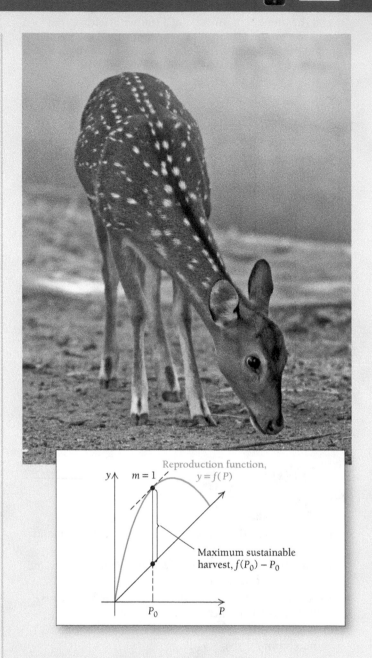

Let the harvest function H be given by

$$H(P) = f(P) - P.$$

Then $H'(P) = f'(P) - 1.$

Now, if we assume that $H'(P)$ exists for all values of P and that there is only one critical value, it follows that the *maximum sustainable harvest* occurs at that value P_0 such that

$$H'(P_0) = f'(P_0) - 1 = 0$$

and $H''(P_0) = f''(P_0) < 0.$

Or, equivalently, we have the following.

> **THEOREM**
>
> The **maximum sustainable harvest** occurs at P_0 such that
>
> $$f'(P_0) = 1 \quad \text{and} \quad f''(P_0) < 0,$$
>
> and is given by
>
> $$H(P_0) = f(P_0) - P_0.$$

Exercises

For Exercises 1–3, do the following.

a) *Graph the reproduction curve, the line $y = P$, and the harvest function using the same viewing window.*

b) *Find the population at which the maximum sustainable harvest occurs. Use both a graphical solution and a calculus solution.*

c) *Find the maximum sustainable harvest.*

1. $f(P) = P(10 - P)$, where P is measured in thousands.

2. $f(P) = -0.025P^2 + 4P$, where P is measured in thousands. This is the reproduction curve in the Hudson Bay area for the snowshoe hare.

3. $f(P) = -0.01P^2 + 2P$, where P is measured in thousands. This is the reproduction curve in the Hudson Bay area for the lynx.

For Exercises 4 and 5, do the following.

a) *Graph the reproduction curve, the line $y = P$, and the harvest function using the same viewing window.*

b) *Graphically determine the population at which the maximum sustainable harvest occurs.*

c) *Find the maximum sustainable harvest.*

4. $f(P) = 40\sqrt{P}$, where P is measured in thousands. Assume that this is the reproduction curve for the brown trout population in a large lake.

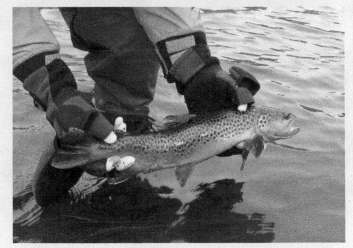

5. $f(P) = 0.237P\sqrt{2000 - P^2}$, where P is measured in thousands.

6. The table below lists data regarding the reproduction of a certain animal.

a) Use REGRESSION to fit a cubic polynomial to these data.

b) Graph the reproduction curve, the line $y = P$, and the harvest function using the same viewing window.

c) Graphically determine the population at which the maximum sustainable harvest occurs.

POPULATION, P (in thousands)	POPULATION, $f(P)$, 1 YEAR LATER
10	9.7
20	23.1
30	37.4
40	46.2
50	42.6

3 Exponential and Logarithmic Functions

What You'll Learn

3.1 Exponential Functions

3.2 Logarithmic Functions

3.3 Applications: Uninhibited and Limited Growth Models

3.4 Applications: Decay

3.5 The Derivatives of a^x and $\log_a x$; Application: Annuities

3.6 A Business Application: Amortization

Why It's Important

In this chapter, we consider two types of functions that are closely related: *exponential functions* and *logarithmic functions*. After learning to find derivatives of such functions, we will study applications in the areas of population growth and decay, continuously compounded interest, annuities and amortization, spread of disease, and carbon dating.

Where It's Used

Microprocessors: In 1971, Intel Corporation released the Intel 4004 microprocessor, which held 2300 transistors. Since then, the number of transistors on a microprocessor has been growing exponentially at the rate of 0.34, or 34%, per year. Approximately how many transistors will be on a microprocessor in 2020? (*This problem appears as Example 5 in Section 3.3.*)

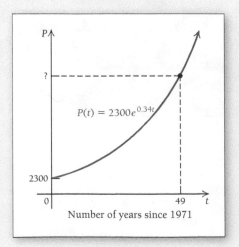

$$P(t) = 2300e^{0.34t}$$

Number of years since 1971

3.1

- Graph exponential functions.
- Differentiate exponential functions.

Exponential Functions

Graphs of Exponential Functions

Consider the following graph. The rapid rise of the graph indicates that it approximates an *exponential function*. In this chapter, we consider such functions and many of their applications.

EXPONENTIAL FUNCTION

Year

(*Source:* epa.gov.)

Recall from Section R.5 that an **exponential function** is given by $f(x) = a_0 \cdot a^x$, where $a > 0$ and $a \neq 1$. The number a is the **base**, the y-intercept is $(0, a_0)$, there are no x-intercepts, and the function is continuous for all real numbers.

The graphs of $f(x) = a_0 \cdot a^x$, for $a > 1$ and for $0 < a < 1$, are shown below, and common characteristics of each are described.

1. The function given by $f(x) = a_0 \cdot a^x$, with $a > 1$, is a positive, increasing, continuous function. As x gets smaller, $a_0 \cdot a^x$ approaches 0. The graph is concave up, and the x-axis is the horizontal asymptote.

2. The function given by $f(x) = a_0 \cdot a^x$, with $0 < a < 1$, is a positive, decreasing, continuous function. As x gets larger, $a_0 \cdot a^x$ approaches 0. The graph is concave up, and the x-axis is the horizontal asymptote.

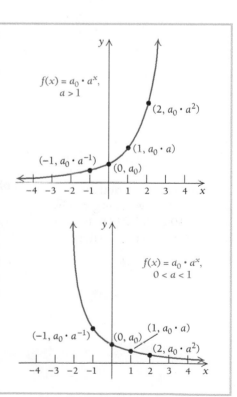

For $a = 1$, we have $f(x) = a_0 \cdot a^x = a_0 \cdot 1^x = a_0 \cdot 1 = a_0$; so, in this case, f is a constant function. This is why we are not interested in 1 as the base of an exponential function.

Recall from Theorem 1 in Section R.1 that if an amount P is invested at interest rate r, compounded annually, then in t years, it will grow to an amount A given by the exponential function

$$A(t) = P(1 + r)^t.$$

This formula can be extended to many situations such as population growth and depreciation.

EXAMPLE 1 **Population Growth.** The city of Woodfork had a population of 5200 on January 1, 2010, and was growing by 2.5% per year. The population, P, of Woodfork t years from January 1, 2010, is given by

$$P(t) = 5200(1.025)^t.$$

a) Graph P.

b) Find $P(8)$ and interpret this result.

c) Find $P(-5)$ and interpret this result.

Solution

a) We begin by finding some function values.

t	$P(t)$
$t = 0$	$P(0) = 5200(1.025)^0 = 5200$
$t = 1$	$P(1) = 5200(1.025)^1 = 5330$
$t = 2$	$P(2) = 5200(1.025)^2 \approx 5463$
$t = 3$	$P(3) = 5200(1.025)^3 \approx 5600$
$t = -1$	$P(-1) = 5200(1.025)^{-1} \approx 5073$
$t = -2$	$P(-2) = 5200(1.025)^{-2} \approx 4949$
$t = -3$	$P(-3) = 5200(1.025)^{-3} \approx 4829$

Number of years from January 1, 2010

Quick Check 1 ✔

The Sandersons deposit $10,000 into a money market fund that earns 4.8% annual interest. The value of their account after t years is given by $V(t) = 10,000(1.048)^t$. Find the value of their account after 6 yr.

We plot these points and connect them with a smooth curve, as shown in the graph. The graph is continuous, has a y-intercept at $(0, 5200)$, and is concave up; also, since $a = 1.025 > 0$, the graph is increasing without bound.

b) We have $P(8) = 5200(1.025)^8 \approx 6336$. The population of Woodfork is estimated to be about 6336 on January 1, 2018.

c) We have $P(-5) = 5200(1.025)^{-5} \approx 4596$. The population of Woodfork was about 4596 on January 1, 2005. **1** ✔

TECHNOLOGY CONNECTION

Exploratory Exercise: Growth

Cut a sheet of $8\frac{1}{2}$-in.-by-11-in. paper into two equal pieces. Then cut these again to obtain four equal pieces. Then cut these to get eight equal pieces, and so on, performing five cutting steps.

Step 1   Step 2   Step 3

a) Stack the pieces and measure the total thickness.

b) A piece of paper is typically 0.004 in. thick. Check the measurement in part (a) by completing the table.

	t	$0.004 \cdot 2^t$
Start	0	$0.004 \cdot 2^0$, or 0.004
Step 1	1	$0.004 \cdot 2^1$, or 0.008
Step 2	2	$0.004 \cdot 2^2$, or 0.016
Step 3	3	
Step 4	4	
Step 5	5	

c) Graph $f(t) = 0.004(2)^t$.

d) Compute the thickness of the stack (in miles) after 25 steps. (*Hint*: 1 mi = 5280 ft.)

The Number e and the Derivative of e^x

To find the derivative of the exponential function

$$f(x) = a^x,$$

we use the definition of the derivative given by

$$f'(x) = \lim_{h \to 0} \frac{f(x + h) - f(x)}{h} \qquad \text{Definition of the derivative}$$

$$= \lim_{h \to 0} \frac{a^{x+h} - a^x}{h} \qquad \text{Substituting } a^{x+h} \text{ for } f(x + h) \text{ and } a^x \text{ for } f(x)$$

$$= \lim_{h \to 0} \frac{a^x \cdot a^h - a^x \cdot 1}{h} \qquad \text{Using the laws for exponents}$$

$$= \lim_{h \to 0} \left(a^x \cdot \frac{a^h - 1}{h} \right) \qquad \text{Factoring}$$

$$= a^x \cdot \lim_{h \to 0} \frac{a^h - 1}{h}. \qquad \begin{array}{l}\text{Noting that } a^x \text{ is constant with respect to } h, \\ \text{and the limit of a constant times a function is} \\ \text{the constant times the limit of that function}\end{array}$$

Thus, $f'(x) = a^x \cdot \lim_{h \to 0} \dfrac{a^h - 1}{h}.$

In the case of $g(x) = 2^x$,

$$g'(x) = 2^x \cdot \lim_{h \to 0} \frac{2^h - 1}{h}. \qquad \text{Substituting 2 for } a$$

h	$\dfrac{2^h - 1}{h}$
0.1	0.7177
0.01	0.6956
0.001	0.6934
0.0001	0.6931...
0.00001	0.6931...
−0.001	0.6929
−0.0001	0.6931...
−0.00001	0.6931...

Note that the limit does not depend on the value of x at which we are evaluating the derivative. In order for $g'(x)$ to exist, we must determine whether $\lim_{h \to 0} \dfrac{2^h - 1}{h}$ exists. Let's investigate this question.

We choose a sequence of numbers h approaching 0 and compute $(2^h - 1)/h$, listing the results in a table, as shown at left. It seems reasonable to infer that $(2^h - 1)/h$ has a limit as h approaches 0 and that its approximate value is 0.6931; thus,

$$g'(x) \approx (0.6931)2^x.$$

h	$\dfrac{3^h - 1}{h}$
0.1	1.1612
0.01	1.1047
0.001	1.0992
0.0001	1.0987
0.00001	1.0986
−0.001	1.0980
−0.0001	1.0986
−0.00001	1.0986

In other words, the derivative is a constant times 2^x. Similarly, for $t(x) = 3^x$,

$$t'(x) = 3^x \cdot \lim_{h \to 0} \frac{3^h - 1}{h}. \qquad \text{Substituting 3 for } a$$

Again, we can find an approximation for the limit that does not depend on the value of x at which we are evaluating the derivative. Consider the table at left. Again, it seems reasonable to infer that $(3^h - 1)/h$ has a limit as h approaches 0. This time, the limit is approximately 1.0986; thus,

$$t'(x) \approx (1.0986)3^x.$$

In other words, the derivative is a constant times 3^x.

Let's now analyze what we have done. We proved that

$$\text{if } f(x) = a^x, \quad \text{then } f'(x) = a^x \cdot \lim_{h \to 0} \frac{a^h - 1}{h}.$$

Consider $\displaystyle\lim_{h \to 0} \frac{a^h - 1}{h}$.

TECHNOLOGY CONNECTION ⌐∿⌐

EXERCISE
Using TBLSET in Ask mode, produce the tables shown above.

1. For $a = 2$,

$$\lim_{h \to 0} \frac{a^h - 1}{h} = \lim_{h \to 0} \frac{2^h - 1}{h} \approx 0.6931.$$

2. For $a = 3$,

$$\lim_{h \to 0} \frac{a^h - 1}{h} = \lim_{h \to 0} \frac{3^h - 1}{h} \approx 1.0986.$$

It seems reasonable to conclude that, for some choice of a between 2 and 3, we have

$$\lim_{h \to 0} \frac{a^h - 1}{h} = 1.$$

To find that a, it suffices to look for a value such that

$$\frac{a^h - 1}{h} = 1. \tag{1}$$

Multiplying both sides by h and then adding 1 to both sides, we have

$$a^h = 1 + h.$$

Raising both sides to the power $1/h$, we have

$$a = (1 + h)^{1/h}. \tag{2}$$

Since equations (1) and (2) are equivalent, it follows that

$$\lim_{h \to 0} \frac{a^h - 1}{h} = \lim_{h \to 0} 1 \quad \text{and} \quad \lim_{h \to 0} a = \lim_{h \to 0} (1 + h)^{1/h}$$

h	$(1 + h)^{1/h}$
0.1	2.5937
0.01	2.7048
0.001	2.7169
0.0001	2.7181
−0.01	2.7320
−0.001	2.7196
−0.0001	2.7184

are also equivalent. Since $\displaystyle\lim_{h \to 0} c = c$,

$$\lim_{h \to 0} \frac{a^h - 1}{h} = 1 \quad \text{and} \quad a = \lim_{h \to 0} (1 + h)^{1/h}$$

are equivalent. Thus, to find the value of a for which $\displaystyle\lim_{h \to 0} \frac{a^h - 1}{h} = 1$, we must have $a = \displaystyle\lim_{h \to 0} (1 + h)^{1/h}$. This last equation gives us the special number we are searching for.* The number is denoted e, in honor of Leonhard Euler (pronounced "Oiler"), the great Swiss mathematician (1707–1783) who did groundbreaking work with it.

DEFINITION

$$e = \lim_{h \to 0} (1 + h)^{1/h} \approx 2.718281828459$$

We call e the *natural base*.

It follows that, for the exponential function $f(x) = e^x$,

$$f'(x) = e^x \cdot \lim_{h \to 0} \frac{e^h - 1}{h}$$

$$= e^x \cdot 1$$

$$= e^x.$$

That is, the derivative of $f(x) = e^x$ is $f'(x) = e^x$.

THEOREM 1

The derivative of the function f given by $f(x) = e^x$ is the function itself:

$$f'(x) = f(x), \quad \text{or} \quad \frac{d}{dx} e^x = e^x.$$

Theorem 1 says that for $f(x) = e^x$, the derivative at x (the slope of the tangent line) is the same as the function value at x. That is, on the graph of $y = e^x$, at the point $(0, 1)$, the slope is $m = 1$; at the point $(1, e)$, the slope is $m = e$; at the point $(2, e^2)$, the slope is $m = e^2$, and so on. The function $y = e^x$ is the *only* exponential function for which this correlation between the function and its derivative is true.

In Section 3.5, we will develop a formula for the derivative of the more general exponential function given by $y = a^x$.

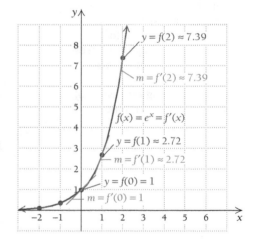

Finding Derivatives of Functions Involving e

We can combine Theorem 1 with earlier theorems to differentiate a variety of functions.

EXAMPLE 2 Find dy/dx:

a) $y = 3e^x$; **b)** $y = x^2 e^x$; **c)** $y = \dfrac{e^x}{x^3}$.

Solution

a) $\dfrac{d}{dx}(3e^x) = 3 \dfrac{d}{dx} e^x$ Recall that $\dfrac{d}{dx}[c \cdot f(x)] = c \cdot f'(x)$.

$\qquad\qquad\quad = 3e^x$ Using Theorem 1

---

*This derivation is based on one presented in Appendix 4 of *e: The Story of a Number*, by Eli Maor (Princeton University Press, 1998).

b) $\dfrac{d}{dx}(x^2 e^x) = x^2 \cdot e^x + e^x \cdot 2x$ Using the Product Rule

$\qquad\qquad\qquad = xe^x(x + 2)$ Factoring

c) $\dfrac{d}{dx}\left(\dfrac{e^x}{x^3}\right) = \dfrac{x^3 \cdot e^x - e^x \cdot 3x^2}{x^6}$ Using the Quotient Rule

$\qquad\qquad\quad = \dfrac{x^2 e^x(x - 3)}{x^6}$ Factoring

$\qquad\qquad\quad = \dfrac{e^x(x - 3)}{x^4}$ Simplifying   **2** ✔

Quick Check 2 ✔

Find dy/dx:

a) $y = 6e^x$;   **b)** $y = x^3 e^x$;

c) $y = \dfrac{e^x}{x^2}$.

TECHNOLOGY CONNECTION 〰

Exploratory

Check each result in Example 2 by entering the function as y_1 and letting $y_2 = \text{nDeriv}$ (y_1, x, x). Then enter the derivative from Example 2 as y_3 and use graphs or a table to compare y_2 and y_3.

Using Graphicus, graph $g(x) = x^2 e^x$ as a first function. Then touch ⊞ and choose Add derivative. Suppose the derivative was mistakenly found to be $g'(x) = 2xe^x$. Graph this incorrect function. What happens? Explain. Then describe a procedure for checking the results of Example 2 using Graphicus.

Suppose we have a more complicated function in the exponent, as in

$$h(x) = e^{x^2 - 5x}.$$

This is a composition of functions. For such a function, we have

$$h(x) = g(f(x)) = e^{f(x)}, \quad \text{where} \quad g(x) = e^x \quad \text{and} \quad f(x) = x^2 - 5x.$$

Now $g'(x) = e^x$. Then by the Chain Rule (Section 1.7), we have

$$h'(x) = g'(f(x)) \cdot f'(x)$$
$$= e^{f(x)} \cdot f'(x).$$

Here $f(x) = x^2 - 5x$, so $f'(x) = 2x - 5$. Then

$$h'(x) = g'(f(x)) \cdot f'(x)$$
$$= e^{f(x)} \cdot f'(x)$$
$$= e^{x^2 - 5x}(2x - 5).$$

The next theorem, which we have proven using the Chain Rule, allows us to find derivatives of functions like the one above.

THEOREM 2

The derivative of e to some power is the product of e to that power and the derivative of the power:

$$\frac{d}{dx} e^{f(x)} = e^{f(x)} \cdot f'(x)$$

or

$$\frac{d}{dx} e^{u} = e^{u} \cdot \frac{du}{dx}.$$

The following gives us a way to remember this rule.

$$h(x) = e^{x^2 - 5x}$$

↓   Rewrite the original function.

$$h'(x) = e^{x^2 - 5x}(2x - 5)$$ Multiply by the derivative of the exponent.

EXAMPLE 3 Differentiate each of the following with respect to x:

a) $y = e^{8x}$;   **b)** $y = e^{-x^2 + 4x - 7}$;   **c)** $e^{\sqrt{x^2 - 3}}$.

Solution

a) $\dfrac{d}{dx} e^{8x} = e^{8x} \cdot 8$ Using the Chain Rule

$\qquad\quad = 8e^{8x}$

b) $\dfrac{d}{dx} e^{-x^2+4x-7} = e^{-x^2+4x-7}(-2x+4)$ Using the Chain Rule

$\qquad\qquad\quad = -2(x-2)e^{-x^2+4x-7}$

c) $\dfrac{d}{dx} e^{\sqrt{x^2-3}} = \dfrac{d}{dx} e^{(x^2-3)^{1/2}}$

$\qquad\quad = e^{(x^2-3)^{1/2}} \cdot \frac{1}{2}(x^2-3)^{-1/2} \cdot 2x$ Using the Chain Rule twice

$\qquad\quad = e^{\sqrt{x^2-3}} \cdot x \cdot (x^2-3)^{-1/2}$

$\qquad\quad = \dfrac{e^{\sqrt{x^2-3}} \cdot x}{\sqrt{x^2-3}}, \quad$ or $\quad \dfrac{xe^{\sqrt{x^2-3}}}{\sqrt{x^2-3}}$ 3 ✔

Quick Check 3 ✔

Differentiate:

a) $f(x) = e^{-4x}$;

b) $g(x) = e^{x^3+8x}$;

c) $h(x) = e^{\sqrt{x^2+5}}$.

Graphs of e^x, e^{-x}, and $1 - e^{-kx}$

Knowing how to differentiate $f(x) = e^x$, we now consider the graph of $f(x) = e^x$ with regard to the curve-sketching techniques discussed in Section 2.2.

EXAMPLE 4   Graph: $f(x) = e^x$. Analyze the graph using calculus.

Solution   We simply find some function values using a calculator, plot the points, and sketch the graph as shown below.

x	$f(x)$
-2	0.135
-1	0.368
0	1
1	2.718
2	7.389

We analyze the graph using calculus as follows.

a) *Derivatives.* Since $f(x) = e^x$, it follows that $f'(x) = e^x$ and $f''(x) = e^x$.

b) *Critical values of f.* Since $f'(x) = e^x > 0$ for all real numbers x, we know that the derivative exists for all real numbers and there is no solution of $f'(x) = 0$. There are no critical values and therefore no maximum or minimum values.

c) *Increasing.* We have $f'(x) = e^x > 0$ for all real numbers x, so the function f is increasing over the entire real line, $(-\infty, \infty)$.

d) *Inflection points.* We have $f''(x) = e^x > 0$ for all real numbers x, so $f''(x) = 0$ has no solution and there are no points of inflection.

e) *Concavity.* Since $f''(x) = e^x > 0$ for all real numbers x, the function f' is increasing and the graph is concave up over the entire real line. ∎

EXAMPLE 5   Graph: $g(x) = e^{-x}$. Analyze the graph using calculus.

Solution   First, we find some function values, plot the points, and sketch the graph.

x	$g(x)$
-2	7.389
-1	2.718
0	1
1	0.368
2	0.135

$g(x) = e^{-x}$

We can then analyze the graph using calculus as follows.

a) *Derivatives.* Since $g(x) = e^{-x}$, we have

$$g'(x) = e^{-x}(-1) = -e^{-x},$$

and

$$g''(x) = -e^{-x}(-1) = e^{-x}.$$

b) *Critical values of g.* Since $e^{-x} = 1/e^x > 0$, we have $g'(x) = -e^{-x} < 0$ for all real numbers x. Thus, the derivative exists for all real numbers, and $g'(x) = 0$ has no solution. There are no critical values and therefore no maximum or minimum values.

c) *Decreasing.* Since the derivative $g'(x) = -e^{-x} < 0$ for all real numbers x, the function g is decreasing over the entire real line.

d) *Inflection points.* We have $g''(x) = e^{-x} > 0$, for all real numbers x, so $g''(x) = 0$ has no solution and there are no points of inflection.

e) *Concavity.* We also know that since $g''(x) = e^{-x} > 0$ for all real numbers x, the function g' is increasing and the graph is concave up over the entire real line.   ■

Functions of the type $f(x) = 1 - e^{-kx}$, with $x \geq 0$, have important applications.

EXAMPLE 6   **Business: Worker Output.**   It is reasonable for a manufacturer to expect the daily output of a new worker to be low at first, increase over time, and then level off. A firm that manufactures 6G smart phones determines that after t working days, the number of phones produced per day by the average worker can be modeled by

$$N(t) = 80 - 70e^{-0.13t}.$$

a) Find $N(0), N(1), N(5), N(10), N(20),$ and $N(30)$.

b) Graph $N(t)$.

c) Find $N'(t)$ and interpret this derivative in terms of rate of change.

d) Find any critical values and intervals over which $N(t)$ is increasing or decreasing.

e) Find $N''(t)$ and any inflection points and intervals over which $N(t)$ is concave up or down.

f) What number of phones seems to determine where worker output levels off?

Solution

a) We make a table of input–output values.

t	0	1	5	10	20	30
$N(t)$	10	18.5	43.5	60.9	74.8	78.6

b) Using these values and/or a graphing calculator, we obtain the graph.

$$N(t) = 80 - 70e^{-0.13t}$$

c) We have $N'(t) = -70e^{-0.13t}(-0.13) = 9.1e^{-0.13t}$; after t days, the rate of change of number of phones produced per day is given by $9.1e^{-0.13t}$.

d) Since $9.1e^{-0.13t} > 0$ for all real numbers t, we know that $N(t)$ is increasing over the interval $(0, \infty)$. There are no critical values.

e) We have $N''(t) = 9.1(-0.13)e^{-0.13t} = -1.183e^{-0.13t}$. Since $-1.183e^{-0.13t} < 0$ for all real numbers t, there are no points of inflection, and the graph of $N(t)$ is concave down over $(0, \infty)$.

f) Examining the graph and expanding the table of function values, it seems that worker output levels off at no more than 80 phones produced per day. **4 ✓**

Quick Check 4 ✓

Business. Repeat Example 6 for the output function

$$N(t) = 80 - 60e^{-0.12t}.$$

In general, for $k > 0$, the graph of $h(x) = 1 - e^{-kx}$ is increasing, which we expect since $h'(x) = ke^{-kx}$ is always positive. Note that $h(x)$ approaches 1 as x approaches ∞.

A word of caution! Functions of the type a^x (for example, 2^x, 3^x, and e^x) are different from functions of the type x^a (for example, x^2, x^3, $x^{1/2}$). For a^x, the variable is in the exponent. For x^a, the variable is in the base. The derivative of a^x is not xa^{x-1}.

Section Summary

- An exponential function is given by $f(x) = a_0 \cdot a^x$, where x is any real number, $a > 0$ and $a \neq 1$. The number a is the base, and the y-intercept is $(0, a_0)$.
- If $a > 1$, then $f(x) = a_0 \cdot a^x$ is increasing, concave up, increasing without bound as x increases, and has a horizontal asymptote $y = 0$ as x approaches $-\infty$.
- If $0 < a < 1$, then $f(x) = a_0 \cdot a^x$ is decreasing, concave up, increasing without bound as x approaches $-\infty$, and has a horizontal asymptote $y = 0$ as x approaches infinity.

- The *exponential function* $f(x) = e^x$, where $e \approx 2.71828$, has the derivative $f'(x) = e^x$. That is, the slope of a tangent line to the graph of $y = e^x$ is the same as the function value at x.
- In general, $\dfrac{d}{dx}e^{f(x)} = e^{f(x)} \cdot f'(x)$.
- The graph of $f(x) = e^x$ is an increasing function with no critical values, no maximum or minimum values, and no points of inflection. The graph is concave up, with

$$\lim_{x \to \infty} f(x) = \infty \quad \text{and} \quad \lim_{x \to -\infty} f(x) = 0.$$

3.1 Exercise Set

Graph.

1. $y = 5^x$

2. $y = 4^x$

3. $y = 2 \cdot 3^x$

4. $y = 3 \cdot 4^x$

5. $y = 5\left(\frac{1}{4}\right)^x$

6. $y = 4\left(\frac{1}{3}\right)^x$

7. $y = 1.3(1.2)^x$

8. $y = 2.4(1.25)^x$

9. $y = 2.6(0.8)^x$

10. $y = 1.13(0.81)^x$

Differentiate.

11. $f(x) = e^x$

12. $f(x) = e^{-x}$

13. $g(x) = e^{2x}$

14. $g(x) = e^{3x}$

15. $f(x) = 6e^x$

16. $f(x) = 4e^x$

17. $F(x) = e^{-7x}$

18. $F(x) = e^{-4x}$

19. $g(x) = 3e^{5x}$

20. $G(x) = 2e^{4x}$

21. $G(x) = -7e^{-x}$

22. $f(x) = -3e^{-x}$

23. $g(x) = \frac{1}{2}e^{-5x}$

24. $f(x) = \frac{1}{3}e^{-4x}$

25. $F(x) = -\frac{2}{3}e^{x^2}$

26. $g(x) = -\frac{4}{5}e^{x^3}$

27. $F(x) = 4 - e^{2x}$

28. $G(x) = 7 + 3e^{5x}$

29. $G(x) = x^3 - 5e^{2x}$

30. $f(x) = x^5 - 2e^{6x}$

31. $g(x) = x^5 e^{2x}$

32. $f(x) = x^7 e^{4x}$

33. $F(x) = \dfrac{e^{2x}}{x^4}$

34. $g(x) = \dfrac{e^{3x}}{x^6}$

35. $f(x) = (x^2 - 2x + 2)e^x$

36. $f(x) = (x^2 + 3x - 9)e^x$

37. $f(x) = \dfrac{e^x}{x^4}$

38. $f(x) = \dfrac{e^x}{x^5}$

39. $f(x) = e^{-x^2 + 8x}$

40. $f(x) = e^{-x^2 + 7x}$

41. $f(x) = e^{x^2/2}$

42. $f(x) = e^{-x^2/2}$

43. $y = e^{\sqrt{x-7}}$

44. $y = e^{\sqrt{x-4}}$

45. $y = \sqrt{e^x - 1}$

46. $y = \sqrt{e^x + 1}$

47. $y = e^x + x^3 - xe^x$

48. $y = xe^{-2x} + e^{-x} + x^3$

49. $y = 1 - e^{-3x}$

50. $y = 1 - e^{-x}$

51. $y = 1 - e^{-kx}$

52. $y = 1 - e^{-mx}$

53. $g(x) = (4x^2 + 3x)e^{x^2 - 7x}$

54. $g(x) = (5x^2 - 8x)e^{x^2 - 4x}$

Graph each function. Then determine any critical values, inflection points, intervals over which the function is increasing or decreasing, and the concavity.

55. $g(x) = e^{-2x}$

56. $f(x) = e^{2x}$

57. $f(x) = e^{(1/3)x}$

58. $g(x) = e^{(1/2)x}$

59. $f(x) = \frac{1}{2}e^{-x}$

60. $g(x) = \frac{1}{3}e^{-x}$

61. $F(x) = -e^{(1/3)x}$

62. $G(x) = -e^{(1/2)x}$

63. $f(x) = 3 - e^{-x}$, for $x \geq 0$

64. $g(x) = 2(1 - e^{-x})$, for $x \geq 0$

65–74. For each function given in Exercises 55–64, graph the function and its first and second derivatives using a graphing utility.

75. Find the slope of the line tangent to the graph of $f(x) = 2e^{-3x}$ at the point $(0, 2)$.

76. Find the slope of the line tangent to the graph of $f(x) = e^x$ at the point $(0, 1)$.

77. Find an equation of the line tangent to the graph of $f(x) = e^{2x}$ at the point $(0, 1)$.

78. Find an equation of the line tangent to the graph of $G(x) = e^{-x}$ at the point $(0, 1)$.

79. and 80. For each of Exercises 77 and 78, graph the function and the tangent line using a graphing utility.

APPLICATIONS

Business and Economics

81. U.S. travel exports. U.S. travel exports (goods and services that international travelers buy while visiting the United States) are increasing exponentially. The value of such exports, t years after 2011, can be approximated by

$$V(t) = 115.32e^{0.094t},$$

where V is in billions of dollars. (*Source*: www.census.gov/foreign-trade/data/index.html.)

a) Estimate the value of U.S. travel exports in 2016 and 2018.

b) Estimate the growth rate for U.S. travel exports in 2016 and 2018.

82. Organic food. More Americans are buying organic fruit and vegetables and products made with organic ingredients. The amount $A(t)$, in billions of dollars, spent on organic food and beverages t years after 1995 can be approximated by

$$A(t) = 2.43e^{0.18t}.$$

(*Source: Nutrition Business Journal, 2004.*)

a) Estimate the amount that Americans spent on organic food and beverages in 2009.

b) Estimate the rate at which spending on organic food and beverages was growing in 2006.

83. Marginal cost. The total cost, in millions of dollars, for Cheevers, Inc., is given by

$$C(t) = 100 - 50e^{-t},$$

where t is the time in years since the start-up date.

Find each of the following.

a) The marginal cost, $C'(t)$

b) $C'(0)$

c) $C'(4)$ (Round to the nearest thousand.)

d) Find $\lim_{t \to \infty} C(t)$ and $\lim_{t \to \infty} C'(t)$.

84. Marginal cost. The total cost, in millions of dollars, for Marcotte Industries is given by

$$C(t) = 200 - 40e^{-t},$$

where t is the time in years since the start-up date.

Find each of the following.

a) The marginal cost $C'(t)$

b) $C'(1)$

c) $C'(5)$ (Round to the nearest thousand.)

d) Find $\lim_{t \to \infty} C(t)$ and $\lim_{t \to \infty} C'(t)$.

85. Marginal demand. At a price of x dollars, the demand, in thousands of units, for a certain turntable is given by the demand function

$$q = 240e^{-0.003x}.$$

a) How many turntables will be bought at a price of $250? Round to the nearest thousand.

b) Graph the demand function for $0 \le x \le 400$.

c) Find the marginal demand, $q'(x)$.

d) Interpret the meaning of the derivative.

86. Marginal supply. At a price of x dollars, the supply function for the turntable in Exercise 85 is given by

$$q = 75e^{0.004x},$$

where q is in thousands of units.

a) How many turntables will be supplied at a price of $250? Round to the nearest thousand.

b) Graph the supply function for $0 \le x \le 400$.

c) Find the marginal supply, $q'(x)$.

d) Interpret the meaning of the derivative.

For Exercises 87–90, use the Tangent *feature from the* DRAW *menu to find the rate of change in part (b).*

87. Growth of a retirement fund. Maria deposits $20,000 in an IRA whose value increases by 5.6% every year. The value of the IRA after t years is modeled by

$$V(t) = 20{,}000(1.056)^t.$$

a) Use the model to estimate the value of Maria's IRA after 7 yr.

b) What is the rate of change in the value of the IRA at the end of 7 yr?

c) When will Maria's IRA have a value of $40,000?

88. Depreciation. Pelican Fabrics purchases a new video surveillance system. The value of the system is modeled by

$$V(t) = 17{,}500(0.92)^t,$$

where V is the value of the system, in dollars, t years after its purchase.

a) Use the model to estimate the value of the system 5 yr after it was purchased.

b) What is the rate of change in the value of the system at the end of 5 yr?

c) When will the system be worth half of its original value?

89. Depreciation. Perriot's Restaurant purchased kitchen equipment on January 1, 2014. The value of the equipment decreases by 15% every year. On January 1, 2016, the value was $14,450.

a) Find an exponential model for the value, V, of the equipment, in dollars, t years after January 1, 2016.

b) What is the rate of change in the value of the equipment on January 1, 2016?

c) What was the original value of the equipment on January 1, 2014?

d) How many years after January 1, 2014 will the value of the equipment have decreased by half?

90. Stock prices. The value (price) of a share of stock in Barrington Gold was $90 on June 15, 2014, and was increasing by 3% every week.

a) Find an exponential model for the value, V, of a share of the stock, in dollars, t weeks after June 15, 2014.

b) What was the rate of change in the value of a share of the stock 6 weeks prior to June 15, 2014?

c) Use the model to estimate the value of a share of the stock 6 weeks prior to June 15, 2014.

d) How many weeks after June 15, 2014, will the stock's share value have doubled?

Life and Physical Sciences

91. Medication concentration. The concentration C, in parts per million, of a medication in the body t hours after ingestion is given by the function

$$C(t) = 10t^2 e^{-t}.$$

a) Find the concentration after 0 hr, 1 hr, 2 hr, 3 hr, and 10 hr.

b) Sketch a graph of the function for $0 \leq t \leq 10$.

c) Find the rate of change of the concentration, $C'(t)$.

d) Find the maximum value of the concentration and the time at which it occurs.

e) Interpret the meaning of the derivative.

Social Sciences

92. Ebbinghaus learning model. Suppose that you are given the task of learning 100% of a block of knowledge. Human nature is such that we retain only a percentage P of knowledge t weeks after we have learned it. The *Ebbinghaus learning model* asserts that P is given by

$$P(t) = Q + (100 - Q)e^{-kt},$$

where Q is the percentage that we would never forget and k is a constant that depends on the knowledge learned. Suppose that $Q = 40$ and $k = 0.7$.

a) Find the percentage retained after 0 weeks, 1 week, 2 weeks, 6 weeks, and 10 weeks.

b) Find $\lim_{t \to \infty} P(t)$.

c) Sketch a graph of P.

d) Find the rate of change of $P(t)$ with respect to time t.

e) Interpret the meaning of the derivative.

SYNTHESIS

Differentiate.

93. $y = (e^{3x} + 1)^5$

94. $y = \dfrac{e^{3t} - e^{7t}}{e^{4t}}$

95. $y = \dfrac{e^x}{x^2 + 1}$

96. $f(x) = e^{\sqrt{x}} + \sqrt{e^x}$

97. $f(x) = e^{x/2} \cdot \sqrt{x - 1}$

98. $f(x) = \dfrac{xe^{-x}}{1 + x^2}$

99. $f(x) = \dfrac{e^x - e^{-x}}{e^x + e^{-x}}$

100. $f(x) = e^{e^x}$

101. Use the results from Exercises 85 and 86 to determine the *equilibrium point* (the point at which supply equals demand) and the rates at which supply and demand are changing at that point.

Exercises 102 and 103 each give an expression for e. Find the function values that are approximations for e. Round to five decimal places.

102. For $f(t) = (1 + t)^{1/t}$, we have $e = \lim_{t \to 0} f(t)$. Find $f(1)$, $f(0.5), f(0.2), f(0.1)$, and $f(0.001)$.

103. For $g(t) = t^{1/(t-1)}$, we have $e = \lim_{t \to 1} g(t)$. Find $g(0.5)$, $g(0.9), g(0.99), g(0.999)$, and $g(0.9998)$.

104. Find the minimum value of $f(x) = xe^x$ over $[-2, 0]$.

105. A student made the following error on a test:

$$\frac{d}{dx}e^x = xe^{x-1}.$$

Identify the error and explain how to correct it.

106. Describe the differences in the graphs of $f(x) = 3^x$ and $g(x) = x^3$.

TECHNOLOGY CONNECTION

Use a graphing calculator (or Graphicus) to graph each function in Exercises 107 and 108, and find all relative extrema.

107. $f(x) = x^2 e^{-x}$

108. $f(x) = e^{-x^2}$

For each of the functions in Exercises 109–112, graph f, f', and f''.

109. $f(x) = e^x$

110. $f(x) = e^{-x}$

111. $f(x) = 2e^{0.3x}$

112. $f(x) = 1000e^{-0.08x}$

113. Graph

$$f(x) = \left(1 + \frac{1}{x}\right)^x.$$

Use the TABLE feature and very large values of x to confirm that e is approached as a limit.

114. Consider the expression 2^π, where $\pi = 3.1415926\ldots$. Recall that π is an irrational number, that is, a number with an infinite, nonrepeating decimal expansion.

a) Using a calculator, complete the following table, giving answers to eight decimal places.

x	2^x
3	
3.1	
3.14	
3.141	
3.1415	
3.14159	
3.141592	
3.1415926	

b) Based on the results from part (a), estimate the value of 2^π.

c) Using a calculator, find 2^π.

d) Use the results of parts (a)–(c) to explain how a base raised to an irrational number can be found as a numerical limit. Does this work for a base raised to any irrational number? Explain.

Answers to Quick Checks

1. $13,248.53   **2. (a)** $6e^x$;   **(b)** $x^2 e^x (x + 3)$;

(c) $\dfrac{e^x (x - 2)}{x^3}$ **3. (a)** $-4e^{-4x}$;   **(b)** $e^{x^3 + 8x} (3x^2 + 8)$;

(c) $\dfrac{xe^{\sqrt{x^2+5}}}{\sqrt{x^2 + 5}}$ **4. (a)** 20, 26.8, 47.1, 61.9, 74.6, 78.4

(b)

(c) $N'(t) = 7.2e^{-0.12t}$; after t days, the rate of change of number of phones produced per day is given by $7.2e^{-0.12t}$.

(d) $N(t)$ is increasing over $(0, \infty)$.   **(e)** $N(t)$ is concave down over $(0, \infty)$.   **(f)** 80 phones produced per day

---

Logarithmic Functions

3.2

- Convert between exponential and logarithmic equations.
- Solve exponential equations.
- Solve problems involving exponential and logarithmic functions.
- Differentiate functions involving natural logarithms.

Logarithmic Functions and Their Graphs

Suppose we want to solve

$$10^y = 1000.$$

We are trying to find the power of 10 that will give 1000. Since $10^3 = 1000$, the answer is 3. The number 3 is called "the logarithm, base 10, of 1000."

DEFINITION

A **logarithm** is defined as follows:

$$\log_a x = y \qquad \text{means} \qquad a^y = x, \quad a > 0, a \neq 1.$$

The number $\log_a x$ is the power y to which we raise a to get x. The number a is called the *logarithmic base*. We read $\log_a x$ as "the logarithm, base a, of x."

For logarithms with base 10, $\log_{10} x$ is the power y such that $10^y = x$. Therefore, a logarithm can be thought of as an exponent. We can convert from a logarithmic equation to an exponential equation, and conversely, as follows.

LOGARITHMIC EQUATION	EXPONENTIAL EQUATION
$\log_a M = N$	$a^N = M$
$\log_{10} 100 = 2$	$10^2 = 100$
$\log_5 \frac{1}{25} = -2$	$5^{-2} = \frac{1}{25}$
$\log_{49} 7 = \frac{1}{2}$	$49^{1/2} = 7$

EXAMPLE 1   Solve for x by writing each logarithmic equation as an equivalent exponential equation.

a) $\log_3 9 = x$ **b)** $\log_x 25 = 2$ **c)** $\log_{16} x = \frac{1}{2}$

Solution

a) We write $\log_3 9 = x$ as $3^x = 9$. Therefore, we have $x = 2$, and we say "the logarithm, base 3, of 9, is 2."

b) We write $\log_x 25 = 2$ as $x^2 = 25$. Since the base must be positive, we have $x = 5$.

c) We write $\log_{16} x = \frac{1}{2}$ as $16^{1/2} = x$. Since $16^{1/2} = \sqrt{16}$, we have $x = 4$.   **1** ✔

In order to graph a logarithmic equation, we can graph its equivalent exponential equation.

EXAMPLE 2   Graph: $y = \log_2 x$.

Solution   We first write the equivalent exponential equation:

$$2^y = x.$$

We select values for y and find the corresponding values of 2^y. Then we plot points, remembering that x is still the first coordinate, and connect the points with a smooth curve.

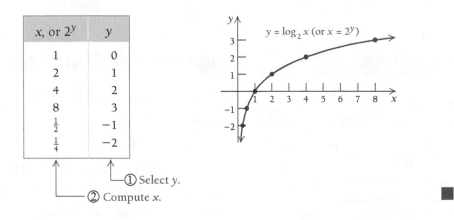

x, or 2^y	y
1	0
2	1
4	2
8	3
$\frac{1}{2}$	-1
$\frac{1}{4}$	-2

① Select y.
② Compute x.

The graphs of $f(x) = 2^x$ and $g(x) = \log_2 x$ are shown below. Note that we can obtain the graph of g by reflecting the graph of f across the line $y = x$. Functions whose graphs can be obtained in this manner are known as *inverses* of each other.

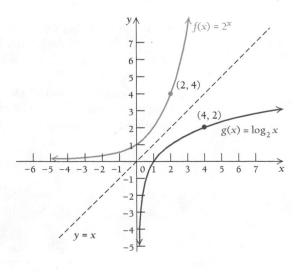

Graphing Logarithmic Functions

To graph $y = \log_2 x$, we first graph $y_1 = 2^x$. We next select the DrawInv option from the DRAW menu and then the Y-VARS option from the VARS menu, followed by ①, ①, and **ENTER** to draw the inverse of y_1. Both graphs are drawn together.

$y_1 = 2^x, \quad y_2 = \log_2 x$

EXERCISES

Graph.

1. $y = \log_3 x$

2. $y = \log_5 x$

3. $f(x) = \log_e x$

4. $f(x) = \log_{10} x$

Although we do not develop inverses in detail here, it is important to note that they "undo" each other. For example,

$$f(3) = 2^3 = 8, \qquad \text{The input 3 gives the output 8.}$$

and $\qquad g(8) = \log_2 8 = 3. \qquad \text{The input 8 gets us back to 3.}$

Basic Properties of Logarithms

The following are some basic properties of logarithms. The proofs of P1–P3 follow from properties of exponents and are outlined in Exercises 119–121 at the end of this section. Properties P4–P6 follow directly from the definition of logarithm, and a proof of P7 is outlined in Exercise 122.

THEOREM 3   **Properties of Logarithms**

For any positive numbers M, N, a, and b, with a, $b \neq 1$, and any real number k:

P1. $\log_a (MN) = \log_a M + \log_a N$

P2. $\log_a \dfrac{M}{N} = \log_a M - \log_a N$

P3. $\log_a (M^k) = k \cdot \log_a M$

P4. $\log_a a = 1$

P5. $\log_a (a^k) = k$

P6. $\log_a 1 = 0$

P7. $\log_b M = \dfrac{\log_a M}{\log_a b}$ (The change-of-base formula)

Let's illustrate these properties.

EXAMPLE 3   Given

$$\log_a 2 = 0.301 \quad \text{and} \quad \log_a 3 = 0.477,$$

find each of the following:

a) $\log_a 6$; **b)** $\log_a \frac{2}{3}$; **c)** $\log_a 81$; **d)** $\log_a \frac{1}{3}$;

e) $\log_a \sqrt{a}$; **f)** $\log_a (2a)$; **g)** $\dfrac{\log_a 3}{\log_a 2}$; **h)** $\log_a 5$.

Solution

a) $\log_a 6 = \log_a (2 \cdot 3)$

$\qquad = \log_a 2 + \log_a 3 \qquad \text{Using Property P1}$

$\qquad = 0.301 + 0.477$

$\qquad = 0.778$

b) $\log_a \frac{2}{3} = \log_a 2 - \log_a 3 \qquad \text{Using Property P2}$

$\qquad = 0.301 - 0.477$

$\qquad = -0.176$

c) $\log_a 81 = \log_a 3^4 \qquad \text{Recognizing 81 as a power of 3}$

$\qquad = 4 \log_a 3 \qquad \text{Using Property P3}$

$\qquad = 4(0.477)$

$\qquad = 1.908$

d) $\log_a \frac{1}{3} = \log_a 1 - \log_a 3$ Using Property P2

$= 0 - 0.477$ Using Property P6

$= -0.477$

e) $\log_a \sqrt{a} = \log_a (a^{1/2}) = \frac{1}{2}$ Using Property P5

f) $\log_a (2a) = \log_a 2 + \log_a a$ Using Property P1

$= 0.301 + 1$ Using Property P4

$= 1.301$

g) $\dfrac{\log_a 3}{\log_a 2} = \dfrac{0.477}{0.301} \approx 1.58$

Here we simply divided and used none of the properties.

h) There is no way to find $\log_a 5$ using the properties of logarithms ($\log_a 5 \neq \log_a 2 + \log_a 3$).   **2** ☑

Quick Check 2 ☑

Given $\log_b 2 = 0.356$ and $\log_b 5 = 0.827$, find each of the following:

a) $\log_b 10$;   **b)** $\log_b \frac{2}{5}$;

c) $\log_b \frac{5}{2}$;   **d)** $\log_b 16$;

e) $\log_b 5b$;   **f)** $\log_b \sqrt{b}$.

Common Logarithms

The number $\log_{10} x$ is the **common logarithm** of x and is abbreviated $\log x$; that is:

DEFINITION

For any positive number x, $\log x = \log_{10} x$.

Thus, when we write "$\log x$" with no base indicated, base 10 is assumed. Note the following comparison of common logarithms and powers of 10.

$1000 = 10^3$	The common logarithms at the right follow from the powers at the left.	$\log 1000 = 3$
$100 = 10^2$		$\log 100 = 2$
$10 = 10^1$		$\log 10 = 1$
$1 = 10^0$		$\log 1 = 0$
$0.1 = 10^{-1}$		$\log 0.1 = -1$
$0.01 = 10^{-2}$		$\log 0.01 = -2$
$0.001 = 10^{-3}$		$\log 0.001 = -3$

Since $\log 100 = 2$ and $\log 1000 = 3$, it seems reasonable that $\log 500$ is somewhere between 2 and 3. Using a calculator with a **LOG** key, we find that $\log 500 \approx 2.6990$.

Before calculators became readily available, common logarithms were listed in tables and used extensively to do certain computations. In fact, computation is the reason logarithms were developed. Since standard notation for numbers is based on 10, it was logical to use base-10, or common, logarithms for computations. Today, computations with common logarithms are mainly of historical interest; the logarithmic functions, base e, are far more important.

Natural Logarithms

The number e, which is approximately 2.71828, was developed in Section 3.1, and has extensive application in many fields. The number $\log_e x$ is the **natural logarithm** of x and is abbreviated $\ln x$.

DEFINITION

For any positive number x, $\ln x = \log_e x$.

The following basic properties of natural logarithms parallel those given earlier for general logarithms.

> **THEOREM 4   Properties of Natural Logarithms**
>
> **P1.** $\ln(MN) = \ln M + \ln N$
>
> **P2.** $\ln \dfrac{M}{N} = \ln M - \ln N$
>
> **P3.** $\ln(a^k) = k \cdot \ln a$
>
> **P4.** $\ln e = 1$
>
> **P5.** $\ln(e^k) = k$
>
> **P6.** $\ln 1 = 0$
>
> **P7.** $\log_b M = \dfrac{\ln M}{\ln b}$ and $\ln M = \dfrac{\log M}{\log e}$

Let's illustrate the properties given in Theorem 4.

EXAMPLE 4   Given

$$\ln 2 = 0.6931 \quad \text{and} \quad \ln 3 = 1.0986,$$

use the properties of natural logarithms to find each of the following:
a) $\ln 6$; **b)** $\ln 81$; **c)** $\ln \frac{1}{3}$; **d)** $\ln(2e^5)$; **e)** $\log_2 3$.

Solution

a) $\ln 6 = \ln(2 \cdot 3) = \ln 2 + \ln 3$ Using Property P1
$$= 0.6931 + 1.0986$$
$$= 1.7917$$

b) $\ln 81 = \ln(3^4)$
$$= 4 \ln 3 \quad \text{Using Property P3}$$
$$= 4(1.0986)$$
$$= 4.3944$$

c) $\ln \frac{1}{3} = \ln 1 - \ln 3$ Using Property P2
$$= 0 - 1.0986 \quad \text{Using Property P6}$$
$$= -1.0986$$

d) $\ln(2e^5) = \ln 2 + \ln(e^5)$ Using Property P1
$$= 0.6931 + 5 \quad \text{Using Property P5}$$
$$= 5.6931$$

e) $\log_2 3 = \dfrac{\ln 3}{\ln 2} = \dfrac{1.0986}{0.6931} \approx 1.5851$ Using Property P7

Quick Check 3 ✔

Given $\ln 2 = 0.6931$ and $\ln 5 = 1.6094$, use the properties of natural logarithms to find each of the following:

a) $\ln 10$; **b)** $\ln \frac{5}{2}$;
c) $\ln \frac{2}{5}$; **d)** $\ln 32$;
e) $\ln 5e^2$; **f)** $\log_5 2$.

Finding Natural Logarithms Using a Calculator

Using a calculator with an **LN** key allows us to find natural logarithms directly.

EXAMPLE 5   Approximate each of the following to six decimal places:

a) $\ln 5.24$; **b)** $\ln 0.001278$.

Solution   We use a calculator with an **LN** key.
a) $\ln 5.24 \approx 1.656321$ **b)** $\ln 0.001278 \approx -6.662459$

Exponential Equations

If an equation contains a variable in an exponent, the equation is **exponential**. We can use logarithms to manipulate or solve exponential equations.

> **EXAMPLE 6** Solve: $e^{-0.04t} = 0.05$.
>
> **Solution** We have
>
> $\ln e^{-0.04t} = \ln 0.05$ Taking the natural logarithm on both sides
>
> $-0.04t = \ln 0.05$ Using Property P5
>
> $t = \dfrac{\ln 0.05}{-0.04}$
>
> $\left.\begin{array}{l} t \approx \dfrac{-2.995732}{-0.04} \\[1.2em] t \approx 75. \end{array}\right\}$ Using a calculator

Quick Check 4 ☑

Solve each equation:

a) $e^t = 80$;

b) $e^{-0.08t} = 0.25$.

4 ☑

In Example 6, we rounded $\ln 0.05$ to -2.995732 in an intermediate step. When using a calculator, you should find

$$\frac{\ln 0.05}{-0.04}$$

by keying in

 LN . 0 5) ÷ (-) . 0 4 ,

pressing **ENTER**, and rounding at the end. Answers at the back of this book have been found in this manner. Remember, the number of places in a table or on a calculator affects the accuracy of the answer. Usually, your answer should agree with that in the Answers section to at least three digits.

TECHNOLOGY CONNECTION

Solving Exponential Equations

Let's solve $e^t = 40$ graphically.

Method 1: The INTERSECT Feature

We change the variable to x and consider the system of equations $y_1 = e^x$ and $y_2 = 40$. We graph the equations in the window $[-1, 8, -10, 70]$ to see the curves and point of intersection.

Then we use the INTERSECT option from the CALC menu to find the point of intersection, about $(3.6888795, 40)$. The x-coordinate, 3.6888795, is the approximate solution of $e^t = 40$.

Method 2: The ZERO Feature

We change the variable to x and get a 0 on one side of the equation: $e^x - 40 = 0$. Then we graph $y = e^x - 40$ in the window $[-1, 8, -10, 10]$.

Using the ZERO option from the CALC menu, we see that the x-intercept is about $(3.6888795, 0)$, so 3.6888795 is the approximate solution.

EXERCISES

Solve graphically using a graphing utility.

1. $e^t = 1000$ 2. $e^{-x} = 60$

3. $e^{-0.04t} = 0.05$ 4. $e^{0.23x} = 41{,}378$

5. $15e^{0.2x} = 34{,}785.13$

Graphs of Natural Logarithmic Functions

There are two ways in which we might graph $y = f(x) = \ln x$. One is to graph the equivalent equation $x = e^y$ by selecting values for y and calculating the corresponding values of e^y. We then plot points, remembering that x is still the first coordinate.

x, or e^y	y
0.1	-2
0.4	-1
1.0	0
2.7	1
7.4	2
20.1	3

① Select y.

② Compute x.

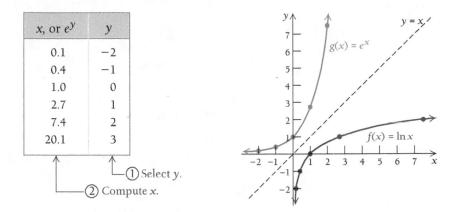

The graph above shows the graph of $g(x) = e^x$ for comparison with that of $f(x) = \ln x$. Note that the functions are inverses of each other. That is, the graph of $y = \ln x$, or $x = e^y$, is a reflection across the line $y = x$ of the graph of $y = e^x$. Any ordered pair (a, b) on the graph of g yields an ordered pair (b, a) on f. Note too that $\lim\limits_{x \to 0^+} \ln x = -\infty$ and the y-axis is a vertical asymptote.

The second method of graphing $y = \ln x$ is to use a calculator to find function values. For example, when $x = 2$, then $y = \ln 2 \approx 0.6931$. This gives the pair $(2, 0.6931)$ shown on the graph.

The following properties can be observed from the graph.

THEOREM 5

$\ln x$ exists only for positive numbers x. The domain is $(0, \infty)$.

> $\ln x < 0$ for $0 < x < 1$.
>
> $\ln x = 0$ when $x = 1$.
>
> $\ln x > 0$ for $x > 1$.

The function given by $f(x) = \ln x$ is always increasing. The range is the entire real line, $(-\infty, \infty)$, or the set of real numbers, $\mathbb{R}$.

Derivatives of Natural Logarithmic Functions

Let's find the derivative of

$$f(x) = \ln x. \tag{1}$$

We first write its equivalent exponential equation:

$$e^{f(x)} = x. \qquad \ln x = \log_e x = f(x), \text{ so } e^{f(x)} = x, \tag{2}$$
$$\text{by the definition of logarithm.}$$

Now we differentiate implicitly on both sides of this equation:

$$\frac{d}{dx} e^{f(x)} = \frac{d}{dx} x$$

$$e^{f(x)} \cdot f'(x) = 1 \qquad \text{Using the Chain Rule}$$

$$x \cdot f'(x) = 1 \qquad \text{Substituting } x \text{ for } e^{f(x)} \text{ from equation (2)}$$

$$f'(x) = \frac{1}{x}.$$

Thus, we have the following.

THEOREM 6

For any positive number x,

$$\frac{d}{dx} \ln x = \frac{1}{x}.$$

To visualize Theorem 6, look back at the graph of $f(x) = \ln x$ on p. 313. Take a straightedge and place it as if its edge were a tangent line. Start on the left and move the straightedge along the curve toward the right, noting how the tangent lines flatten out. Think about the slopes of these tangent lines. The slopes approach 0 as a limit, though they never actually become 0. This is consistent with the formula

$$\frac{d}{dx} \ln x = \frac{1}{x}, \quad \text{because } \lim_{x \to \infty} \frac{1}{x} = 0.$$

Theorem 6 states that to find the slope of the tangent line at x for the function $f(x) = \ln x$, we need only take the reciprocal of x. This is true only for positive values of x, since $\ln x$ is defined only for positive numbers. Note that

$$\frac{d}{dx} \ln(cx) = \frac{1}{cx} \cdot c = \frac{1}{x}, \quad \text{for } cx > 0$$

and

$$\frac{d}{dx} \ln(-x) = \frac{1}{(-x)} \cdot (-1) = \frac{1}{x}, \quad \text{for } x < 0.$$

Thus, $y = \ln x$ is not the only function for which $dy/dx = 1/x$. In particular, note that for $x < 0$, the function given by $y = \ln x$ is undefined. However, for $x < 0$, the function given by $y = \ln(-x)$ is defined. Since

$$y = \ln |x| \text{ is equivalent to } y = \begin{cases} \ln x, & \text{if } x > 0, \\ \ln(-x), & \text{if } x < 0, \end{cases}$$

it follows that

$$\frac{dy}{dx} \ln |x| = \frac{1}{x}, \quad \text{for all } x \neq 0.$$

This result will be important for our work in Chapter 4. In general, when we write $y = \ln x$, we assume $x > 0$. For example, for the function given by $y = \ln(x^2 + 5x)$, we assume that x is chosen so that $x^2 + 5x > 0$.

Let's find some derivatives.

EXAMPLE 7 Differentiate:

a) $y = 3 \ln x;$ **b)** $y = x^2 \ln x + 5x;$ **c)** $y = \dfrac{\ln |2x|}{x^3}.$

Solution

a) $\dfrac{d}{dx}(3 \ln x) = 3 \dfrac{d}{dx} \ln x = \dfrac{3}{x}$

b) $\dfrac{d}{dx}(x^2 \ln x + 5x) = x^2 \cdot \dfrac{1}{x} + 2x \cdot \ln x + 5$ Using the Product Rule on $x^2 \ln x$

$= x + 2x \cdot \ln x + 5$ Simplifying

c) $\dfrac{d}{dx}\left(\dfrac{\ln |2x|}{x^3}\right) = \dfrac{x^3 \cdot (1/2x) \cdot 2 - \ln |2x| (3x^2)}{(x^3)^2}$ Using the Quotient Rule

$= \dfrac{x^2 - 3x^2 \ln |2x|}{x^6}$

$= \dfrac{x^2(1 - 3 \ln |2x|)}{x^6}$ Factoring

$= \dfrac{1 - 3 \ln |2x|}{x^4}$ Simplifying   **5** ✔

Quick Check 5 ✔

Differentiate:

a) $y = 5 \ln x;$

b) $y = x^3 \ln x + 4x;$

c) $y = \dfrac{\ln |4x|}{x^2}.$

Suppose we want to differentiate a function of the form $h(x) = \ln f(x)$, such as

$$h(x) = \ln (x^2 - 8x).$$

This can be regarded as a composition of functions,

$$h(x) = g(f(x)), \quad \text{where} \quad g(x) = \ln x \quad \text{and} \quad f(x) = x^2 - 8x.$$

Now $g'(x) = 1/x$, so by the Chain Rule (Section 1.7), we have

$$h'(x) = g'(f(x)) \cdot f'(x)$$

$$= \dfrac{1}{f(x)} \cdot f'(x).$$

For the above case, $f(x) = x^2 - 8x$, so $f'(x) = 2x - 8$. Then

$$h'(x) = \dfrac{1}{x^2 - 8x} \cdot (2x - 8) = \dfrac{2x - 8}{x^2 - 8x}.$$

The following rule, which results directly from the Chain Rule, allows us to find derivatives of functions like the one above.

THEOREM 7

The derivative of the natural logarithm of a function is the derivative of the function divided by the function:

$$\dfrac{d}{dx} \ln f(x) = \dfrac{1}{f(x)} \cdot f'(x) = \dfrac{f'(x)}{f(x)},$$

or

$$\dfrac{d}{dx} \ln u = \dfrac{1}{u} \cdot \dfrac{du}{dx}.$$

The following gives us a way of remembering this rule.

$$h(x) = \ln\,(x^2 - 8x)$$

① Differentiate the "inside" function.

$$h'(x) = \frac{2x - 8}{x^2 - 8x}$$

② Divide by the "inside" function.

EXAMPLE 8 Differentiate:

a) $y = \ln\,(3x)$; **b)** $y = \ln\,(x^2 - 5)$; **c)** $f(x) = \ln\left(\dfrac{x^3 + 4}{x}\right)$.

Solution

a) If $y = \ln\,(3x)$, then

$$\frac{dy}{dx} = \frac{3}{3x} = \frac{1}{x}.$$

Note that we could have done this using the fact that $\ln\,(MN) = \ln M + \ln N$:

$$\ln\,(3x) = \ln 3 + \ln x;$$

then, since $\ln 3$ is a constant, we have

$$\frac{d}{dx}\ln\,(3x) = \frac{d}{dx}\ln 3 + \frac{d}{dx}\ln x = 0 + \frac{1}{x} = \frac{1}{x}.$$

b) If $y = \ln\,(x^2 - 5)$, then

$$\frac{dy}{dx} = \frac{2x}{x^2 - 5}.$$

c) If $f(x) = \ln\left(\dfrac{x^3 + 4}{x}\right)$, then, since $\ln\dfrac{M}{N} = \ln M - \ln N$, we have

$$f'(x) = \frac{d}{dx}\left[\ln\,(x^3 + 4) - \ln x\right] \qquad \text{Using P2 avoids use of the Quotient Rule.}$$

$$= \frac{3x^2}{x^3 + 4} - \frac{1}{x}$$

$$\left.\begin{array}{l} = \dfrac{3x^2}{x^3 + 4}\cdot\dfrac{x}{x} - \dfrac{1}{x}\cdot\dfrac{x^3 + 4}{x^3 + 4} \\[2mm] = \dfrac{(3x^2)x - (x^3 + 4)}{x(x^3 + 4)} \\[2mm] = \dfrac{3x^3 - x^3 - 4}{x(x^3 + 4)} = \dfrac{2x^3 - 4}{x(x^3 + 4)}. \end{array}\right\}$$

Finding a common denominator

Simplifying

6 ✔

TECHNOLOGY CONNECTION

Exploratory

To check part (a) of Example 8, we let $y_1 = \ln\,(3x)$, $y_2 = \text{nDeriv}(y_1, x, x)$, and $y_3 = 1/x$. Either GRAPH or TABLE can then be used to show that $y_2 = y_3$. Use this approach to check parts (b) and (c) of Example 8. (Or use Graphicus to check those results.)

Quick Check 6 ✔

Differentiate:

a) $y = \ln 5x$;

b) $y = \ln\,(3x^2 + 4)$;

c) $y = \ln\,(\ln 5x)$;

d) $y = \ln\left(\dfrac{x^5 - 2}{x}\right)$.

Applications

EXAMPLE 9 **Social Science: Forgetting.** In a psychological experiment, students were shown a set of nonsense syllables, such as POK, RIZ, DEQ, and so on, and asked to recall them every minute thereafter. The percentage $R(t)$ who retained the syllables after t minutes was found to be given by the logarithmic learning model

$$R(t) = 80 - 27\ln t, \quad \text{for} \quad t \geq 1.$$

a) What percentage of students retained the syllables after 1 min?

b) Find $R'(2)$, and explain what it represents.

Solution

a) $R(1) = 80 - 27 \cdot \ln 1 = 80 - 27 \cdot 0 = 80\%$

b) $\dfrac{d}{dt}(80 - 27 \ln t) = 0 - 27 \cdot \dfrac{1}{t} = -\dfrac{27}{t},$

so $R'(2) = -\dfrac{27}{2} = -13.5.$

This result indicates that 2 min after students have been shown the syllables, the percentage of them who remember the syllables is shrinking at the rate of 13.5% per minute. ■

EXAMPLE 10 **Business: An Advertising Model.** Sawtelle Inc. begins a radio advertising campaign in New York City to market its new energy drink. The percentage of the "target market" that buys a product is normally a function of the duration of the advertising campaign. The radio station estimates this percentage, as a decimal, by using $f(t) = 1 - e^{-0.04t}$ for this type of product, where t is the number of days of the campaign. The target market is approximately 1,000,000 people, and the price per unit is $1.50. If the campaign costs $1000 per day, how long should it last in order to maximize profit?

Solution The radio station's model for the percentage of the target market that buys the product seems reasonable if we graph f. The function increases from 0 (0%) toward 1 (100%). The longer the advertising campaign, the larger the percentage of the market that has bought the product.

The total-profit function, here expressed in terms of time t, is given by

Profit = Revenue − Cost

$$P(t) = R(t) - C(t).$$

We find $R(t)$ and $C(t)$:

$$R(t) = (\text{Percentage buying}) \cdot (\text{Target market}) \cdot (\text{Price per unit})$$
$$= (1 - e^{-0.04t})(1{,}000{,}000)(1.5) = 1{,}500{,}000 - 1{,}500{,}000e^{-0.04t},$$

and

$$C(t) = (\text{Advertising costs per day}) \cdot (\text{Number of days}) = 1000t.$$

Next, we find $P(t)$ and its derivative:

$$P(t) = R(t) - C(t)$$
$$= 1{,}500{,}000 - 1{,}500{,}000e^{-0.04t} - 1000t,$$
$$P'(t) = -1{,}500{,}000e^{-0.04t}(-0.04) - 1000$$
$$= 60{,}000e^{-0.04t} - 1000.$$

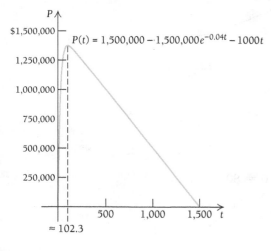

$P(t) = 1{,}500{,}000 - 1{,}500{,}000e^{-0.04t} - 1000t$

We then set the first derivative equal to 0 and solve:

$$60{,}000e^{-0.04t} - 1000 = 0$$
$$60{,}000e^{-0.04t} = 1000$$
$$e^{-0.04t} = \frac{1000}{60{,}000} = 0.0167$$
$$\ln e^{-0.04t} = \ln 0.0167$$
$$-0.04t = \ln 0.0167$$
$$t = \frac{\ln 0.0167}{-0.04}$$
$$t \approx 102.3.$$

Quick Check 7 ☑

Business: An Advertising Model.
Repeat Example 10 using the function

$$f(t) = 1 - e^{-0.08t}$$

and assuming that the campaign costs $2000 per day.

We have only one critical value, so we can use the second derivative to determine whether we have a maximum:

$$P''(t) = 60{,}000e^{-0.04t}(-0.04)$$
$$= -2400e^{-0.04t}.$$

Since exponential functions are positive, $e^{-0.04t} > 0$ for all numbers t. Thus, since $-2400e^{-0.04t} < 0$ for all t, we have $P''(102.3) < 0$, and we have a maximum.

The advertising campaign should run for 103 days (since we need to round up to a whole day) in order to maximize profit.   **7** ☑

Section Summary

- A logarithmic function $y = \log_a x$ is defined by $a^y = x$, for $a > 0$ and $a \neq 1$.
- The common logarithmic function g is defined by $g(x) = \log_{10} x = \log x$, for $x > 0$.
- The natural logarithm function f is defined by $f(x) = \log_e |x| = \ln |x|$, where $e \approx 2.71828$. When we write $f(x) = \ln x$, we assume $x > 0$. The derivative of f is $f'(x) = \dfrac{1}{x}$. The slope of a tangent line to the graph of f at x is found by taking the reciprocal of x.

- The graph of $f(x) = \ln x$ is an increasing function with no critical values, no maximum or minimum values, and no points of inflection. The domain is $(0, \infty)$. The range is $(-\infty, \infty)$, or $\mathbb{R}$. The graph is concave down, with

$$\lim_{x \to \infty} f(x) = \infty \quad \text{and} \quad \lim_{x \to 0^+} f(x) = -\infty.$$

- Properties of logarithms are described in Theorems 3 and 4.

3.2 Exercise Set

Write an equivalent exponential equation.

1. $\log_3 81 = 4$

2. $\log_2 8 = 3$

3. $\log_{27} 3 = \frac{1}{3}$

4. $\log_8 2 = \frac{1}{3}$

5. $\log_a J = K$

6. $\log_a K = J$

7. $-\log_b V = w$

8. $-\log_{10} h = p$

Solve for x.

9. $\log_7 49 = x$

10. $\log_5 125 = x$

11. $\log_x 32 = 5$

12. $\log_x 64 = 3$

13. $\log_3 x = 5$

14. $\log_6 x = -1$

15. $\log_{11} \sqrt{11} = x$

16. $\log_4 1/16 = x$

Write an equivalent logarithmic equation.

17. $e^t = p$

18. $e^M = b$

19. $10^3 = 1000$

20. $10^2 = 100$

21. $10^{-2} = 0.01$

22. $10^{-1} = 0.1$

23. $Q^n = T$

24. $M^p = V$

Given $\log_b 3 = 1.099$ and $\log_b 5 = 1.609$, find each value.

25. $\log_b \frac{1}{5}$

26. $\log_b \frac{5}{3}$

27. $\log_b \sqrt{b^3}$

28. $\log_b 15$

29. $\log_b 75$

30. $\log_b (5b)$

Given $\ln 4 = 1.3863$ and $\ln 5 = 1.6094$, find each value. Do not use a calculator.

31. $\ln 80$

32. $\ln 20$

33. $\ln \frac{1}{5}$

34. $\ln \frac{5}{4}$

35. $\ln (4e)$

36. $\ln (5e)$

37. $\ln \sqrt{e^8}$

38. $\ln \sqrt{e^6}$

39. $\ln \frac{4}{5}$

40. $\ln \frac{1}{4}$

41. $\ln \left(\frac{4}{e} \right)$

42. $\ln \left(\frac{e}{5} \right)$

Find each logarithm. Round to six decimal places.

43. $\ln 99{,}999$

44. $\ln 5894$

45. $\ln 0.0182$

46. $\ln 0.00087$

47. $\ln 0.011$

48. $\ln 8100$

Solve for t.

49. $e^t = 80$

50. $e^t = 10$

51. $e^{3t} = 900$

52. $e^{2t} = 1000$

53. $e^{-t} = 0.01$

54. $e^{-t} = 0.1$

55. $e^{-0.02t} = 0.06$

56. $e^{0.07t} = 2$

Differentiate.

57. $y = -9 \ln x$

58. $y = -8 \ln x$

59. $y = 7 \ln |x|$

60. $y = 4 \ln |x|$

61. $y = x^6 \ln x - \frac{1}{4} x^4$

62. $y = x^4 \ln x - \frac{1}{2} x^2$

63. $f(x) = \ln (9x)$

64. $f(x) = \ln (6x)$

65. $f(x) = \ln |5x|$

66. $f(x) = \ln |10x|$

67. $g(x) = x^5 \ln (3x)$

68. $g(x) = x^2 \ln (7x)$

69. $g(x) = x^4 \ln |6x|$

70. $g(x) = x^9 \ln |2x|$

71. $y = \dfrac{\ln x}{x^5}$

72. $y = \dfrac{\ln x}{x^4}$

73. $y = \dfrac{\ln |3x|}{x^2}$

74. $y = \dfrac{\ln |11x|}{x^8}$

75. $y = \ln \dfrac{x^2}{4}$ $\left(Hint: \ln \dfrac{A}{B} = \ln A - \ln B. \right)$

76. $y = \ln \dfrac{x^4}{2}$

77. $y = \ln (3x^2 + 2x - 1)$

78. $y = \ln (7x^2 + 5x + 2)$

79. $f(x) = \ln \left(\dfrac{x^2 - 7}{x} \right)$

80. $f(x) = \ln \left(\dfrac{x^2 + 5}{x} \right)$

81. $g(x) = e^x \ln x^2$

82. $g(x) = e^{2x} \ln x$

83. $f(x) = \ln (e^x + 1)$

84. $f(x) = \ln (e^x - 2)$

85. $g(x) = (\ln x)^4$ (*Hint:* Use the Extended Power Rule.)

86. $g(x) = (\ln x)^3$

87. $f(x) = \ln (\ln (8x))$

88. $f(x) = \ln (\ln (3x))$

89. $g(x) = \ln (5x) \cdot \ln (3x)$

90. $g(x) = \ln (2x) \cdot \ln (7x)$

91. Find the equation of the line tangent to the graph of $y = (x^2 - x) \ln (6x)$ at $x = 2$.

92. Find the equation of the line tangent to the graph of $y = e^{3x} \cdot \ln (1x)$ at $x = 1$.

93. Find the equation of the line tangent to the graph of $y = (\ln x)^2$ at $x = 3$.

94. Find the equation of the line tangent to the graph of $y = \ln(4x^2 - 7)$ at $x = 2$.

APPLICATIONS

Business and Economics

95. Advertising.   A model for consumers' response to advertising is given by

$$N(a) = 2000 + 500 \ln a, \quad a \geq 1,$$

where $N(a)$ is the number of units sold and a is the amount spent on advertising, in thousands of dollars.

   a) How many units were sold after spending $1000 on advertising?
   b) Find $N'(a)$ and $N'(10)$.
   c) Find the maximum and minimum values, if they exist.
   d) Find $\lim\limits_{a \to \infty} N'(a)$. Discuss whether it makes sense to continue to spend more and more on advertising.

96. Advertising.   A model for consumers' response to advertising is given by

$$N(a) = 1000 + 200 \ln a, \quad a \geq 1,$$

where $N(a)$ is the number of units sold and a is the amount spent on advertising, in thousands of dollars.

   a) How many units were sold after spending $1000 on advertising?
   b) Find $N'(a)$ and $N'(10)$.
   c) Find the maximum and minimum values of N, if they exist.
   d) Find $N'(a)$. Discuss $\lim\limits_{a \to \infty} N'(a)$. Does it make sense to spend more and more on advertising? Why or why not?

97. An advertising model.   Solve Example 10 if the advertising campaign costs $2000 per day.

98. An advertising model.   Solve Example 10 if the advertising campaign costs $4000 per day.

99. Marginal revenue.   The demand for a new computer game can be modeled by

$$p(x) = 53.5 - 8 \ln x,$$

where $p(x)$ is the price consumers will pay, in dollars, and x is the number of games sold, in thousands. Recall that total revenue is given by $R(x) = x \cdot p(x)$.

   a) Find $R(x)$.
   b) Find the marginal revenue, $R'(x)$.
   c) Is there any price at which revenue will be maximized? Why or why not?

100. Growth of a stock.   The value, $V(t)$, in dollars, of a share of Cypress Mills stock t months after it is purchased is modeled by

$$V(t) = 58(1 - e^{-1.1t}) + 20.$$

$V(t) = 58(1 - e^{-1.1t}) + 20$

   a) Find $V(1)$ and $V(12)$.
   b) Find $V'(t)$.
   c) After how many months will the value of a share of the stock first reach $75?
   d) Find $\lim\limits_{t \to \infty} V(t)$. Discuss the value of a share over a long period of time. Is this trend typical?

101. Marginal profit.   The profit, in thousands of dollars, from the sale of x thousand candles can be estimated by

$$P(x) = 2x - 0.3x \ln x.$$

   a) Find the marginal profit, $P'(x)$.
   b) Find $P'(150)$, and explain what this number represents.
   c) How many thousands of candles should be sold to maximize profit?

Life and Physical Sciences

102. Acceptance of a new medicine.   The percentage P of doctors who prescribe a certain new medicine is

$$P(t) = 100(1 - e^{-0.2t}),$$

where t is the time, in months.

   a) Find $P(1)$ and $P(6)$.
   b) Find $P'(t)$.
   c) How many months will it take for 90% of doctors to prescribe the new medicine?
   d) Find $\lim\limits_{t \to \infty} P(t)$, and discuss its meaning.

Social Sciences

103. Forgetting.   Students in a botany class took a final exam. They took equivalent forms of the exam at monthly intervals thereafter. After t months, the average score $S(t)$, as a percentage, was found to be

$$S(t) = 78 - 20 \ln(t + 1), \quad t \geq 0.$$

   a) What was the average score when the students initially took the test?
   b) What was the average score after 4 months?
   c) What was the average score after 24 months?
   d) What percentage of their original answers did the students retain after 2 years (24 months)?
   e) Find $S'(t)$.
   f) Find the maximum value, if one exists.
   g) Find $\lim\limits_{t \to \infty} S(t)$, and discuss its meaning.

104. Forgetting. As part of a study, students in a psychology class took a final exam. They took equivalent forms of the exam at monthly intervals thereafter. After t months, the average score $S(t)$, as a percentage, was found to be given by

$$S(t) = 78 - 15 \ln (t + 1), \quad t \geq 0.$$

a) What was the average score when they initially took the test, $t = 0$?
b) What was the average score after 4 months?
c) What was the average score after 24 months?
d) What percentage of their original answers did the students retain after 2 years (24 months)?
e) Find $S'(t)$.
f) Find the maximum and minimum values, if they exist.
g) Find $\lim_{t \to \infty} S(t)$ and discuss its meaning.

105. Walking speed. Bornstein and Bornstein found in a study that the average walking speed v, in feet per second, of a person living in a city of population p, in thousands, is

$$v(p) = 0.37 \ln p + 0.05.$$

(*Source*: M. H. Bornstein and H. G. Bornstein, "The Pace of Life," *Nature*, Vol. 259, pp. 557–559 (1976).)

a) The population of Seattle is 635,000 ($p = 635$). What is the average walking speed of a person living in Seattle?
b) The population of New York is 8,340,000. What is the average walking speed of a person living in New York?
c) Find $v'(p)$.
d) Interpret $v'(p)$ found in part (c).

106. Hullian learning model. A keyboarder learns to type W words per minute after t weeks of practice, where W is given by

$$W(t) = 100(1 - e^{-0.3t}).$$

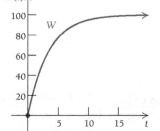

a) Find $W(1)$ and $W(8)$.
b) Find $W'(t)$.
c) After how many weeks will the keyboarder's speed be 95 words per minute?
d) Find $\lim_{t \to \infty} W(t)$, and discuss its meaning.

SYNTHESIS

107. Solve $P = P_0 e^{kt}$ for t.

Differentiate.

108. $f(x) = \ln (x^3 + 1)^5$

109. $g(x) = [\ln (x + 5)]^4$

110. $f(t) = \ln [(t^3 + 3)(t^2 - 1)]$

111. $f(t) = \ln \left| \dfrac{1 - t}{1 + t} \right|$

112. $y = \ln \left| \dfrac{x^5}{(8x + 5)^2} \right|$

113. $f(x) = \log_5 x$

114. $f(x) = \log_7 x$

115. $y = \ln \sqrt{5 + x^2}$

116. $f(t) = \dfrac{\ln t^2}{t^2}$

117. $y = \dfrac{x^{n+1}}{n + 1}\left(\ln x - \dfrac{1}{n + 1} \right)$

118. $f(x) = \ln \dfrac{1 + \sqrt{x}}{1 - \sqrt{x}}$

To prove Properties P1, P2, P3, and P7 of Theorem 3, let $X = \log_a M$ and $Y = \log_a N$, and give reasons for the steps listed in Exercises 119–122.

119. Proof of P1 of Theorem 3.

$M = a^X$ and $N = a^Y$, _____

so $MN = a^X \cdot a^Y = a^{X+Y}$. _____

Thus, $\log_a (MN) = X + Y$ _____

$= \log_a M + \log_a N$. _____

120. Proof of P2 of Theorem 3.

$M = a^X$ and $N = a^Y$, _____

so $\dfrac{M}{N} = \dfrac{a^X}{a^Y} = a^{X-Y}$. _____

Thus, $\log_a \dfrac{M}{N} = X - Y$ _____

$= \log_a M - \log_a N$. _____

121. Proof of P3 of Theorem 3.

$M = a^X$, _____

so $M^k = (a^X)^k$ _____

$= a^{Xk}$. _____

Thus, $\log_a M^k = Xk$ _____

$= k \cdot \log_a M$. _____

122. Proof of P7 of Theorem 3.

Let $\log_b M = R$.

Then $b^R = M$, _____

and $\log_a (b^R) = \log_a M$. _____

Thus, $R \cdot \log_a b = \log_a M$, _____

and $R = \dfrac{\log_a M}{\log_a b}$. _____

It follows that

$$\log_b M = \dfrac{\log_a M}{\log_a b}.$$ _____

123. Find $\lim_{h \to 0} \dfrac{\ln (1 + h)}{h}$.

124. For any $k > 0$, $\ln(kx) = \ln k + \ln x$. Use this fact to show graphically why

$$\frac{d}{dx}\ln(kx) = \frac{d}{dx}\ln x = \frac{1}{x}.$$

125. Use natural logarithms to determine which is larger, 81^{81} or 9^{160}.

126. Explain why $\log_a 0$ is not defined. (*Hint:* Rewrite it as an equivalent exponential expression.)

TECHNOLOGY CONNECTION

Find the minimum value of each function in Exercises 127 and 128. Use a graphing calculator or Graphicus.

127. $f(x) = x \ln x$ **128.** $f(x) = x^2 \ln x$

129. Let $f(x) = \ln|x|$.

    a) Using a graphing utility, sketch the graph of f.

    b) Find the slopes of the tangent lines at $x = -3$, $x = -2$ and $x = -1$.

c) How do your answers for part (b) compare to the slopes of the tangent lines at $x = 3$, $x = 2$ and $x = 1$?

d) In your own words, explain how the Chain Rule can be used to show that $\dfrac{d}{dx}\ln(-x) = \dfrac{1}{x}$.

Answers to Quick Checks

1. (a) 4; **(b)** 36; **(c)** 1   **2. (a)** 1.183; **(b)** -0.471; **(c)** 0.471; **(d)** 1.424; **(e)** 1.827; **(f)** $\frac{1}{2}$ **3. (a)** 2.3025; **(b)** 0.9163; **(c)** -0.9163; **(d)** 3.4655; **(e)** 3.6094; **(f)** 0.4307   **4. (a)** $t \approx 4.3820$; **(b)** $t \approx 17.329$ **5. (a)** $\dfrac{5}{x}$; **(b)** $x^2 + 3x^2 \ln x + 4$; **(c)** $\dfrac{1 - 2\ln|4x|}{x^3}$ **6. (a)** $\dfrac{1}{x}$; **(b)** $\dfrac{6x}{3x^2 + 4}$; **(c)** $\dfrac{1}{x(\ln 5x)}$; **(d)** $\dfrac{4x^5 + 2}{x(x^5 - 2)}$ **7.** The advertising campaign should run for about 51 days to maximize profit.

Applications: Uninhibited and Limited Growth Models

3.3

- Find functions that satisfy $dP/dt = kP$.
- Convert between growth rate and doubling time.
- Solve application problems using exponential growth and limited growth models.

Quick Check 1 ☑

Differentiate $f(x) = 5e^{4x}$. Then express $f'(x)$ in terms of $f(x)$.

Exponential Growth

Consider the function given by

$$f(x) = 2e^{3x}.$$

Differentiating, we get

$$f'(x) = 2e^{3x} \cdot 3$$
$$= f(x) \cdot 3.$$

Graphically, this says that the derivative, or slope of the tangent line, is 3 times the function value.   **1** ☑

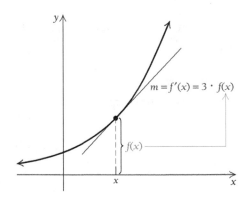

Although we do not prove it here, the exponential function $f(x) = ce^{kx}$ is the only function for which the derivative is a constant times the function itself.

THEOREM 8

A function $y = f(x)$ satisfies

$$\frac{dy}{dx} = ky \qquad \text{or} \qquad f'(x) = k \cdot f(x)$$

if and only if

$$y = ce^{kx} \qquad \text{or} \qquad f(x) = ce^{kx}$$

for some constant c.

EXAMPLE 1   Find the general form of the function that satisfies each equation.

a) $\dfrac{dA}{dt} = 5A$ **b)** $\dfrac{dP}{dt} = kP$

Solution

a) The desired function is given by $A(t) = ce^{5t}$, where c is an arbitrary constant. As a check, note that

$$A'(t) = ce^{5t} \cdot 5 = 5 \cdot A(t).$$

Quick Check 2 ✔

Find the general form of the function that satisfies the equation

$$\dfrac{dN}{dt} = kN.$$

b) The desired function is given by $P(t) = ce^{kt}$, where c is an arbitrary constant. As a check, note that

$$\dfrac{dP}{dt} = ce^{kt} \cdot k = kP.$$

     2 ✔

Whereas the solution of an algebraic equation is a number, the solutions of the equations in Example 1 are functions. For example, the solution of $2x + 5 = 11$ is the number 3, and the solution of the equation $dP/dt = kP$ is the function $P(t) = ce^{kt}$. An equation like $dP/dt = kP$, which includes a derivative and which has a function as a solution, is called a *differential equation*.

EXAMPLE 2   Solve the differential equation

$$f'(z) = k \cdot f(z).$$

Solution   The solution is $f(z) = ce^{kz}$. *Check:* $f'(z) = ce^{kz} \cdot k = f(z) \cdot k$.   ■

We will discuss differential equations in more depth in Section 5.7.

Uninhibited Population Growth

The equation

$$\dfrac{dP}{dt} = kP \quad \text{or} \quad P'(t) = kP(t), \quad \text{with } k > 0,$$

is the basic model of uninhibited (unrestrained) population growth, whether the population is comprised of humans, bacteria in a culture, or dollars invested with interest compounded continuously. In the absence of inhibiting or stimulating factors, a population normally reproduces at a rate proportional to its size, and this is exactly what $dP/dt = kP$ says. The only function that satisfies this differential equation is given by

$$P(t) = ce^{kt},$$

where t is time and k is the rate expressed in decimal notation. Note that

$$P(0) = ce^{k \cdot 0} = ce^{0} = c \cdot 1 = c,$$

so c represents the initial population, which we denote as P_0:

$$P(t) = P_0 e^{kt}.$$

The graph of $P(t) = P_0 e^{kt}$, for $k > 0$, shows how uninhibited growth produces a "population explosion."

The constant k is the **rate of exponential growth**, or the **exponential growth rate**. This is *not* the instantaneous rate of change of the population size, which varies according to

$$\frac{dP}{dt} = kP,$$

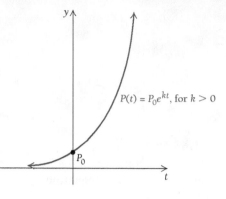

$P(t) = P_0 e^{kt}$, for $k > 0$

but the constant by which P must be multiplied in order to get the instantaneous rate of change at any point in time. It is similar to the daily interest rate paid by a bank. If the daily interest rate is $0.07/365$, then any given balance P is growing at the rate of $(0.07/365) \cdot P$ dollars per day. Because of compounding, after 1 year, the interest earned will exceed 7% of P. When interest is compounded continuously, the interest rate is a true exponential growth rate.

> **EXAMPLE 3** **Business: Interest Compounded Continuously.** Suppose P_0, in dollars, is invested in the Von Neumann Hi-Yield Fund, with interest compounded continuously at 7% per year. That is, the balance P grows at the rate
>
> $$\frac{dP}{dt} = 0.07P.$$

a) Find the function that satisfies the equation. Write it in terms of P_0 and 0.07.

b) Suppose that $100 is invested. What is the balance after 1 yr?

c) In what period of time will an investment of $100 double itself?

Solution

a) $P(t) = P_0 e^{0.07t}$ Note that $P(0) = P_0$.

b) $P(1) = 100e^{0.07(1)} = 100e^{0.07}$

$$\approx \$107.25 \qquad \text{Using a calculator and rounding}$$

c) We are looking for a number T such that $P(T) = \$200$. The number T is called the **doubling time**. To find T, we solve

$$200 = 100e^{0.07 \cdot T}$$
$$2 = e^{0.07T}$$
$$\ln 2 = \ln e^{0.07T} \qquad \text{Finding the natural logarithm of both sides}$$
$$\ln 2 = 0.07T \qquad \text{Using Property P5 of logarithms: } \ln e^k = k$$
$$\frac{\ln 2}{0.07} = T$$
$$9.9 \approx T.$$

Quick Check 3 ✔

Business: Interest Compounded Continuously. Repeat Example 3 for interest compounded continuously at 4% per year.

Thus, at 7% compounded continuously, $100 will double in approximately 9.9 yr.

3 ✔

To find a general expression relating the exponential growth rate k and the doubling time T, we solve the following:

$$2P_0 = P_0 e^{kT}$$
$$2 = e^{kT} \qquad \text{Dividing by } P_0$$
$$\ln 2 = \ln e^{kT} \qquad \text{Finding the natural logarithm of both sides}$$
$$\ln 2 = kT.$$

Note that this relationship between k and T does not depend on P_0. It takes as long for $1 to double as for $1000. We have the following theorem.

THEOREM 9

The *exponential growth rate k* and the *doubling time T* are related by

$$kT = \ln 2 \approx 0.693147, \qquad \text{or} \qquad k = \frac{\ln 2}{T} \approx \frac{0.693147}{T},$$

and $T = \dfrac{\ln 2}{k} \approx \dfrac{0.693147}{k}.$

EXAMPLE 4 **Business: Facebook Membership.** The social-networking Web site Facebook connects people with other members they designate as friends. During its period of heaviest growth, membership in Facebook was doubling every 6 months. What was the exponential growth rate of Facebook membership, as a percentage?

Solution   We have

$$k = \frac{\ln 2}{T} \approx \frac{0.693147}{6 \text{ months}} \qquad \begin{array}{l} \text{If possible, enter the calculation as } (\ln 2)/6 \\ \text{without approximating the logarithmic value.} \end{array}$$

$$\approx 0.116 \cdot \frac{1}{\text{month}}.$$

The exponential growth rate of Facebook membership was 11.6% per month.   **4** ✔

EXAMPLE 5 **Physical Science: Integrated Circuits.** In 1971, Intel Corporation released the Intel 4004 microprocessor, which held 2300 transistors. Since then, the number of transistors on a microprocessor has been growing exponentially at the rate of 0.34, or 34%, per year. (How was this estimate determined? The answer is in the model we develop in the following Technology Connection.) That is,

$$\frac{dP}{dt} = 0.34P,$$

where t is the number of years since 1971. (*Sources*: www.intel.com; www.motorola.com; www.microsoft.com.)

a) Find the function that satisfies this equation. Assume $P_0 = 2300$ and $k = 0.34$.

b) Estimate the number of transistors on a microprocessor in 2020.

c) Find the time needed for the number of transistors on a microprocessor to double.

Solution
a) $P(t) = 2300e^{0.34t}$

b) Since 2020 is 49 years after 1971, we have $P(49) = 2300e^{0.34(49)} \approx 39.5$ billion.

c) $T = \dfrac{\ln 2}{k} = \dfrac{\ln 2}{0.34} \approx 2.04$ yr. The fact that the number of transistors doubles every 2 years is known as Moore's Law, after Intel co-founder Gordon Moore, who foresaw this growth back in 1965.   **5** ✔

Quick Check 4 ✔

Business: Internet Use. Worldwide use of the Internet is increasing at an exponential rate, with traffic doubling every 100 days. What is the exponential growth rate of Internet use?

Quick Check 5 ✔

Life Science: Population Growth in China. In 2006, the population of China was 1.314 billion, and the exponential growth rate was 0.6% per year. Thus,

$$\frac{dP}{dt} = 0.006P,$$

where t is the time, in years, after 2006. Assume uninhibited growth. (*Source: Time Almanac, 2007.*)

a) Find the function that satisfies the equation. Assume $P_0 = 1.314$ and $k = 0.006$.

b) Estimate the population of China at the beginning of 2020.

c) After what period of time will the population be double that in 2006?

TECHNOLOGY CONNECTION

Exponential Models Using Regression

Transistors on Microprocessors

The table below shows data regarding the number of transistors on a microprocessors.

YEAR	NUMBER OF TRANSISTORS
1971 (Intel 4004)	2300
1979 (Intel 8088)	29,000
1984 (Motorola 68020)	200,000
1993 (Intel Pentium I)	3,100,000
2000 (Intel Pentium IV)	42,000,000
2010 (Intel Itanium Tukwila)	2,000,000,000
2013 (Microsoft Xbox One)	5,000,000,000

What is the projected number of transistors on a microprocessor in 2020? The graph of this data shows a rapidly growing transistor count that can be modeled with an exponential function. We carry out the regression procedure exactly as we did in Section R.6, but select ExpReg rather than LinReg.

Note that this gives us an exponential model of the type $y = a \cdot b^x$, where y is the number of transistors x years after 1971:

$$y = 1914.094222 \cdot 1.419271605^x.$$

Since $b = e^{\ln b}$, we can write this function as an exponential function, with base e:

$$y = 1914.094222 \cdot 1.419271605^x$$
$$= 1914.094222(e^{\ln 1.419271605})^x$$
$$= 1914.094222e^{0.3501437858x}$$

Thus, in 2020 ($t = 49$), the number of transistors on a microprocessor is estimated to be

$$y = 1914.094222e^{0.3501437858(49)} = 54.1 \text{ billion.}$$

EXERCISES

Estimate the number of transistors on a microprocessor in each of the following years.

1. 2025   2. 2030

3. 2050   4. 2100

5. Explain why this model differs slightly from the one used in Example 5. Do both models accurately estimate the number of transistors on a microprocessor over the years 1971–2020?

Projecting College Costs

For Exercises 6 and 7, use the data regarding projected college costs (tuition and room and board) listed in the table below.

SCHOOL YEAR, *x* YEARS SINCE 2004–2005	COSTS OF ATTENDING A PUBLIC 4-YEAR COLLEGE OR UNIVERSITY (2009–2010 dollars)
2004–2005, 0	12,918
2005–2006, 1	13,188
2006–2007, 2	13,587
2007–2008, 3	13,748
2008–2009, 4	14,400
2009–2010, 5	15,014
2010–2011, 6	15,605

(*Source*: National Center for Education Statistics, *Annual Digest of Education Statistics*: 2014.)

EXERCISES

6. Use REGRESSION to fit an exponential function $y = a \cdot b^x$ to the data. Let the school year 2004–2005 be represented by $x = 0$ and let $y =$ the cost, in dollars.

7. Use the exponential function found in Exercise 6 to estimate college costs in the school years 2016–2017, 2017–2018, and 2020–2021.

It is possible to use two representative data points to determine P_0 and k in $P(t) = P_0 e^{kt}$, as we will see next.

EXAMPLE 6 **Business: Batman Comic Book.** A 1939 comic book with the first appearance of the "Caped Crusader," Batman, sold at auction in Dallas in 2010 for a record $1.075 million. The comic book originally cost 10¢ (or $0.10). Using the two data points (0, $0.10) and (71, $1,075,000), we can model the increasing value of the comic book. The modeling assumption is that the value V of the comic book grows exponentially, as given by

$$\frac{dV}{dt} = kV.$$

(*Source*: Heritage Auction Galleries.)

a) Find the function that satisfies this equation. Assume $V_0 = \$0.10$.

b) Estimate the value of the comic book in 2020.

c) What is the doubling time for the value of the comic book?

d) In what year will the value of the comic book be $30 million, assuming there is no change in the growth rate?

Solution

a) Because of the modeling assumption, we have $V(t) = V_0 e^{kt}$. Since $V_0 = \$0.10$, it follows that

$$V(t) = 0.10 e^{kt}.$$

We have made use of the data point (0, $0.10). Next, we use the data point (71, $1,075,000) to determine k. We solve

$$V(t) = 0.10 e^{kt}, \quad \text{or} \quad 1,075,000 = 0.10^{k(71)}$$

for k, using natural logarithms:

$$1,075,000 = 0.10 e^{k(71)} = 0.10 e^{71k}$$

$$\frac{1,075,000}{0.10} = e^{71k} \qquad \text{Dividing to simplify}$$

$$10,750,000 = e^{71k}$$

$$\ln 10,750,000 = \ln e^{71k} \qquad \text{Finding the logarithm of both sides}$$

$$\ln 10,750,000 = 71k \qquad \text{Using Property P5}$$

$$\frac{\ln(10,750,000)}{71} = k$$

$$0.228 \approx k. \qquad \text{Using a calculator and rounding to the nearest thousandth}$$

The desired function is $V(t) = 0.10 e^{0.228t}$, where V is in dollars and t is the number of years since 1939.

b) To estimate the value of the comic book in 2020, which is $2020 - 1939 = 81$ years after 1939, we substitute 81 for t in the equation:

$$V(t) = 0.10 e^{0.228t}$$

$$V(81) = 0.10 e^{0.228(81)} \approx \$10,484,567.$$

c) The doubling time T is given by

$$T = \frac{\ln 2}{k} = \frac{\ln 2}{0.228} \approx 3.04 \text{ yr.}$$

Quick Check 6 ☑

Business: Batman Comic Book.
In Example 6, the consigner had bought the comic book in the late 1960s for $100. (*Source*: Heritage Auction Galleries.) Assume that the year of purchase was 1969 and that the value V of the comic book has since grown exponentially, as given by

$$\frac{dV}{dt} = kV,$$

where t is the number of years since 1969.

a) Use the data points (0, $100) and (41, $1,075,000) to find the function that satisfies the equation.

b) Estimate the value of the comic book in 2020, and compare your answer to that of Example 6.

c) What is the doubling time for the value of the comic book?

d) In what year will the value of the comic book be $30 million? Compare your answer to that of Example 6.

d) We substitute $30,000,000 for $V(t)$ and solve for t:

$$V(t) = 0.10e^{0.228t}$$
$$30,000,000 = 0.10e^{0.228t}$$
$$\frac{30,000,000}{0.10} = e^{0.228t}$$
$$300,000,000 = e^{0.228t}$$
$$\ln 300,000,000 = \ln e^{0.228t}$$
$$\ln 300,000,000 = 0.228t$$
$$\frac{\ln 300,000,000}{0.228} = t$$
$$86 \approx t. \qquad \text{Using a calculator and rounding to the nearest year}$$

We add 86 to 1939 to get 2025 as the year in which the value of the comic book will reach $30 million.   **6** ☑

Models of Limited Growth

We have seen that the growth model $P(t) = P_0 e^{kt}$ applies to *unlimited*, or *unrestricted*, population growth. However, there are often factors that prevent a population from exceeding some limiting value L—perhaps a limitation on food, living space, or other natural resources. One model of such growth is

$$P(t) = \frac{L}{1 + be^{-kt}}, \quad \text{for} \quad k > 0,$$

which is called the *logistic equation,* or *logistic function.*

$$P(t) = \frac{L}{1 + be^{-kt}},$$
for $k > 0$

EXAMPLE 7   **Business: Satellite Radio Subscribers.**   Satellite radio companies provide subscribers with clear signals of over 100 radio stations. The providers XM and Sirius at first experienced what seemed like exponential growth, but the slowing of this growth led Sirius to buy out XM in 2008, forming Sirius XM. The combined number of subscribers N, in millions, t years after 2000, can be modeled by the logistic equation

$$N(t) = \frac{24.691}{1 + 34.348e^{-0.585t}}.$$

(*Source*: Sirius XM Radio, Inc.)

a) Find the number of subscribers in 2010 and 2013.

b) Find the rate at which the number of subscribers was growing in 2010.

c) Graph the equation.

d) Explain why an uninhibited growth model is inappropriate but a logistic equation is appropriate to model this growth.

Solution

a) We use a calculator to find the function values:

$$N(10) = 22.468 \text{ million and } N(13) = 24.276 \text{ million.}$$

After 10 yr, there were about 22,468,000 subscribers.
After 13 yr, there were about 24,276,000 subscribers.

b) We find the rate of change using the Quotient Rule:

$$N'(t) = \frac{(1 + 34.348e^{-0.585t}) \cdot 0 - 24.691(34.348e^{-0.585t})(-0.585)}{(1 + 34.348e^{-0.585t})^2}$$

$$= \frac{496e^{-0.585t}}{(1 + 34.348e^{-0.585t})^2}.$$

Next, we use a calculator to evaluate the derivative at $t = 10$:

$$N'(10) = 1.183.$$

In 2010, the number of subscribers was growing at a rate of 1.183 million, or 1,183,000, per year.

c) Using a graphing utility, we obtain the following graph.

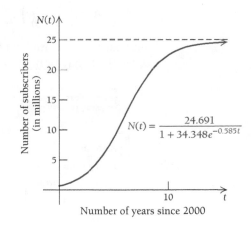

d) An uninhibited growth model is inappropriate because as more and more subscribers are added, the population contains fewer who have not subscribed, perhaps because of the cost or a lack of interest, or simply because the population is finite. The logistic equation, graphed in part (c), displays the rapid early rise in the number of subscribers as well as the slower growth in later years. It would appear that the limiting value of subscribers is between 24 and 25 million.   **7** ✔

Another model of limited growth is provided by

$$P(t) = L(1 - e^{-kt}), \text{ for } k > 0,$$

which is graphed below. This function increases over its domain, $[0, \infty)$, but increases most rapidly at the beginning, unlike a logistic function.

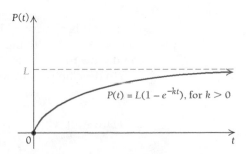

Quick Check 7 ✔

Life Science: Spread of an Epidemic. In a town whose population is 3500, an epidemic of a disease occurs. The number of people N infected t days after the disease first appears is given by

$$N(t) = \frac{3500}{1 + 19.9e^{-0.6t}}.$$

a) How many people are initially infected with the disease $(t = 0)$?

b) Find the number infected after 2 days, 8 days, and 18 days.

c) Graph the equation.

d) Find the rate at which the disease is spreading after 16 days.

e) Will all 3500 residents ever be infected? Why or why not?

Business Application: An Alternative Derivation of e and $P(t) = P_0e^{kt}$

The number e can also be found using the *compound-interest formula* (which was developed in Chapter R),

$$A = P\left(1 + \frac{r}{n}\right)^{nt},$$

where A is the amount that an initial investment P will be worth after t years at interest rate r, expressed as a decimal, compounded n times per year.

Suppose that \$1 is invested at 100% interest ($r = 100\% = 1$) for 1 yr (though obviously no bank would pay this). The formula becomes

$$A = \left(1 + \frac{1}{n}\right)^n.$$

Suppose that the number of compounding periods, n, increases indefinitely. Let's investigate the behavior of the function. We obtain the following table of values and graph.

COMPOUNDING PERIOD	FREQUENCY, n	$A = \left(1 + \frac{1}{n}\right)^n$
Annually	1	\$2.00000
Every 6 months	2	\$2.25000
Every 4 months	3	\$2.37037
Quarterly	4	\$2.44141
Monthly	12	\$2.61304
Weekly	52	\$2.69260
Daily	365	\$2.71457
Every hour	8,760	\$2.71813
Every minute	525,600	\$2.71828

With *continuous* compounding, we have $A = \lim\limits_{n \to \infty} \left(1 + \frac{1}{n}\right)^n$, or equivalently,

$$A = \lim_{h \to \infty}\left(1 + \frac{1}{1/h}\right)^{1/h}, \quad \text{or} \quad A = \lim_{h \to 0}(1 + h)^{1/h}.$$

Recall from Section 3.1 that $\lim\limits_{h \to 0}(1 + h)^{1/h} = e$. Thus,

$$\lim_{n \to \infty}\left(1 + \frac{1}{n}\right)^n = e.$$

This result is confirmed by the graph and table above. If \$1 were invested at an interest rate of 100% with increasingly frequent compounding periods, the greatest value it could grow to in 1 yr is about \$2.7183.

To develop the formula

$$P(t) = P_0e^{kt},$$

we again start with the compound-interest formula,

$$A = P\left(1 + \frac{r}{n}\right)^{nt},$$

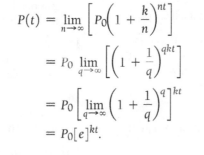

Exploratory

Graph

$$y = \left(1 + \frac{1}{x}\right)^x$$

using the viewing window $[0, 5000, 0, 5]$, with Xscl $= 1000$ and Yscl $= 1$. Trace along the graph. Why does the graph appear to be horizontal? As you trace to the right, note the value of the y-coordinate. Is it approaching a constant? What seems to be its limiting value?

and assume that interest is compounded continuously. Let $P = P_0$ and $r = k$:

$$P(t) = P_0\left(1 + \frac{k}{n}\right)^{nt}.$$

We are interested in what happens as n approaches ∞. To find this limit, we first let

$$\frac{k}{n} = \frac{1}{q}, \quad \text{so that} \quad qk = n.$$

Note that since k is a positive constant, as n gets large, so must q. Thus,

$$P(t) = \lim_{n \to \infty}\left[P_0\left(1 + \frac{k}{n}\right)^{nt}\right] \qquad \text{Letting the number of compounding periods become infinite}$$

$$= P_0 \lim_{q \to \infty}\left[\left(1 + \frac{1}{q}\right)^{qkt}\right] \qquad \text{Substituting } 1/q \text{ for } k/n \text{ and } qk \text{ for } n \text{ and } q \to \infty \text{ for } n \to \infty$$

$$= P_0\left[\lim_{q \to \infty}\left(1 + \frac{1}{q}\right)^q\right]^{kt} \qquad \text{Using Limit Property L2 from Section 1.2}$$

$$= P_0[e]^{kt}.$$

Section Summary

- Uninhibited growth can be modeled by a *differential equation* of the form $\dfrac{dP}{dt} = kP$, which has the solution $P(t) = P_0 e^{kt}$.
- The *exponential growth rate k* and the *doubling time T* are related by the equation $T = \dfrac{\ln 2}{k}$, or $k = \dfrac{\ln 2}{T}$.

- Certain kinds of limited growth can be modeled by equations such as $P(t) = \dfrac{L}{1 + be^{-kt}}$ and $P(t) = L(1 - e^{-kt})$, for $k > 0$.

3.3 Exercise Set

1. Find the general form of f if $f'(x) = 4f(x)$.

2. Find the general form of g if $g'(x) = 6g(x)$.

3. Find the general form of the function that satisfies $dA/dt = -9A$.

4. Find the general form of the function that satisfies $dP/dt = -3P(t)$.

5. Find the general form of the function that satisfies $dQ/dt = kQ$.

6. Find the general form of the function that satisfies $dR/dt = kR$.

APPLICATIONS

Business and Economics

7. **U.S. patents.** The number of applications for patents, N, grew dramatically in recent years, with growth averaging about 5.8% per year. That is,

$$N'(t) = 0.058N(t).$$

(*Source:* Based on data from the U.S. Patent and Trademark office, 2009–2013.)

   a) Find the function that satisfies this equation. Assume that $t = 0$ corresponds to 2009, when approximately 483,000 patent applications were received.
   b) Estimate the number of patent applications in 2020.
   c) Estimate the doubling time for $N(t)$.

8. **Franchise expansion.** Pete Zah's, Inc., is selling franchises for pizza shops throughout the country. The marketing manager estimates that the number of franchises, N, will increase at the rate of 10% per year, that is,

$$\frac{dN}{dt} = 0.10N.$$

   a) Find the function that satisfies this equation. Assume that the number of franchises at $t = 0$ is 50.
   b) How many franchises will there be in 20 yr?
   c) In what period of time will the initial number of 50 franchises double?

9. Compound interest. If an amount P_0 is invested in the Mandelbrot Bond Fund and interest is compounded continuously at 5.9% per year, the balance P grows at the rate given by

$$\frac{dP}{dt} = 0.059P.$$

a) Find the function that satisfies the equation. Write it in terms of P_0 and 0.059.

b) Suppose $1000 is invested. What is the balance after 1 yr? After 2 yr?

c) When will an investment of $1000 double itself?

10. Compound interest. If an amount P_0 is invested in a savings account and interest is compounded continuously at 4.3% per year, the balance P grows at the rate given by

$$\frac{dP}{dt} = 0.043P.$$

a) Find the function that satisfies the equation. Write it in terms of P_0 and 0.043.

b) Suppose $20,000 is invested. What is the balance after 1 yr? After 2 yr?

c) When will an investment of $20,000 double itself?

11. Bottled water sales. Since 2000, sales of bottled water have increased at the rate of approximately 9.3% per year. That is, the volume of bottled water sold, G, in billions of gallons, t years after 2000 is growing at the rate given by

$$\frac{dG}{dt} = 0.093G.$$

(*Source*: The Beverage Marketing Corporation.)

a) Find the function that satisfies the equation, given that approximately 4.7 billion gallons of bottled water were sold in 2000.

b) Predict the number of gallons of water sold in 2025.

c) What is the doubling time for $G(t)$?

12. Annual net sales. Green Mountain Coffee Roasters produces many varieties of flavored coffees, teas, and K-cups. Since 2008, the net sales S of the company have grown exponentially at the rate of 46.3% per year. This growth can be approximated by

$$\frac{dS}{dt} = 0.463S,$$

where t is the number of years since 2008. (*Source*: Green Mountain Coffee Roasters financial statements.)

a) Find the function that satisfies the equation, given that net sales in 2008 ($t = 0$) were approximately $500,000.

b) Estimate net sales in 2012 and 2016.

c) What is the doubling time for $S(t)$?

13. Annual interest rate. Euler Bank advertises that it compounds interest continuously and that it will double your money in 15 yr. What is its annual interest rate?

14. Annual interest rate. Hardy Bank advertises that it compounds interest continuously and that it will double your money in 12 yr. What is its annual interest rate?

15. Oil demand. The growth rate of the demand for oil in the United States is 10% per year. When will the demand be double that of 2012?

16. Coal demand. The growth rate of the demand for coal in the world is 4% per year. When will the demand be double that of 2006?

Interest compounded continuously. *For Exercises 17–20, complete the following.*

	Initial Investment at $t = 0$, P_0	Interest Rate, k	Doubling Time, T (in years)	Amount after 5 yr
17.	$75,000	6.2%	____	_____
18.	$5,000	____	____	$7,130.90
19.	_____	8.4%	____	$11,414.71
20.	_____	____	11	$17,539.32

21. Art masterpieces. In 2004, a collector paid $104,168,000 for Pablo Picasso's "Garcon à la Pipe." The same painting sold for $30,000 in 1950. (*Source*: BBC News, 5/6/04.)

Boy with a Pipe (1905), Pablo Picasso. © 2011 Picasso Estate/ARS

a) Find the exponential growth rate k, to three decimal places, and determine the exponential growth function V, for which $V(t)$ is the painting's value, in dollars, t years after 1950.

b) Predict the value of the painting in 2015.

c) What is the doubling time for the value of the painting?

d) How long after 1950 will the value of the painting be $1 billion?

22. Per capita income.   In 2009, U.S. per capita personal income *I* was $48,040. In 2012, it was $52,430. (*Source:* data.worldbank.org.) Assume that the growth of U.S. per capita personal income follows an exponential model.

a) Letting $t = 0$ be 2009, write the function.

b) Predict what U.S. per capita income will be in 2020.

c) In what year will U.S. per capita income be double that of 2009?

23. Federal receipts.   In 2011, U.S. federal receipts (money taken in) totaled $2.30 trillion. In 2013, total federal receipts were $2.77 trillion. (*Source:* usgovernmentrevenue.com.) Assume that the growth of total federal receipts, *F*, can be modeled by an exponential function and use 2011 as the base year ($t = 0$).

a) Find the growth rate *k* to six decimal places, and write the exponential function $F(t)$, for total receipts in trillions of dollars.

b) Estimate total federal receipts in 2015.

c) When will total federal receipts be $10 trillion?

24. Consumer price index.   The *consumer price index* compares the costs, *c*, of goods and services over various years, where 1983 is used as a base ($t = 0$). The same goods and services that cost $100 in 1983 cost $226 in 2012. (*Source:* Bureau of Labor Statistics.)

a) Model *c* as an exponential function rounding the growth rate *k* to five decimal places.

b) Estimate what the goods and services costing $100 in 1983 will cost in 2020.

c) In what year did the same goods and services cost twice the 1983 price?

Total mobile data traffic.   The following graph shows the predicted monthly mobile data traffic for the years 2013–2018. Use these data in Exercises 25 and 26.

MOBILE DATA TRAFFIC

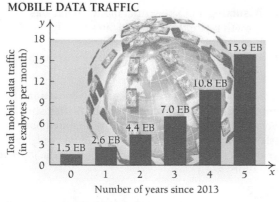

(*Source:* Cisco VNI Mobile, 2014.)

25. a) Use REGRESSION to fit an exponential function $y = a \cdot b^x$ to the data. Let *y* be the monthly mobile data traffic in exabytes (EB, 1 exabyte = 1 billion gigabytes) and *x* the number of years since 2013. Then convert the function to an exponential function, base *e*, using the fact that $b = e^{\ln b}$.

b) What is the exponential growth rate, as a percentage?

c) Estimate the monthly mobile data traffic in 2020.

d) When will monthly mobile data traffic exceed 50 exabytes?

e) What is the doubling time for monthly mobile data traffic?

26. a) Find an exponential function, base *e*, that fits the data, using the points (0, 1.5) and (2, 4.4). Let *x* represent the number of years since 2013.

b) Estimate the total monthly mobile data traffic in 2019 and 2022.

c) When will total monthly mobile data traffic exceed 50 exabytes?

d) What is the doubling time for total monthly mobile traffic?

e) Compare your answers with those from parts (c)–(e) of Exercise 25. Decide which exponential function seems to fit the data better, and explain why.

27. Value of Manhattan Island.   Peter Minuit of the Dutch West India Company purchased Manhattan Island from the natives living there in 1626 for $24 worth of merchandise. Assuming an exponential rate of inflation of 5%, how much will Manhattan be worth in 2020?

28. Total revenue.   Intel, a computer chip manufacturer, reported $1265 million in total revenue in 1986. In 2012, the total revenue was $53.3 billion. (*Source:* intel.com.) Assuming an exponential model, find the growth rate *k*, to four decimal places, and determine the revenue function *R*, with $R(t)$ in billions of dollars. Then predict the company's total revenue for 2020.

29. The U.S. Forever Stamp.   The U.S. Postal Service sells the Forever Stamp, which is always valid as first-class postage on standard envelopes weighing 1 ounce or less, regardless of any subsequent increases in the first-class rate. (*Source:* U.S. Postal Service.)

a) The cost of a first-class postage stamp was 4¢ in 1962 and 49¢ in 2014. This increase represents exponential growth. Write the function *S* for the cost of a stamp *t* years after 1962 ($t = 0$).

b) What was the growth rate in the cost?

c) Predict the cost of a first-class postage stamp in 2016, 2018, and 2020.

d) An advertising firm spent $4900 on 10,000 first-class postage stamps at the beginning of 2014. Knowing it will need 10,000 first-class stamps in each of the years 2015–2024, it decides to try to save money by also buying enough stamps to cover those years at the time of the 2014 purchase. Assuming there is a postage increase in each of the years 2016, 2018, and 2020 to the cost predicted in part (c), how much money will the firm save by buying the Forever Stamps in 2014?

e) Discuss the pros and cons of the purchase decision described in part (d).

30. Average salary of Major League baseball players. In 1970, the average salary of Major League baseball players was $29,303. In 2013, the average salary was $3,390,000. (*Source*: mlb.com.) Assuming exponential growth occurred, what was the growth rate to the nearest hundredth of a percent? What will the average salary be in 2020? In 2025? Round your answers to the nearest thousand.

31. Effect of advertising. Suppose that SpryBorg Inc. introduces a new computer game in Houston using television advertisements. Surveys show that $P\%$ of the target audience buys the game after x ads are broadcast, satisfying

$$P(x) = \frac{100}{1 + 49e^{-0.13x}}.$$

a) What percentage buys the game without seeing a TV ad ($x = 0$)?

b) What percentage buys the game after the ad is run 5 times? 10 times? 20 times? 30 times? 50 times? 60 times?

c) Find the rate of change, $P'(x)$.

d) Sketch a graph of the function.

32. Cost of a Hershey bar. The cost of a Hershey bar was $0.05 in 1962 and $0.99 in 2013 (in a supermarket, not in a movie theater).

a) Find an exponential function that fits the data.

b) Predict the cost of a Hershey bar in 2020 and 2025.

33. Superman comic book. In August 2014, a 1938 comic book featuring the first appearance of Superman sold at auction for a record price of $3.2 million. The comic book originally cost 10¢ ($0.10). (*Sources*: eBay; money.cnn.com.) Use the two data points (0, $0.10) and (76, $3,200,000), and assume that the value V of the comic book has grown exponentially, as given by

$$\frac{dV}{dt} = kV.$$

(In the summer of 2010, a family faced foreclosure on their mortgage. As they were packing, they came across some old comic books in the basement, and one of them was a copy of this first Superman comic. They sold it and saved their house.)

a) Find the function that satisfies this equation. Assume that $V_0 = \$0.10$.

b) Estimate the value of the comic book in 2020.

c) What is the doubling time for the value of the comic book?

d) After what time will the value of the comic book be $30 million, assuming there is no change in the growth rate?

34. Batman comic book. Refer to Example 6. In what year will the value of the comic book be $5 million?

35. Batman comic book. Refer to Example 6. In what year will the value of the comic book be $10 million?

Life and Physical Sciences

Population growth. *For Exercises 36–40, complete the following.*

	Population	Exponential Growth Rate, k	Doubling Time, T (in years)
36.	Mexico	3.5%/yr	_____
37.	Europe	_____	69.31
38.	Oil reserves	_____	6.931
39.	Coal reserves	_____	17.3
40.	Alaska	2.794%/yr	_____

41. Bicentennial growth of the United States. The population of the United States in 1776 was about 2,508,000. In the country's bicentennial year, the population was about 216,000,000.

a) Assuming an exponential model, what was the growth rate of the United States through its bicentennial year?

b) Is exponential growth a reasonable assumption? Why or why not?

42. Limited population growth: human population. Seventeen adults came ashore from the British ship *HMS Bounty* in 1790 to settle on the uninhabited South Pacific island Pitcairn. The population, $P(t)$, of the island t years after 1790 can be approximated by the logistic equation

$$P(t) = \frac{3400}{17 + 183e^{-0.982t}}.$$

(*Source*: www.government.pn.)

a) Find the population of the island after 10 yr, 50 yr, and 75 yr.

b) Find the rate of change in the population, $P'(t)$.

c) Find the rate of change in the population after 10 yr, 50 yr, and 75 yr.

d) What is the limiting value for the population of Pitcairn? (The limiting value is the number to which the population gets closer and closer but never reaches.)

43. Limited population growth: tortoise population. The tortoise population, $P(t)$, in a square mile of the Mojave Desert after t years can be approximated by the logistic equation

$$P(t) = \frac{3000}{20 + 130e^{-0.214t}}$$

(*Source*: www.deserttortoise.org.)

a) Find the tortoise population after 0 yr, 5 yr, 15 yr, and 25 yr.

b) Find the rate of change in the population, $P'(t)$.

c) Find the rate of change in the population after 0 yr, 5 yr, 15, yr, and 25 yr.

d) What is the limiting value (see Exercise 42) for the population of tortoises in a square mile of the Mojave Desert?

44. Limited population growth. A lake is stocked with 400 rainbow trout. The size of the lake, the availability of food, and the number of other fish restrict population growth to a limiting value of 2500 trout. (See Exercise 42.) The population of trout in the lake after time t, in months, is approximated by

$$P(t) = \frac{2500}{1 + 5.25e^{-0.32t}}.$$

a) Find the population after 0 months, 1 month, 5 months, 10 months, 15 months, and 20 months.

b) Find the rate of change, $P'(t)$.

c) Sketch a graph of the function.

Social Sciences

45. Women college graduates. The number of women earning a bachelor's degree from a 4-yr college in the United States grew from 48,869 in 1930 to approximately 920,000 in 2010. (*Source*: National Center for Education Statistics.) Find an exponential function that fits the data, and the exponential growth rate, rounded to the nearest hundredth of a percent.

46. Hullian learning model. The Hullian learning model asserts that the probability p of mastering a task after t learning trials is approximated by

$$p(t) = 1 - e^{-kt},$$

where k is a constant that depends on the task to be learned. Suppose a new dance is taught to an aerobics class. For this particular dance, assume $k = 0.28$.

a) What is the probability of mastering the dance in 1 trial? 2 trials? 5 trials? 11 trials? 16 trials? 20 trials?

b) Find the rate of change, $p'(t)$.

c) Sketch a graph of the function.

47. Spread of infection. Spread by skin-to-skin contact or via shared towels or clothing, methicillin-resistant *Staphylococcus aureus* (MRSA) can easily infect growing numbers of students at a university. Left unchecked, the number of cases of MRSA on a university campus t weeks after the first 9 cases occur can be modeled by

$$N(t) = \frac{568.803}{1 + 62.200e^{-0.092t}}.$$

(*Source*: Vermont Department of Health, Epidemiology Division.)

a) Find the number of infected students beyond the first 9 cases after 3 weeks, 40 weeks, and 80 weeks.

b) Find the rate at which the disease is spreading after 20 weeks.

c) Explain why an unrestricted growth model is inappropriate but a logistic equation *is* appropriate for this situation. Then use a calculator to graph the equation.

48. Diffusion of information. Pharmaceutical firms invest significantly in testing new medications. After a drug is approved by the Federal Drug Administration, it still takes time for physicians to fully accept and start prescribing it. The acceptance by physicians approaches a *limiting value* of 100%, or 1, after t months. Suppose that the percentage P of physicians prescribing a new cancer medication after t months is approximated by

$$P(t) = 100(1 - e^{-0.4t}).$$

a) What percentage of doctors are prescribing the medication after 0 months? 1 month? 2 months? 3 months? 5 months? 12 months? 16 months?

b) Find $P'(7)$, and interpret its meaning.

c) Sketch a graph of the function.

49. Spread of a rumor. The rumor "People who study math all get scholarships" spreads across a college campus. Data in the following table show the number of students N who have heard the rumor after time t, in days.

TIME, t (in days)	NUMBER, N, WHO HAVE HEARD THE RUMOR
1	1
2	2
3	4
4	7
5	12
6	18
7	24
8	26
9	28
10	28
11	29
12	30

a) Use REGRESSION to fit a logistic equation,

$$N(t) = \frac{c}{1 + ae^{-bt}},$$

to the data.

b) Estimate the limiting value of the function. At most, how many students will hear the rumor?

c) Graph the function.

d) Find the rate of change, $N'(t)$.

e) Find $\lim_{t \to \infty} N'(t)$, and explain its meaning.

SYNTHESIS

We have now studied models for linear, quadratic, exponential, and logistic growth. In the real world, understanding which is the most appropriate type of model for a given situation is an important skill. For each situation in Exercises 50–60, identify the most appropriate type of model and explain why you chose that model. List any restrictions you would place on the domain of the function.

50. The growth in value of a U.S. savings bond

51. The growth in the length of Zachary's hair following a haircut

52. The growth in sales of electric cars

53. The drop and rise of a lake's water level during and after a drought

54. The rapidly growing sales of organic foods

55. The number of manufacturing jobs that have left the United States since 1995

56. The life expectancy of the average American

57. The occupancy (number of apartments rented) of a newly opened apartment complex

58. The decrease in population of a city after its principal industry closes

59. The weight of a dog from birth to adulthood

60. The efficiency of an employee as a function of number of hours worked

61. Find an expression relating the exponential growth rate k and the *quadrupling time* T_4.

62. Find an expression relating the exponential growth rate k and the *tripling time* T_3.

63. Quantity Q_1 grows exponentially with a doubling time of 1 yr. Quantity Q_2 grows exponentially with a doubling time of 2 yr. If the initial amounts of Q_1 and Q_2 are the same, how long will it take for Q_1 to be twice the size of Q_2?

64. To what exponential growth rate per hour does a growth rate of 100% per day correspond?

65. Complete the table below, which relates growth rate k and doubling time T.

Growth Rate, k (per year)	1%	2%			14%
Doubling Time, T (in years)			15	10	

Graph $T = (\ln 2)/k$. Is this a linear relationship? Explain.

66. Describe the differences in the graphs of an exponential function and a logistic function.

The Rule of 70. *The relationship between doubling time T and growth rate k is the basis of the Rule of 70. Since*

$$T = \frac{\ln 2}{k} = \frac{0.693147}{k} = \frac{69.3147}{100k} \approx \frac{70}{100k},$$

we can estimate the length of time needed for a quantity to double by dividing the growth rate k (expressed as a percentage) into 70.

67. Estimate the time needed for an amount of money to double, if the interest rate is 7%, compounded continuously.

68. Estimate the time needed for the population in a city to double, if the growth rate is 3.5%, compounded continuously.

69. Using a calculator, find the exact doubling times for the amount of money in Exercise 67 and the population in Exercise 68.

70. Describe two situations where it would be preferable to use the Rule of 70 instead of the formula $T = \ln(2)/k$. Explain why it would be acceptable to use this rule in these situations.

71. Business: total revenue. The revenue of Red Rocks, Inc., in millions of dollars, is given by the function

$$R(t) = \frac{4000}{1 + 1999e^{-0.5t}},$$

where t is measured in years.

a) What is $R(0)$, and what does it represent?
b) Find $\lim_{t \to \infty} R(t)$. Call this value $R_{\max}$, and explain what it means.
c) Find the value of t (to the nearest integer) for which $R(t) = 0.99R_{\max}$.

Answers to Quick Checks

1. $f'(x) = 20e^{4x}; f'(x) = 4f(x)$ **2.** $N(t) = ce^{kt}$, where c is an arbitrary constant   **3. (a)** $P(t) = P_0 e^{0.04t}$;
(b) \$104.08; **(c)** 17.3 yr   **4.** 0.69% per day
5. (a) $P(t) = 1.314e^{0.006t}$; **(b)** 1.429 billion; **(c)** 115.5 yr
6. (a) $V(t) = 100e^{0.226t}$, which is almost the same as the growth rate found in Example 6; **(b)** \$10,131,604, which is quite close to the estimate found in Example 6; **(c)** 3.07 yr;
(d) after 55.8 yr, or in 2025, again about the same as was found in Example 6   **7. (a)** 167; **(b)** 500, 3007, 3499
(c)   **(d)** After 16 days, the number of people infected is growing at the rate of about 2.8 people per day.

(e) According to the model, $\lim_{t \to \infty} N(t) = 3500$, so virtually all of the town's residents will be affected.

3.4

- Find a function that satisfies $dP/dt = -kP$.
- Convert between decay rate and half-life.
- Solve applied problems involving exponential decay.

Exploratory

Using the same set of axes, graph $y_1 = e^{2x}$ and $y_2 = e^{-2x}$. Compare the graphs.

Then, using the same set of axes, graph $y_1 = 100e^{-0.06x}$ and $y_2 = 100e^{0.06x}$. Compare each pair of graphs.

Applications: Decay

In the equation of population growth, $dP/dt = kP$, the constant k is given by

$$k = (\text{Birth rate}) - (\text{Death rate}).$$

Thus, a population "grows" only when the birth rate is greater than the death rate. When the birth rate is less than the death rate, k is negative, and the population is decreasing, or "decaying," at a rate proportional to its size. For convenience in our computations, we will express such a negative value as $-k$, where $k > 0$. The equation

$$\frac{dP}{dt} = -kP, \quad \text{where } k > 0,$$

shows P to be *decreasing* as a function of time, and the solution

$$P(t) = P_0 e^{-kt}$$

shows P to be decreasing exponentially. This is called **exponential decay**. The amount present initially at $t = 0$ is again P_0.

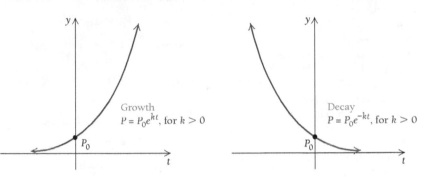

Radioactive Decay

Radioactive elements decay exponentially; that is, they disintegrate at a rate that is proportional to the amount present.

EXAMPLE 1   **Life Science: Decay.**   Strontium-90 has a decay rate of 2.8% per year. The rate of change of an amount N of this radioactive isotope is given by

$$\frac{dN}{dt} = -0.028N.$$

a) Find the function that satisfies the equation. Let N_0 represent the amount present at $t = 0$.

b) Suppose that 1000 grams (g) of strontium-90 is present at $t = 0$. How much will remain after 70 yr?

c) After how long will exactly half of the 1000 g remain?

Solution

a) $N(t) = N_0 e^{-0.028t}$

b) $N(70) = 1000e^{-0.028(70)}$

$$= 1000e^{-1.96}$$

$$\approx 140.8584209. \quad \text{Using a calculator}$$

After 70 yr, about 140.9 g of the strontium-90 remains.

Quick Check 1 ✔

Life Science: Decay. Xenon-133 has a decay rate of 14% per day. The rate of change of an amount N of this radioactive isotope is given by

$$\frac{dN}{dt} = -0.14N.$$

a) Find the function that satisfies the equation. Let N_0 represent the amount present at $t = 0$.

b) Suppose 1000 g of xenon-133 is present at $t = 0$. How much will remain after 10 days?

c) After how long will half of the 1000 g remain?

How can scientists determine that the remains of an animal or plant have lost 30% of the carbon-14? The assumption is that the percentage of carbon-14 in the atmosphere and in living plants and animals is the same. When a plant or animal dies, its carbon-14 decays exponentially. A scientist burns the remains and uses a Geiger counter to determine the percentage of carbon-14 in the smoke. The amount by which this varies from the percentage in the atmosphere indicates how much carbon-14 was lost through decay.

The process of carbon-14 dating was developed by the American chemist Willard F. Libby in 1952. It is known that the radioactivity of a living plant measures 16 disintegrations per gram per minute. Since the half-life of carbon-14 is 5730 years, a dead plant with an activity of 8 disintegrations per gram per minute is 5730 years old, one with an activity of 4 disintegrations per gram per minute is about 11,500 years old, and so on. Carbon-14 dating can be used to determine the age of organic objects from 30,000 to 40,000 years old. Beyond such an age, it is too difficult to measure the radioactivity, and other methods are used.

c) We are asking, "At what time T will $N(T)$ be half of N_0, or $\frac{1}{2} \cdot 1000$?" The number T is called the **half-life** of strontium-90. To find T, we solve

$$500 = 1000e^{-0.028T} \qquad \text{We use 500 because } 500 = \tfrac{1}{2} \cdot 1000.$$
$$\tfrac{1}{2} = e^{-0.028T} \qquad \text{Dividing both sides by 1000}$$
$$\ln \tfrac{1}{2} = \ln e^{-0.028T} \qquad \text{Taking the natural logarithm of both sides}$$
$$\ln 1 - \ln 2 = -0.028T \qquad \text{Using the properties of logarithms}$$
$$0 - \ln 2 = -0.028T$$
$$\frac{-\ln 2}{-0.028} = T \qquad \text{Dividing both sides by } -0.028$$
$$\frac{\ln 2}{0.028} = T$$
$$25 \approx T. \qquad \text{Using a calculator}$$

Thus, the half-life of strontium-90 is about 25 yr.   **1** ✔

To find a general expression relating decay rate k and half-life T, we solve

$$\tfrac{1}{2} P_0 = P_0 e^{-kT}$$
$$\tfrac{1}{2} = e^{-kT}$$
$$\ln \tfrac{1}{2} = \ln e^{-kT}$$
$$\ln 1 - \ln 2 = -kT$$
$$0 - \ln 2 = -kT$$
$$-\ln 2 = -kT$$
$$\ln 2 = kT.$$

Again, we have the following.

THEOREM 10

The *decay rate, k,* and the *half-life, T,* are related by

$$kT = \ln 2 \approx 0.693147,$$

or

$$k = \frac{\ln 2}{T} \quad \text{and} \quad T = \frac{\ln 2}{k}.$$

Thus, half-life, T, depends only on decay rate, k, and is independent of the initial population size.

The effect of half-life is shown in the radioactive decay curve at right. Note that the exponential function gets close to, but never reaches, 0 as t gets larger. Thus, in theory, a radioactive substance never completely decays.

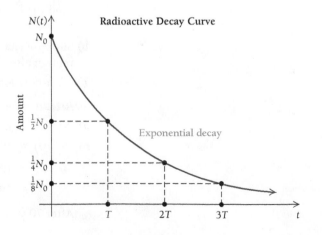

Radioactive Decay Curve

EXAMPLE 2 **Life Science: Half-life.** Plutonium-239, a common product of a functioning nuclear reactor, can be deadly to people exposed to it. Its decay rate is about 0.0028% per year. What is its half-life?

Solution We have

$$T = \frac{\ln 2}{k}$$

$$= \frac{\ln 2}{0.000028} \qquad \text{Converting 0.0028\% to decimal notation}$$

$$\approx 24{,}755.$$

Thus, the half-life of plutonium-239 is about 24,755 yr. **2** ✔

EXAMPLE 3 **Life Science: Carbon Dating.** The radioactive element carbon-14 has a half-life of 5730 yr. The percentage of carbon-14 present in the remains of plants and animals is used to determine age. Archaeologists found that the linen wrapping from one of the Dead Sea Scrolls had lost 22.3% of its carbon-14. How old was the linen wrapping?

Solution Our plan is to find an exponential equation of the form $N(t) = N_0 e^{-kt}$, replace $N(t)$ with $(1 - 0.223)N_0$, and solve for t. First, however, we find the decay rate, k:

$$k = \frac{\ln 2}{T} \approx \frac{0.693147}{5730} \approx 0.00012097, \quad \text{or} \quad 0.012097\% \text{ per year.}$$

Thus, the amount $N(t)$ that remains from an initial amount N_0 after t years is given by:

$$N(t) = N_0 e^{-0.00012097t}. \qquad \text{Remember: } k \text{ is positive, so } -k \text{ is negative.}$$

(*Note:* This equation can be used for all subsequent carbon-dating problems.)
If the linen wrapping of a Dead Sea Scroll lost 22.3% of its carbon-14 from an initial amount N_0, then $77.7\% \cdot N_0$ remains. To find the age t of the wrapping, we solve the following equation for t:

$$77.7\% \, N_0 = N_0 e^{-0.00012097t}$$
$$0.777 = e^{-0.00012097t}$$
$$\ln 0.777 = \ln e^{-0.00012097t}$$
$$\ln 0.777 = -0.00012097t$$
$$\frac{\ln 0.777}{-0.00012097} = t$$
$$2086 \approx t.$$

Thus, the linen wrapping of the Dead Sea Scroll is about 2086 yr old. **3** ✔

A Business Application: Present Value

Bankers and financial planners are often asked about problems like the following.

EXAMPLE 4 **Business: Present Value.** Following the birth of their granddaughter, two grandparents want to make an initial investment, P_0, that will grow to $10,000 by the child's 20th birthday. Interest is compounded continuously at 4%. What should the initial investment be?

Quick Check 2 ✔

Life Science: Half-life.
a) The decay rate of cesium-137 is 2.3% per year. What is its half-life?
b) The half-life of barium-140 is 13 days. What is its decay rate?

In 1947, a Bedouin youth looking for a stray goat climbed into a cave at Kirbet Qumran on the shores of the Dead Sea near Jericho and came upon earthenware jars containing an incalculable treasure of ancient manuscripts, which concern the Jewish books of the Bible. Shown here are fragments of those so-called Dead Sea Scrolls, a portion of some 600 or so texts found so far. Officials date them before A.D. 70, making them the oldest biblical manuscripts by 1000 years.

Quick Check 3 ✔

Life Science: Carbon Dating.
How old is a skeleton found at an archaeological site if tests show that it has lost 60% of its carbon-14?

Solution Using $P = P_0e^{kt}$, we find P_0 such that

$$10,000 = P_0e^{0.04 \cdot 20},$$

or

$$10,000 = P_0e^{0.8}.$$

Now

$$\frac{10,000}{e^{0.8}} = P_0,$$

or

$$10,000e^{-0.8} = P_0,$$

and, using a calculator, we have

$$P_0 = 10,000e^{-0.8}$$
$$\approx 4493.29.$$

Thus, the grandparents should deposit $4493.29, which will grow to $10,000 by the child's 20th birthday.

Economists call $4493.29 the *present value* of $10,000 due 20 yr from now at 4%, compounded continuously. The process of computing present value is called **discounting**. Another way to pose this problem is to ask "What must I invest now, at 4%, compounded continuously, in order to have $10,000 in 20 years?" The answer is $4493.29, and it is the present value of $10,000 due in 20 yr.

Computing present value can be interpreted as exponential decay from the future back to the present.

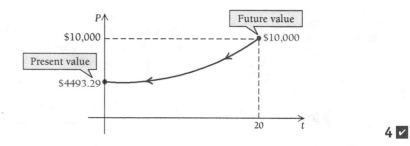

Quick Check 4 ☑

Business: Present Value. Repeat Example 4 for an interest rate of 6%.

4 ☑

In general, the present value P_0 of an amount P due t years later is found by solving the following equation for P_0:

$$P_0e^{kt} = P$$

$$P_0 = \frac{P}{e^{kt}} = Pe^{-kt}.$$

THEOREM 11

The **present value** P_0 of an amount P due t years later, at interest rate k, compounded continuously, is given by

$$P_0 = Pe^{-kt}.$$

Newton's Law of Cooling

Consider the following situation. A hot cup of soup, at a temperature of 200°, is placed in a 70° room.* The temperature of the soup decreases over time t, in minutes, according to the model known as **Newton's Law of Cooling**.

Newton's Law of Cooling

The temperature T of a cooling object drops at a rate that is proportional to the difference $T - C$, where C is the constant temperature of the surrounding medium. Thus,

$$\frac{dT}{dt} = -k(T - C). \tag{1}$$

The function that satisfies equation (1) is

$$T = T(t) = ae^{-kt} + C. \tag{2}$$

To check that $T(t) = ae^{-kt} + C$ is the solution, find dT/dt and substitute dT/dt and $T(t)$ into equation (1). This check is left to the student.

EXAMPLE 5 **Life Science: Scalding Coffee.** McDivett's Pie Shoppes, a national chain, finds that the temperature of its freshly brewed coffee is 130°. The company fears that if customers spill hot coffee on themselves, lawsuits might result. Room temperature in the restaurants is generally 72°. The temperature of the coffee cools to 120° after 4.3 min. McDivett's decides that it is safer to serve coffee at 105°. How long does it take a cup of coffee to cool to 105°?

Solution Note that C, the surrounding air temperature, is 72°. To find the value of a in equation (2) for Newton's Law of Cooling, we observe that at $t = 0$, we have $T(0) = 130°$. We solve for a as follows:

$$130 = ae^{-k\cdot 0} + 72$$
$$130 = a + 72$$
$$58 = a. \quad \text{Noting that } a = 130 - 72, \text{ the difference between the original temperatures}$$

Next, we find k using the fact that $T(4.3) = 120$:

$$120 = 58e^{-k\cdot(4.3)} + 72$$
$$48 = 58e^{-4.3k}$$
$$\frac{48}{58} = e^{-4.3k}$$
$$\ln\frac{48}{58} = \ln e^{-4.3k}$$
$$\ln\frac{48}{58} = -4.3k \quad \text{Using Property P5 of logarithms}$$
$$\frac{\ln\dfrac{48}{58}}{-4.3} = k$$
$$k \approx 0.044. \quad \text{Using a calculator}$$

---

*Assume throughout this section that all temperatures are in degrees Fahrenheit unless noted otherwise.

We now have $T(t) = 58e^{-0.044t} + 72$. To see how long it will take the coffee to cool to 105°, we set $T(t) = 105$ and solve for t:

$$105 = 58e^{-0.044t} + 72$$

$$33 = 58e^{-0.044t}$$

$$\frac{33}{58} = e^{-0.044t}$$

$$\ln\frac{33}{58} = \ln e^{-0.044t}$$

$$\ln\frac{33}{58} = -0.044t \qquad \text{Using Property P5 of logarithms}$$

$$\frac{\ln\frac{33}{58}}{-0.044} = t$$

$$t \approx 12.8 \text{ min.} \qquad \text{Using a calculator}$$

Thus, to cool to 105°, the coffee should be allowed to cool for about 13 min. **5** ✔

Quick Check 5 ✔

Life Science: Scalding Coffee. Repeat Example 5, but assume that the coffee is sold in an ice cream shop, where room temperature is 70°, and it cools to a temperature of 120° in 4 min.

The graph of $T(t) = ae^{-kt} + C$ shows that $\lim_{t \to \infty} T(t) = C$. The temperature of the object decreases toward the temperature of the surrounding medium.

Mathematically, this model demonstrates that the object's temperature never quite reaches C. In practice, the temperature of the cooling object will get so close to that of the surrounding medium that no device could detect a difference. Let's now use Newton's Law of Cooling to solve a crime.

EXAMPLE 6 **Forensics: When Was the Murder Committed?** A body is found slumped over a desk in a study. The coroner arrives at noon, immediately takes the temperature of the body, and finds it to be 94.6°. She waits 1 hr, takes the temperature again, and finds it to be 93.4°. She also notes that the temperature of the room is 70°. When was the murder committed?

Solution Note that C, the surrounding air temperature, is 70°. To find a in $T(t) = ae^{-kt} + C$, we assume that the temperature of the body was normal when the murder occurred. Thus, $T = 98.6°$ at $t = 0$:

$$98.6 = ae^{-k \cdot 0} + 70,$$

$$a = 28.6.$$

This gives $T(t) = 28.6e^{-kt} + 70$.

To find the number of hours N since the murder was committed, we must first determine k. From the two temperature readings the coroner made, we have

$$94.6 = 28.6e^{-kN} + 70, \qquad \text{or} \quad 24.6 = 28.6e^{-kN}; \tag{3}$$

$$93.4 = 28.6e^{-k(N+1)} + 70, \quad \text{or} \quad 23.4 = 28.6e^{-k(N+1)}. \tag{4}$$

Dividing equation (3) by equation (4), we get

$$\frac{24.6}{23.4} = \frac{28.6e^{-kN}}{28.6e^{-k(N+1)}}$$

$$= e^{-kN + k(N+1)}$$

$$= e^{-kN + kN + k} = e^{k}.$$

We solve this equation for k:

$$\ln\frac{24.6}{23.4} = \ln e^k \qquad \text{Taking the natural logarithm on both sides}$$

$$0.05 \approx k. \qquad \text{Using a calculator}$$

Next, we substitute $k \approx 0.05$ into equation (3) and solve for N:

$$24.6 = 28.6e^{-0.05N}$$

$$\frac{24.6}{28.6} = e^{-0.05N}$$

$$\ln\frac{24.6}{28.6} = \ln e^{-0.05N}$$

$$\frac{\ln\dfrac{24.6}{28.6}}{-0.05} = N$$

$$3 \approx N. \qquad \text{Using a calculator}$$

Quick Check 6 ☑

Forensics. Repeat Example 6, assuming that the coroner arrives at 2 A.M., immediately takes the temperature of the body, and finds it to be 92.8°. She waits 1 hr, takes the temperature again, and finds it to be 90.6°. She also notes that the temperature of the room is 72°. When was the murder committed?

Since the coroner arrived at noon, or 12 o'clock, the murder occurred at about 9:00 A.M.

6 ☑

Section Summary

- The *decay rate*, k, and the *half-life*, T, are related by $kT = \ln 2$, or

$$k = \frac{\ln 2}{T} \quad \text{and} \quad T = \frac{\ln 2}{k}.$$

- The *present value* P_0 of an amount P due t years later, at an interest rate k, compounded continuously, is given by $P_0 = Pe^{-kt}$.

- According to *Newton's Law of Cooling*, the temperature T of a cooling object drops at a rate proportional to the difference $T - C$, when C is the surrounding room temperature. Thus, we have

$$\frac{dT}{dt} = -k(T - C), \quad \text{and} \quad T(t) = ae^{-kt} + C.$$

3.4 Exercise Set

In Exercises 1–8, find the half-life for each situation.

1. An element loses 12% of its mass every year.

2. An population of bacteria decreases by 5.75% per month.

3. A vehicle loses 0.8% of its value every month.

4. A city loses 3.9% of its population every year.

5. The value of a dollar decreases by 3% every year.

6. An element loses 1.75% of its mass every day.

7. An investment loses 1.9% of its value every week.

8. A motor home loses 0.5% of its value every week.

APPLICATIONS

Life and Physical Sciences

9. **Radioactive decay.** Iodine-131 has a decay rate of 9.6% per day. The rate of change of an amount N of iodine-131 is given by

$$\frac{dN}{dt} = -0.096N,$$

where t is the number of days since decay began.

a) Let N_0 represent the amount of iodine-131 present at $t = 0$. Find the exponential function that models the situation.

b) Suppose 500 g of iodine-131 is present at $t = 0$. How much will remain after 4 days?

c) After how many days will half of the 500 g of iodine-131 remain?

10. Radioactive decay. Carbon-14 has a decay rate of 0.012097% per year. The rate of change of an amount N of carbon-14 is given by

$$\frac{dN}{dt} = -0.00012097N,$$

where t is the number of years since decay began.

a) Let N_0 represent the amount of carbon-14 present at $t = 0$. Find the exponential function that models the situation.

b) Suppose 200 g of carbon-14 is present at $t = 0$. How much will remain after 800 yr?

c) After how many years will half of the 200 g of carbon-14 remain?

11. Chemistry. Substance A decomposes at a rate proportional to the amount of A present.

a) Write an equation that gives the amount A left of an initial amount A_0 after time t.

b) It is found that 10 lb of A will reduce to 5 lb in 3.3 hr. After how long will there be only 1 lb left?

12. Chemistry. Substance A decomposes at a rate proportional to the amount of A present.

a) Write an equation that gives the amount A left of an initial amount A_0 after time t.

b) It is found that 8 g of A will reduce to 4 g in 3 hr. After how long will there be only 1 g left?

Radioactive decay. *For Exercises 13–16, complete the following.*

Radioactive Substance	Decay Rate, k	Half-life, T
13. Polonium-218	_____	3 min
14. Radium-226	_____	1600 yr
15. Lead-210	3.15%/yr	_____
16. Strontium-90	2.77%/yr	_____

17. Half-life. Of an initial amount of 1000 g of lead-210, how much will remain after 100 yr? See Exercise 15 for the value of k.

18. Half-life. Of an initial amount of 1000 g of polonium-218, how much will remain after 20 min? See Exercise 13 for the value of k.

19. Carbon dating. How old is an ivory tusk that has lost 40% of its carbon-14?

20. Carbon dating. How old is a piece of wood that has lost 90% of its carbon-14?

21. Cancer treatment. Iodine-125 is often used to treat cancer and has a half-life of 60.1 days. In a sample, the amount of iodine-125 decreased by 25% while in storage. How long was the sample in storage?

22. Carbon dating. How old is a Chinese artifact that has lost 60% of its carbon-14?

23. Carbon dating. Recently, while digging in Chaco Canyon, New Mexico, archaeologists found corn pollen that had lost 38.1% of its carbon-14. The age of this corn pollen was evidence that Indians had been cultivating crops in the Southwest centuries earlier than previously thought. (*Source: American Anthropologist.*) What was the age of the pollen?

Chaco Canyon, New Mexico

Business and Economics

24. Present value. Following the birth of a child, a parent wants to make an initial investment P_0 that will grow to $30,000 by the child's 20th birthday. Interest is compounded continuously at 6%. What should the initial investment be?

25. Present value. Following the birth of their child, the Irwins want to make an initial investment P_0 that will grow to $40,000 by the child's 20th birthday. Interest is compounded continuously at 5.3%. What should the initial investment be?

26. Present value. Desmond wants to have $15,000 available in 5 yr to pay for new siding. Interest is 4.3%, compounded continuously. How much money should be invested?

27. Sports salaries. An athlete signs a contract that guarantees a $9-million salary 6 yr from now. Assuming that money can be invested at 4.7%, with interest compounded continuously, what is the present value of that year's salary?

28. Actors' salaries. An actor signs a film contract that will pay $12 million when the film is completed 3 yr from now. Assuming that money can be invested at 4.2%, with interest compounded continuously, what is the present value of that payment?

29. Estate planning. Shannon has a trust fund that will yield $80,000 in 13 yr. A CPA is preparing a financial statement for Shannon and wants to take into account the present value of the trust fund in computing her net worth. Interest is compounded continuously at 4.8%. What is the present value of the trust fund?

30. Supply and demand. The supply and demand for stereos produced by Blaster Sound, Inc., are given by

$$S(x) = \ln x \quad \text{and} \quad D(x) = \ln \frac{163{,}000}{x},$$

where $S(x)$ is the number of stereos that the company is willing to sell for x dollars each and $D(x)$ is the quantity that the public is willing to buy at price x. Find the equilibrium point. (See Section R.5.)

31. Salvage value. Lucas Mining estimates that the salvage value $V(t)$, in dollars, of a piece of machinery after t years is given by

$$V(t) = 40{,}000e^{-t}.$$

a) What did the machinery cost initially?
b) What is the salvage value after 2 yr?
c) Find the rate of change of the salvage value, and explain its meaning.

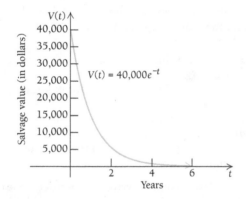

V(t) = 40,000e^{-t}

Salvage value (in dollars) — Years

32. Salvage value. Wills Investments tracks the value of a particular photocopier over a period of years. The data in the table below show the value of the copier at time t, in years, after the date of purchase.

Time, t (in years)	Salvage Value
0	$34,000
1	22,791
2	15,277
3	10,241
4	6,865
5	4,600
6	3,084

(*Source*: International Data Corporation.)

a) Use REGRESSION to fit an exponential function $y = a \cdot b^x$ to the data. Then convert that formula to $V(t) = V_0 e^{-kt}$, where V_0 is the value when the copier is purchased and t is the time, in years, from the date of purchase. (See the Technology Connection on p. 326.)
b) Estimate the salvage value of the copier after 7 yr; 10 yr.

c) After what amount of time will the salvage value be $1000?
d) After how long will the copier be worth half of its original value?
e) Find the rate of change of the salvage value, and interpret its meaning.

33. Actuarial science. An actuary works for an insurance company and calculates insurance premiums. Given an actual mortality rate (probability of death) for a given age, actuaries sometimes need to project future expected mortality rates of people of that age. For example,

$$Q(t) = (Q_0 - 0.00055)e^{0.163t} + 0.00055,$$

where t is the number of years into the future and Q_0 is the mortality rate when $t = 0$, projects future mortality rates.

a) Suppose the actual mortality rate of a group of females aged 25 is 0.014 (14 deaths per 1000). What is the future expected mortality rate of this group of females 3, 5, and 10 yr in the future?
b) Sketch the graph of the mortality function $Q(t)$ for the group in part (a) for $0 \le t \le 10$.

34. Actuarial science. Use the formula from Exercise 33.

a) Suppose the actual mortality rate of a group of males aged 25 is 0.023 (23 deaths per 1000). What is the future expected mortality rate of this group of males 3, 5, and 10 yr in the future?
b) Sketch the graph of the mortality function $Q(t)$ for the group in part (a) for $0 \le t \le 10$.
c) What is the ratio of the mortality rate for 25-year-old males 10 yr in the future to that for 25-year-old females 10 yr in the future (Exercise 33a)?

35. U.S. farms. The number N of farms in the United States has declined continually since 1950. In 1950, there were 5,650,000 farms, and in 2012, that number had decreased to 2,170,000. (*Sources*: U.S. Department of Agriculture; National Agricultural Statistics Service.)

5,650,000

2,170,000

Number of farms (in millions) — Number of years since 1950

Assuming the number of farms decreased according to the exponential decay model:

a) Find the value of k, and write an exponential function that describes the number of farms after time t, where t is the number of years since 1950.
b) Estimate the number of farms in 2016 and in 2020.
c) At this decay rate, when will only 1,000,000 farms remain?

Social Sciences

36. Forgetting. In an art history class, students took a test. They were subsequently retested with an equivalent test at weekly intervals. Their average retest scores t weeks later are given in the following table.

Time, t (in weeks)	Score, y
1	84.9%
2	84.6%
3	84.4%
4	84.2%
5	84.1%
6	83.9%

a) Use REGRESSION to fit a logarithmic function $y = a + b \ln x$ to the data.
b) Use the function to predict the average test score after 8 weeks, 10 weeks, 24 weeks, and 36 weeks.
c) After how long will the test scores fall below 82%?
d) Find the rate of change of the scores, and interpret its meaning.

37. Decline in beef consumption. Annual consumption of beef per person was about 64.6 lb in 2000 and about 61.2 lb in 2008. Assuming that $B(t)$, the annual beef consumption t years after 2000, is decreasing according to the exponential decay model:

a) Find the value of k, and write the equation.
b) Estimate the consumption of beef in 2015.
c) In what year (theoretically) will the consumption of beef be 20 lb per person?

38. Population decrease of Russia. The population of Russia dropped from 150 million in 1995 to 142.5 million in 2013. (*Source: CIA–The World Factbook.*) Assume that $P(t)$, the population, in millions, t years after 1995, is decreasing according to the exponential decay model.

a) Find the value of k, and write the equation.
b) Estimate the population of Russia in 2018.
c) When will the population of Russia be 100 million?

39. Population decrease of Ukraine. The population of Ukraine dropped from 51.9 million in 1995 to 44.5 million in 2013. (*Source: CIA–The World Factbook.*) Assume that $P(t)$, the population, in millions, t years after 1995, is decreasing according to the exponential decay model.

a) Find the value of k, and write the equation.
b) Estimate the population of Ukraine in 2018.
c) In what year will the population of Ukraine be 40 million, according to this model?

Life and Natural Sciences

40. Cooling. After warming the water in a hot tub to 100°, the heating element fails. The surrounding air temperature is 40°, and in 5 min the water temperature drops to 95°.

a) Find the value of the constant a in Newton's Law of Cooling.
b) Find the value of the constant k. Round to five decimal places.
c) What is the water temperature after 10 min?
d) How long does it take the water to cool to 41°?
e) Find the rate of change of the water temperature, and interpret its meaning.

41. Cooling. The temperature in a whirlpool bath is 102°, and the room temperature is 75°. The water cools to 90° in 10 min.

a) Find the value of the constant a in Newton's Law of Cooling.
b) Find the value of the constant k. Round to five decimal places.
c) What is the water temperature after 20 min?
d) How long does it take the water to cool to 80°?
e) Find the rate of change of the water temperature, and interpret its meaning.

42. Forensics. A coroner arrives at a murder scene at 2 A.M. He takes the temperature of the body and finds it to be 61.6°. He waits 1 hr, takes the temperature again, and finds it to be 57.2°. The body is in a freezer, where the temperature is 10°. When was the murder committed?

43. Forensics. A coroner arrives at a murder scene at 11 P.M. She finds the temperature of the body to be 85.9°. She waits 1 hr, takes the temperature again, and finds it to be 83.4°. She notes that the room temperature is 60°. When was the murder committed?

44. Prisoner-of-war protest. The initial weight of a prisoner of war is 140 lb. To protest the conditions of her imprisonment, she begins a fast. Her weight t days after her last meal is approximated by
$$W = 140e^{-0.009t}.$$

a) How much does the prisoner weigh after 25 days?
b) At what rate is the prisoner's weight changing after 25 days?

45. Political protest. A monk weighing 170 lb begins a fast to protest a war. His weight after t days is given by
$$W = 170e^{-0.008t}.$$

a) When the war ends 20 days later, how much does the monk weigh?
b) At what rate is the monk losing weight after 20 days (before any food is consumed)?

46. Atmospheric pressure. Atmospheric pressure P at altitude a is given by

$$P = P_0 e^{-0.00005a},$$

where P_0 is the pressure at sea level. Assume that $P_0 = 14.7 \text{ lb/in}^2$ (pounds per square inch).

a) Find the pressure at an altitude of 1000 ft.
b) Find the pressure at an altitude of 20,000 ft.
c) At what altitude is the pressure 14.7 lb/in^2?
d) Find the rate of change of the pressure, and interpret its meaning.

47. Satellite power. The power supply of a satellite is a radioisotope (radioactive substance). The power output P, in watts (W), decreases at a rate proportional to the amount present and P is given by

$$P = 50 e^{-0.004t},$$

where t is the time, in days.

a) How much power will be available after 375 days?
b) What is the half-life of the power supply?
c) The satellite cannot operate on less than 10 W of power. How long can the satellite stay in operation?
d) How much power did the satellite have to begin with?
e) Find the rate of change of the power output, and interpret its meaning.

48. Cases of tuberculosis. The number of cases N of tuberculosis in the United States has decreased continually since 1956. In 1956, there were 69,895 cases. By 2012, this number had decreased by over 80%, to 10,521 cases.

a) Find the value of k, and write an exponential function that describes the number of tuberculosis cases after time t, where t is the number of years since 1956.
b) Estimate the number of cases in 2016 and in 2020.
c) At this decay rate, in what year will there be 5000 cases?

Modeling

For each of the scatterplots in Exercises 49–58, determine which, if any, of these functions might be used as a model for the data:

a) Quadratic: $f(x) = ax^2 + bx + c$
b) Polynomial, not quadratic
c) Exponential: $f(x) = ae^{kx}, k > 0$
d) Exponential: $f(x) = ae^{-kx}, k > 0$
e) Logarithmic: $f(x) = a + b \ln x$
f) Logistic: $f(x) = \dfrac{a}{1 + be^{-kx}}$

49.

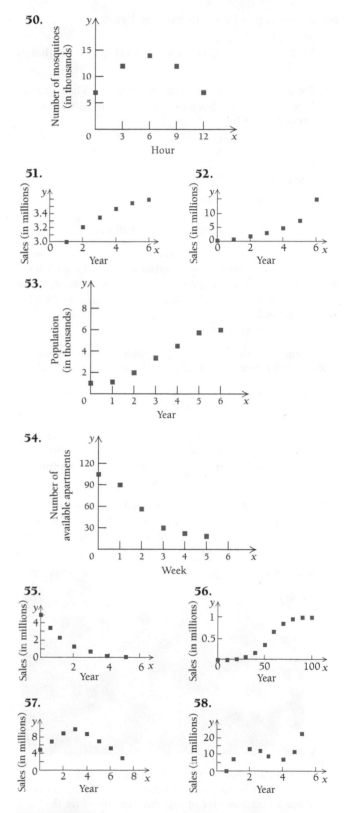

SYNTHESIS

59. A sample of an element lost 25% of its mass in 5 weeks.

a) Find the half-life.
b) After how many weeks will the sample have lost 75% of its mass?

60. A vehicle lost 15% of its value in 2 yr.
   a) Find the half-life.
   b) After how many years will the vehicle be worth 40% of its original value?

61. Economics: supply and demand elasticity. The demand, $D(x)$, and supply, $S(x)$, functions for a multipurpose printer are as follows:

$$D(x) = q = 480e^{-0.003x}$$

and

$$S(x) = q = 150e^{0.004x}.$$

   a) Find the equilibrium point. Assume that x is the price in dollars.
   b) Find the elasticity of demand when $x = \$100$.

The Beer–Lambert Law. *A beam of light enters a medium such as water or smoky air with initial intensity I_0. Its intensity is decreased depending on the thickness (or concentration) of the medium. The intensity I at a depth (or concentration) of x units is given by*

$$I = I_0 e^{-\mu x}.$$

The constant μ ("mu"), called the coefficient of absorption, varies with the medium. Use this law for Exercises 62 and 63.

62. Light through smog. Concentrations of particulates in the air due to pollution reduce sunlight. In a smoggy area, $\mu = 0.01$ and x is the concentration of particulates measured in micrograms per cubic meter (mcg/m^3). What change is more significant—dropping pollution levels from 100 mcg/m^3 to 90 mcg/m^3 or dropping them from 60 mcg/m^3 to 50 mcg/m^3? Why?

63. Light through sea water. Sea water has $\mu = 1.4$ and x is measured in meters. What would increase cloudiness more —dropping x from 2 m to 5 m or dropping x from 7 m to 10 m? Explain.

64. Newton's Law of Cooling. Consider the following exploratory situation. Fill a glass with hot tap water. Place a thermometer in the glass and measure the temperature. Check the temperature every 30 min thereafter. Plot your data on this graph, and connect the points with a smooth curve.

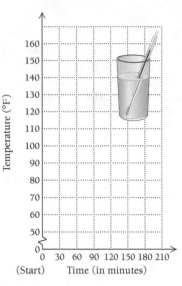

   a) What was the temperature of the water when you began?
   b) At what temperature does there seem to be a leveling off of the graph?
   c) What is the difference between your answers to parts (a) and (b)?
   d) How does the water temperature in part (b) compare with the room temperature?
   e) Find an equation that fits the data. Use this equation to check values of other data points. How do they compare?
   f) Is it ever "theoretically" possible for the temperature of the water to be the same as the room temperature? Explain.
   g) Find the rate of change of the temperature, and interpret its meaning.

65. An interest rate decreases from 8% to 7.2%. Explain why this increases the present value of an amount due 10 yr later.

66. The city of Rayburn loses half its population every 12 yr.
   a) Explain why Rayburn's population will not be zero after 2 half-lives, or 24 yr.
   b) What percentage of the original population remains after 2 half-lives?
   c) What percentage of the original population remains after 4 half-lives?

Answers to Quick Checks

1. (a) $N(t) = N_0 e^{-0.14t}$; **(b)** 246.6 g; **(c)** 4.95 days
2. (a) 30.1 yr; **(b)** 5.3% per day   **3.** 7574 yr
4. \$3011.94 **5.** 11.7 min   **6.** $N = 2.2$ hr, so the murder was committed 2 hr and 12 min before the coroner arrived, at about 11:48 P.M. on the previous day.

3.5

- Differentiate functions involving a^x.
- Differentiate functions involving $\log_a x$.
- Find the future value and the rate of growth of an annuity.

The Derivatives of a^x and $\log_a x$; Application: Annuities

The Derivative of a^x

To find the derivative of a^x, for any base a, we first express a^x as a power of e. To do this, recall that $\log_b x$ is the power to which b is raised in order to get x. Thus,

$$b^{\log_b x} = x.$$

In particular, it follows that

$$e^{\log_e A} = A, \quad \text{or} \quad e^{\ln A} = A.$$

If we replace A with a^x, we have

$$e^{\ln a^x} = a^x, \quad \text{or} \quad a^x = e^{\ln a^x}. \tag{1}$$

To find the derivative of a^x, we differentiate both sides:

$$\frac{d}{dx} a^x = \frac{d}{dx} e^{\ln a^x}$$

$$= \frac{d}{dx} e^{x \ln a} \qquad \text{Using a property of logarithms}$$

$$= \frac{d}{dx} e^{(\ln a)x}$$

$$= e^{(\ln a)x} \cdot \ln a \qquad \text{Differentiating and using the Chain Rule}$$

$$= e^{\ln a^x} \cdot \ln a \qquad \text{Using a property of logarithms}$$

$$= a^x \cdot \ln a. \qquad \text{Using equation (1)}$$

Thus, we have the following theorem.

> **THEOREM 12**
>
> $$\frac{d}{dx} a^x = (\ln a)a^x$$

EXAMPLE 1   Differentiate: **a)** $y = 2^x$;   **b)** $y = (1.4)^x$;   **c)** $f(x) = 3^{2x}$.

Solution

a) $\dfrac{d}{dx} 2^x = (\ln 2)2^x$ Using Theorem 12

Note that $\ln 2 \approx 0.6931$, so this equation verifies our earlier approximation (in Section 3.1) of the derivative of 2^x as $(0.6931)2^x$.

b) $\dfrac{d}{dx} (1.4)^x = (\ln 1.4)(1.4)^x$

Quick Check 1 ✔

Differentiate:

a) $y = 5^x$;
b) $f(x) = 4^x$;
c) $y = 7^{2x}$.

c) Since $f(x) = 3^{2x}$ is of the form $f(x) = 3^{g(x)}$, the Chain Rule applies:

$$f'(x) = (\ln 3)3^{2x} \cdot \frac{d}{dx}(2x)$$

$$= \ln 3 \cdot 3^{2x} \cdot 2 = 2\ln 3 \cdot 3^{2x}.$$

1 ✔

Compare these formulas:

$$\frac{d}{dx} a^x = (\ln a)a^x \quad \text{and} \quad \frac{d}{dx} e^x = e^x.$$

The simplicity of the latter formula is a reason for the use of base e in calculus. The many applications of e in natural phenomena provide additional reasons.

THEOREM 13

$$\ln a = \lim_{h \to 0} \frac{a^h - 1}{h}$$

The Derivative of $\log_a x$

Just as the derivative of a^x is expressed in terms of $\ln a$, so too is the derivative of $\log_a x$. To find this derivative, we first express $\log_a x$ in terms of $\ln a$ using the change-of-base formula (P7 of Theorem 3) from Section 3.2:

$$\frac{d}{dx} \log_a x = \frac{d}{dx}\left(\frac{\log_e x}{\log_e a}\right) \qquad \text{Using the change-of-base formula}$$

$$= \frac{d}{dx}\left(\frac{\ln x}{\ln a}\right)$$

$$= \frac{1}{\ln a} \cdot \frac{d}{dx}(\ln x) \qquad \frac{1}{\ln a} \text{ is a constant.}$$

$$= \frac{1}{\ln a} \cdot \frac{1}{x}.$$

THEOREM 14

$$\frac{d}{dx} \log_a x = \frac{1}{\ln a} \cdot \frac{1}{x}$$

Comparing this equation with

$$\frac{d}{dx} \ln x = \frac{1}{x},$$

we see another advantage of using base e in calculus: with base e, the constant $1/(\ln a)$ is simply 1.

EXAMPLE 2   Differentiate:

a) $y = \log_8 x;$ **b)** $y = \log x;$

c) $f(x) = \log_3 (x^2 + 1);$ **d)** $f(x) = x^3 \log_5 x.$

Solution

a) $\dfrac{d}{dx} \log_8 x = \dfrac{1}{\ln 8} \cdot \dfrac{1}{x}$ Using Theorem 14

b) $\dfrac{d}{dx} \log x = \log_{10} x$ $\log x$ means $\log_{10} x.$

$$= \frac{1}{\ln 10} \cdot \frac{1}{x}$$

Quick Check 2 ✔

Differentiate:

a) $y = \log_2 x$;
b) $f(x) = -7 \log x$;
c) $g(x) = x^6 \log x$;
d) $y = \log_8 (x^3 - 7)$.

c) Note that $f(x) = \log_3 (x^2 + 1)$ is of the form $f(x) = \log_3 (g(x))$, so the Chain Rule is required:

$$f'(x) = \frac{1}{\ln 3} \cdot \frac{1}{x^2 + 1} \cdot \frac{d}{dx}(x^2 + 1) \qquad \text{Using the Chain Rule}$$

$$= \frac{1}{\ln 3} \cdot \frac{1}{x^2 + 1} \cdot 2x$$

$$= \frac{2x}{(\ln 3)(x^2 + 1)}.$$

d) Since $f(x) = x^3 \log_5 x$ is of the form $f(x) = g(x) \cdot h(x)$, we use the Product Rule:

$$f'(x) = x^3 \cdot \frac{d}{dx} \log_5 x + \log_5 x \cdot \frac{d}{dx} x^3 \qquad \text{Using the Product Rule}$$

$$= x^3 \cdot \frac{1}{\ln 5} \cdot \frac{1}{x} + \log_5 x \cdot 3x^2 \qquad \text{Differentiating}$$

$$= \frac{x^2}{\ln 5} + 3x^2 \log_5 x, \quad \text{or} \quad x^2 \left(\frac{1}{\ln 5} + 3 \log_5 x \right). \qquad \text{2 ✔}$$

Business Application: Annuities

A savings account into which deposits of equal size (called *payments*) are made on a regular basis is called an **annuity**. Many people use annuities to save for retirement or for college.

If we let p represent the amount paid into the annuity on a regular basis, r the annual interest rate, n the number of compounding periods per year (which is also the number of payments made per year), and t the time in years, then the future value of the annuity, A, is given by

$$A(t) = \frac{p\left[\left(1 + \dfrac{r}{n}\right)^{nt} - 1\right]}{\dfrac{r}{n}}.$$

EXAMPLE 3 **Value of an Annuity.** Javier deposits $150 every month into an annuity with an annual interest rate of 4.5%. Assume that interest is compounded monthly.

a) Find a function $A(t)$ that gives the value of Javier's annuity after t years.

b) What is the value of Javier's annuity after 5 years?

c) What is the rate of change in the value of Javier's annuity after 5 years?

Solution

a) We have $p = 150$, $r = 0.045$, and $n = 12$. Thus, we substitute and simplify:

$$A(t) = \frac{150\left[\left(1 + \dfrac{0.045}{12}\right)^{12t} - 1\right]}{\dfrac{0.045}{12}} \qquad \begin{array}{l}\text{Substituting 150 for } p, 0.045 \text{ for } r, \text{ and} \\ \text{12 for } n.\end{array}$$

$$= 40{,}000[(1.00375)^{12t} - 1]. \qquad \text{Simplifying}$$

b) In 5 yr, the value of Javier's annuity will be

$$A(5) = 40{,}000[(1.00375)^{12 \cdot 5} - 1]$$

$$= \$10{,}071.83.$$

c) To find the rate of change in the value of Javier's annuity, we first find the derivative of $A(t)$:

$$\frac{d}{dt}A(t) = \frac{d}{dt}\left(40{,}000\left[(1.00375)^{12t} - 1\right]\right)$$

$$A'(t) = 40{,}000 \, \frac{d}{dt}\left[(1.00375)^{12t} - 1\right]$$

$$= 40{,}000(1.00375)^{12t} \cdot \ln(1.00375) \cdot 12 \qquad \text{Using } \frac{d}{dt}a^u = a^u \cdot \ln a \cdot \frac{du}{dt}$$

$$= 1796.63(1.00375)^{12t} \qquad \text{Simplifying}$$

After 5 yr, the value of Javier's annuity is changing at the rate of

$$A'(5) = 1796.63(1.00375)^{12 \cdot 5} = \$2249.01/\text{yr}. \qquad \boxed{3 \checkmark}$$

Quick Check 3 ☑

Kerrie deposits \$10,000 every 3 months into an annuity. Assume an annual interest rate of 3.75%, compounded quarterly.

a) Find $A(t)$, the value of Kerrie's annuity after t years.
b) What is the value of Kerrie's annuity after 10 yr?
c) What is the rate of change in the value of Kerrie's annuity after 10 yr?

Section Summary

- The following rules apply when we differentiate exponential and logarithmic functions for any base a:

$$\frac{d}{dx}a^x = (\ln a)a^x, \quad \text{and} \quad \frac{d}{dx}\log_a x = \frac{1}{\ln a} \cdot \frac{1}{x}.$$

- The value of an annuity is given by

$$A = \frac{p\left[\left(1 + \dfrac{r}{n}\right)^{nt} - 1\right]}{\dfrac{r}{n}},$$

where p is the amount of the regular payment, r the annual percentage rate, and n the number of compounding periods per year.

3.5 Exercise Set

Differentiate.

1. $y = 6^x$

2. $y = 7^x$

3. $f(x) = 8^x$

4. $f(x) = 15^x$

5. $g(x) = x^5(3.7)^x$

6. $g(x) = x^3(5.4)^x$

7. $y = 7^{x^4 + 2}$

8. $y = 4^{x^2 + 5}$

9. $y = e^{x^2}$

10. $y = e^{8x}$

11. $f(x) = 3^{x^4 + 1}$

12. $f(x) = 12^{7x - 4}$

13. $y = \log_8 x$

14. $y = \log_4 x$

15. $y = \log_{17} x$

16. $y = \log_{23} x$

17. $g(x) = \log_{32}(9x - 2)$

18. $g(x) = \log_6(5x + 1)$

19. $F(x) = \log(6x - 7)$

20. $G(x) = \log(5x + 4)$

21. $y = \log_9(x^4 - x)$

22. $y = \log_8(x^3 + x)$

23. $f(x) = 4\log_7\left(\sqrt{x} - 2\right)$

24. $g(x) = -\log_6\left(\sqrt[3]{x} + 5\right)$

25. $y = 5^x \cdot \log_2 x$

26. $y = 6^x \cdot \log_7 x$

27. $G(x) = (\log_{12} x)^5$

28. $F(x) = (\log_9 x)^7$

29. $f(x) = \dfrac{6^x}{5x - 1}$

30. $g(x) = \dfrac{7^x}{4x + 1}$

31. $y = 5^{2x^3 - 1} \cdot \log(6x + 5)$

32. $y = \log(7x + 3) \cdot 4^{2x^4 + 8}$

33. $G(x) = \log_9 x \cdot (4^x)^6$

34. $F(x) = 7^x \cdot (\log_4 x)^9$

35. $f(x) = (3x^5 + x)^5 \log_3 x$

36. $g(x) = \sqrt{x^3 - x}\,(\log_5 x)$

APPLICATIONS

Business and Economics

37. Double declining balance depreciation. An office machine is purchased for $5200. Under certain assumptions, its salvage value, V, in dollars, is depreciated according to a method called *double declining balance*, by basically 80% each year, and is given by

$$V(t) = 5200(0.80)^t,$$

where t is the time, in years, after purchase.

a) Find $V'(t)$.
b) Interpret the meaning of $V'(t)$.

38. Recycling aluminum cans. It is known that 45% of all aluminum cans distributed are recycled each year. A beverage company uses 250,000 lb of aluminum cans. After recycling, the amount of aluminum, in pounds, still in use after t years is given by

$$N(t) = 250,000(0.45)^t.$$

(*Source*: The Container Recycling Institute.)

a) Find $N'(t)$.
b) Interpret the meaning of $N'(t)$.

39. Recycling glass. In 2012, 34.1% of all glass containers were recycled. A beverage company used 400,000 lb of glass containers per year. After recycling, the amount of glass, in pounds, still in use after t years is given by

$$N(t) = 400,000(0.341)^t.$$

(*Source*: www.gpi.org.)

a) Find $N'(t)$
b) Interpret the meaning of $N'(t)$.

40. Household liability. The total financial liability, in billions of dollars, of U.S. households can be modeled by

$$L(t) = 1547(1.083)^t,$$

where t is the number of years after 1980. The graph of this function follows.

a) Using this model, predict the total financial liability of U.S. households in 2012.
b) Find $L'(25)$.
c) Interpret the meaning of $L'(25)$.

41. Small business. The number of nonfarm proprietorships, in thousands, in the United States can be modeled by

$$N(t) = 8400 \ln t - 10,500,$$

where t is the number of years after 1970. The graph of this function is given below.

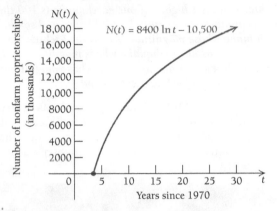

a) Using this model, predict the number of nonfarm proprietorships in the United States in 2020.
b) Find $N'(45)$.
c) Interpret the meaning of $N'(45)$.

42. Annuities. Yukiko opens a savings account to pay for her new baby's college education. She deposits $200 every month into the account at an annual interest rate of 4.2%, compounded monthly.

a) Find $A(t)$, the value of Yukiko's account after t years.
b) What is the value of Yukiko's account after 8 yr?
c) What is the rate of change in the value of Yukiko's account after 8 yr?

43. Annuities. Nasim opens a retirement savings account, and she deposits $1000 every 4 months into the account, which has an annual interest rate of 3.8%, compounded every 4 months.

a) Find $A(t)$, the value of Nasim's account after t years.
b) What is the value of Nasim's account after 12 yr?
c) What is the rate of change in the value of Nasim's account after 12 yr?

Life and Physical Sciences

44. Agriculture. Farmers wishing to avoid the use of genetically modified (GMO) seeds are increasingly concerned about inadvertently growing GMO plants as a result of pollen drifting from nearby farms. Assuming that these farmers raise their own seeds, the fractional portion of their crop that remains free of GMO plants t years later can be approximated by

$$P(t) = (0.98)^t.$$

a) Using this model, predict the fractional portion of the crop that will be GMO-free 10 yr after a neighboring farm begins to use GMO seeds.
b) Find $P'(15)$.
c) Interpret the meaning of $P'(15)$.

Earthquake magnitude. *The magnitude R (measured on the Richter scale) of an earthquake of intensity I is defined as*

$$R = \log \frac{I}{I_0},$$

where I_0 is a minimum intensity used for comparison. If one earthquake is 10 times as intense as another, its magnitude on the Richter scale is 1 higher; if one earthquake is 100 times as intense as another, its magnitude is 2 higher, and so on. Thus, an earthquake whose magnitude is 6 on the Richter scale is 10 times as intense as an earthquake whose magnitude is 5, and 100 times as intense as an earthquake whose magnitude is 4. Use this information for Exercises 45 and 46.

45. On January 12, 2010, a devastating earthquake struck the Caribbean nation of Haiti. It had an intensity that was 10,000,000, or 10^7, times as intense as I_0. What was this earthquake's magnitude on the Richter scale? (*Hint:* Let $I = 10^7 \cdot I_0$.)

46. Find the magnitude of an earthquake that is 5,600,000 times as intense as I_0.

If two earthquakes have magnitudes R_1 and R_2, where $R_1 > R_2$, their relative intensity is given by

$$R_1 - R_2 = \log \frac{I_1}{I_2}.$$

Thus, comparing an earthquake of magnitude 8.0 with another earthquake of magnitude 5.5, we have

$8.0 - 5.5 = \log \dfrac{I_1}{I_2}$, *or* $2.5 = \log \dfrac{I_1}{I_2}$, *and* $I_1 = 10^{2.5} I_2$. *Since*

$10^{2.5} \approx 316$, *an earthquake of magnitude 8.0 is about 316 times as intense as an earthquake of magnitude 5.5. Use this information for Exercises 47 and 48.*

47. The following table shows the magnitudes of selected large earthquakes.

EARTHQUAKE	MAGNITUDE
Sumatran-Andaman, 2004	9.2
Japan, 2011	9.0
San Francisco, 1906	8.0
Baja California, 2010	7.2
San Fernando, 1971	6.6

a) How many times more intense was the Japanese earthquake of 2011 than the Baja California earthquake of 2010?

b) How many times more intense was the Sumatran-Andaman earthquake of 2004 than the San Fernando earthquake of 1971?

48. An earthquake of magnitude 5.0 is considered "moderate," with the potential to damage unreinforced structures. How many times more intense was the San Francisco earthquake of 1906 than a "moderately damaging" earthquake with a magnitude 5.0?

49. Earthquake intensity.   The intensity of an earthquake is given by

$$I = I_0 10^R,$$

where R is the magnitude on the Richter scale and I_0 is the minimum intensity, at which $R = 0$, used for comparison.

a) Find I, in terms of I_0, for an earthquake of magnitude 7 on the Richter scale.

b) Find I, in terms of I_0, for an earthquake of magnitude 8 on the Richter scale.

c) Compare your answers to parts (a) and (b).

d) Find the rate of change dI/dR.

e) Interpret the meaning of dI/dR.

50. Intensity of sound.   The intensity of a sound is given by

$$I = I_0 10^{0.1L},$$

where L is the loudness of the sound measured in decibels and I_0 is the minimum intensity detectable by the human ear.

a) Find I, in terms of I_0, for the loudness of a power mower, which is 100 decibels.

b) Find I, in terms of I_0, for the loudness of a just audible sound, which is 10 decibels.

c) Compare your answers to parts (a) and (b).

d) Find the rate of change dI/dL.

e) Interpret the meaning of dI/dL.

51. Earthquake magnitude. The magnitude R (measured on the Richter scale) of an earthquake of intensity I is defined as

$$R = \log \frac{I}{I_0},$$

where I_0 is the minimum intensity (used for comparison).

a) Find the rate of change dR/dI.

b) Interpret the meaning of dR/dI.

52. Loudness of sound. The loudness L of a sound of intensity I is defined as

$$L = 10 \log \frac{I}{I_0},$$

where I_0 is the minimum intensity detectable by the human ear and L is the loudness measured in decibels.

a) Find the rate of change dL/dI.

b) Interpret the meaning of dL/dI.

53. Response to drug dosage. The response y to a dosage x of a drug can be approximated by

$$y = m \log x + b,$$

where m and b are constants. This response may be hard to measure with a number. The patient might perspire more, have an increase in temperature, or faint.

a) Find the rate of change dy/dx.
b) Interpret the meaning of dy/dx.

SYNTHESIS

Finding natural logarithms as limits. *Given that the derivative of* $f(x) = a^x$ *is* $f'(x) = a^x(\ln a)$, *in Section 3.1, we showed that*

$$f'(x) = a^x \cdot \lim_{h \to 0} \frac{a^h - 1}{h}.$$

Thus, we can define

$$\ln a = \lim_{h \to 0} \frac{a^h - 1}{h}.$$

In Exercises 54–57, use this definition to find each limit.

54. $\displaystyle \lim_{h \to 0} \frac{3^h - 1}{h}$

55. $\displaystyle \lim_{h \to 0} \frac{5^h - 1}{h}$

56. $\displaystyle \lim_{h \to 0} \frac{e^h - 1}{h}$

57. $\displaystyle \lim_{h \to 0} \frac{\sqrt{e^h} - 1}{h}$

Use the Chain Rule, implicit differentiation, and other techniques to differentiate each function given in Exercises 58–65.

58. $f(x) = 3^{(2^x)}$

59. $y = 2^{x^4}$

60. $y = x^x$, for $x > 0$

61. $y = \log_3 (\log x)$

62. $f(x) = x^{e^x}$, for $x > 0$

63. $y = a^{f(x)}$

64. $y = \log_a f(x)$, for $f(x)$ positive

65. $y = [f(x)]^{g(x)}$, for $f(x)$ positive

66. Consider the function $y = x^x$, with $x > 0$.

a) Find $\dfrac{dy}{dx}$. (*Hint:* Take the natural logarithm of both sides and differentiate implicitly.)
b) Find the minimum value of y on $(0, \infty)$.

67. In your own words, derive the formula for the derivative of $f(x) = a^x$.

68. In your own words, derive the formula for the derivative of $f(x) = \log_a x$.

A Business Application: Amortization*

The value of an investment typically grows (or decays) exponentially. In Section R.1, we saw that an initial amount P, invested at an annual interest rate r, compounded n times per year for t years, grows to an amount $A(t)$, given by

$$A(t) = P\left(1 + \frac{r}{n}\right)^{nt}.$$

The amount $A(t)$ is called the **compound interest future value**. The formula assumes that amount P is invested once and r does not change.

If an investor chooses to make regular, equal-size payments p into a savings account, the account is an *annuity*, as we saw in Section 3.5. The **annuity future value**, $A(t)$, is given by

$$A(t) = \frac{p\left[\left(1 + \dfrac{r}{n}\right)^{nt} - 1\right]}{\dfrac{r}{n}}.$$

In this case, the investor deposits amount p in each of the n compounding periods per year.

- Find the regular payment needed to amortize a loan.
- Use the amortization formula to solve applied problems.
- Complete an amortization schedule.

---

*This section does use calculus and is not relied on in later chapters.

Amortization

Most large purchases, such as a house or a car, are made with an amortized loan, which is paid off in equal payments. This payment process is called **amortization**; it is represented graphically below.

Original loan amount (does not include any down payments) → P

The loan amount, P, gains interest before the first payment is received.
The first payment is received, and the balance owed is reduced.
However, the remaining balance grows in value until the next payment is received.

The process repeats every payment period.

The last payment reduces the balance to zero, and the loan is paid off.

Amount owed (vertical axis)
Time (horizontal axis)

Suppose you buy a new car. After making a down payment, you elect to finance the balance using a loan on which you will make monthly payments. However, the money borrowed accrues interest as long as the loan is active. We let P represent the loan amount and p represent the regular payment needed to pay off (*amortize*) the loan in the specified number of years. To determine p, assuming that r, n, and t have been agreed on, we combine the above two expressions for $A(t)$ into one **amortization formula**.

DEFINITION

A loan amount P is financed at an annual interest rate r compounded n times per year for t years. The payment amount p must satisfy the *amortization formula*:

$$P\left(1 + \frac{r}{n}\right)^{nt} = \frac{p\left[\left(1 + \frac{r}{n}\right)^{nt} - 1\right]}{\frac{r}{n}}.$$

EXAMPLE 1   **Amortization: Car Loan.**   Henri buys a new car for $20,000, with 30% down and the rest financed through an amortized loan at 7%, compounded monthly for 5 yr.

a) Find Henri's monthly loan payment.

b) Assuming that Henri makes every payment, find the total amount he will pay.

Solution

a) Henri pays 30% of $20,000, or $6000, as a down payment and finances the rest of the car's cost through an amortized loan. Since 70% of $20,000 is $14,000, we have $P = \$14{,}000$, $n = 12$, $t = 5$, and $r = 0.07$. These are substituted into the amortization formula

$$P\left(1 + \frac{r}{n}\right)^{nt} = \frac{p\left[\left(1 + \frac{r}{n}\right)^{nt} - 1\right]}{\frac{r}{n}} \qquad \text{Using the amortization formula}$$

$$14{,}000\left(1 + \frac{0.07}{12}\right)^{12 \cdot 5} = \frac{p\left[\left(1 + \frac{0.07}{12}\right)^{12 \cdot 5} - 1\right]}{\frac{0.07}{12}}$$

Quick Check 1 ☑

The Sharmas purchase a new home for $275,000. Suppose they put 40% down and finance the rest through a mortgage (an amortized home loan) at an annual rate of 4.1%, compounded monthly for 30 yr.

a) Find their monthly payment.
b) If the Sharmas make every payment, what is the total amount they will pay?
c) Find the total interest they will pay on their mortgage, assuming that they make all payments.

Quick Check 2 ☑

Mr. and Mrs. Urrutia qualify for a 30-yr mortgage at 4.5%, compounded monthly. They are able to make payments of $2000 per month. What is the largest loan amount they can afford?

$$19{,}846.75363 = p(71.59290165)$$

$$p = \frac{19{,}846.75363}{71.59290165} = \$277.22. \qquad \text{Solving for } p$$

Thus, Henri's monthly car payment is $277.22.

b) If Henri makes the minimum monthly payment every month for 60 months, he will pay a total of $277.22 · 60 = $16,633.20 to cover the loan. **1** ☑

Sometimes, a person will want to specify a payment amount p and use that to find loan amount P that is affordable.

EXAMPLE 2 **Business: Car Loan.** Chelsea wants to buy a new car and can afford to make payments of $300 per month. She qualifies for a car loan at 5%, compounded monthly for 6 years. What is the largest loan amount she can afford?

Solution We use the amortization formula and make the substitutions:

$$P\left(1 + \frac{r}{n}\right)^{nt} = \frac{p\left[\left(1 + \frac{r}{n}\right)^{nt} - 1\right]}{\frac{r}{n}} \qquad \begin{array}{l}\text{Using the amortization}\\\text{formula}\end{array}$$

$$P\left(1 + \frac{0.05}{12}\right)^{12 \cdot 6} = \frac{300\left[\left(1 + \frac{0.05}{12}\right)^{12 \cdot 6} - 1\right]}{\frac{0.05}{12}} \qquad \text{Substituting}$$

$$P(1.349017744) = 25129.27758$$

$$P = \frac{25129.27758}{1.349017744} = \$18{,}627.83. \qquad \text{Solving for } P$$

Chelsea can afford a loan of up to $18,627.83. **2** ☑

Amortization Schedules

To see the effect each payment has on a loan, we can set up an *amortization schedule*.

EXAMPLE 3 **Amortization Schedule.** From Example 1, Henri's car loan amount is $P = \$14{,}000$ and his monthly payment is $277.22. Fill in the first two rows of the amortization schedule shown below.

Balance	Payment	Portion of Payment Applied to Interest	Portion of Payment Applied to Principal	New Balance
$14,000	$277.22			

Solution During the first month, interest is calculated once. Therefore, we use the simple interest formula to determine 1 month's interest on $14,000 at the annual interest rate of $r = 7\% = 0.07$, with $t = \frac{1}{12}$ representing 1 month:

$$I = Prt$$
$$= \$14{,}000 \cdot 0.07 \cdot \tfrac{1}{12}$$
$$= \$81.67.$$

Henri's payment of $277.22 is split into two parts: $81.67 pays off the first month's interest, and the remainder, $277.22 − $81.67 = $195.55, is applied toward the principal. The new balance is $14,000 − $195.55 = $13,804.45.

Balance	Payment	Portion of Payment Applied to Interest	Portion of Payment Applied to Principal	New Balance
$14,000	$277.22	$81.67	$195.55	$13,804.45
$13,804.45	$277.22			

We repeat the process: The second month's interest is calculated based on $P = \$13,804.45$. We obtain $I = \$13,804.45 \cdot 0.07 \cdot \frac{1}{12} = \$80.53$. The second payment of $277.22 is also split in two parts: $80.53 pays off the interest for the month, and the rest, $277.22 - \$80.53 = \$196.69$, is applied to the principal. The new balance is $\$13,804.45 - \$196.69 = \$13,607.76$.

Balance	Payment	Portion of Payment Applied to Interest	Portion of Payment Applied to Principal	New Balance
$14,000	$277.22	$81.67	$195.55	$13,804.45
$13,804.45	$277.22	$80.53	$196.69	$13,607.76

Quick Check 3 ☑

Complete the first two rows of an amortization schedule for the Sharmas' mortgage (see Quick Check 1).

Slowly, the portion of the monthly payment applied to interest decreases and the portion applied to principal increases. Eventually, very little interest accrues on the balance, and nearly all of the payment is applied to the principal.   **3** ☑

TECHNOLOGY CONNECTION

Amortization Schedules on a Spreadsheet

An amortization schedule like that in Example 3 can be created with a spreadsheet. In cells A1 through E1, enter the headings shown below. In cell A2, enter 14000, and in cell B2, enter 277.22. Highlight the whole sheet and click on the $ button to convert all cells to dollar format:

	A	B	C	D	E
1	Balance Forward	Payment	Portion to Interest	Portion to Principal	New Balance
2	$ 14,000.00	$ 277.22			
3					

Next, in cell C2, enter =A2*0.07/12; in cell D2, enter =B2-C2; in cell E2, enter =A2-D2; and in cell A3, enter =E2. Then copy cells B2 through E2 and paste them into cells B3 through E3. Finally, copy cells A3 through E3 and paste them into cells A4 through E61. This process generates the amortization schedule for all 60 months of the loan period.

   Note that the monthly portion devoted to interest decreases steadily. The final payment reduces the balance to zero. Due to rounding error, small fluctuations in the last row usually occur.

	A	B	C	D	E
1	Balance Forward	Payment	Portion to Interest	Portion to Principal	New Balance
2	$ 14,000.00	$ 277.22	$ 81.67	$ 195.55	$ 13,804.45
3	$ 13,804.45	$ 277.22	$ 80.53	$ 196.69	$ 13,607.75
4	$ 13,607.75	$ 277.22	$ 79.38	$ 197.84	$ 13,409.91
5	$ 13,409.91	$ 277.22	$ 78.22	$ 199.00	$ 13,210.92
6	$ 13,210.92	$ 277.22	$ 77.06	$ 200.16	$ 13,010.76
7	$ 13,010.76	$ 277.22	$ 75.90	$ 201.32	$ 12,809.44
8	$ 12,809.44	$ 277.22	$ 74.72	$ 202.50	$ 12,606.94
9	$ 12,606.94	$ 277.22	$ 73.54	$ 203.68	$ 12,403.26
10	$ 12,403.26	$ 277.22	$ 72.35	$ 204.87	$ 12,198.39
11	$ 12,198.39	$ 277.22	$ 71.16	$ 206.06	$ 11,992.33
12	$ 11,992.33	$ 277.22	$ 69.96	$ 207.26	$ 11,785.06
13	$ 11,785.06	$ 277.22	$ 68.75	$ 208.47	$ 11,576.59
49	$ 3,460.68	$ 277.22	$ 20.19	$ 257.03	$ 3,203.65
50	$ 3,203.65	$ 277.22	$ 18.69	$ 258.53	$ 2,945.12
51	$ 2,945.12	$ 277.22	$ 17.18	$ 260.04	$ 2,685.08
52	$ 2,685.08	$ 277.22	$ 15.66	$ 261.56	$ 2,423.52
53	$ 2,423.52	$ 277.22	$ 14.14	$ 263.08	$ 2,160.44
54	$ 2,160.44	$ 277.22	$ 12.60	$ 264.62	$ 1,895.82
55	$ 1,895.82	$ 277.22	$ 11.06	$ 266.16	$ 1,629.66
56	$ 1,629.66	$ 277.22	$ 9.51	$ 267.71	$ 1,361.95
57	$ 1,361.95	$ 277.22	$ 7.94	$ 269.28	$ 1,092.67
58	$ 1,092.67	$ 277.22	$ 6.37	$ 270.85	$ 821.82
59	$ 821.82	$ 277.22	$ 4.79	$ 272.43	$ 549.40
60	$ 549.40	$ 277.22	$ 3.20	$ 274.02	$ 275.38
61	$ 275.38	$ 277.22	$ 1.61	$ 275.61	$ (0.23)

EXERCISES

1. Suppose Henri decides to pay $300 per month. Make the necessary changes to the amortization schedule. By how many months is the length of the loan reduced, and how much interest does he save?

2. Suppose Henri decides to pay $350 per month. Make the necessary changes to the amortization schedule. By how many months is the length of the loan reduced, and how much interest does he save?

Section Summary

- *Amortization* is a process in which a loan amount P at an annual interest rate r compounded n times per year for t years is paid off (*amortized*) in equal-sized payments p, according to the formula

$$P\left(1 + \frac{r}{n}\right)^{nt} = \frac{p\left[\left(1 + \frac{r}{n}\right)^{nt} - 1\right]}{\frac{r}{n}}.$$

3.6 | Exercise Set

In Exercises 1–10, find the payment amount p needed to amortize the given loan amount. Assume that a payment is made in each of the n compounding periods per year.

1. $P = \$7000;\ r = 6\%;\ t = 5$ yr, compounded monthly

2. $P = \$8000;\ r = 5\%;\ t = 8$ yr, compounded monthly

3. $P = \$12,000;\ r = 5.7\%;\ t = 6$ yr, compounded quarterly

4. $P = \$20,000;\ r = 6.2\%;\ t = 7$ yr, compounded quarterly

5. $P = \$500;\ r = 4.1\%;\ t = 1$ yr, compounded monthly

6. $P = \$800;\ r = 3.8\%;\ t = 2$ yr, compounded monthly

7. $P = \$150,000;\ r = 5.15\%;\ t = 30$ yr, compounded semiannually

8. $P = \$235,000;\ r = 4.35\%;\ t = 30$ yr, compounded semiannually

9. $P = \$75,000;\ r = 8\%;\ t = 15$ yr, compounded annually

10. $P = \$90,000;\ r = 7\%;\ t = 12$ yr, compounded annually

11. Car loans. Todd purchases a new Honda Accord LX for $22,150. He makes a $4000 down payment and finances the remainder through an amortized loan at an annual interest rate of 6.5%, compounded monthly for 5 yr.

  a) Find Todd's monthly car payment.
  b) Assume that Todd makes every payment for the life of the loan. Find his total payments.
  c) How much interest does Todd pay over the life of the loan?

12. Car loans. Katie purchases a new Jeep Wrangler Sport for $23,000. She makes a $5000 down payment and finances the remainder through an amortized loan at an annual interest rate of 5.7%, compounded monthly for 7 yr.

  a) Find Katie's monthly car payment.
  b) Assume that Katie makes every payment for the life of the loan. Find her total payments.
  c) How much interest does Katie pay over the life of the loan?

13. Home mortgages. The Hogansons purchase a new home for $195,000. They make a 25% down payment and finance the remainder with a 30-yr mortgage at an annual interest rate of 5.2%, compounded monthly.

  a) Find the Hogansons' monthly mortgage payment.
  b) Assume that the Hogansons make every payment for the life of the loan. Find their total payments.
  c) How much interest do the Hogansons pay over the life of the loan?

14. Mortgages. Andre purchases an office building for $450,000. He makes a 30% down payment and finances the remainder through a 15-yr mortgage at an annual interest rate of 4.15%, compounded monthly.

  a) Find Andre's monthly mortgage payment.
  b) Assume that Andre makes every payment for the life of the loan. Find his total payments.
  c) How much interest does Andre pay over the life of the loan?

15. Credit cards. Joanna uses her credit card to finance a $500 purchase. Her card charges an annual interest rate of 22.75%, compounded monthly, and assumes a 10-yr term. Assume that Joanna makes no further purchases on her credit card.

  a) Find Joanna's monthly credit card payment.
  b) Assume that Joanna makes every payment for the life of the loan. Find her total payments.
  c) How much interest does Joanna pay over the life of the loan?

16. Credit cards. Isaac uses his credit card to finance a $1200 purchase. His card charges an annual interest rate of 19.25%, compounded monthly, and assumes a 10-yr term. Assume that Isaac makes no further purchases on his credit card.

  a) Find Isaac's monthly credit card payment.
  b) Assume that Isaac makes every payment for the life of the loan. Find his total payments.
  c) How much interest does Isaac pay over the life of the loan?

In Exercises 17–22, complete the first two lines of an amortization schedule for each situation, using a table as shown below.

Balance	Payment	Portion of Payment Applied to Interest	Portion of Payment Applied to Principal	New Balance

17. Todd's car loan in Exercise 11

18. Katie's car loan in Exercise 12

19. The Hogansons' home loan in Exercise 13

20. Andre's office building loan in Exercise 14

21. Joanna's credit card loan in Exercise 15

22. Isaac's credit card loan in Exercise 16

23. Maximum loan amount. Desmond plans to purchase a new car. He qualifies for a loan at an annual interest rate of 5.8%, compounded monthly for 6 yr. He is willing to pay up to $300 per month. What is the largest loan he can afford?

24. Maximum loan amount. Curtis plans to purchase a new car. He qualifies for a loan at an annual interest rate of 7%, compounded monthly for 5 yr. He is willing to pay up to $200 per month. What is the largest loan he can afford?

25. Maximum loan amount. The Daleys plan to purchase a new home. They qualify for a mortgage at an annual interest rate of 4.15%, compounded monthly for 30 yr. They are willing to pay up to $1800 per month. What is the largest loan they can afford?

26. Maximum loan amount. Martina plans to purchase a new home. She qualifies for a mortgage at an annual interest rate of 4.45%, compounded monthly for 20 yr. She is willing to pay up to $2000 per month. What is the largest loan she can afford?

27. Comparing loan options. Kathy plans to finance $12,000 for a new car through an amortized loan. The lender offers two options: (1) a 5-yr term at an annual interest rate of 5.2%, compounded monthly, and (2) a 6-yr term at an annual interest rate of 5%, compounded monthly.

a) Find the monthly payments for options 1 and 2.

b) Assume that Kathy makes every monthly payment. Find her total payments for options 1 and 2.

c) Assume that Kathy intends to make every monthly payment. Which option will result in less interest paid, and how much less?

28. Comparing loan options. The Aubrys plan to finance a new home through an amortized loan of $275,000. The lender offers two options: (1) a 30-yr term at an annual interest rate of 4%, compounded monthly, and (2) a 20-yr term at an annual interest rate of 5%, compounded monthly.

a) Find the monthly payments for options 1 and 2.

b) Assume that the Aubrys make every monthly payment. Find their total payments for options 1 and 2.

c) Assume that the Aubrys intend to make every monthly payment. Which option will result in less interest paid, and by how much?

29. Comparing rates. Darnell plans to finance $200,000 for a new home through a 30-yr mortgage.

a) Find his monthly payment, assuming an annual interest rate of 5%, compounded monthly.

b) Find his monthly payment, assuming an annual interest rate of 6%, compounded monthly.

c) Assume that Darnell makes every payment. How much will he save in interest over 30 yr if he selects the 5% rate?

30. Comparing rates. The Salazars plan to finance $300,000 for a new home through a 20-yr mortgage.

a) Find their monthly payment assuming an annual interest rate of 4.25%, compounded monthly.

b) Find their monthly payment assuming an annual interest rate of 4.75%, compounded monthly.

c) Assume that the Salazars make every payment. How much will they save in interest over 30 yr if they select the 4.25% rate?

SYNTHESIS

31. Retirement planning. Dwight is 25 years old. He plans to retire at age 60 and by then wants to have saved a sum of money that will allow him to withdraw $500 per month for 25 more years (until age 85), at which time the sum will be depleted (amortized). Assume a fixed annual interest rate of 4.5%, compounded monthly for the entire duration.

a) Find the amount of money Dwight will need at age 60.

b) Find the monthly deposit Dwight needs to make in order to reach this sum, assuming that he starts saving immediately.

32. Retirement planning. Kenna is 30 years old. She plans to retire at age 55 and by then wants to have saved a sum of money that will allow her to withdraw $700 per month for 25 more years (until age 80), at which time the sum will be depleted (amortized). Assume a fixed annual interest rate of 5%, compounded monthly for the entire duration.

a) Find the amount of money Kenna will need at age 55.

b) Find the monthly deposit Kenna needs to make in order to reach this sum, assuming that she starts saving immediately.

33. Lottery winnings. Suppose you win $5,000,000 (after taxes) in a lottery. Instead of a one-time payment, you accept a structured plan of annual payments over 20 yr. Under this plan, you receive yearly payments W that assume an annual interest rate of 5% and that will accrue to $5,000,000 over 20 yr. Find the annual payment W you receive under this plan.

34. Structured settlement. Suppose you won a $700,000 (after taxes) settlement in court, to be paid in quarterly payments at an annual interest rate of 4%, compounded quarterly for 5 yr. Find your quarterly payment.

Shortening the life of a loan. *Amortization gives the borrower an advantage: by paying more than the minimum required payment, the borrower can pay off (amortize) the principal faster and save money in interest. Assume P is the loan amount or principal, r is the interest rate, n is the compounding frequency, and t is the time in years. The amortization formula is used to determine the payment amount p that will amortize the loan in t years. However, if the borrower consistently pays Q, where Q > p, the formula for the time needed to amortize the loan amount P is*

$$t = \frac{\ln(nQ) - \ln(nQ - Pr)}{n \ln\left(1 + \frac{r}{n}\right)}.$$

35. Business: home loan. The Begays finance $200,000 for a 30-yr home mortgage at an annual interest rate of 5%, compounded monthly.

a) Find the monthly payment needed to amortize this loan in 30 yr.

b) Assuming that the Begays make the payment found in part (a) every month for 30 yr, find the total interest they will pay.

c) Suppose the Begays pay an extra 15% every month (thus, $Q = 1.15 \cdot p$). Find the time needed to amortize the $200,000 loan.

d) About how much total interest will the Begays pay if they pay Q every month?

e) About how much will the Begays save on interest if they pay Q rather than p every month?

36. Business: car loan. Gwen finances a $15,000 car loan at an annual interest rate of 6%, compounded monthly over a 5-yr term.

a) Find the payment amount needed to amortize this loan in 5 yr.

b) Assuming that Gwen makes the payment found in part (a) every month for 5 yr, find the total interest she will pay.

c) Suppose Gwen pays an extra 20% every month. Find the time needed to amortize the $15,000 loan.

d) About how much total interest will Gwen pay if she pays Q every month?

e) About how much will Gwen save on interest if she pays Q rather than p every month?

37. Derive the formula for t given before Exercise 35.

38. If you are shopping for a car, you will likely be offered loans at different interest rates and/or for different terms. For example, a longer term usually results in a lower monthly payment. Is increasing the term of the loan a good long-term strategy? In general, what is always a good strategy when choosing among various loan options?

TECHNOLOGY CONNECTION

39–44. Use a spreadsheet to complete the first twelve lines of an amortization schedule for each loan in Exercises 11–16.

Answers to Quick Checks

1. (a) $797.28; (b) $287,020.80; (c) $122,020.80
2. $394,722.32   3. First row: $165,000, $797.28, $563.75, $233.53, $164,766.47; second row: $164,766.47, $797.28, $562.95, $234.33, $164,532.14

KEY TERMS AND CONCEPTS	**EXAMPLES**

An **exponential function** f is a function of the form $f(x) = a_0 \cdot a^x$, where x is any real number and a, the **base**, is any positive number other than 1.

The y-intercept of f is $(0, a_0)$; there are no x-intercepts. The domain of an exponential function is $(-\infty, \infty)$.

$$f(x) = \left(\tfrac{1}{2}\right)^x \qquad g(x) = 3 \cdot 2^x$$

The natural base e is such that

$$\frac{d}{dx} e^x = e^x,$$

where $e = \lim_{h \to 0} (1 + h)^{1/h} \approx 2.718$,

and $\dfrac{d}{dx} e^{f(x)} = f'(x) e^{f(x)}$.

$$\frac{d}{dx}(e^{x^2+3x}) = e^{x^2+3x} \cdot (2x + 3) = (2x + 3)e^{x^2+3x}$$

A **logarithmic function** g is any function of the form $g(x) = \log_a x$, where a, the **base**, is a positive number other than 1:

$$y = \log_a x \quad \text{means} \quad a^y = x.$$

Logarithmic functions are inverses of exponential functions.

$$\log_2 8 = 3 \text{ means } 2^3 = 8;$$

$$\log_3 \frac{1}{3} = -1 \text{ means } 3^{-1} = \frac{1}{3};$$

and $\qquad \log_8 64 = x$ means $8^x = 64$, so $x = 2$.

The graph of $y = \log_3 x$:

Remember that $\log_b c$ *is the exponent to which b is raised to get c.* The notation for common and natural logarithms is

$$\log c = \log_{10} c \quad \text{and} \quad \ln c = \log_e c.$$

- $\log 1000 = \log_{10} 10^3 = 3$ and $\ln e^{\sqrt{5}} = \log_e e^{\sqrt{5}} = \sqrt{5}$
- Using a calculator, $\log 50 \approx 1.69897$, and so $10^{1.69897} \approx 50$.

The following properties of logarithms allow us to manipulate expressions. We assume that M, N, and a are positive, with $a \neq 1$, and k is a real number:

$$\log_a (MN) = \log_a M + \log_a N$$
$$\log_a \frac{M}{N} = \log_a M - \log_a N$$
$$\log_a (M^k) = k \log_a M$$
$$\log_a a = 1$$
$$\log_a a^k = k$$
$$\log_a 1 = 0$$
$$\log_b M = \frac{\log_a M}{\log_a b}$$

- $\log_2 8x = \log_2 8 + \log_2 x = 3 + \log_2 x$
- $\log_3 \dfrac{9}{x} = \log_3 9 - \log_3 x = 2 - \log_3 x$
- $\log_4 x^5 = 5 \log_4 x$
- $\log_6 6 = 1$
- $\log_5 25 = \log_5 5^2 = 2$
- $\log_7 1 = 0$
- $\log_3 5 = \dfrac{\log_a 5}{\log_a 3}$. If $a = 10$, then $\log_3 5 = \dfrac{\log 5}{\log 3} \approx 1.465$.

KEY TERMS AND CONCEPTS	**EXAMPLES**

SECTION 3.2 (*continued*)

Logarithms are used to solve certain exponential equations.

Solve: $5e^{2t} = 80$.

We have

$$
\begin{aligned}
5e^{2t} &= 80 \\
e^{2t} &= 16 &&\text{Dividing both sides by 5} \\
\ln e^{2t} &= \ln 16 &&\text{Taking the natural logarithm of both sides} \\
2t &= \ln 16 &&\text{Using a property of logarithms} \\
t &= \frac{\ln 16}{2} \\
t &\approx 1.386
\end{aligned}
$$

The **natural logarithm** is defined by $f(x) = \log_e |x| = \ln |x|$, where $e \approx 2.71828$ and $x \neq 0$. When we write $y = \ln x$, we assume $x > 0$.

The derivative of the natural logarithm of x is the reciprocal of x:

$$
\frac{d}{dx}\ln |x| = \frac{1}{x}, \text{ for } x \neq 0, \text{ and}
$$

$$
\frac{d}{dx}\ln x = \frac{1}{x}, \text{ for } x > 0.
$$

The derivative of $y = \ln f(x)$ is

$$
\frac{d}{dx}\ln f(x) = \frac{f'(x)}{f(x)}.
$$

- $\dfrac{d}{dx}[\ln (x^2 + 8)] = \dfrac{1}{x^2 + 8} \cdot 2x = \dfrac{2x}{x^2 + 8}$

- $\dfrac{d}{dx}\big[\ln (5x) \cdot (x^3 - 7x)\big] = \ln (5x) \cdot \dfrac{d}{dx}(x^3 - 7x) + (x^3 - 7x) \cdot \dfrac{d}{dx}[\ln (5x)]$

  Using the product rule

  $= \ln (5x) \cdot (3x^2 - 7) + (x^3 - 7x) \cdot \dfrac{1}{5x} \cdot 5$

  Simplifying

  $= (3x^2 - 7) \ln (5x) + (x^2 - 7)$

SECTION 3.3

Because exponential functions are the only functions for which the derivative (rate of change) is directly proportional to the function value for any input value, they can model many real-world situations involving uninhibited growth.

If $\dfrac{dP}{dt} = kP$, with $k > 0$, then

$P(t) = P_0 e^{kt}$, where P_0 is the initial population at $t = 0$.

Business. The balance P in an account with Turing Mutual Funds grows at a rate given by

$$
\frac{dP}{dt} = 0.04P,
$$

where t is time, in years. Find the function that satisfies the equation (let $P(0) = P_0$). After what period of time will an initial investment, P_0, double itself?

The function is given by

$$
P = P_0 e^{0.04t}.
$$

Check:

$$
\frac{d}{dt} P_0 e^{0.04t} = P_0 e^{0.04t} \cdot 0.04
$$

$$
= 0.04 P_0 e^{0.04t}
$$

$$
= 0.04P
$$

To find the doubling time, we set $P = 2P_0$ and solve for t:

$$
\begin{aligned}
2P_0 &= P_0 e^{0.04t} \\
2 &= e^{0.04t} &&\text{Dividing both sides by } P_0 \\
\ln 2 &= \ln (e^{0.04t}) &&\text{Taking the natural logarithm of both sides} \\
\ln 2 &= 0.04t \\
\frac{\ln 2}{0.04} &= t, \quad \text{or} \quad t \approx 17.3 \text{ yr.}
\end{aligned}
$$

(*continued*)

KEY TERMS AND CONCEPTS	EXAMPLES

SECTION 3.3 (continued)

The **exponential growth rate** k and the **doubling time** T are related by

$$k = \frac{\ln 2}{T} \quad \text{and} \quad T = \frac{\ln 2}{k}.$$

Two models for limited and inhibited growth are

$$P(t) = \frac{L}{1 + be^{-kt}},$$

and

$$P(t) = L(1 - e^{-kt}),$$

where $k > 0$ and L is the limiting value.

If the exponential growth rate is 4% per year, then the doubling time is

$$T = \frac{\ln 2}{4\%} \approx \frac{0.693147}{0.04} \approx 17.3 \text{ yr}.$$

The doubling time for the number of downloads per day from iSongs is 614 days. The exponential growth rate is

$$k = \frac{\ln 2}{T} \approx \frac{0.693147}{614} \approx 0.0011289 = 0.11\% \text{ per day}.$$

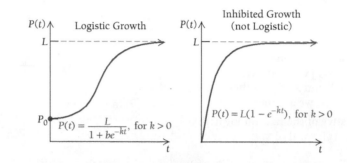

SECTION 3.4

Exponential growth is modeled by $P(t) = P_0e^{kt}$, $k > 0$, and **exponential decay** is modeled by $P(t) = P_0e^{-kt}$, $k > 0$.

Exponential decay characterizes many real-world phenomena. One of the most common is *radioactive decay*.

Physical Science. Lead-210 has a decay rate of 3.15% per year. The rate of change of an amount N of lead-210 is given by

$$\frac{dN}{dt} = -0.0315N.$$

Find the function that satisfies the equation. How much of an 80-g sample of lead-210 will remain after 20 yr?

The function is given by $N(t) = N_0e^{-0.0315t}$.

Check:

$$\frac{d}{dt}(N_0e^{-0.0315t}) = N_0e^{-0.0315t}(-0.0315)$$

$$= -0.0315 \cdot N(t).$$

The amount of an 80-g sample remaining after 20 yr is $N(20) = 80e^{-0.0315(20)} \approx 42.6$ g.

KEY TERMS AND CONCEPTS	EXAMPLES

SECTION 3.4 (continued)

Half-life, T, and *decay rate*, k, are related by

$$k = \frac{\ln 2}{T} \quad \text{and} \quad T = \frac{\ln 2}{k}.$$

The decay equation, $P_0 = Pe^{-kt}$, can also be used to calculate the present value of P dollars due t years in the future.

The half-life of a radioactive isotope is 38 days. The decay rate is

$$T = \frac{\ln 2}{38} = \frac{0.693147}{38} \approx 0.0182 = 1.82\% \text{ per day.}$$

If a sample of an element loses 20% of it mass in 5 yr, then $0.8A = Ae^{-k\cdot 5}$, and

$$k = \frac{\ln 0.8}{5} \approx 0.0446. \text{ Thus, the element's half-life is}$$

$$T = \frac{\ln 2}{0.0446} \approx 15.54 \text{ yr.}$$

The **present value** P_0 of an amount P due t years later, at interest rate k, compounded continuously, is given by

$$P_0 = Pe^{-kt}.$$

The present value of \$200,000 due 8 yr from now, at 4.6% interest, compounded continuously, is given by

$$P_0 = Pe^{-kt} = 200,000e^{-0.046\cdot 8} = \$138,423.44.$$

SECTION 3.5

Formulas can be used to differentiate exponential and logarithmic functions for any base a, other than e:

$$\frac{d}{dx}a^x = (\ln a)a^x \text{ and } \frac{d}{dx}\log_a x = \frac{1}{\ln a}\cdot\frac{1}{x}.$$

$$\frac{d}{dx}7^x = \ln 7 \cdot 7^x$$

$$\frac{d}{dx}\log_6 x = \frac{1}{\ln 6}\cdot\frac{1}{x}$$

An **annuity** is a savings account into which deposits of equal size (called payments) are made on a regular basis.

The **annuity future value**, A, is given by

$$A(t) = \frac{p\left[\left(1 + \frac{r}{n}\right)^{nt} - 1\right]}{\frac{r}{n}},$$

where p is the amount of each regular payment, r is the annual interest rate, n is the number of compounding periods per year (and the number of payments per year), and t is the time in years.

Matt deposits \$500 every month into an annuity that has an annual interest rate of 4.2%, compounded monthly. The value, A, of Matt's annuity after t years is given by

$$A(t) = \frac{500\left[\left(1 + \frac{0.042}{12}\right)^{12t} - 1\right]}{\frac{0.042}{12}} = 142,857.14[(1.0035)^{12t} - 1].$$

The value of Matt's annuity after 6 yr is

$$A(6) = 142,857.14[(1.0035)^{12\cdot 6} - 1] \approx \$40,861.44.$$

The rate of change in the value of the annuity is given by

$$A'(t) = 142,857.14(1.0035)^{12t}(\ln 1.0035)(12) = 5989.52(1.0035)^{12t}.$$

After 6 yr, the annuity is increasing in value at the rate of

$$A'(6) = 5989.52(1.0035)^{12\cdot 6} = \$7702.70/\text{yr.}$$

SECTION 3.6

Amortization is a process in which a loan amount P is paid off in $n \cdot t$ equal payments over a period of t years. The loan amount P and the payment amount p are related by

$$P\left(1 + \frac{r}{n}\right)^{nt} = \frac{p\left[\left(1 + \frac{r}{n}\right)^{nt} - 1\right]}{\frac{r}{n}}.$$

Andy buys a 2014 Nissan Sentra for \$25,000. He pays \$5000 and finances the rest through a 5-yr loan at an annual interest rate of 6%. His monthly car payment is p:

$$20,000\left(1 + \frac{0.06}{12}\right)^{60} = \frac{p\left[\left(1 + \frac{0.06}{12}\right)^{60} - 1\right]}{\frac{0.06}{12}}$$

$$26977.00305 = p(69.77003051)$$

$$p = \frac{26977.00305}{69.77003051} = \$386.66.$$

CHAPTER 3
Review Exercises

These review exercises are for test preparation. They can also be used as a practice test. Answers are at the back of the book. The red bracketed section references tell you what part(s) of the chapter to restudy if your answer is incorrect.

CONCEPT REINFORCEMENT

In Exercises 1–6, match each equation in column A with the most appropriate graph in column B [3.1–3.4]

Column A
Column B

1. $P(t) = 50e^{0.03t}$

2. $P(t) = \dfrac{50}{1 + 2e^{-0.02t}}$

3. $P(t) = 50e^{-0.20t}$

4. $P(t) = \ln t$

5. $P(t) = 50(1 - e^{-0.04t})$

6. $P(t) = 50 + \ln t$

Classify each statement as either true or false.

7. The base a in the exponential function given by $f(x) = a^x$ must be greater than 1. [3.1]

8. The base a in the logarithmic function given by $g(x) = \log_a x$ must be greater than 0. [3.2]

9. If $f'(x) = c \cdot f(x)$ for $c \neq 0$ and $f(x) \neq 0$, then f must be an exponential function. [3.3]

10. With exponential growth, the doubling time depends on the size of the original population. [3.3]

11. A radioactive isotope's half-life can be used to determine the value of its decay constant. [3.4]

12. A radioactive isotope's half-life depends on how much of the substance is initially present. [3.4]

13. For any exponential function of the form $f(x) = a^x$, it follows that $f'(x) = \ln a \cdot a^x$. [3.5]

14. For any logarithmic function of the form $g(x) = \log_a x$, it follows that $g'(x) = \dfrac{1}{a} \cdot \dfrac{1}{x}$. [3.5]

15. It is possible to amortize a loan faster by paying more than the minimum amount for each payment. [3.6]

REVIEW EXERCISES

16. Find x. [3.5]
    a) $\log_2 \frac{1}{8} = x$
    b) $\log_x 9 = \frac{1}{2}$
    c) $\log_4 x = 5$

Differentiate each function.

17. $y = \ln x$ [3.2]

18. $y = e^x$ [3.1]

19. $y = \ln (x^4 + 5)$ [3.2]

20. $y = e^{2\sqrt{x}}$ [3.1]

21. $f(x) = \ln \sqrt{x}$ [3.2]

22. $f(x) = x^4 e^{3x}$ [3.1]

23. $f(x) = \dfrac{\ln x}{x^3}$ [3.2]

24. $f(x) = e^{x^2} \cdot \ln 4x$ [3.1, 3.2]

25. $f(x) = e^{4x} - \ln \dfrac{x}{4}$ [3.1, 3.2]

26. $y = \dfrac{\ln e^x}{e^x}$ [3.1, 3.2]

27. $F(x) = 9^x$ [3.5]

28. $g(x) = \log_2 x$ [3.5]

29. $y = 3^x \cdot \log_4 (2x + 1)$ [3.5]

Graph each function. [3.1]

30. $f(x) = 4^x$

31. $g(x) = \left(\frac{1}{3}\right)^x$

Given $\log_a 2 = 1.8301$ *and* $\log_a 7 = 5.0999$, *find each logarithm.* [3.2]

32. $\log_a 14$

33. $\log_a \frac{2}{7}$

34. $\log_a 28$

35. $\log_a 3.5$

36. $\log_a \sqrt{7}$

37. $\log_a \frac{1}{4}$

38. Find the function Q that satisfies $dQ/dt = 7Q$, given that $Q = 25$ when $t = 0$. [3.3]

39. Life science: population growth. The population of Boomtown doubled in 16 yr. What was the growth rate of the city? Round to the nearest tenth of a percent. [3.3]

40. Business: interest compounded continuously. Suppose $8300 is invested in Noether Bond Fund, for which the interest rate is 3.8%, compounded continuously. How long will it take for the $8300 to double? Round to the nearest tenth of a year. [3.3]

41. Business: cost of a prime-rib dinner. Suppose the average cost C of a prime-rib dinner was $15.81 in 1986 and $27.95 in 2014. Assuming that the exponential growth model applies: [3.3]

   a) Find the exponential growth rate to three decimal places, and write the function that models the situation.

   b) What will the cost of such a dinner be in 2018? In 2024?

42. Business: cost of Oreo cookies. The average cost, C, of Oreo Cookies was $2.69/lb in 1990 and $5.14/lb in 2013. (*Source*: foodtimeline.org.) Assuming that the exponential growth model applies: [3.3]

   a) Find the exponential growth rate to three decimal places, and write the function that models the situation.

   b) What will the cost of 1 lb of Oreo Cookies be in 2020? In 2030?

43. Business: franchise growth. Fashionista Clothing is selling franchises throughout the United States and Canada. It is estimated that the number of franchises N will increase at the rate of 12% per year, that is,

$$\frac{dN}{dt} = 0.12N,$$

where t is the time, in years. [3.3]

   a) Find the function that satisfies the equation, assuming that the number of franchises in 2014 ($t = 0$) is 60.

   b) How many franchises will there be in 2018?

   c) After how long will the number of franchises be 300? Round to the nearest tenth of a year.

44. Business: franchise growth. The Coffee Casa is selling franchises throughout the southwestern United States. It is estimated that the number of franchises N will increase at the rate of 7% per year, that is,

$$\frac{dN}{dt} = 0.07N,$$

where t is the time, in years. [3.3]

   a) Find the function that satisfies the equation, assuming that the number of franchises in 2010 ($t = 0$) was 24.

   b) How many franchises will there be in 2017?

   c) After how long will the number of franchises be double what it was 2010? Round to the nearest tenth of a year.

45. Life science: decay rate. The decay rate of a certain radioactive substance is 13% per year. What is its half-life? Round to the nearest tenth of a year. [3.4]

46. Life science: half-life. The half-life of radon-222 is 3.8 days. What is its decay rate? Round to the nearest tenth of a percent. [3.4]

47. Life science: decay rate. A certain radioactive isotope has a decay rate of 7% per day, that is,

$$\frac{dA}{dt} = -0.07A,$$

where A is the amount of isotope present after t days. [3.4]

   a) Find a function that satisfies the equation if the amount of the isotope present at $t = 0$ is 800 g.

   b) After 20 days, how much of the 800 g will remain? Round to the nearest gram.

   c) After how long will half of the original amount remain?

48. Social science: Hullian learning model. The probability $p(t)$ of mastering a certain assembly-line task after t learning trials is given by

$$p(t) = 1 - e^{-0.7t}. \quad [3.3]$$

   a) What is the probability of learning the task after 1 trial? 2 trials? 5 trials? 10 trials? 14 trials?

   b) Find the rate of change, $p'(t)$.

   c) Interpret the meaning of $p'(t)$.

   d) Sketch a graph of the function.

49. Business: present value. Find the present value of $1,000,000 due 40 yr later at 4.2%, compounded continuously. [3.4]

50. Business: annuity. Patrice deposits $50 into a savings account every month at an annual interest rate of 4.7%, compounded monthly. [3.5]

   a) How much will her account contain after 8 yr, assuming she makes no withdrawals?

   b) What is the rate of change in the value of Patrice's account after 8 yr?

51. Business: car loan. Glenda buys a used Subaru Outback for $13,000. She pays 25% down and finances the rest at an annual interest rate of 6.5%, compounded monthly for 5 yr. [3.6]

a) Find Glenda's monthly car payment.

b) If Glenda makes every payment for the life of the loan, find the total interest she will pay.

52. Business: home mortgage. The Savards qualify for a 30-yr mortgage at an annual interest rate of 4.25%, compounded monthly. They are willing to pay up to $2500 per month as their mortgage payment. What is the most they can afford to borrow? [3.6]

53. Business: credit card. Vicki uses her credit card to buy $1200 in goods. Her credit card has an annual interest rate of 20.75%, compounded monthly over a 10-yr term. Assume that Vicki makes no additional purchases with this credit card. [3.6]

a) Find the amount of Vicki's monthly payment.

b) Assume that Vicki pays the amount found in part (a). In the first month, what will she pay in interest, and what will she pay toward the principal?

SYNTHESIS

54. Differentiate: $y = \dfrac{e^{2x} + e^{-2x}}{e^{2x} - e^{-2x}}$. [3.1]

55. Find the minimum value of $f(x) = x^4 \ln (4x)$. [3.2]

56. Graph: $f(x) = \dfrac{e^{1/x}}{(1 + e^{1/x})^2}$. [3.1]

57. Find $\lim\limits_{x \to 0} \dfrac{e^{1/x}}{(1 + e^{1/x})^2}$. [3.1]

58. Business: shopping on the Internet. Online sales of all types of consumer products increased at an exponential rate in recent years. Data in the following table show online retail sales in the United States, in billions of dollars. [3.3]

Years, t, after 2010	U.S. Online Retail Sales (in billions)
0	$167
1	194
2	231
3	262
4	291

(*Sources*: Internetretailer.com; www.census.gov.)

a) Use REGRESSION to fit an exponential function $y = a \cdot b^x$ to the data. Then convert that formula to an exponential function, base e, where t is the number of years after 2010, and determine the exponential growth rate.

b) Estimate online sales in 2016 and in 2020.

c) After what amount of time will online sales be $1 trillion?

d) What is the doubling time for online sales?

CHAPTER 3
Test

Differentiate.

1. $y = 2e^{3x}$

2. $y = (\ln x)^4$

3. $f(x) = e^{-x^2}$

4. $f(x) = \ln \dfrac{x}{7}$

5. $f(x) = e^x - 5x^3$

6. $f(x) = 3e^x \ln x$

7. $y = 7^x + 3^x$

8. $y = \log_{14} x$

9. Solve:

a) $\log_2 32 = x$;

b) $\log_8 x = \frac{1}{3}$.

Given $\log_b 2 = 0.2560$ *and* $\log_b 9 = 0.8114$, *find each of the following.*

10. $\log_b 18$

11. $\log_b 4.5$

12. $\log_b 3$

13. Find the function that satisfies $dM/dt = 6M$, if $M = 2$ at $t = 0$.

14. The doubling time for a certain bacteria population is 3 hr. What is the growth rate? Round to the nearest tenth of a percent.

APPLICATIONS

15. Business: interest compounded continuously. An investment is made at 6.931% per year, compounded continuously. What is the doubling time? Round to the nearest tenth of a year.

16. Business: cost of milk. The cost C of a gallon of milk was $3.22 in 2006. In 2013, it was $3.50. (*Source*: U.S. Department of Labor, Bureau of Labor Statistics.) Assuming that the exponential growth model applies:

a) Find the exponential growth rate to the nearest tenth of a percent, and write the equation.

b) Estimate the cost of a gallon of milk in 2016 and in 2020.

17. Life science: drug dosage. A dose of a drug is injected into the body of a patient. The drug amount in the body decreases at the rate of 10% per hour, that is,

$$\frac{dA}{dt} = -0.1A,$$

where A is the amount in the body and t is the time, in hours.

a) A dose of 3 cubic centimeters (cc) is administered. Assuming $A_0 = 3$, find the function that satisfies the equation.

b) How much of the initial dose of 3 cc remains after 10 hr?

c) After how long does half of the original dose remain?

18. Life science: decay rate. The decay rate of radium-226 is 4.209% per century. What is its half-life?

19. Life science: half-life. The half-life of bohrium-267 is 17 sec. What is its decay rate? Express the rate as a percentage rounded to four decimal places.

20. Business: effect of advertising. Twin City Roasters introduced a new coffee in a trial run. The firm advertised the coffee on television and found that the percentage $P(t)$ of people who bought the coffee after t ads had been run was

$$P(t) = \frac{100}{1 + 24e^{-0.28t}}.$$

a) What percentage of people bought the coffee before seeing the ad ($t = 0$)?

b) What percentage bought the coffee after the ad had been run 1 time? 5 times? 10 times? 20 times? 30 times?

c) Find the rate of change, $P'(t)$.

d) Interpret the meaning of $P'(t)$.

e) Sketch a graph of the function.

21. Business: annuity. Jill deposits $20 per week into an account for holiday shopping. The account has an annual interest rate of 3.3%, compounded weekly.

a) Find the future value of Jill's account after 1 yr (52 weeks).

b) What is the rate of change in the value of her account after 1 yr?

22. Business: amortized loan. The Langways purchase a new home for $450,000. They pay 20% down and finance the rest through a 30-yr mortgage at an annual interest rate of 3.75%, compounded monthly.

a) How much is the Langways' monthly mortgage payment?

b) Assuming that the Langways make the monthly payment found in part (a) for the life of the loan, how much will they pay in total?

c) How much interest will they pay?

23. Business: car loan. Giselle qualifies for a car loan at an annual interest rate of 5.75%, compounded monthly for

5 yr. She is willing to pay up to $400 per month in car payments. What is the maximum loan amount she can afford?

SYNTHESIS

24. Differentiate: $y = x(\ln x)^2 - 2x\ln x + 2x$.

25. Find the maximum and minimum values of $f(x) = x^4 e^{-x}$ over $[0, 10]$.

TECHNOLOGY CONNECTION

26. Graph: $f(x) = \dfrac{e^x - e^{-x}}{e^x + e^{-x}}$.

27. Find $\displaystyle\lim_{x \to 0} \dfrac{e^x - e^{-x}}{e^x + e^{-x}}$.

28. Business: average price of a television commercial. The cost of a 30-sec television commercial that runs during the Super Bowl was increasing exponentially from 1991 to 2014. Data in the table below show costs for those years.

Years, t, after 1990	Cost of Commercial
1	$800,000
3	850,000
5	1,000,000
8	1,300,000
13	2,100,000
16	2,600,000
22	3,500,000
24	4,000,000

(*Source*: National Football League.)

a) Use REGRESSION to fit an exponential function $y = a \cdot b^x$ to the data. Then convert that formula to an exponential function, base e, where t is the number of years after 1990.

b) Estimate the cost of a commercial run during the Super Bowl in 2017 and 2020.

c) After what amount of time will the cost be $1 billion?

d) What is the doubling time of the cost of a commercial run during the Super Bowl?

e) The cost of a Super Bowl commercial in 2009 turned out to be $3 million, and in 2010 it dropped to about $2.8 million, possibly due to the decline in the world economy. Expand the table of costs, and make a scatterplot of the data. Does the cost still seem to follow an exponential function? Explain. What kind of curve seems to fit the data best? Fit that curve using REGRESSION, and predict the cost of a Super Bowl commercial in 2017 and 2020. Compare your answers to those for part (b).

The Business of Motion Picture Revenue and DVD Release

There has been increasing pressure by motion picture executives to narrow the gap between theater release of a movie and release to DVD. The executives want to reduce marketing expenses, adapt to the increasing consumption of on-demand movies, and boost decreasing DVD sales. Theater owners, on the other hand, want to protect sales. The owners are fearful that if movie executives shorten the time between theater release and DVD release, the number of ticket buyers will drop, as many people will wait for the DVD.

The table to the right gives the number of days between theater release and DVD release for 10 movies. Note that the average gap in time is about 4 months.

Let's examine the data for *Monsters University*. The table on the facing page presents the weekly estimates of gross revenue, G, for the movie. The total revenue, R, is approximated by adding each week's gross revenue to the previous week's total revenue.

Exercises

1. A movie executive wants to fit a function to the data. Make a scatterplot of the data points (t, G); then use **REGRESSION** to fit linear, quadratic, cubic, and exponential functions to the data, and graph each equation with the scatterplot. Which function fits best? Why?

2. Use the exponential function to predict gross revenue, G, for weeks 9 through 13.

MOVIE	RELEASE DATES	NUMBER OF DAYS SEPARATING RELEASE DATES
Dallas Buyers Club	Theater: Nov. 1, 2013 DVD: Feb. 4, 2014	96
12 Years a Slave	Theater: Oct. 18, 2013 DVD: Mar. 4, 2014	137
American Hustle	Theater: Dec. 13, 2013 DVD: Mar. 18, 2014	95
Lee Daniels' The Butler	Theater: Aug. 16, 2013 DVD: Jan. 14, 2014	151
Captain Phillips	Theater: Oct. 11, 2013 DVD: Jan. 21, 2014	102
Rush	Theater: Sept. 20, 2013 DVD: Jan. 28, 2014	130
Monsters University	Theater: June 21, 2013 DVD: Oct. 29, 2013	130
Man of Steel	Theater: June 14, 2013 DVD: Dec. 12, 2013	181
Star Trek: Into Darkness	Theater: May 17, 2013 DVD: Sept. 10, 2013	116
World War Z	Theater: June 21, 2013 DVD: Sept. 17, 2013	88

Average = 122 days, or about 4 months

(*Source*: www.imdb.com.)

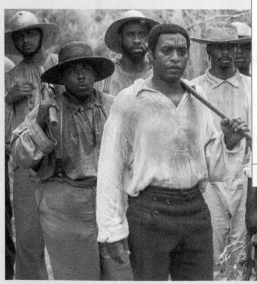

3. Use your predictions from Exercise 2 to compute total revenue, R, for weeks 9 through 13.

4. Use REGRESSION to fit a logistic function of the form $R(t) = c/(1 + ae^{-bt})$ to the data points (t, R) for weeks 1–8. Based on these results, what seems to be a limiting value for the total revenue from *Monsters University*?

5. Find the rate of change $R'(t)$, and explain what it means. Find $\lim_{t \to \infty} R'(t)$, and explain what it represents.

6. The DVD release for *Monsters University* was October 29, 2013. Based on the given data, do you think this release date was appropriate? What other factors might influence the release date of a DVD?

7. Now, consider the data for *Dallas Buyer's Club*, shown in the table to the right. This movie was released in selected theaters on November 1, 2013, and released nationwide (United States and Canada) on November 22, 2013. Make a scatterplot of the data points (t, G) for weeks 1 through 8, and fit linear, quadratic, cubic, and exponential functions to the data. Which function, if any, best estimates the weekly gross revenue for weeks 9 through 14?

8. Make a scatterplot of the data points (t, G) for weeks 4 through 8, and fit linear, quadratic, cubic and exponential functions to the data. Which function, if any, best estimates the weekly gross revenue for the weeks 9 through 14?

9. Using procedures similar to Exercises 2–4, find a limiting value for the total revenue of *Dallas Buyers Club*. The DVD's release date was February 4, 2014, or 14 weeks after theater release. Was the release date appropriate? Why or why not?

Revenue for *Monsters University*

WEEK IN RELEASE, t (week 1 = June 20–26, 2013)	WEEKLY REVENUE, G (current week estimates, in millions)	TOTAL REVENUE, R (or cumulative box office revenue, in millions)
1. June 26	$115.33	$115.33
2. July 2	$70.57	$185.90
3. July 9	$36.09	$221.99
4. July 16	$19.23	$241.22
5. July 23	$9.72	$250.94
6. July 30	$5.49	$256.43
7. Aug. 6	$2.66	$259.09
8. Aug. 13	$1.37	$260.46
9. Aug. 20	?	?
10. Aug. 27	?	?
11. Sept. 3	?	?
12. Sept. 10	?	?
13. Sept. 17	?	?

(*Source:* www.the-numbers.com.)

Revenue for *Dallas Buyers Club*

WEEK IN RELEASE, t (week 1 = November 1–7, 2013)	WEEKLY REVENUE, G (current week estimates, in millions)	TOTAL REVENUE, R (or cumulative box office revenue, in millions)
1. Nov. 7	$0.35	$0.35
2. Nov. 14	$0.91	$1.26
3. Nov. 21	$2.43	$3.69
4. Nov. 28	$4.01	$7.70
5. Dec. 5	$3.25	$10.95
6. Dec. 12	$2.18	$13.13
7. Dec. 19	$1.64	$14.77
8. Dec. 26	$0.68	$15.45
9. Jan. 2, 2014	?	?
10. Jan. 9	?	?
11. Jan. 16	?	?
12. Jan. 23	?	?
13. Jan. 30	?	?
14. Feb. 6 (week of DVD release)	?	?

(*Source:* www.the-numbers.com.)

Cumulative Review

1. Write an equation of the line with slope -4 and containing the point $(-7, 1)$.

2. Find the slope and the y-intercept of $2x - 6y = 9$.

3. For $f(x) = x^2 - 5$, find $f(x + h)$.

4. a) Graph:
$$f(x) = \begin{cases} 5 - x, & \text{for } x \neq 2, \\ -3, & \text{for } x = 2. \end{cases}$$
   b) Find $\lim\limits_{x \to 2} f(x)$.
   c) Find $f(2)$.
   d) Is f continuous at 2?

5. a) Graph: $g(x) = \begin{cases} 9 - x^2, & x \leq 1, \\ x + 7, & x > 1. \end{cases}$
   b) Find $\lim\limits_{x \to 1} g(x)$.
   c) Find $g(1)$.
   d) Is g continuous at 1?

Find each limit, if it exists. If a limit does not exist, state that fact.

6. $\lim\limits_{x \to 1} \sqrt{x^3 + 8}$

7. $\lim\limits_{x \to -4} \dfrac{x^2 - 16}{x + 4}$

8. $\lim\limits_{x \to 3} \dfrac{4}{x - 3}$

9. $\lim\limits_{x \to \infty} \dfrac{12x - 7}{3x + 2}$

10. $\lim\limits_{x \to \infty} \dfrac{2x^3 - x}{8x^5 - x^2 + 1}$

11. If $f(x) = x^2 + 3$, find $f'(x)$ by determining
$$\lim_{h \to 0} \frac{f(x + h) - f(x)}{h}.$$

For exercises 12–14, refer to the following graph of $y = h(x)$.

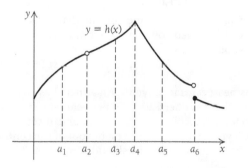

12. Identify the input values for which h has no limit.

13. Identify the input values for which h is discontinuous.

14. Identify the input values for which the derivative of h does not exist.

Differentiate.

15. $y = -9x + 3$

16. $y = x^2 - 7x + 3$

17. $y = x^{1/4}$

18. $f(x) = x^{-6}$

19. $f(x) = \sqrt[3]{2x^5 - 8}$

20. $f(x) = \dfrac{5x^3 + 4}{2x - 1}$

21. $y = \ln(x^2 + 5)$

22. $y = e^{\ln x}$

23. $y = e^{3x} + x^2$

24. $y = e^{\sqrt{x-3}}$

25. $f(x) = \ln(e^x - 4)$

26. For $y = x^2 - \dfrac{2}{x}$, find d^2y/dx^2.

27. **Business: average cost.** Doubletake Clothing finds that the cost, in dollars, of producing x pairs of jeans is given by $C(x) = 320 + 9\sqrt{x}$. Find the rate at which the average cost is changing when 100 pairs of jeans have been produced.

28. Differentiate implicitly to find dy/dx if $x^3 + x/y = 7$.

29. Find an equation of the tangent line to the graph of $y = e^x - x^2 - 3$ at the point $(0, -2)$.

30. Find the x-value(s) at which the tangent line to $f(x) = x^3 - 2x^2$ has a slope of -1.

Sketch the graph of each function. List and label the coordinates of any extrema and points of inflection. State where the function is increasing or decreasing, where it is concave up or concave down, and where any asymptotes occur.

31. $f(x) = x^3 - 3x + 1$

32. $f(x) = 2x^2 - x^4 - 3$

33. $f(x) = \dfrac{8x}{x^2 + 1}$

34. $f(x) = \dfrac{8}{x^2 - 4}$

Find the absolute maximum and minimum values, if they exist, over the indicated interval. If no interval is indicated, consider the entire real number line.

35. $f(x) = 3x^2 - 6x - 4$

36. $f(x) = -5x + 1$

37. $f(x) = \frac{1}{3}x^3 - x^2 - 3x + 5$; $[-2, 0]$

38. **Business: maximizing profit.** Detailed Clothing's total revenue and total cost, in dollars, from the sale of x custom sweatshirts are given by
$$R(x) = 4x^2 + 11x + 110,$$
$$C(x) = 4.2x^2 + 5x + 10.$$
Find the number of sweatshirts, x, that must be produced and sold in order to maximize profit.

39. Business: minimizing inventory costs. An electronics store sells 450 sets of earbuds each year. It costs $4 to store a set for a year. When placing an order, there is a fixed cost of $1 plus $0.75 for each set. How many times per year should the store reorder earbuds, and in what lot size, in order to minimize inventory costs?

40. Let $y = 3x^2 - 2x + 1$. Use differentials to find the approximate change in y when $x = 2$ and $\Delta x = 0.05$.

41. Business: exponential growth. Frieda's Frozen Yogurt is experiencing growth of 10% per year in the number, N, of franchises it owns; that is,

$$\frac{dN}{dt} = 0.1N,$$

where N is the number of franchises and t is the time, in years, from 2011.

a) Given that there were 8000 franchises in 2011, find the solution of the equation, assuming that $N_0 = 8000$ and $k = 0.1$.

b) Predict the number of franchises in 2019.

c) What is the doubling time for the number of franchises?

42. Economics: elasticity of demand. Consider the demand function given by

$$q = D(x) = 240 - 20x,$$

where q is the quantity of coffee mugs demanded at a price of x dollars per mug.

a) Find the elasticity.

b) Find the elasticity at $x = \$2$, and state whether the demand is elastic or inelastic.

c) Find the elasticity at $x = \$9$, and state whether the demand is elastic or inelastic.

d) At a price of $2, will a small increase in price cause total revenue to increase or decrease?

e) Find the value of x for which the total revenue is a maximum.

43. Business: approximating cost overage. A square plot of ground measures 75 ft by 75 ft, with a tolerance of ± 4 in. Landscapers are going to cover the plot with grass sod. Each square of sod costs $8 and measures 3 ft by 3 ft.

a) Use differentials to estimate the change in area when the measurement tolerance is taken into acount.

b) How many extra squares of sod should the landscapers bring to the job, and how much extra will this cost?

44. Gail deposits $250 every month into an annuity at an annual interest rate of 3.35%, compounded monthly.

a) Find a function $A(t)$ that gives the value of Gail's annuity after t years.

b) Find the value of Gail's annuity after 3 yr.

c) What is the rate of change in the value of Gail's annuity after 3 yr?

45. Garth purchases a new Toyota Highlander for $31,050. He makes a down payment of $7500 and finances the rest of the cost through a 6-yr amortized loan at an annual interest rate of 5.25%, compounded monthly.

a) Find Garth's monthly payment.

b) Assume that Garth makes every payment for the life of the loan. Find the total of his payments.

c) How much total interest will Garth pay?

d) Fill in the two rows of Garth's amortization schedule below.

Balance	Payment	Portion of Payment Applied to Interest	Portion of Payment Applied to Principal	New Balance
$23,550				

Evaluate.

46. $\displaystyle\int 3x^5\, dx$

47. $\displaystyle\int_{-1}^{0} (2e^x + 1)\, dx$

48. $\displaystyle\int \frac{x}{(7 - 3x)^2}\, dx$ (Use Table 1 on pp. 431–432.)

49. $\displaystyle\int x^3 e^{x^4}\, dx$

50. $\displaystyle\int (x + 3) \ln x\, dx$

51. $\displaystyle\int \frac{75}{x}\, dx$

52. $\displaystyle\int_{0}^{1} 3\sqrt{x}\, dx$

53. Find the area under the graph of $y = x^2 + 3x$ over the interval $[1, 5]$.

54. Business: present value. Find the present value of $250,000 due in 30 yr at 6%, compounded continuously.

55. Business: value of a fund. Leigh Ann wants to have $50,000 saved in 10 yr.

a) She makes a one-time deposit at an APR of 5.45%, compounded continuously. Find the amount she should deposit.

b) Calculate the interest earned in part (a).

56. Business: contract buyout. An athlete has an 8-yr contract that pays her $200,000 per year. She invests the money at an APR of 4.85%, compounded continuously. After 5 yr, the team offers her a buyout of the contract. What is the lowest amount she should accept?

57. Determine whether the following improper integral is convergent or divergent, and calculate its value if it is convergent:

$$\int_{3}^{\infty} \frac{1}{x^7}\, dx.$$

58. Economics: supply and demand. Demand and supply functions are given by

$$p = D(x) = (x - 20)^2$$

and

$$p = S(x) = x^2 + 10x + 50,$$

where p is the price per unit, in dollars, when x units are sold. Find the equilibrium point and the consumer's surplus.

59. Find the volume of the solid of revolution generated by rotating the region under the graph of $y = e^{-x}$, from $x = 0$ to $x = 5$, around the x-axis.

60. Find the volume of the solid of revolution generated by rotating the region under the graph of $y = (x^2 + 1)^2$, from $x = 0$ to $x = 2$, around the y-axis.

61. Consider the data in the following table.

Age of Business (in years)	1	3	5
Profit (in tens of thousands of dollars)	4	7	12

a) Find the regression line, $y = mx + b$.
b) Use the regression line to predict the profit when the business is 10 years old.
c) Find the exponential regression curve, $y = ae^{bx}$.
d) Use the exponential regression curve to predict the profit when the business is 10 years old.

Given $f(x, y) = e^y + 4x^2y^3 + 3x$, *find each of the following.*

62. f_x **63.** f_{yy}

64. Find the relative maximum and minimum values of $f(x, y) = x^2 + y^2 - xy - 8x + 7y + 9$.

65. Maximize $f(x, y) = 4x + 2y - x^2 - y^2 + 4$, subject to the constraint $x + 2y = 9$.

66. Evaluate $\int_0^3 \int_{-1}^2 e^x \, dy \, dx$.

67. Business: demographics. The number of shoppers, in hundreds per square mile, who shop at Los Arcos Mall is modeled by $f(x, y) = 10 - x - y^2$, where x is miles from the mall toward the east and y is miles from the mall toward the north. The graph below shows a shaded region to the northeast of the mall, which is at $(0, 0)$. Find the total number of mall shoppers in the region.

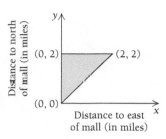

68. Solve the differential equation $dy/dx = xy$.

69. Solve the differential equation $y' + 4xy = 3x$, where $y = 3$ when $x = -1$.

70. Suppose the rate of change of y with respect to x is directly proportional to the square root of y. Assume $y \geq 0$.

a) Write a differential equation that models this situation.
b) Find the general solution of the equation from part (a).

71. A jar contains 12 yellow candies, 15 red candies, and 20 green candies. A single candy is chosen at random.

a) Find the probability that a yellow candy is chosen.
b) Find the probability that a green candy is not chosen.
c) Find the probability that a red or green candy is chosen.
d) Find the probability that a blue candy is chosen.

72. Business: distribution of weights. The weight, in pounds, of a box of a certain cereal is uniformly distributed between 2 lb and 2.25 lb. Find the probability that a randomly chosen box of this cereal weighs between 2.07 lb and 2.1 lb.

73. Business: wait times. The wait time t, in minutes, between customers at Teri's Book Nook can be modeled by the probability density function $f(t) = 0.45e^{-0.45t}$, for $0 \leq t < \infty$.

a) What is the probability that the wait time is at most 2 min?
b) What is the probability that the wait time is greater than 5 min?

74. Let $f(x) = \dfrac{c}{x^2}$ be a probability density function over the interval $[1, 3]$.

a) Find c.
b) Find the mean μ and the standard deviation σ.
c) Find $P([1.5, 2.5])$.

75. Business: distribution of salaries. The salaries paid by a large corporation are normally distributed with a mean $\mu = \$75,000$ and a standard deviation $\sigma = \$6,000$.

a) Find the probability that a randomly chosen employee earns between $72,000 and $85,000 per year.
b) An executive of the corporation earns $90,000 per year. In what percentile of the salaries does this salary place him?
c) A new employee insists on a salary that is in the top 2% of salaries. What is the minimum salary that this employee would accept?

Review of Basic Algebra

- Manipulate exponential expressions.
- Multiply and factor algebraic expressions.
- Solve equations, inequalities, and applied problems.

This appendix covers most of the algebraic topics essential to a study of calculus. It can be used in conjunction with Chapter R or as needed throughout the book.

Exponential Notation

Let's review the meaning of an expression

$$a^n,$$

where a is any real number and n is an integer; that is, n is a number in the set $\{\ldots, -3, -2, -1, 0, 1, 2, 3, \ldots\}$. The number a is the **base** and n is the **exponent**.

For an integer n greater than 1,

$$a^n = \underbrace{a \cdot a \cdot a \cdots a}_{n \text{ factors}}.$$

In other words, a^n is the product of n **factors**, each of which is a.

EXAMPLE 1 Write equivalent expressions without exponents.

a) 4^3 **b)** $(-2)^5$ **c)** $(-2)^4$ **d)** -2^4 **e)** $\left(\dfrac{1}{2}\right)^3$

Quick Check 1 ✔

Write equivalent expressions without exponents.

a) 3^5

b) $(-5)^2$

c) $\left(\frac{2}{3}\right)^4$

Solution

a) $4^3 = 4 \cdot 4 \cdot 4 = 64$

b) $(-2)^5 = (-2)(-2)(-2)(-2)(-2) = -32$

c) $(-2)^4 = (-2)(-2)(-2)(-2) = 16$

d) $-2^4 = -(2^4) = -(2)(2)(2)(2) = -16$ The base is 2 , not -2.

e) $\left(\dfrac{1}{2}\right)^3 = \dfrac{1}{2} \cdot \dfrac{1}{2} \cdot \dfrac{1}{2} = \dfrac{1}{8}$

1 ✔

We define an exponent of 1 as follows:

$a^1 = a$, for any real number a.

In other words, any real number to the first power is that number itself.
We define an exponent of 0 as follows:

$a^0 = 1$, for any nonzero real number a.

EXAMPLE 2 Write equivalent expressions without exponents.

a) $(-2x)^0$ **b)** $(-2x)^1$ **c)** $\left(\dfrac{1}{2}\right)^0$ **d)** $-e^0$ **e)** e^1 **f)** $\left(\dfrac{1}{2}\right)^1$

Quick Check 2 ✔

Write equivalent expressions without exponents.

a) $\left(\frac{2}{5}\right)^0$

b) $\left(\frac{2}{5}\right)^1$

c) -4^0

Solution

a) $(-2x)^0 = 1$

b) $(-2x)^1 = -2x$

c) $\left(\frac{1}{2}\right)^0 = 1$

d) $-e^0 = -1$

e) $e^1 = e$

f) $\left(\frac{1}{2}\right)^1 = \frac{1}{2}$ 2 ✔

The meaning of a negative integer as an exponent is as follows:

$$a^{-n} = \left(\frac{1}{a}\right)^n = \frac{1}{a^n}, \text{ for any nonzero real number } a.$$

That is, any nonzero real number a to the $-n$ power is (the reciprocal of a)^n, or equivalently, the reciprocal of a^n.

EXAMPLE 3   Write equivalent expressions without negative exponents.

a) 2^{-5} **b)** $\left(\frac{3}{4}\right)^{-2}$ **c)** $2x^{-5}$ **d)** e^{-k} **e)** $\frac{1}{t^{-1}}$

Quick Check 3 ✔

Write equivalent expressions without negative exponents.

a) 3^{-2}

b) $\frac{1}{4^{-3}}$

c) $8x^{-5}$

Solution

a) $2^{-5} = \frac{1}{2^5} = \frac{1}{2 \cdot 2 \cdot 2 \cdot 2 \cdot 2} = \frac{1}{32}$

b) $\left(\frac{3}{4}\right)^{-2} = \left(\frac{4}{3}\right)^2 = \frac{4^2}{3^2} = \frac{16}{9}$

c) $2x^{-5} = \frac{2}{x^5}$

d) $e^{-k} = \frac{1}{e^k}$

e) $\frac{1}{t^{-1}} = \left(\frac{1}{t}\right)^{-1} = t^1 = t$ 3 ✔

Properties of Exponents

Note the following:

$$b^5 \cdot b^{-3} = (b \cdot b \cdot b \cdot b \cdot b) \cdot \frac{1}{b \cdot b \cdot b}$$
$$= \frac{b \cdot b \cdot b}{b \cdot b \cdot b} \cdot b \cdot b$$
$$= 1 \cdot b \cdot b = b^2.$$

We can obtain the same result by adding the exponents. This is true in general.

THEOREM 1

For any nonzero real number a and any integers n and m,
$$a^n \cdot a^m = a^{n+m}.$$

(To multiply when the bases are the same, add the exponents.)

EXAMPLE 4 Multiply:

a) $x^5 \cdot x^6$ b) $x^{-5} \cdot x^6$ c) $2x^{-3} \cdot 5x^{-4}$ d) $r^2 \cdot r$ e) $x^3 \cdot x^7 \cdot x^{-2}$

Solution

a) $x^5 \cdot x^6 = x^{5+6} = x^{11}$

b) $x^{-5} \cdot x^6 = x^{-5+6} = x$

c) $2x^{-3} \cdot 5x^{-4} = 10x^{-3+(-4)} = 10x^{-7}$, or $\dfrac{10}{x^7}$

d) $r^2 \cdot r = r^{2+1} = r^3$

e) $x^3 \cdot x^7 \cdot x^{-2} = x^{3+7+(-2)} = x^8$

Quick Check 4 ✔

Multiply.

a) $t^5 \cdot t^3$
b) $4x^2 \cdot 7x^{-5}$
c) $y^4 y^{-9} y$

4 ✔

Note the following:

$$b^5 \div b^2 = \frac{b^5}{b^2} = \frac{b \cdot b \cdot b \cdot b \cdot b}{b \cdot b}$$

$$= \frac{b \cdot b}{b \cdot b} \cdot b \cdot b \cdot b$$

$$= 1 \cdot b \cdot b \cdot b = b^3.$$

We can obtain the same result by subtracting the exponents. This is true in general.

THEOREM 2

For any nonzero real number a and any integers n and m,

$$\frac{a^n}{a^m} = a^{n-m}.$$

(To divide when the bases are the same, subtract the exponent in the denominator from the exponent in the numerator.)

EXAMPLE 5 Divide:

a) $\dfrac{a^3}{a^2}$ b) $\dfrac{x^7}{x^7}$ c) $\dfrac{e^3}{e^{-4}}$ d) $\dfrac{e^{-4}}{e^{-1}}$ e) $\dfrac{c^2 c^8}{c^{12}}$

Solution

a) $\dfrac{a^3}{a^2} = a^{3-2} = a^1 = a$

b) $\dfrac{x^7}{x^7} = x^{7-7} = x^0 = 1$

c) $\dfrac{e^3}{e^{-4}} = e^{3-(-4)} = e^{3+4} = e^7$

d) $\dfrac{e^{-4}}{e^{-1}} = e^{-4-(-1)} = e^{-4+1} = e^{-3}$, or $\dfrac{1}{e^3}$

e) $\dfrac{c^2 c^8}{c^{12}} = c^{2+8-12} = c^{-2}$, or $\dfrac{1}{c^2}$

Quick Check 5 ✔

Divide.

a) $\dfrac{d^7}{d^2}$

b) $\dfrac{t^3}{t^{-5}}$

c) $\dfrac{u^5 u^{12}}{u^3}$

5 ✔

Note the following:

$$(b^2)^3 = b^2 \cdot b^2 \cdot b^2 = b^{2+2+2} = b^6.$$

We can obtain the same result by multiplying the exponents. The other results in Theorem 3 can be similarly motivated.

THEOREM 3

For any nonzero real numbers a and b, and any integers n and m,

$$(a^n)^m = a^{nm}, \qquad (ab)^n = a^n b^n, \quad \text{and} \quad \left(\frac{a}{b}\right)^n = \frac{a^n}{b^n}.$$

EXAMPLE 6 Simplify:

a) $(x^{-2})^3$ **b)** $(e^x)^2$ **c)** $(2x^4y^{-5}z^3)^{-3}$ **d)** $\left(\dfrac{x^2}{p^4 q^5}\right)^3$

Solution

a) $(x^{-2})^3 = x^{-2 \cdot 3} = x^{-6}, \quad \text{or} \quad \dfrac{1}{x^6}$ **b)** $(e^x)^2 = e^{2x}$

c) $(2x^4 y^{-5} z^3)^{-3} = 2^{-3}(x^4)^{-3}(y^{-5})^{-3}(z^3)^{-3}$

$$= \frac{1}{2^3} x^{-12} y^{15} z^{-9}, \quad \text{or} \quad \frac{y^{15}}{8x^{12} z^9}$$

Quick Check 6 ✔

Simplify.

a) $(x^5)^7$

b) $(z^{-2})^8$

c) $\left(\dfrac{4x}{y^2 z^{-1}}\right)^4$

d) $\left(\dfrac{x^2}{p^4 q^5}\right)^3 = \dfrac{(x^2)^3}{(p^4 q^5)^3} = \dfrac{x^6}{(p^4)^3(q^5)^3}$

$$= \frac{x^6}{p^{12} q^{15}}$$

6 ✔

Multiplication

The distributive law is important when multiplying. This law is as follows.

The Distributive Law

For any numbers A, B, and C,

$$A(B + C) = AB + AC.$$

Because subtraction can be regarded as addition of an additive inverse, it follows that

$$A(B - C) = AB - AC.$$

EXAMPLE 7 Multiply:

a) $3(x - 5)$ **b)** $P(1 + r)$ **c)** $(x - 5)(x + 3)$ **d)** $(a + b)(a + b)$

Solution

a) $3(x - 5) = 3 \cdot x - 3 \cdot 5 = 3x - 15$ **b)** $P(1 + r) = P \cdot 1 + P \cdot r = P + Pr$

c) $(x - 5)(x + 3) = (x - 5)x + (x - 5)3$

$$= x \cdot x - 5x + 3x - 5 \cdot 3$$

$$= x^2 - 2x - 15$$

Quick Check 7 ✔

Multiply.

a) $-4(x - 3)$

b) $x(y + 3z)$

c) $(x + 1)(2x - 7)$

d) $(a + b)(a + b) = (a + b)a + (a + b)b$

$$= a \cdot a + ba + ab + b \cdot b$$

$$= a^2 + 2ab + b^2$$

7 ✔

The following formulas, which are obtained using the distributive law, are also useful. All three are used in Example 8, which follows.

$$(A + B)^2 = A^2 + 2AB + B^2$$
$$(A - B)^2 = A^2 - 2AB + B^2$$
$$(A - B)(A + B) = A^2 - B^2$$

EXAMPLE 8 Multiply:

Quick Check 8 ☑

Multiply.

a) $(2x + 3)^2$

b) $(3x - 1)^2$

c) $(y - 5z)(y + 5z)$

a) $(x + h)^2$

b) $(2x - t)^2$

c) $(3c + d)(3c - d)$

Solution

a) $(x + h)^2 = x^2 + 2xh + h^2$

b) $(2x - t)^2 = (2x)^2 - 2(2x)t + t^2 = 4x^2 - 4xt + t^2$

c) $(3c + d)(3c - d) = (3c)^2 - d^2 = 9c^2 - d^2$

8 ☑

Factoring

Factoring is the reverse of multiplication. That is, to factor an expression, we find an equivalent expression that is a product. Always remember to look first for a common factor.

EXAMPLE 9 Factor:

a) $P + Pi$

b) $2xh + h^2$

c) $x^2 - 6xy + 9y^2$

d) $x^2 - 5x - 14$

e) $6x^2 + 7x - 5$

f) $x^2 - 9t^2$

Solution

a) $P + Pi = P \cdot 1 + P \cdot i = P(1 + i)$ ⎫ Using the distributive law

b) $2xh + h^2 = h(2x + h)$ ⎭

Quick Check 9 ☑

Factor.

a) $2m^2n + 4mn^2$

b) $x^2 - 10x + 25$

c) $3x^2 + 10x + 3$

d) $16t^2 - 81u^2$

c) $x^2 - 6xy + 9y^2 = (x - 3y)^2$

d) $x^2 - 5x - 14 = (x - 7)(x + 2)$ Finding factors of -14 whose sum is -5

e) $6x^2 + 7x - 5 = (2x - 1)(3x + 5)$ Considering ways of factoring the first term—for example, $(2x\ )(3x\ )$; then looking for factors of -5 that yield the desired product

f) $x^2 - 9t^2 = (x - 3t)(x + 3t)$ Using the formula $(A - B)(A + B) = A^2 - B^2$ 9 ☑

Some expressions with four terms can be factored by first looking for a common binomial factor. This is called **factoring by grouping**.

EXAMPLE 10 Factor:

a) $t^3 + 6t^2 - 2t - 12$

b) $x^3 - 7x^2 - 4x + 28$

Solution

a) $t^3 + 6t^2 - 2t - 12 = t^2(t + 6) - 2(t + 6)$ Factoring the first two terms and then the second two terms

$$= (t + 6)(t^2 - 2)$$ Factoring out the common binomial factor, $(t + 6)$

b) $x^3 - 7x^2 - 4x + 28 = x^2(x - 7) - 4(x - 7)$ Factoring the first two terms and then the second two terms

Quick Check 10 ☑

Factor.

a) $u^3 + 4u^2 + 3u + 12$

b) $x^3 + 2x^2 - x - 2$

$$= (x - 7)(x^2 - 4)$$ Factoring out the common binomial factor, $(x - 7)$

$$= (x - 7)(x - 2)(x + 2)$$ Using $(A - B)(A + B) = A^2 - B^2$ 10 ☑

Solving Equations

Basic to the solution of many equations are the *Addition Principle* and the *Multiplication Principle*. We can add (or subtract) the same number on both sides of an equation and obtain an equivalent equation, that is, a new equation that has the same solutions as the original equation. We can also multiply (or divide) by a nonzero number on both sides of an equation and obtain an equivalent equation.

The Addition Principle	**The Multiplication Principle**
For any real numbers a, b, and c, $a = b$ is equivalent to $a + c = b + c$.	For any real numbers a, b, and c, with $c \neq 0$, $a = b$ is equivalent to $a \cdot c = b \cdot c$.

When solving a linear equation, we use these principles and other properties of real numbers to get the variable alone on one side. Then it is easy to determine the solution.

EXAMPLE 11 Solve: $-\frac{5}{6}x + 10 = \frac{1}{2}x + 2$.

Solution We first multiply by 6 on both sides to clear the fractions:

$$6\left(-\frac{5}{6}x + 10\right) = 6\left(\frac{1}{2}x + 2\right) \qquad \text{Using the Multiplication Principle}$$
$$6\left(-\frac{5}{6}x\right) + 6 \cdot 10 = 6\left(\frac{1}{2}x\right) + 6 \cdot 2 \qquad \text{Using the distributive law}$$
$$-5x + 60 = 3x + 12 \qquad \text{Simplifying}$$
$$60 = 8x + 12 \qquad \text{Using the Addition Principle: adding } 5x \text{ on both sides}$$
$$48 = 8x \qquad \text{Adding } -12 \text{, or subtracting 12, on both sides}$$
$$\frac{1}{8} \cdot 48 = \frac{1}{8} \cdot 8x \qquad \text{Multiplying by } \frac{1}{8} \text{ on both sides}$$
$$6 = x.$$

Quick Check 11 ✔

Solve:
$3x - 15 = \frac{1}{2}x + 4$.

The variable is now alone on one side, and we see that 6 is the solution. You can check by substituting 6 into the original equation. **11** ✔

Another principle for solving equations is the *Principle of Zero Products*.

The Principle of Zero Products
For any numbers a and b, if $ab = 0$, then $a = 0$ or $b = 0$; and if $a = 0$ or $b = 0$, then $ab = 0$.

To solve an equation using this principle, we must have 0 on one side and the other side must be a product. Solutions are then obtained by setting each factor equal to 0 and solving the resulting equations.

EXAMPLE 12 Solve: $3x(x - 2)(5x + 4) = 0$.

Solution We have

$$3x(x - 2)(5x + 4) = 0$$
$$3x = 0 \quad \text{or} \quad x - 2 = 0 \quad \text{or} \quad 5x + 4 = 0 \qquad \text{Using the Principle of Zero Products}$$
$$\frac{1}{3} \cdot 3x = \frac{1}{3} \cdot 0 \quad \text{or} \qquad x = 2 \quad \text{or} \qquad 5x = -4 \qquad \text{Solving each equation separately}$$
$$x = 0 \quad \text{or} \qquad x = 2 \quad \text{or} \qquad x = -\frac{4}{5}.$$

Quick Check 12 ✔

Solve:
$2x(3x - 1)(x + 5) = 0$.

The solutions are 0, 2, and $-\frac{4}{5}$. **12** ✔

Note that the Principle of Zero Products applies *only* when a product is 0.

EXAMPLE 13 Solve: $4x^3 = x$.

Solution We have

$$4x^3 = x$$
$$4x^3 - x = 0 \qquad \text{Adding } -x \text{ to both sides to get 0 on one side}$$
$$x(4x^2 - 1) = 0 \quad \left.\right\}$$
$$x(2x - 1)(2x + 1) = 0 \quad \left.\right\} \text{Factoring}$$
$$x = 0 \quad or \quad 2x - 1 = 0 \quad or \quad 2x + 1 = 0 \qquad \text{Using the Principle of Zero Products}$$
$$x = 0 \quad or \qquad 2x = 1 \quad or \qquad 2x = -1$$
$$x = 0 \quad or \qquad x = \tfrac{1}{2} \quad or \qquad x = -\tfrac{1}{2}.$$

Quick Check 13 ✔

Solve: $9x^3 = 4x$.

The solutions are $0, \tfrac{1}{2}$, and $-\tfrac{1}{2}$.

13 ✔

Rational Equations

Expressions like the following are polynomials in one variable:

$$x^2 - 4, \qquad x^3 + 7x^2 - 8x + 9, \qquad t - 19.$$

The **least common multiple, LCM,** of two polynomials is found by factoring and using each factor the greatest number of times that it occurs in any one factorization.

EXAMPLE 14 Find the LCM: $x^2 + 2x + 1, 5x^2 - 5x$, and $x^2 - 1$.

Solution

Quick Check 14 ✔

Find the LCM:
$x^2 + 2x + 1, x^2 - 9$,
and $x^2 + 4x + 3$.

$$\left. \begin{aligned} x^2 + 2x + 1 &= (x + 1)(x + 1); \\ 5x^2 - 5x &= 5x(x - 1); \\ x^2 - 1 &= (x + 1)(x - 1) \end{aligned} \right\} \text{Factoring}$$
$$\text{LCM} = 5x(x + 1)(x + 1)(x - 1)$$

14 ✔

A **rational expression** is a ratio of polynomials. Each of the following is a rational expression:

$$\frac{x^2 - 6x + 9}{x^2 - 4}, \qquad \frac{x - 2}{x - 3}, \qquad \frac{a + 7}{a^2 - 16}, \qquad \frac{5}{5t - 15}.$$

A **rational equation** is an equation containing one or more rational expressions. Here are some examples:

$$\frac{2}{3} - \frac{5}{6} = \frac{1}{x}, \qquad x + \frac{6}{x} = 5, \qquad \frac{2x}{x - 3} - \frac{6}{x} = \frac{18}{x^2 - 3x}.$$

To solve a rational equation, we first clear the equation of fractions by multiplying both sides by the LCM of all the denominators. The resulting equation might have solutions that are *not* solutions of the original equation. Thus, we must check all possible solutions in the original equation.

EXAMPLE 15 Solve: $\dfrac{2x}{x - 3} - \dfrac{6}{x} = \dfrac{18}{x^2 - 3x}$.

Solution Note that $x^2 - 3x = x(x - 3)$. The LCM of the denominators is $x(x - 3)$. We multiply by $x(x - 3)$.

$$x(x - 3)\left(\frac{2x}{x - 3} - \frac{6}{x}\right) = x(x - 3)\left(\frac{18}{x^2 - 3x}\right) \qquad \text{Multiplying by the LCM on both sides}$$

$$x(x - 3) \cdot \frac{2x}{x - 3} - x(x - 3) \cdot \frac{6}{x} = x(x - 3)\left(\frac{18}{x^2 - 3x}\right) \qquad \text{Using the distributive law}$$

$$2x^2 - 6(x - 3) = 18 \qquad \text{Simplifying}$$
$$2x^2 - 6x + 18 = 18$$
$$2x^2 - 6x = 0$$
$$2x(x - 3) = 0$$
$$2x = 0 \quad or \quad x - 3 = 0$$
$$x = 0 \quad or \qquad x = 3$$

The numbers 0 and 3 are possible solutions. But each makes a denominator in the original equation 0. Since division by 0 is not allowed, we see that $x \neq 0$ and $x \neq 3$. We can also carry out a check, as follows.

Check

For 0:

$$\frac{2x}{x-3} - \frac{6}{x} = \frac{18}{x^2 - 3x}$$

$$\frac{2(0)}{0-3} - \frac{6}{0} \; \overset{?}{\underset{|}{}} \; \frac{18}{0^2 - 3(0)}$$

$$0 - \frac{6}{0} \; \bigg| \; \frac{18}{0} \qquad \text{UNDEFINED;}$$
$$\text{FALSE}$$

For 3:

$$\frac{2x}{x-3} - \frac{6}{x} = \frac{18}{x^2 - 3x}$$

$$\frac{2(3)}{3-3} - \frac{6}{3} \; \overset{?}{\underset{|}{}} \; \frac{18}{3^2 - 3(3)}$$

$$\frac{6}{0} - 2 \; \bigg| \; \frac{18}{0} \qquad \text{UNDEFINED;}$$
$$\text{FALSE}$$

The equation has *no solution*.

EXAMPLE 16   Solve: $\dfrac{x^2}{x-2} = \dfrac{4}{x-2}$.

Solution   Note first that $x \neq 2$. The LCM of the denominators is $x - 2$. We multiply both sides by $x - 2$.

$$(x-2) \cdot \frac{x^2}{x-2} = (x-2) \cdot \frac{4}{x-2}$$

$$x^2 = 4 \qquad \text{Simplifying}$$

$$x^2 - 4 = 0$$

$$(x+2)(x-2) = 0$$

$$x = -2 \quad or \quad x = 2 \qquad \text{Using the Principle of Zero Products}$$

Check

For 2:

$$\frac{x^2}{x-2} = \frac{4}{x-2}$$

$$\frac{2^2}{2-2} \; \overset{?}{\underset{|}{}} \; \frac{4}{2-2}$$

$$\frac{4}{0} \; \bigg| \; \frac{4}{0} \qquad \text{UNDEFINED;}$$
$$\text{FALSE}$$

For -2:

$$\frac{x^2}{x-2} = \frac{4}{x-2}$$

$$\frac{(-2)^2}{-2-2} \; \overset{?}{\underset{|}{}} \; \frac{4}{-2-2}$$

$$\frac{4}{-4} \; \bigg| \; \frac{4}{-4}$$
$$-1 \; \bigg| \; -1 \qquad \text{TRUE}$$

The number -2 is a solution, but 2 is not (it results in division by 0).   **15** ✓

Quick Check 15 ✓

Solve: $\dfrac{t^2}{t+3} = \dfrac{9}{t+3}$.

Square Roots and Equations of the Type $x^2 = a$

When we raise a number to the second power, we say that we have *squared* the number. Sometimes, we may need to find the number that was squared. We call this process *finding the square root* of a number.

> **DEFINITION**
>
> The number c is a **square root** of a if $c^2 = a$. The positive square root of a is written $\sqrt{a}$.

For example, 5 is a square root of 25 since $5^2 = 25$, and -5 is also a square root of 25 since $(-5)^2 = 25$. Thus, we can write $\sqrt{25} = 5$ and $\sqrt{25} = -5$. However, -4 does <u>not</u> have a real-number square root since there is no real number c such that $c^2 = -4$. That is, $\sqrt{-4}$ is not a real number.

Properties of the Square Root

- Every positive real number a has two real-number square roots. For $a > 0$, the square roots of a are $\sqrt{a}$ and $-\sqrt{a}$. We often represent the two square roots using the plus-minus symbol: $\pm\sqrt{a}$.
- The number 0 has just one square root, 0 itself.
- Negative numbers do not have real-number square roots.

Consider the equation $x^2 = 25$. The solutions are the two square roots of 25, so $x = \pm 5$. In general, we conclude that if $x^2 = a$, then its solutions are $x = \pm\sqrt{a}$. This is the *Principle of Square Roots*.

The Principle of Square Roots

The solutions of $x^2 = a$ are $x = \pm\sqrt{a}$.

- When $a > 0$, the solutions are two real numbers.
- When $a = 0$, the solution is 0.
- When $a < 0$, there are no real-number solutions.

EXAMPLE 17   Use the Principle of Square Roots to solve each equation.

a) $x^2 = 81$ **b)** $x^2 = 7$ **c)** $x^2 = -16$ **d)** $3x^2 = 12$ **e)** $(2x + 1)^2 = 36$

Solution

a) We have

$$x^2 = 81$$
$$x = \pm\sqrt{81} \qquad \text{Using the Principle of Square Roots}$$
$$x = \pm 9. \qquad \text{Simplifying}$$

b) We have

$$x^2 = 7$$
$$x = \pm\sqrt{7} \qquad \text{Using the Principle of Square Roots}$$
$$x \approx \pm 2.646. \qquad \text{Using a calculator}$$

c) Since $-16 < 0$, there is no real-number solution of $x^2 = -16$.

d) We have

$$3x^2 = 12$$
$$\tfrac{1}{3} \cdot 3x = \tfrac{1}{3} \cdot 12 \qquad \text{Multiplying both sides by } \tfrac{1}{3}$$
$$x^2 = 4 \qquad \text{Simplifying}$$
$$x = \pm\sqrt{4} \qquad \text{Using the Principle of Square Roots}$$
$$x = \pm 2. \qquad \text{Simplifying}$$

The solutions are 2 and -2.

e) We have

$$(2x + 1)^2 = 36$$

$2x + 1 = 6$	or $2x + 1 = -6$	Using the Principle of Square Roots
$2x = 5$	$2x = -7$	Simplifying
$x = \tfrac{5}{2}$	$x = -\tfrac{7}{2}.$	

The solutions are $\tfrac{5}{2}$ and $-\tfrac{7}{2}$.

Quick Check 16 ✔

Use the Principle of Square Roots to solve each equation.

a) $x^2 = 121$
b) $t^2 = 13$
c) $4(3 - 5r)^2 = 100$

16 ✔

Solving Inequalities

Two inequalities are **equivalent** if they have the same solutions. For example, the inequalities $x > 4$ and $4 < x$ are equivalent. Principles for solving inequalities are similar to those for solving equations. We can add the same number to both sides of an inequality. We can also multiply on both sides by the same nonzero number, but if that number is negative, we must reverse the inequality sign. The following are the inequality-solving principles.

The Inequality-Solving Principles

For any real numbers a, b, and c,

$$a < b \quad \text{is equivalent to} \quad a + c < b + c.$$

For any real numbers a, b, and any *positive* number c,

$$a < b \quad \text{is equivalent to} \quad ac < bc.$$

For any real numbers a, b, and any *negative* number c,

$$a < b \quad \text{is equivalent to} \quad ac > bc.$$

Similar statements hold for $\le$ and $\ge$.

EXAMPLE 18   Solve: $17 - 8x \ge 5x - 4$.

Solution   We have

$$17 - 8x \ge 5x - 4$$
$$-8x \ge 5x - 21 \qquad \text{Adding } -17 \text{ to both sides}$$
$$-13x \ge -21 \qquad \text{Adding } -5x \text{ to both sides}$$
$$-\tfrac{1}{13}(-13x) \le -\tfrac{1}{13}(-21) \qquad \text{Multiplying both sides by } -\tfrac{1}{13} \text{ and } \textit{reversing} \text{ the inequality sign}$$
$$x \le \tfrac{21}{13}.$$

Quick Check 17 ✔

Solve:
$3x + 4 < 5x - 2$.

Any number less than or equal to $\tfrac{21}{13}$ is a solution.   **17** ✔

Applications

To solve applied problems, we first translate to mathematical language, usually an equation. Then we solve the equation and check to see whether the solution of the equation is a solution of the problem.

EXAMPLE 19   **Life Science: Weight Gain.**   After a 5% gain in weight, a grizzly bear weighs 693 lb. What was its original weight?

Solution   We first translate to an equation:

$$\underbrace{Original\ weight}_{w} + 5\%\ of\ the \underbrace{original\ weight}_{w} = 693$$
$$w \quad + 0.05 \quad \cdot \quad w \quad = 693.$$

Now we solve the equation:

$$1 \cdot w + 0.05 \cdot w = 693$$
$$w(1 + 0.05) = 693$$
$$1.05w = 693$$
$$w = \frac{693}{1.05} = 660.$$

Quick Check 18 ✔

Including a sales tax of 6%, the cost of a set of dinner plates is $132.50. What is the price of the plates without the tax?

Check: $600 + 5\% \cdot 660 = 660 + 0.05 \cdot 660 = 660 + 33 = 693.$

The original weight of the bear was 660 lb.   **18** ✔

Quick Check 19 ✔

Shoe Express determines that its total revenue, in dollars, from the sale of x pairs of shoes is given by

$$85x + 120.$$

How many pairs of shoes must the store sell to ensure that its total revenue will be more than $30,000?

EXAMPLE 20   **Business: Total Sales.**   Raggs, Ltd., a clothing firm, determines that its total revenue, in dollars, from the sale of x suits is given by

$$200x + 50.$$

Determine the number of suits that the firm must sell to ensure that its total revenue will be more than $70,050.

Solution   We translate to an inequality and solve:

$$200x + 50 > 70{,}050$$
$$200x > 70{,}000 \qquad \text{Adding } -50 \text{ to both sides}$$
$$x > 350. \qquad \text{Multiplying both sides by } \tfrac{1}{200}$$

Thus the company's total revenue will exceed $70,050 when it sells more than 350 suits.   **19** ✔

A   Exercise Set

Express as an equivalent expression without exponents.

1. 5^3

2. 7^2

3. $(-7)^2$

4. $(-5)^3$

5. $(1.01)^2$

6. $(1.01)^3$

7. $\left(\dfrac{1}{2}\right)^4$

8. $\left(\dfrac{1}{4}\right)^3$

9. $(6x)^0$

10. $(6x)^1$

11. $-t^1$

12. $-t^0$

13. $\left(\dfrac{1}{3}\right)^0$

14. $\left(\dfrac{1}{3}\right)^1$

Express as an equivalent expression without negative exponents.

15. 3^{-2}

16. 4^{-2}

17. $\left(\dfrac{1}{2}\right)^{-3}$

18. $\left(\dfrac{7}{2}\right)^{-2}$

19. $\dfrac{1}{3^{-2}}$

20. $\dfrac{1}{4^{-1}}$

21. 10^{-1}

22. 10^{-4}

23. e^{-b}

24. t^{-k}

25. b^{-1}

26. h^{-1}

Multiply.

27. $x^2 \cdot x^3$

28. $t^3 \cdot t^4$

29. $x^{-7} \cdot x$

30. $x^5 \cdot x$

31. $5x^2 \cdot 7x^3$

32. $4t^3 \cdot 2t^4$

33. $x^{-4} \cdot x^7 \cdot x$

34. $x^{-3} \cdot x \cdot x^3$

35. $e^{-t} \cdot e^t$

36. $e^k \cdot e^{-k}$

Divide.

37. $\dfrac{x^5}{x^2}$

38. $\dfrac{x^7}{x^3}$

39. $\dfrac{x^2}{x^5}$

40. $\dfrac{x^3}{x^7}$

41. $\dfrac{e^k}{e^k}$

42. $\dfrac{t^k}{t^k}$

43. $\dfrac{e^t}{e^4}$

44. $\dfrac{e^k}{e^3}$

45. $\dfrac{t^6}{t^{-8}}$

46. $\dfrac{t^5}{t^{-7}}$

47. $\dfrac{t^{-9}}{t^{-11}}$

48. $\dfrac{t^{-11}}{t^{-7}}$

49. $\dfrac{ab(a^2b)^3}{ab^{-1}}$

50. $\dfrac{x^2y^3(xy^3)^2}{x^{-3}y^2}$

Simplify.

51. $(t^{-2})^3$

52. $(t^{-3})^4$

53. $(e^x)^4$

54. $(e^x)^5$

55. $(2x^2y^4)^3$

56. $(2x^2y^4)^5$

57. $(3x^{-2}y^{-5}z^4)^{-4}$

58. $(5x^3y^{-7}z^{-5})^{-3}$

59. $(-3x^{-8}y^7z^2)^2$

60. $(-5x^4y^{-5}z^{-3})^4$

61. $\left(\dfrac{cd^3}{2q^2}\right)^4$

62. $\left(\dfrac{4x^2y}{a^3b^3}\right)^3$

Multiply.

63. $5(x - 7)$

64. $x(1 + t)$

65. $(x - 5)(x - 2)$

66. $(x - 4)(x - 3)$

67. $(a - b)(a^2 + ab + b^2)$

68. $(x^2 - xy + y^2)(x + y)$

69. $(2x + 5)(x - 1)$

70. $(3x + 4)(x - 1)$

71. $(a - 2)(a + 2)$

72. $(3x - 1)(3x + 1)$

73. $(5x + 2)(5x - 2)$

74. $(t - 1)(t + 1)$

75. $(a - h)^2$

76. $(a + h)^2$

77. $(5x + t)^2$

78. $(7a - c)^2$

79. $5x(x^2 + 3)^2$

80. $-3x^2(x^2 - 4)(x^2 + 4)$

Use the following equation for Exercises 81–84.

$$\begin{aligned}
(x + h)^3 &= (x + h)(x + h)^2 \\
&= (x + h)(x^2 + 2xh + h^2) \\
&= (x + h)x^2 + (x + h)2xh + (x + h)h^2 \\
&= x^3 + x^2h + 2x^2h + 2xh^2 + xh^2 + h^3 \\
&= x^3 + 3x^2h + 3xh^2 + h^3
\end{aligned}$$

81. $(a + b)^3$

82. $(a - b)^3$

83. $(x - 5)^3$

84. $(2x + 3)^3$

Factor.

85. $x - xt$

86. $x + xh$

87. $x^2 + 6xy + 9y^2$

88. $x^2 - 10xy + 25y^2$

89. $x^2 - 2x - 15$

90. $x^2 + 8x + 15$

91. $x^2 - x - 20$

92. $x^2 - 9x - 10$

93. $49x^2 - t^2$

94. $9x^2 - b^2$

95. $36t^2 - 16m^2$

96. $25y^2 - 9z^2$

97. $a^3b - 16ab^3$

98. $2x^4 - 32$

99. $a^8 - b^8$

100. $36y^2 + 12y - 35$

101. $10a^2x - 40b^2x$

102. $x^3y - 25xy^3$

103. $2 - 32x^4$

104. $2xy^2 - 50x$

105. $9x^2 + 17x - 2$

106. $6x^2 - 23x + 20$

107. $x^3 + 8$ (*Hint:* See Exercise 68.)

108. $a^3 - 27$ (*Hint:* See Exercise 67.)

109. $y^3 - 64t^3$

110. $m^3 + 1000p^3$

111. $3x^3 - 6x^2 - x + 2$

112. $5y^3 + 2y^2 - 10y - 4$

113. $x^3 - 5x^2 - 9x + 45$ **114.** $t^3 + 3t^2 - 25t - 75$

Solve.

115. $-7x + 10 = 5x - 11$ **116.** $-8x + 9 = 4x - 70$

117. $5x - 17 - 2x = 6x - 1 - x$

118. $5x - 2 + 3x = 2x + 6 - 4x$

119. $x + 0.8x = 216$ **120.** $x + 0.5x = 210$

121. $x + 0.08x = 216$ **122.** $x + 0.05x = 210$

123. $2x(x + 3)(5x - 4) = 0$

124. $7x(x - 2)(2x + 3) = 0$

125. $x^2 + 1 = 2x + 1$ **126.** $2t^2 = 9 + t^2$

127. $t^2 - 2t = t$

128. $6x - x^2 = x$

129. $6x - x^2 = -x$

130. $2x - x^2 = -x$

131. $9x^3 = x$

132. $16x^3 = x$

133. $(x - 3)^2 = x^2 + 2x + 1$

134. $(x - 5)^2 = x^2 + x + 3$

135. $\dfrac{4x}{x + 5} + \dfrac{20}{x} = \dfrac{100}{x^2 + 5x}$

136. $\dfrac{x}{x + 1} + \dfrac{3x + 5}{x^2 + 4x + 3} = \dfrac{2}{x + 3}$

137. $\dfrac{50}{x} - \dfrac{50}{x - 2} = \dfrac{4}{x}$ **138.** $\dfrac{60}{x} = \dfrac{60}{x - 5} + \dfrac{2}{x}$

139. $0 = 2x - \dfrac{250}{x^2}$ **140.** $5 - \dfrac{35}{x^2} = 0$

141. $x^2 = 64$ **142.** $x^2 = 144$

143. $u^2 = 30$ **144.** $w^2 = 97$

145. $4t^2 = 49$ **146.** $100k^2 = 169$

147. $9x^2 = 20$ **148.** $25y^2 = 3$

149. $5z^2 = 4$ **150.** $3b^2 = 144$

151. $(3x - 2)^2 = 1$ **152.** $(6x + 5)^2 = 400$

153. $(2 - 5x)^2 = 10$ **154.** $(1 - 4y)^2 = 2$

155. $3 - x \leq 4x + 7$ **156.** $x + 6 \leq 5x - 6$

157. $5x - 5 + x > 2 - 6x - 8$

158. $3x - 3 + 3x > 1 - 7x - 9$

159. $-7x < 4$ **160.** $-5x \geq 6$

161. $5x + 2x \leq -21$ **162.** $9x + 3x \geq -24$

163. $2x - 7 < 5x - 9$ **164.** $10x - 3 \geq 13x - 8$

165. $8x - 9 < 3x - 11$ **166.** $11x - 2 \geq 15x - 7$

167. $8 < 3x + 2 < 14$ **168.** $2 < 5x - 8 \leq 12$

169. $3 \leq 4x - 3 \leq 19$ **170.** $9 \leq 5x + 3 < 19$

171. $-7 \leq 5x - 2 \leq 12$ **172.** $-11 \leq 2x - 1 < -5$

APPLICATIONS

Business and Economics

173. Investment increase. An investment is made at $8\frac{1}{2}\%$, compounded annually. It grows to $705.25 at the end of 1 yr. How much was invested originally?

174. Investment increase. An investment is made at 7%, compounded annually. It grows to $856 at the end of 1 yr. How much was invested originally?

175. Total revenue. Sunshine Products determines that the total revenue, in dollars, from the sale of x flowerpots is $3x + 1000$. Determine the number of flowerpots that must be sold so that the total revenue will be more than $22,000.

176. Total revenue. Beeswax Inc. determines that the total revenue, in dollars, from the sale of x candles is $5x + 1000$. Determine the number of candles that must be sold so that the total revenue will be more than $22,000.

Life and Physical Sciences

177. Weight gain. After a 6% gain in weight, an elk weighs 508.8 lb. What was its original weight?

178. Weight gain. After a 7% gain in weight, a deer weighs 363.8 lb. What was its original weight?

Social Sciences

179. Population increase. After a 2% increase, the population of Burnside City is 826,200. What was the city's former population?

180. Population increase. After a 3% increase, the student population of Glen Oaks College is 5356. What was the former student population?

General Interest

181. Grade average. To get a B in a course, a student's average must be greater than or equal to 80% (at least 80%) and less than 90%. On the first three tests, Claudia scores 78%, 90%, and 92%. Determine the scores on the fourth test that will guarantee her a B.

182. Grade average. To get a C in a course, a student's average must be greater than or equal to 70% and less than 80%. On the first three tests, Horace scores 65%, 83%, and 82%. Determine the scores on the fourth test that will guarantee him a C.

183. Auditorium seating. The seats at Ardon Auditorium are arranged in a square, with n rows, each containing n seats. If the auditorium can seat 324 people, how many people can be seated in one row?

184. Tiling a room. The conference room at the Fireside Hotel is square, and the floor is covered by 5625 equal-sized square tiles. How many tiles run along each edge of the room?

Answers to Quick Checks

1. (a) 243; (b) 25, (c) $\frac{16}{81}$ **2.** (a) 1; (b) $\frac{2}{5}$; (c) -1

3. (a) $\frac{1}{9}$; (b) 64; (c) $\frac{8}{x^5}$ **4.** (a) t^8; (b) $\frac{28}{x^3}$; (c) $\frac{1}{y^4}$

5. (a) d^5; (b) t^8; (c) u^{14} **6.** (a) x^{35}; (b) $\frac{1}{z^{16}}$;

(c) $\frac{256x^4z^4}{y^8}$ **7.** (a) $-4x + 12$; (b) $xy + 3xz$;

(c) $2x^2 - 5x - 7$ **8.** (a) $4x^2 + 12x + 9$;

(b) $9x^2 - 6x + 1$; (c) $y^2 - 25z^2$ **9.** (a) $2mn(m + 2n)$;

(b) $(x - 5)^2$; (c) $(x + 3)(3x + 1)$;

(d) $(4t + 9u)(4t - 9u)$ **10.** (a) $(u + 4)(u^2 + 3)$;

(b) $(x + 2)(x - 1)(x + 1)$ **11.** $x = \frac{38}{5}$ **12.** $0, \frac{1}{3}, -5$

13. $0, \frac{2}{3}, -\frac{2}{3}$ **14.** $(x + 1)^2(x^2 - 9)$ **15.** $t = 3$

16. (a) $x = \pm 11$; (b) $t = \pm\sqrt{13}$; (c) $r = -\frac{2}{5}, \frac{8}{5}$

17. $x > 3$ **18.** $125 **19.** $x \geq 352$

Regression and Microsoft Excel

- Use Microsoft Excel to perform regression

Using Excel 2013

We can use Microsoft Excel to enter and plot data and to find lines of best fit using regression. Suppose we are given the following data:

x	0	2	4	5	6
y	3	4.7	6	6.8	8

Step 1: We open a blank workbook and enter the data into two columns, as shown in Fig. 1.

Step 2: We highlight the columns of data (see Fig. 2). Then within the Insert tab, we select Scatter in Charts. Next, we choose the first option that appears, with the markers shown as distinct points.

FIGURE 1

FIGURE 2

Step 3: A scatterplot of the data appears, as shown in Fig. 3. We click on ⊕ near the upper-right corner of the graph. We select Trendline, then click on the pointer and choose More Options... (see Fig. 4).

FIGURE 3

FIGURE 4

FIGURE 5

Step 4: A Format Trendline box opens (Fig. 5), with Linear selected as the default. At the bottom, we check the box next to Display Equation ON CHART, as well as the box next to Display R-squared VALUE ON CHART.

The line of best fit is now displayed on the scatterplot, along with its equation and the R^2 value, as shown in Fig. 6. The R^2 value is called the *squared correlation coefficient*. An R^2 value close to 1 indicates that the data have a strong linear trend.

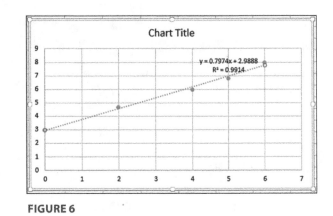

FIGURE 6

In this book, regression is also used to fit exponential and polynomial functions to data. The student can experiment with the various regression options under Format Trendline.

Using Excel for Mac 2011

The steps for finding the line of best fit using Excel for Mac 2011 are given below. There are three toolbar levels in Excel for Mac: the primary toolbar across the top of the screen, a secondary toolbar with icons directly below the primary toolbar, and a tertiary toolbar below the secondary one.

Step 1: Choose the Workbook option (the default).
Step 2: Enter the data into two columns.
Step 3: Highlight the data; then under Charts in the tertiary toolbar, select Scatter. Next, select the first choice, Marked Scatter. A scatterplot of the data appears on the screen.
Step 4: Click on the points to "activate" them. They will appear as X's.
Step 5: From the Chart option in the primary toolbar, select Add Trendline from the drop-down menu. A Format Trendline window appears. Select Options.
Step 6: Check the boxes next to Display Equation on chart and Display R-squared value on chart. The equation and the R^2 value will appear on the scatterplot, along with the trendline.

B Exercise Set

1. Use Excel to find the line of best fit for the following data.

x	4	6	8	10	12
y	15	22	27	33	44

2. Use Excel to find the line of best fit for the following data.

x	−5	−1	3	8
y	2	10	19	35

3. Use Excel to find a quadratic function (polynomial of power 2) that best fits the data in Exercise 2.

Areas for a Standard Normal Distribution

Entries in the table represent area under the curve between $z = 0$ and a positive value of z. Because of the symmetry of the curve, area under the curve between $z = 0$ and a negative value of z are found in a similar manner.

Area = Probability
$$= P(0 \leq x \leq z)$$
$$= \int_0^z \frac{1}{\sqrt{2\pi}} e^{-x^2/2} \, dx$$

z	0.00	0.01	0.02	0.03	0.04	0.05	0.06	0.07	0.08	0.09
0.0	.0000	.0040	.0080	.0120	.0160	.0199	.0239	.0279	.0319	.0359
0.1	.0398	.0438	.0478	.0517	.0557	.0596	.0636	.0675	.0714	.0753
0.2	.0793	.0832	.0871	.0910	.0948	.0987	.1026	.1064	.1103	.1141
0.3	.1179	.1217	.1255	.1293	.1331	.1368	.1406	.1443	.1480	.1517
0.4	.1554	.1591	.1628	.1664	.1700	.1736	.1772	.1808	.1844	.1879
0.5	.1915	.1950	.1985	.2019	.2054	.2088	.2123	.2157	.2190	.2224
0.6	.2257	.2291	.2324	.2357	.2389	.2422	.2454	.2486	.2517	.2549
0.7	.2580	.2611	.2642	.2673	.2704	.2734	.2764	.2794	.2823	.2852
0.8	.2881	.2910	.2939	.2967	.2995	.3023	.3051	.3078	.3106	.3133
0.9	.3159	.3186	.3212	.3238	.3264	.3289	.3315	.3340	.3365	.3389
1.0	.3413	.3438	.3461	.3485	.3508	.3531	.3554	.3577	.3599	.3621
1.1	.3643	.3665	.3686	.3708	.3729	.3749	.3770	.3790	.3810	.3830
1.2	.3849	.3869	.3888	.3907	.3925	.3944	.3962	.3980	.3997	.4015
1.3	.4032	.4049	.4066	.4082	.4099	.4115	.4131	.4147	.4162	.4177
1.4	.4192	.4207	.4222	.4236	.4251	.4265	.4279	.4292	.4306	.4319
1.5	.4332	.4345	.4357	.4370	.4382	.4394	.4406	.4418	.4429	.4441
1.6	.4452	.4463	.4474	.4484	.4495	.4505	.4515	.4525	.4535	.4545
1.7	.4554	.4564	.4573	.4582	.4591	.4599	.4608	.4616	.4625	.4633
1.8	.4641	.4649	.4656	.4664	.4671	.4678	.4686	.4693	.4699	.4706
1.9	.4713	.4719	.4726	.4732	.4738	.4744	.4750	.4756	.4761	.4767
2.0	.4772	.4778	.4783	.4788	.4793	.4798	.4803	.4808	.4812	.4817
2.1	.4821	.4826	.4830	.4834	.4838	.4842	.4846	.4850	.4854	.4857
2.2	.4861	.4864	.4868	.4871	.4875	.4878	.4881	.4884	.4887	.4890
2.3	.4893	.4896	.4898	.4901	.4904	.4906	.4909	.4911	.4913	.4916
2.4	.4918	.4920	.4922	.4925	.4927	.4929	.4931	.4932	.4934	.4936
2.5	.4938	.4940	.4941	.4943	.4945	.4946	.4948	.4949	.4951	.4952
2.6	.4953	.4955	.4956	.4957	.4959	.4960	.4961	.4962	.4963	.4964
2.7	.4965	.4966	.4967	.4968	.4969	.4970	.4971	.4972	.4973	.4974
2.8	.4974	.4975	.4976	.4977	.4977	.4978	.4979	.4979	.4980	.4981
2.9	.4981	.4982	.4982	.4983	.4984	.4984	.4985	.4985	.4986	.4986
3.0	.4987	.4987	.4987	.4988	.4988	.4989	.4989	.4989	.4990	.4990

Answers

CHAPTER R

Technology Connection, p. 6

1–20. Left to the student

Exercise Set R.1, p. 10

1.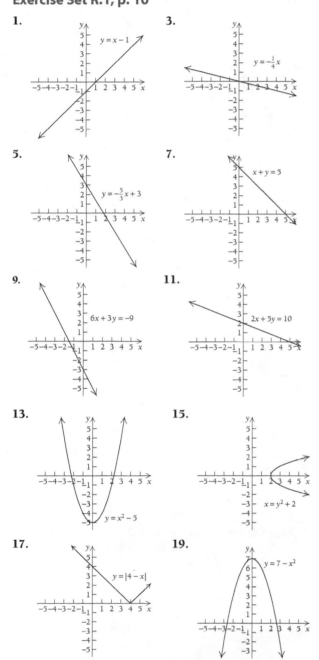

3.

5.

7.

9.

11.

13.

15.

17.

19.

21.

23. 344.4 mg **25.** About 27.25 mi/hr, or mph **27.** (a) About 1.8 million, about 4.2 million, about 5.4 million, about 6.1 million; (b) about 39 and 82; (c) about 63; (d) ✏

29. (a) \$102,800.00; (b) \$102,819.60; (c) \$102,829.54; (d) \$102,839.46; (e) \$102,839.56 **31.** (a) \$33,745.92; (b) \$33,784.87; (c) \$33,804.75; (d) \$33,824.68; (e) \$33,824.90

33. \$550.86 **35.** \$97,881.97 **37.** (a) 2007–2012; (b) 2005; (c) 2012; (d) 2002 **39.** (a) \$88,382.67; (b) \$42,000; \$46,382.67 **41.** 5.43% **43.** 3.82% **45.** (a) Western: 4.5%, Commonwealth: 4.52%; (b) Commonwealth **47.** $4.1\overline{2}\%$

49. **51.**

53. **55.**

Technology Connection, p. 16

1. 951; 42,701 **2.** 21,813

Technology Connection, p. 17

1. 6; 3.99; 150; $-1.\overline{5}$, or $-\frac{14}{9}$ **2.** -21.3; -18.39; -117.3; $3.2\overline{5}$, or $\frac{293}{90}$ **3.** -75; -65.466; -420.6; $1.6\overline{8}$, or $\frac{76}{45}$

Technology Connection, p. 20

1–3. Left to the student

Exercise Set R.2, p. 21

1. Yes **3.** Yes **5.** Yes **7.** Yes **9.** Yes **11.** Yes **13.** Yes **15.** No **17.** Yes

A ✏ indicates that the exercise asks for a written interpretation or explanation; answers will vary.

19. (a)

x	5.1	5.01	5.001	5
$f(x)$	17.4	17.04	17.004	17

(b) $f(4) = 13, f(3) = 9, f(-2) = -11, f(k) = 4k - 3,$
$f(1 + t) = 4t + 1, f(x + h) = 4x + 4h - 3$
21. $g(-1) = -2, g(0) = -3, g(1) = -2, g(5) = 22,$
$g(u) = u^2 - 3, g(a + h) = a^2 + 2ah + h^2 - 3,$ and
$\dfrac{g(a + h) - g(a)}{h} = 2a + h, h \neq 0$ **23. (a)** $f(4) = \dfrac{1}{49},$

$f(0) = \dfrac{1}{9}, f(a) = \dfrac{1}{(a + 3)^2}, f(t + 4) = \dfrac{1}{(t + 7)^2},$

$f(x + h) = \dfrac{1}{(x + h + 3)^2},$ and $\dfrac{f(x + h) - f(x)}{h} =$

$\dfrac{-2x - h - 6}{(x + h + 3)^2(x + 3)^2}, h \neq 0$ **(b)** Take an input, square it, add
six times the input, add 9, and then take the reciprocal of the result.

25. (a) $f(x) = 4x + 2$ **27. (a)** $h(x) = x^2 + x$
(b)   **(b)**

29.   **31.**

33.   **35.**

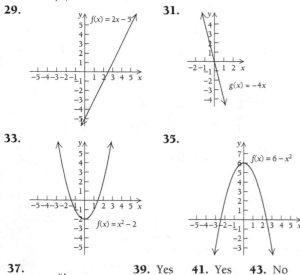

37.   **39.** Yes   **41.** Yes   **43.** No
                     45. No   **47.** Yes   **49.** Yes
                     51. No

53. (a)   **(b)** No

55. $\dfrac{f(x + h) - f(x)}{h} = 2x + h - 3, h \neq 0$

57. $f(-1) = 3, f(1) = -2$ **59.** $f(0) = 17, f(10) = 6$
61.   **63.**

65.   **67.**

69.   **71.** \$530.80   **73. (a)** 1.818 m²;
                     (b) 2.173 m²; **(c)** 1.537 m²
                     75. (a) Yes; a unique "scale of
impact" number is assigned to
each event. **(b)** The inputs are
the events; the outputs are the
scale of impact numbers.

77. $y = \pm\sqrt{\dfrac{x + 5}{2}}$; this is *not* a function.

79. $y = 2 \cdot \sqrt[3]{x}$; this is a function.   **81.** ✏️

83.

X	Y1
−3	.6
−2	ERR:
−1	−1
0	−.75
1	−1
2	ERR:
3	.6
X = −3	

85. Left to the student

87. (a) $f(x) = 5(x + 2); g(x) = 5x + 2$
(b)   **(c)** No   **89.** $a = 2$

Technology Connection, p. 28

1.

X	Y1
-3	.2
-2.5	.4444
-2	ERR:
-1.5	-.5714
-1	-.3333
-.5	-.2667
0	-.25

X = -3

2. Answers may vary.

Technology Connection, p. 30

1. Domain $= \mathbb{R}$; range $= [-4, \infty)$
2. Domain $= \mathbb{R}$; range $= \mathbb{R}$
3. Domain $= \{x \mid x$ is a real number and $x \neq -1\}$;
range $= \{y \mid y$ is a real number and $y \neq 0\}$
4. Domain $= \mathbb{R}$; range $= [-8, \infty)$
5. Domain $= [-4, \infty)$; range $= [0, \infty)$
6. Domain $= [-3, 3]$; range $= [0, 3]$
7. Domain $= [-3, 3]$; range $= [-3, 0]$
8. Domain $= \mathbb{R}$; range $= \mathbb{R}$

Exercise Set R.3, p. 31

1. $(-1, 3)$ **3.** $(0, 5)$ **5.** $(-9, -5]$ **7.** $[x, x + h]$
9. $(-\infty, q]$ **11.** $[-2, 2]$
13. $(6, 20]$
15. $(-3, \infty)$
17. $(-2, 3]$
19. $[12.5, \infty)$
21. (a) 3; (b) $\{-3, -1, 1, 3, 5\}$; (c) 3; (d) $\{-2, 0, 2, 3, 4\}$
23. (a) 4; (b) $\{-5, -3, 1, 2, 3, 4, 5\}$; (c) $\{-5, -3, 4\}$;
(d) $\{-3, 2, 4, 5\}$ **25.** (a) -1; (b) $[-2, 4]$; (c) 3; (d) $[-3, 3]$
27. (a) -2; (b) $[-4, 2]$; (c) -2; (d) $[-3, 3]$ **29.** (a) 3;
(b) $[-3, 3]$; (c) about -1.4 and 1.4; (d) $[-5, 4]$ **31.** (a) 1;
(b) $[-5, 5)$; (c) $[3, 5)$; (d) $\{-2, -1, 0, 1, 2\}$
33. $\{x \mid x$ is a real number and $x \neq 2\}$ **35.** $\{x \mid x \geq 0\}$ **37.** $\mathbb{R}$
39. $\{x \mid x$ is a real number and $x \neq 2\}$ **41.** $\mathbb{R}$
43. $\{x \mid x$ is a real number and $x \neq 3.5\}$ **45.** $\{x \mid x \geq -\frac{4}{5}\}$
47. $\mathbb{R}$ **49.** $\{x \mid x$ is a real number and $x \neq 5, x \neq -5\}$ **51.** $\mathbb{R}$
53. $\{x \mid x$ is a real number and $x \neq 5, x \neq 1\}$ **55.** $[-1, 2]$
57. (a) $A(t) = 5000\left(1 + \dfrac{0.031}{2}\right)^{2t}$; (b) $\{t \mid t \geq 0\}$
59. (a) $[25, 102]$; (b) approximately $[0, 455]$; (c)
61. (a) $[0, 70]$; (b) $[8, 75]$ **63.**   **65.** $(-\infty, 0) \cup (0, \infty)$;
$[0, \infty)$; $\left\{\dfrac{1}{6}\right\}$; $(-\infty, 0) \cup (0, \infty)$; $[0, \infty)$

Technology Connection, p. 35

1. The line slants up from left to right, intersects the y-axis at
$(0, 1)$, and is steeper than $y = 10x + 1$.   **2.** The line slants
up from left to right, passes through the origin, and is less steep
than $y = \frac{2}{31}x$.   **3.** The line slants down from left to right, passes through the origin, and is steeper than $y = -10x$.   **4.** The
line slants down from left to right, intersects the y-axis at
$(0, -1)$, and is less steep than $y = -\frac{5}{32}x - 1$.

Technology Connection, p. 38

1. The graph of y_2 is a shift 3 units up of the graph of y_1, and y_2
has y-intercept $(0, 3)$. The graph of y_3 is a shift 4 units down
of the graph of y_1, and y_3 has y-intercept $(0, -4)$. The graph

of $y = x - 5$ is a shift 5 units down of the graph of $y = x$, and
$y = x - 5$ has y-intercept $(0, -5)$. All lines are parallel.
2. For any x-value, the y_2-value is 3 more than the y_1-value,
and the y_3-value is 4 less than the y_1-value.

Exercise Set R.4, p. 44

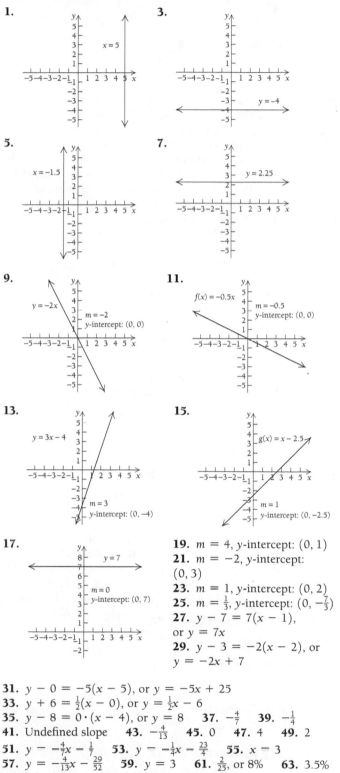

19. $m = 4$, y-intercept: $(0, 1)$
21. $m = -2$, y-intercept:
$(0, 3)$
23. $m = 1$, y-intercept: $(0, 2)$
25. $m = \frac{1}{3}$, y-intercept: $\left(0, -\frac{7}{3}\right)$
27. $y - 7 = 7(x - 1)$,
or $y = 7x$
29. $y - 3 = -2(x - 2)$, or
$y = -2x + 7$

31. $y - 0 = -5(x - 5)$, or $y = -5x + 25$
33. $y + 6 = \frac{1}{2}(x - 0)$, or $y = \frac{1}{2}x - 6$
35. $y - 8 = 0 \cdot (x - 4)$, or $y = 8$ **37.** $-\frac{4}{7}$ **39.** $-\frac{1}{4}$
41. Undefined slope   **43.** $-\frac{4}{13}$ **45.** 0   **47.** 4   **49.** 2
51. $y - \frac{4}{7}x - \frac{1}{7}$ **53.** $y - \frac{1}{4}x - \frac{23}{4}$ **55.** $x - 3$
57. $y = -\frac{4}{13}x - \frac{29}{52}$ **59.** $y = 3$ **61.** $\frac{2}{25}$, or 8%   **63.** 3.5%
65. (a) $I(s) = 0.0057s$; (b) 18 cartridges
67. (a) $C(x) = 80x + 45,000$; (b) $R(x) = 450x$;

(c) $P(x) = 370x - 45,000$;
(d) profit of $1,065,000; **(e)** 122 pairs

69. (a) $V(t) = 5200 - 512.5t$;
(b) $V(0) = \$5200$, $V(1) = \$4687.50$, $V(2) = \$4175$,
$V(3) = \$3662.50$, $V(4) = \$3150$, $V(7) = \$1612.50$,
$V(8) = \$1100$ **71.** $V(3) = \$25,200$ **73.** About 91%
(don't round up, for legal reasons!)   **75.** \$232.50/yr
77. 1.8 billion/yr   **79.** $t \approx 0.02$ sec   **81. (a)** $B(W) = 0.025W$;
(b) $0.025 = 2.5\%$, so $M = 2.5\% \cdot W$, and the weight of the
brain is 2.5% of the body weight; **(c)** 4 lb
83. (a) $D(5) = 6$ ft,   **(b)**   **(c)**
$D(10) = 11.5$ ft,
$D(20) = 22.5$ ft,
$D(50) = 55.5$ ft,
$D(65) = 72$ ft

85. (a) $y = 0.057x - 113.85$; **(b)** approximately 94.8%;
(c) 2015; **(d)**   **87. (a)** $N = 1.02P$; **(b)** $N = 204,000$
people; **(c)** $P = 360,000$ people   **89.** $y = 25$
91. (a) Graph III; **(b)** graph IV; **(c)** graph I; **(d)** graph II
93. Answers may vary.

Technology Connection, p. 50

1–2. Left to the student

Technology Connection, p. 51

1. (a) 2 and 4; **(b)** 2 and −5; **(c)** and **(d)** left to the student

Technology Connection, p. 53

1. −5 and 2   **2.** −4 and 6   **3.** −2 and 1   **4.** 0, −1.414,
and 1.414 (approx.)   **5.** 0 and 700   **6.** −2.079, 0.463, and
3.116 (approx.)   **7.** −3.096, −0.646, 0.646, and 3.096 (approx.)
8. −1 and 1   **9.** −0.387 and 1.721 (approx.)   **10.** 6.133
11. −2, −1.414, 1, and 1.414 (approx.)   **12.** −3, −1, 2, and 3

Technology Connection, p. 54

Left to the student

Technology Connection, p. 55

1. Left to the student   **2.** For $x = 3$, y_1 is ERR and y_2 is 6.

Technology Connection, p. 56

1–8. Left to the student

Technology Connection, p. 57

1–2. Left to the student

Technology Connection, p. 63

1. Approximately (14, 266)

Exercise Set R.5, p. 64

1.   **3.**

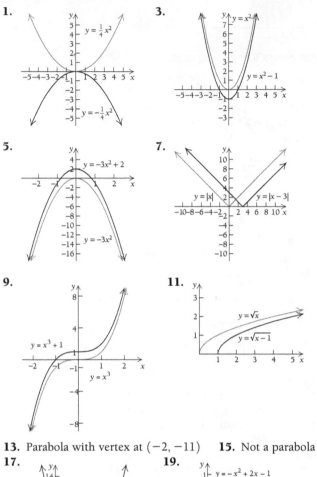

5.   **7.**

9.   **11.**

13. Parabola with vertex at $(-2, -11)$ **15.** Not a parabola

17.   **19.**

21.   **23.**

25.   **27.**

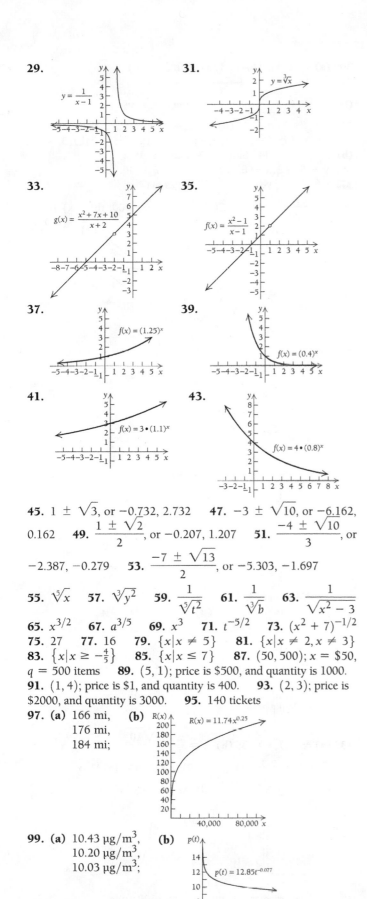

29.

$y = \dfrac{1}{x-1}$

31.

$y = \sqrt[3]{x}$

33.

$g(x) = \dfrac{x^2 + 7x + 10}{x + 2}$

35.

$f(x) = \dfrac{x^2 - 1}{x - 1}$

37.

$f(x) = (1.25)^x$

39.

$f(x) = (0.4)^x$

41.

$f(x) = 3 \cdot (1.1)^x$

43.

$f(x) = 4 \cdot (0.8)^x$

45. $1 \pm \sqrt{3}$, or $-0.732, 2.732$ **47.** $-3 \pm \sqrt{10}$, or -6.162, 0.162 **49.** $\dfrac{1 \pm \sqrt{2}}{2}$, or $-0.207, 1.207$ **51.** $\dfrac{-4 \pm \sqrt{10}}{3}$, or $-2.387, -0.279$ **53.** $\dfrac{-7 \pm \sqrt{13}}{2}$, or $-5.303, -1.697$

55. $\sqrt[5]{x}$ **57.** $\sqrt[3]{y^2}$ **59.** $\dfrac{1}{\sqrt[5]{t^2}}$ **61.** $\dfrac{1}{\sqrt[3]{b}}$ **63.** $\dfrac{1}{\sqrt{x^2 - 3}}$

65. $x^{3/2}$ **67.** $a^{3/5}$ **69.** x^3 **71.** $t^{-5/2}$ **73.** $(x^2 + 7)^{-1/2}$

75. 27 **77.** 16 **79.** $\{x \,|\, x \neq 5\}$ **81.** $\{x \,|\, x \neq 2, x \neq 3\}$

83. $\{x \,|\, x \geq -\frac{4}{5}\}$ **85.** $\{x \,|\, x \leq 7\}$ **87.** $(50, 500)$; $x = \$50$, $q = 500$ items **89.** $(5, 1)$; price is $500, and quantity is 1000.

91. $(1, 4)$; price is $1, and quantity is 400. **93.** $(2, 3)$; price is $2000, and quantity is 3000. **95.** 140 tickets

97. (a) 166 mi, 176 mi, 184 mi; **(b)**

$R(x) = 11.74x^{0.25}$

99. (a) 10.43 µg/m³, 10.20 µg/m³, 10.03 µg/m³; **(b)**

$p(t) = 12.85t^{-0.077}$

101. 24 cities; 47 cities **103.** **105.** $-1.831, -0.856, 3.188$ **107.** $1.489, 5.673$ **109.** $-2, 3$ **111.** $[-1, 2]$

113. Approximately $(10.33, 8.83)$; produce 8830 units at a price of $10.33 each

Technology Connection, p. 72

1. (a) $y = 2.7x + 63.8$ **(b)** 93.5; **(c)**

Technology Connection, p. 74

1. (a) $y = 0.00112141561x^4 - 0.1159429698x^3 + 3.670845719x^2 - 32.77404732x + 2.857997859$ **(b)**

2. (a) $y = -62.8327x^2 + 5417.8404x - 57264.7856$

(b) $y = -1.6519x^3 + 145.6606x^2 - 2658.3088x + 36491.7730$

(c) $y = -0.0771x^4 + 11.3952x^3 - 639.2276x^2 + 17037.1915x - 135483.9938$

(d) quartic function; **(e)** $38,853, $58,887

3. $y = 93.2857x^2 - 1336x + 5460.8286$

Exercise Set R.6, p. 75

1. Linear   **3.** Quadratic, $a < 0$ **5.** Quadratic, $a < 0$
7. Quadratic, $a < 0$ **9. (a)** $y = -1.5x + 65.4$;
(b) 47.4 million   **11. (a)** $y = -44\frac{1}{3}x^2 + 188\frac{2}{3}x$; **(b)** 45.3 mg;
(c) ✐   **13. (a)** $y = 0.144x^2 - 4.63x + 60$; **(b)** 188.5 ft;
(c) ✐   **15.** Answers will vary.   **17. (a)** $y = 11.421(1.020)^x$;
(b) **(c)** 30.7 million

$y = 11.421(1.020)^x$

19. (a) $y = 107.850(1.031)^x$ **(b)**

$y = 107.850(1.031)^x$

(c) $365.74 **(d)** ✐   **21.** ✐   **23.** ✐
25. (a) $y = -1.5964x + 66.2607$; **(b)** 47.10 million **(c)** The answers are very close, giving essentially the same information.
(d) $y = 66.332 \cdot (0.975)^x$, 48.95 million; **(e)** ✐

Chapter R Review Exercises, p. 85

1. (d)   **2.** (b)   **3.** (f)   **4.** (a)   **5.** (e)   **6.** (g)   **7.** (c)
8. True   **9.** False   **10.** True   **11.** True   **12.** False
13. False   **14.** True   **15. (a)** 4.1 million; **(b)** 32, 85;
(c) ✐   **16.** $5017.60   **17.** $1340.24   **18.** Not a function.
One input, Elizabeth, has three outputs.
19. (a) $f(3) = -6$; **(b)** $f(-5) = -30$; **(c)** $f(a) = -a^2 + a$;
(d) $f(x + h) = -x^2 - 2xh - h^2 + x + h$
20.

$f(x) = (x - 2)^2$

21.

$y = |x + 1|$

22.

$f(x) = \frac{x^2 - 16}{x + 4}$

23.

$g(x) = \sqrt{x} + 1$

24. Not a function   **25.** Function   **26.** Function
27. Not a function   **28. (a)** $f(2) = 1$; **(b)** $[-4, 4]$;
(c) $x = -3$; **(d)** $[-1, 3]$
29. (a) $f(-1) = 1$, **(b)**
  $f(1.5) = 4$,
  $f(6) = 3$

$y = f(x)$

30. (a) $[-2, 5]$; **(b)** $(-1, 3]$; **(c)** $(-\infty, a)$
31. (a) $[-4, 5)$;

(b) $(2, \infty)$;

32. (a) $f(-3) = -2$; **(b)** $\{-3, -2, -1, 0, 1, 2, 3\}$;
(c) $-1, 3$; **(d)** $\{-2, 1, 2, 3, 4\}$ **33. (a)** $(-\infty, 5)\cup(5, \infty)$;
(b) $[-6, \infty)$ **34.** Slope, -3; y-intercept, 2
35. $y + 5 = \frac{1}{4}(x - 8)$, or $y = \frac{1}{4}x - 7$ **36.** -3
37. $-$$350 per year   **38.** 75 pages per day
39. $A = \dfrac{7}{200}V$ **40. (a)** $C(x) = 0.50x + 4000$; **(b)** $R(x) = 10x$;
(c) $P(x) = 9.5x - 4000$ **(d)** 422 CDs

41. (a)

$y = \sqrt{x}$
$y = \sqrt{x} - 3$

(b)

$y = (x - 1)^3$
$y = x^3$

42. (a)

$f(x) = x^2 - 6x + 8$

(b)

$g(x) = \sqrt[3]{x} + 2$

Vertex at $(3, -1)$

(c)

$y = -\dfrac{1}{x}$

(d)

$y = \dfrac{x^2 + x - 6}{x - 2}$

43. (a) $x = 1, x = 3$; **(b)** $x = \dfrac{2 \pm \sqrt{10}}{2}$ **44. (a)** $x^{4/5}$;
(b) t^4; **(c)** $m^{-2/3}$; **(d)** $(x^2 - 9)^{-1/2}$ **45. (a)** $\sqrt[5]{x^2}$
(b) $\dfrac{1}{\sqrt[5]{m^3}}$; **(c)** $\sqrt{x^2 - 5}$; **(d)** $\sqrt{3t}$ **46.** $\left[\frac{9}{2}, \infty\right)$

47. (a)

$y = \frac{1}{2} \cdot (4)^x$
$(0, \frac{1}{2})$

(b)

$y = 3 \cdot \left(\frac{1}{4}\right)^x$
$(0, 3)$

48. $(3, 16)$; price $=$ $3, quantity $= 1600$ units
49. About 3.3 hr

50. (a) $y = 0.2x + 160$ **(b)**
(c) 173.4 beats/min

51. (a)
(b) Data fit a quadratic function.
(c) $y = 2.0x^2 - 89.8\overline{4}x + 870$;
(d) About $-\$25.33$; **(e)**

52. (a) 525,375 lb; **(b)** $4.31/lb
53. $f(x) = x^3 - 9x^2 + 27x + 50$ **54.**
$y = \sqrt[3]{|4 - x^2|} + 1$

Zero: $x = -1.25$;
domain: $\mathbb{R}$; range: $\mathbb{R}$

Zero: none; domain: $\mathbb{R}$;
range: $[1, \infty)$

55. $(-1.21, 2.36)$ **56. (a)** $y = 0.2x + 160$;
(b) 173.4 beats/min; **(c)**
57. (a) $y = 1.86x^2 - 84.18x + 943.86$; **(b)** $95.46; **(c)**
58. (a) $y = 37.58x + 294.48$;
$y = -0.59x^2 + 74.61x - 117.72$;
$y = 0.02x^3 - 2.60x^2 + 125.71x - 439.65$;
$y = 0.003x^4 - 0.324x^3 + 11.46x^2 - 88.51x + 507.84$

(b)
$y_1 = 37.58x + 294.48$
$y_2 = -0.59x^2 + 74.61x - 117.72$
$y_3 = 0.02x^3 - 2.60x^2 + 125.71x - 439.65$
$y_4 = 0.003x^4 - 0.324x^3 + 11.46x^2 - 88.51x + 507.84$
(c)

Chapter R Test, p. 88

1. [R.1] $750 **2.** [R.2] **(a)** $f(-3) = -4$;
(b) $f(a + h) = -a^2 - 2ah - h^2 + 5$ **3.** [R.4] Slope, $\frac{4}{5}$;
y-intercept, $-\frac{2}{3}$ **4.** [R.4] $y - 7 = \frac{1}{4}(x + 3)$, or $y = \frac{1}{4}x + \frac{31}{4}$
5. [R.4] $-\frac{1}{2}$ **6.** [R.4] $-\$700/yr$ **7.** [R.4] $\frac{1}{2}$ lb/bag
8. [R.4] $F = \frac{2}{3}W$ **9.** [R.4] **(a)** $C(x) = 0.08x + 8000$;
(b) $R(x) = 0.50x$; **(c)** $P(x) = 0.42x - 8000$; **(d)** 19,048 cards
10. [R.5] $(3, 25)$; $x = \$3$, $q = 25$ thousand units
11. [R.2] Yes **12.** [R.2] No **13.** [R.3] **(a)** $f(1) = -4$;
(b) $\mathbb{R}$ **(c)** $x = \pm3$; **(d)** $[-5, \infty)$

14. [R.5]
$f(x) = \frac{8}{x}$

15. [R.5] $t^{-1/2}$
16. [R.5] $\dfrac{1}{\sqrt[5]{t^3}}$

17. [R.5]
$f(x) = \frac{x^2 - 1}{x + 1}$

18. [R.5] $(-\infty, -7) \cup (-7, 2) \cup (2, \infty)$ **19.** [R.5] $(-2, \infty)$
20. [R.3] $[c, d)$
21. [R.2]
$f(x) = \begin{cases} x^2 + 2, & \text{for } x \geq 0 \\ x^2 - 2, & \text{for } x < 0 \end{cases}$
22. [R.5]
$(0, \frac{1}{2})$ $f(x) = \frac{1}{2} \cdot (3)^x$

23. [R.6] **(a)**   **(b)** yes;

(c) $y = -1.94x^2 + 102.74x + 1253.49$; **(d)** 2589.9 calories;
(e)   **24.** [R.5] $\frac{1}{16}$ **25.** [R.5] Domain: $(-\infty, \frac{5}{3}]$;
zero: $x = -798\frac{2}{3}$ **26.** [R.5] Answers will vary. One possibility
is $(x + 3)(x - 1)(x - 4) = 0$. **27.** [R.4] $\frac{51}{7}$
28. [R.5] Zeros: $\pm\sqrt{8} \approx \pm2.828$, $y = \sqrt[3]{|9 - x^2|} - 1$
$\pm\sqrt{10} \approx \pm3.162$;
domain: $\mathbb{R}$; range: $[-1, \infty)$

29. [R.6] **(a)** $y = -1.51x^2 + 79.98x + 1436.93$;
(b) 2480.4 calories; **(c)**

Extended Technology Application, p. 91

1. (a) $y = 0.121x - 0.465$
(b) **(c)** $7.40, $8.01. Not reasonable estimates. The data are increasing, but these prices seem lower than the trend of the curve indicates. **(d)** 2119; seems too far in the future.

2. (a) $y = 0.002x^2 + 0.024x + 0.420$
(b) **(c)** $10.43, $11.90. Yes, the curve seems to better follow the trend in the data. **(d)** 2043; seems more reasonable.

3. (a) $y = 0.000009x^3 + 0.00082x^2 + 0.0426x + 0.347$
(b) **(c)** $9.05, $10.43. Yes, the curve seems to follow the trend in the data, but the resulting ticket prices are virtually the same as those found with the quadratic function. **(d)** 2046; seems reasonable.

4. (a) $y = 0.000002x^4 - 0.00023x^3 + 0.0098x^2 - 0.067x + 0.558$
(b) **(c)** $10.15, $13.02. Yes, but the estimates are higher than those found using the quadratic or cubic function. **(d)** 2028; seems too soon.

5. (a) $y = 0.521453(1.049459)^x$
(b) **(c)** $12.02, $15.30. Yes, but the curve rises much faster as x increases. **(d)** 2025, seems too soon.

6. (a) If the scatterplot and the linear function are graphed on the same axes, the predicted prices seem lower than the trend of the curve indicates.
(b) Graphing the scatterplot, the linear function, and the quadratic function, we see that the quadratic function seems to better follow the trend of the data.

(c) The exponential function seems to fit the data more closely than the quadratic function does. The trend of the data seems to suggest an exponential model.

CHAPTER 1

Technology Connection, p. 95

1. 5   **2.** −4   **3.** $g(x) = 475.24, 492.1, 493.81, 494.19, 495.9, 513.24$ **4.** 494   **5.** −1

Exercise Set 1.1, p. 102

1. −2   **3.** The limit, as x approaches 4, of $f(x)$ **5.** The limit, as x approaches 5 from the left, of $F(x)$ **7.** $\lim_{x \to 2^+}$ **9.** $\lim_{x \to 5}$ **11.** 1; 2; does not exist   **13.** 4; 2; does not exist   **15.** 4   **17.** 0   **19.** 0   **21.** 4   **23.** 3   **25.** −1   **27.** Does not exist   **29.** 0   **31.** 1   **33.** 1   **35.** 2   **37.** Does not exist   **39.** 1   **41.** −1   **43.** 2   **45.** Does not exist   **47.** 0   **49.** 2

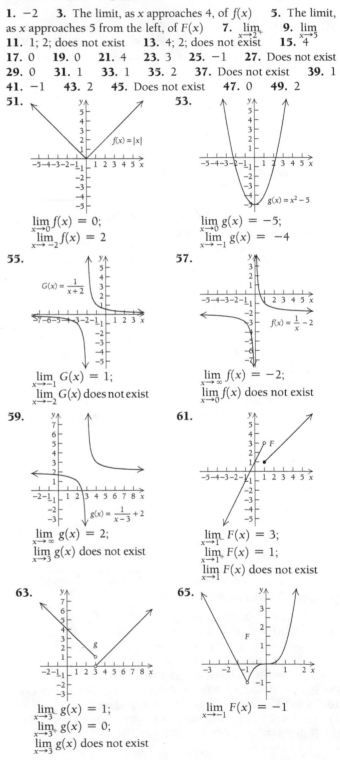

51. $\lim_{x \to 0} f(x) = 0;$ $\lim_{x \to -2} f(x) = 2$

53. $\lim_{x \to 0} g(x) = -5;$ $\lim_{x \to -1} g(x) = -4$

55. $\lim_{x \to -1} G(x) = 1;$ $\lim_{x \to -2} G(x)$ does not exist

57. $\lim_{x \to \infty} f(x) = -2;$ $\lim_{x \to 0} f(x)$ does not exist

59. $\lim_{x \to \infty} g(x) = 2;$ $\lim_{x \to 3} g(x)$ does not exist

61. $\lim_{x \to 1^-} F(x) = 3;$ $\lim_{x \to 1^+} F(x) = 1;$ $\lim_{x \to 1} F(x)$ does not exist

63. $\lim_{x \to 3^-} g(x) = 1;$ $\lim_{x \to 3^+} g(x) = 0;$ $\lim_{x \to 3} g(x)$ does not exist

65. $\lim_{x \to -1} F(x) = -1$

67.

$\lim_{x \to 0} H(x)$ does not exist;

$\lim_{x \to 1} H(x) = 2$

69. $3.50, $3.50, $3.50   **71.** $4.00, $4.50, limit does not exist
73. $1.19, $1.40, limit does not exist   **75.** Limit does not exist.
77. 10%, 15%, limit does not exist   **79.** 25%, limit does not exist
81. 15%, 25%, limit does not exist   **83.** 3   **85.** −1
87. Limit does not exist; 2   **89.** Limit does not exist; $\frac{1}{6}$

Technology Connection, p. 109

1. 53   **2.** 2.8284   **3.** 0.25   **4.** 0.16667

Exercise Set 1.2, p. 113

1. False   **3.** True   **5.** False   **7.** False   **9.** 3   **11.** −3
13. 4   **15.** 15   **17.** −4   **19.** 6   **21.** $\frac{3}{2}$ **23.** $\frac{13}{4}$ **25.** −12
27. $\frac{1}{10}$ **29.** Limit does not exist.   **31.** 3   **33.** Limit does
not exist.   **35.** 0   **37.** Not continuous   **39.** Continuous
41. Not continuous   **43. (a)** −1, 2, limit does not exist;
(b) −1; **(c)** no, the limit does not exist; **(d)** 3; **(e)** 3;
(f) yes, $\lim_{x \to -2} f(x) = f(-2)$ **45. (a)** 2; **(b)** does not exist;
(c) no, $k(-1)$ does not exist; **(d)** −2; **(e)** −2; **(f)** yes,
$\lim_{x \to 3} k(x) = k(3)$ **47. (a)** 3; **(b)** 1; **(c)** limit does not exist;
(d) 1; **(e)** no, $\lim_{x \to 3} G(x)$ does not exist; **(f)** yes, $\lim_{x \to 0} G(x) = G(0)$;
(g) yes, $\lim_{x \to 2.9} G(x) = G(2.9)$ **49.** Yes; $\lim_{x \to 4} g(x) = g(4)$
51. No; $\lim_{x \to 0} G(x)$ does not exist and $G(0)$ does not exist.
53. Yes; $\lim_{x \to 4} f(x) = f(4)$ **55.** No; $\lim_{x \to 4} F(x)$ does not exist.
57. No; $g(4)$ does not exist.   **59.** No; $\lim_{x \to 2} G(x)$ does not equal
$G(2)$.   **61.** Yes; $\lim_{x \to 4} G(x) = G(4)$ **63.** No; $g(5)$ does not
exist and $\lim_{x \to 5} g(x)$ does not exist.   **65.** No; $\lim_{x \to 2} G(x)$ does not
exist and $G(2)$ does not exist.   **67.** Yes; $g(x)$ is continuous over
$(-4, 4)$ because $\lim_{x \to a} g(x) = g(a)$ for all a in $(-4, 4)$.   **69.** No;
$G(x)$ is not continuous at $x = 1$.   **71.** Yes; $g(x)$ is continuous at
each real number because $\lim_{x \to a} g(x) = g(a)$ for all real numbers a.
73. 30, 25, does not exist   **75.** 120, 120, 120   **77.** $k = 2$
79. 0.5   **81.** 0.5   **83.** 0.378, or $\frac{1}{\sqrt{7}}$ **85.** 0

Exercise Set 1.3, p. 122

1. (a) $10x + 5h$; **(b)** 60, 55, 50.5, 50.05   **3. (a)** $-10x - 5h$;
(b) −60, −55, −50.5, −50.05   **5. (a)** $2x + h - 1$;
(b) 11, 10, 9.1, 9.01   **7. (a)** $\dfrac{-9}{x \cdot (x + h)}$;
(b) $-\frac{9}{35}, -\frac{3}{10}, -\frac{6}{17}, -\frac{60}{167}$ **9. (a)** 2; **(b)** 2, 2, 2, 2
11. (a) $36x^2 + 36xh + 12h^2$; **(b)** 1308, 1092, 918.12, 901.8012
13. (a) $2x + h - 4$; **(b)** 8, 7, 6.1, 6.01   **15. (a)** $2x + h - 3$;
(b) 9, 8, 7.1, 7.01   **17.** About 0.275%/yr, about 0.16%/yr,
about 0.211%/yr   **19.** About 0.35%/yr, about 0.26%/yr,
about 0.3%/yr   **21.** About −0.025%/yr, about −0.12%/yr,
about −0.078%/yr   **23.** About 0.05%/yr, about 0.72%/yr, about
0.422%/yr **25.** 1.268 quadrillion BTUs/yr, 1.187 quadrillion BTUs/yr,
−0.255 quadrillion BTUs/yr   **27. (a)** 70 pleasure units/unit of
product, 39 pleasure units/unit of product, 29 pleasure units/

unit of product, 23 pleasure units/unit of product; **(b)**
29. (a) $27.16; **(b)** $29.56; **(c)** $2.40; **(d)** $1.20, which
means the average price of a ticket increases by $1.20/yr.
31. −116; Payton County lost 116 people per year on average
from the 5th to the 8th year after the last census.   **33.** The
average cost of production of between 300 and 305 holders is
$19.80 per unit.   **35. (a)** 1.0 lb/month; **(b)** 0.54 lb/month;
(c) 0.77 lb/month; **(d)** 0.67 lb/month; **(e)** growth rate is
greatest in the first 3 months.   **37. (a)** Approximately
1.49 hectares/g; **(b)** 1.09 represents the average growth rate,
in hectares/g, of home range with respect to body weight when
the mammal grows from 200 to 300 g.   **39. (a)** 1.25 words/
min, 1.25 words/min, 0.625 word/min, 0 words/min, 0 words/
min; **(b)**   **41. (a)** 256 ft; **(b)** 128 ft/sec
43. (a) 125 million people/yr for both countries; **(b)**
(c) A: 290 million people/yr, −40 million people/yr,
−50 million people/yr, 300 million people/yr,
B: 125 million people/yr in all intervals; **(d)**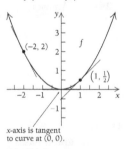
45. (a) 2006–07; **(b)** 2003–04, 2008–09; **(c)** about $7970
for public and about $20,130 for private   **47.** $2ax + b + ah$
49. $4x^3 + 6x^2h + 4xh^2 + h^3$
51. $5ax^4 + 10ax^3h + 10ax^2h^2 + 5axh^3 + ah^4 + 4bx^3 +$
$6bx^2h + 4bxh^2 + bh^3$ **53.** $\dfrac{1}{(1 - x - h)(1 - x)}$
55. $\dfrac{2}{\sqrt{2x + 2h + 1} + \sqrt{2x + 1}}$

Technology Connection, p. 131

$y = -\frac{3}{4}x - 3; y = -12x - 12$

Technology Connection, p. 134

1–8. Left to the student

Exercise Set 1.4, p. 135

1. (a) and **(b)**

x-axis is tangent
to curve at (0, 0).

(c) $f'(x) = x$;
(d) −2, 0, 1

5. (a) and **(b)**

x-axis is tangent
to curve at (0, 0).

(c) $f'(x) = -3x^2$;
(d) −12, 0, −3

3. (a) and **(b)**

x-axis is tangent
to curve at (0, 0).

(c) $f'(x) = -4x$;
(d) 8, 0, −4

7. (a) and **(b)** All tangent lines
are identical to the graph of the
original function.

(c) $f'(x) = 2$;
(d) 2, 2, 2

9. (a) and **(b)** All tangent lines are identical to the graph of the original function.

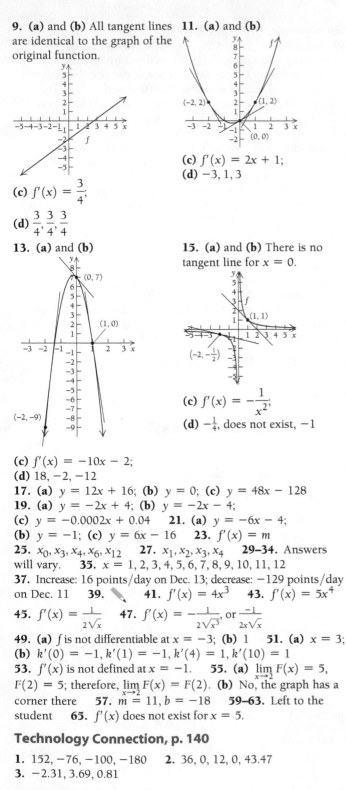

(c) $f'(x) = \frac{3}{4}$;

(d) $\frac{3}{4}, \frac{3}{4}, \frac{3}{4}$

11. (a) and **(b)**

(c) $f'(x) = 2x + 1$;
(d) $-3, 1, 3$

13. (a) and **(b)**

(c) $f'(x) = -10x - 2$;
(d) $18, -2, -12$

15. (a) and **(b)** There is no tangent line for $x = 0$.

(c) $f'(x) = -\frac{1}{x^2}$;
(d) $-\frac{1}{4}$, does not exist, -1

17. (a) $y = 12x + 16$; **(b)** $y = 0$; **(c)** $y = 48x - 128$
19. (a) $y = -2x + 4$; **(b)** $y = -2x - 4$;
(c) $y = -0.0002x + 0.04$ **21. (a)** $y = -6x - 4$;
(b) $y = -1$; **(c)** $y = 6x - 16$ **23.** $f'(x) = m$
25. $x_0, x_3, x_4, x_6, x_{12}$ **27.** x_1, x_2, x_3, x_4 **29–34.** Answers
will vary.   **35.** $x = 1, 2, 3, 4, 5, 6, 7, 8, 9, 10, 11, 12$
37. Increase: 16 points/day on Dec. 13; decrease: -129 points/day
on Dec. 11   **39.** 🖉   **41.** $f'(x) = 4x^3$ **43.** $f'(x) = 5x^4$
45. $f'(x) = \frac{1}{2\sqrt{x}}$ **47.** $f'(x) = -\frac{1}{2\sqrt{x^3}}$, or $\frac{-1}{2x\sqrt{x}}$
49. (a) f is not differentiable at $x = -3$; **(b)** 1   **51. (a)** $x = 3$;
(b) $k'(0) = -1, k'(1) = -1, k'(4) = 1, k'(10) = 1$
53. $f'(x)$ is not defined at $x = -1$.   **55. (a)** $\lim\limits_{x \to 2} F(x) = 5$,
$F(2) = 5$; therefore, $\lim\limits_{x \to 2} F(x) = F(2)$. **(b)** No, the graph has a
corner there   **57.** $m = 11, b = -18$ **59–63.** Left to the
student   **65.** $f'(x)$ does not exist for $x = 5$.

Technology Connection, p. 140

1. $152, -76, -100, -180$ **2.** $36, 0, 12, 0, 43.47$
3. $-2.31, 3.69, 0.81$

Technology Connection, p. 144

1. Tangent line is horizontal at $\left(2, \frac{8}{3}\right)$.

Exercise Set 1.5, p. 145

1. $8x^7$ **3.** -0.5 **5.** 0   **7.** $30x^9$ **9.** $-8x^{-9}$ **11.** $-15x^{-6}$
13. $4x^3 - 7$ **15.** $\frac{2}{\sqrt{x}}$ **17.** $0.7x^{-0.3}$ **19.** $-1.6x^{-2/3}$

21. $-\frac{24}{x^5}$ **23.** $\frac{3}{4}$ **25.** $\frac{1}{4\sqrt[4]{x^3}} + \frac{3}{x^2}$ **27.** $-\frac{10}{3}\sqrt[3]{x^2}$

29. $10x - 7$ **31.** $0.36x^{0.2}$ **33.** $\frac{3}{4}$ **35.** $-\frac{12}{5x^7}$

37. $-\frac{4}{x^2} - \frac{3}{5}x^{-2/5}$ **39.** 7   **41.** $\frac{1}{2}x^{1/2}$ **43.** $-0.02x + 0.4$

45. $-\frac{3}{4}x^{-7/4} - 2x^{-1/3} + \frac{5}{4}x^{1/4} - \frac{8}{x^5}$ **47.** $\frac{1}{7} - \frac{7}{x^2}$ **49.** $\frac{1}{4}$

51. -5 **53.** $\frac{1}{12}$ **55.** $-\frac{3}{640}$ **57. (a)** $y = \frac{3}{2}x - \frac{3}{2}$;
(b) $y = \frac{31}{4}x - 17$; **(c)** $y = \frac{107}{6}x - \frac{165}{2}$ **59. (a)** $y = -\frac{2}{3}x + \frac{1}{3}$;
(b) $y = \frac{2}{3}x + \frac{1}{3}$; **(c)** $y = \frac{1}{3}x + \frac{4}{3}$ **61.** $(0, 4)$ **63.** $(0, -2)$
65. $(0.3, 7.55)$ **67.** $(20, 54)$ **69.** None   **71.** The
tangent line is horizontal at *all* points of the graph.
73. $\left(-1, -55\frac{1}{3}\right), \left(11, 111\frac{1}{3}\right)$ **75.** $\left(\sqrt{2}, 1 - 4\sqrt{2}\right)$,
or approximately $(1.41, -4.66)$; $(-\sqrt{2}, 1 + 4\sqrt{2})$,
or approximately $(-1.41, 6.66)$ **77.** $(3, 0)$ **79.** $(2.5, 8.75)$

81. $(50, 75)$ **83.** $(1 + \sqrt{6}, -\frac{11}{3} - 3\sqrt{6})$, or approximately
$(3.45, -11.02)$; $(1 - \sqrt{6}, -\frac{11}{3} + 3\sqrt{6})$, or approximately
$(-1.45, 3.68)$ **85. (a)** $C'(r) = 6.28$;   **(b)** 6.28 cm;
(c) 🖉   **87. (a)** $w'(t) = 1.82 - 0.1192t + 0.002274t^2$;
(b) about 21 lb; **(c)** about 0.86 lb/month

89. (a) $R'(v) = -\frac{6000}{v^2}$; **(b)** 75 beats/min;

(c) -0.94 beat/min per mL   **91. (a)** $\frac{dP}{dt} = 4000t$;

(b) 300,000 people; **(c)** 40,000 people/yr; **(d)** 🖉

93. (a) $V' = \frac{0.61}{\sqrt{h}}$; **(b)** 244 mi; **(c)** 0.0031 mi/ft; **(d)** 🖉

95. $(2, \infty)$ **97.** $(0, 4)$, $\left(-\sqrt{\frac{2}{3}}, -\frac{40}{9}\right)$, and $\left(\sqrt{\frac{2}{3}}, -\frac{40}{9}\right)$
99. $f'(x) = 5x^4 + 3x^2$, which is greater than or equal to 0 for all x.

101. $k'(x) = -\frac{2}{x^3}$, which is less than 0 for all x **103.** $2x + 1$

105. $3x^2 - 1$ **107.** $\frac{\sqrt{7}}{2\sqrt{x}}$ **109.** $1 - \frac{1}{x^2}$ **111.** 🖉

113.

$$y = \frac{5x^2 + 8x - 3}{3x^2 + 2}$$

$(-0.346, -2.191)$,
$(1.929, 2.358)$

115.

$f'(1) = 1$

117.

$f'(1) = 1.2$

Technology Connection, p. 152

1. (c)   **2–5.** Left to the student

Technology Connection, p. 153

1–2. Left to the student

Exercise Set 1.6, p. 154

1. $13x^{12}$ **3.** $12x + 7$ **5.** $18x^5 - 60x^4$ **7.** $\frac{15}{2}x^{3/2} + 4x$

9. $18x^2 + 14x - 18$ **11.** $\frac{9\sqrt{t}}{2} - \frac{1}{2\sqrt{t}} + 2$ **13.** $2x$, for $x \neq 0$

15. $18x^5 - 2x$, for $x \neq 0$ **17.** $8x + 2$, for $x \neq \frac{1}{2}$

19. 1, for $t \neq -4$ **21.** $40x^3 - 21x^2 - 26x + 13$

23. $\dfrac{-2x(5x^3 - 3x - 15)}{(2x^3 + 3)^2}$ **25.** $-\frac{105}{2}x^{3/2} - 6x + 42x^{-1/2} + 4$

27. $\dfrac{3}{(3 - t)^2} + 15t^2$ **29.** $50x - 40$ **31.** $2x(x^2 - 4)(3x^2 - 4)$

33. $-36x^{-2} - 120x^{-3} + 144x^{-4} - 72x^{-5}$

35. $3t^2 - 1 + \dfrac{6}{t^2}$ **37.** $\dfrac{x^4 + 3x^2 + 2x}{(x^2 + 1)^2} + 12x^2$

39. $\dfrac{(x^{1/2} + 3)(\frac{1}{3}x^{-2/3}) - (x^{1/3} - 7)(\frac{1}{2}x^{-1/2})}{(\sqrt{x} + 3)^2}$, or

$\dfrac{6 - \sqrt{x} + 21x^{1/6}}{6x^{2/3}(\sqrt{x} + 3)^2}$ **41.** $\dfrac{-2x^{-1}}{(x + x^{-1})^2}$, or $\dfrac{-2x}{(x^2 + 1)^2}$, for $x \neq 0$

43. $\dfrac{-1}{(t - 4)^2}$ **45.** $\dfrac{5x^2 - 6x + 5}{(x^2 - 1)^2}$

47. $\dfrac{(t^2 - 2t + 4)(-2t + 3) - (-t^2 + 3t + 5)(2t - 2)}{(t^2 - 2t + 4)^2}$, or

$\dfrac{-t^2 - 18t + 22}{(t^2 - 2t + 4)^2}$ **49.** **(a)** $y = 2$; **(b)** $y = \frac{1}{2}x + 2$

51. **(a)** $y = x + 5$; **(b)** $y = \frac{21}{4}x - \frac{21}{4}$ **53.** $-\$0.0925$/belt

55. $-\$0.0153$/belt   **57.** $\$0.0772$/belt   **59.** $\$1.64$/vase

61. **(a)** $P'(t) = 57.6t^{0.6} - 104$; **(b)** $\$461.4$ billion/yr;

(c)   **63.** **(a)** $T'(t) = \dfrac{-4(t^2 - 1)}{(t^2 + 1)^2}$; **(b)** $100.2°F$;

(c) $-0.48°F$/hr   **65.** $30t^2 + 10t - 15$

67. $3x^2\left(\dfrac{x^2 + 1}{x^2 - 1}\right) + \dfrac{-4x}{(x^2 - 1)^2}(x^3 - 8)$, or

$\dfrac{3x^6 - 4x^4 - 3x^2 + 32x}{(x^2 - 1)^2}$ **69.** $\dfrac{-x^6 + 4x^3 - 24x^2}{(x^4 - 3x^3 - 5)^2}$

71. **(a)** $f'(x) = \dfrac{-2x}{(x^2 - 1)^2}$; **(b)** $g'(x) = \dfrac{-2x}{(x^2 - 1)^2}$; **(c)**

73.   **75.** **(a)** Definition of derivative; **(b)** adding and subtracting the same quantity is the same as adding 0; **(c)** the limit of a sum is the sum of the limits; **(d)** factoring; **(e)** the limit of a product is the product of the limits and $\lim_{h \to 0} f(x + h) = f(x)$; **(f)** definition of derivative; **(g)** using Leibniz notation

77. $\$13.24$/belt; $\$0.078$/belt

79.

There are no points at which the tangent line is horizontal.

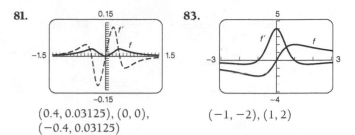

81. $(0.4, 0.03125)$, $(0, 0)$, $(-0.4, 0.03125)$

83. $(-1, -2)$, $(1, 2)$

Exercise Set 1.7, p. 163

1. $8x - 12$ **3.** $-55(7 - x)^{54}$ **5.** $\dfrac{-1}{2\sqrt{1 - x}}$ **7.** $\dfrac{3x}{\sqrt{3x^2 - 4}}$

9. $-400x(4x^2 + 1)^{-51}$ **11.** $4(x - 4)^7(2x + 3)^5(7x - 6)$

13. $\dfrac{-8}{(4x + 5)^3}$ **15.** $\dfrac{4x(5x + 14)}{(7 - 5x)^4}$ **17.** $15x^2(3 + x^3)^4 -$

$28x^6(1 + x^7)^3$ **19.** $4x - 400$ **21.** $\dfrac{2}{3\sqrt[3]{(2x - 1)^2}} - 8 + 2x$

23. $-5(2x - 3)^3(10x - 3)$

25. $(5x + 2)^3(2x - 3)^7(120x - 28)$,

or $4(5x + 2)^3(2x - 3)^7(30x - 7)$ **27.** $\dfrac{2x(5x - 1)}{\sqrt{4x - 1}}$

29. $\dfrac{2x - 5}{4(x^2 - 5x + 2)^{3/4}}$ **31.** $\dfrac{44(3x - 1)^3}{(5x + 2)^5}$

33. $\dfrac{13}{2(2x + 3)^{1/2}(5 - x)^{3/2}}$

35. $200(2x^3 - 3x^2 + 4x + 1)^{99}(3x^2 - 3x + 2)$

37. $\dfrac{-5(7x - 2)^4}{(3x - 1)^6}$ **39.** $\dfrac{-1}{(x - 1)^{3/2}(x + 1)^{1/2}}$

41. $\dfrac{(5x - 4)^6(120x + 107)}{(6x + 1)^4}$ **43.** $\dfrac{(3x - 4)^{1/4}(138x - 19)}{(2x + 1)^{1/3}}$

45. $\dfrac{-45}{u^4}$, 2, $\dfrac{-90}{(2x + 1)^4}$ **47.** $50u^{49}$, $12x^2 - 4x$,

$50(4x^3 - 2x^2)^{49}(12x^2 - 4x)$ **49.** $2u$, $3x^2$, $6x^2(x^3 + 1)$

51. $3x^2(10x^3 + 13)$ **53.** $\dfrac{-3x}{\sqrt{34 - 3x^2}}$

55. $\dfrac{3(-6t - 11)}{(5 + 3t)^2(6 + 3t)^2}$, or $\dfrac{-6t - 11}{3(t + 2)^2(3t + 5)^2}$ **57.** $y = 0$

59. $y = 4x - 3$ **61.** **(a)** $\dfrac{-64(6x + 1)}{(2x - 5)^3}$; **(b)** $\dfrac{-64(6x + 1)}{(2x - 5)^3}$;

(c)   **63.** -216 **65.** $4(13)^{-2/3}$, or about 0.72

67. $f'(x) = 6[2x^3 + (4x - 5)^2]^5[6x^2 + 8(4x - 5)]$

69. $f'(x) = \dfrac{1}{2\sqrt{x^2 + \sqrt{1 - 3x}}}\left(2x - \dfrac{3}{2\sqrt{1 - 3x}}\right)$

71. $\$1,000,000$/airplane

73. $P'(x) = \dfrac{500(2x - 0.1)}{\sqrt{x^2 - 0.1x}} - \dfrac{4000x}{3(x^2 + 2)^{2/3}}$

75. **(a)** $37.04x^3 - 255.81x^2 + 574.48x - 309.12$ **(b)**

(c) $\$1929.24$ billion/yr   **77.** **(a)** $\dfrac{da}{dr} = 5000\left(1 + \dfrac{r}{4}\right)^{19}$; **(b)**

79. **(a)** $P(t) = 2t^2 + 400.8t + 80.08$; **(b)** $\$592.80$/month

81. **(a)** $D(c) = 4.25c + 106.25$, $c(w) = \dfrac{95w}{43.2} \approx 2.199w$

(b) 4.25 mg/unit of creatine clearance; **(c)** 2.199 units of creatine clearance/kg; **(d)** 9.35 mg/kg; **(e)**

83. $1 + \dfrac{1}{2\sqrt{x}} + \dfrac{1}{2\sqrt{x + \sqrt{x}}} \cdot \left(1 + \dfrac{1}{2\sqrt{x}}\right)$ **85.** $\frac{1}{27}x^{-26/27}$

87. $\dfrac{6x^7 + 32x^5 + 5x^4}{(x^3 + 6x + 1)^{2/3}}$ **89.** $3x^2(x^2 + 1)^{3/2} + 3x^4(x^2 + 1)^{1/2}$,

or $(3x^2 + 6x^4)\sqrt{1 + x^2}$ **91.** $\dfrac{3(x^2 - x - 1)^2(x^2 + 4x - 1)}{(x^2 + 1)^4}$

93. $\dfrac{6\sqrt{t} + 1}{4\sqrt{t}\sqrt{3t + \sqrt{t}}}$

95. (a) $\dfrac{d}{dx}[f(x)]^3 = \dfrac{d}{dx}[f(x)^2 \cdot f(x)]$

$= f(x)^2 \cdot f'(x) + 2f(x) \cdot f'(x) \cdot f(x)$
$= f(x)^2 \cdot f'(x) + 2f(x)^2 \cdot f'(x)$
$= 3f(x)^2 \cdot f'(x);$

(b) $\dfrac{d}{dx}[f(x)]^4 = \dfrac{d}{dx}[f(x)^3 \cdot f(x)]$

$= f(x)^3 \cdot f'(x) + 3f(x)^2 \cdot f'(x) \cdot f(x)$
$= f(x)^3 \cdot f'(x) + 3f(x)^3 \cdot f'(x) = 4f(x)^3 \cdot f'(x)$

97.

$(-2.14476, -7.728),$
$(2.14476, 7.728)$

99. $\dfrac{4 - 2x^2}{\sqrt{4 - x^2}}$

Exercise Set 1.8, p. 172

1. $12x^2$ **3.** $24x^2$ **5.** 8 **7.** 0 **9.** $\dfrac{12}{x^5}$ **11.** $\dfrac{-1}{4x^{3/2}}$

13. $6x - \dfrac{10}{x^3}$ **15.** $\dfrac{-4}{25x^{9/5}}$ **17.** $\dfrac{12}{x^4}$

19. $14(x^2 + 3x)^5(13x^2 + 39x + 27)$
21. $10(3x^2 + 2x + 1)^3(81x^2 + 54x + 11)$

23. $\dfrac{3(x^2 + 2)}{4(x^2 + 1)^{5/4}}$ **25.** $\dfrac{3}{4\sqrt{x}}$ **27.** $\dfrac{45x^4 - 54x^2 - 3}{16(x^3 - x)^{5/4}}$

29. $\frac{4}{3}x^{-2/3} + \frac{1}{4}x^{-3/2}$ **31.** $24x^{-5} + 6x^{-4}$ **33.** $60x^2 + 6x$

35. $\dfrac{44}{(2x - 3)^3}$ **37.** $120x$ **39.** $720x$

41. $-2520x^{-8} + \dfrac{1760}{243}x^{-14/3}$ **43.** 0

45. (a) $v(t) = -20t + 2$; (b) $a(t) = -20$; (c) $v(1) = -18$ m/sec, $a(1) = -20$ m/sec^2 **47.** (a) $v(t) = 3$; (b) $a(t) = 0$; (c) $v(2) = 3$ mi/hr, $a(2) = 0$ mi/hr^2; (d) ✏ **49.** (a) 144 ft; (b) 96 ft/sec; (c) 32 ft/sec^2 **51.** $v(2) = 19.62$ m/sec, $a(2) = 9.81$ m/sec^2 **53.** (a) The velocity is greatest at time 0. The slope of a tangent line is greatest there. (b) The acceleration is negative, since the slopes of tangent lines are decreasing.
55. (a) $(7, 11)$; (b) $(2, 4), (7, 11), (13, 15)$; (c) $(0, 2), (11, 13)$; (d) $(4, 7)$; (e) ✏ **57.** (a) \$146,000/month, \$84,000/month, $-\$4000$/month; (b) $-\$68,000$/month^2, $-\$56,000$/month^2, $-\$32,000$/month^2; (c) ✏ **59.** (a) 11.34, 1.98, 0.665;
(b) $-0.789, -0.0577, -0.0112$; (c) ✏

61. $\dfrac{6}{(1 - x)^4}$ **63.** $\dfrac{3x^{1/2} - 1}{2x^{3/2}(x^{1/2} - 1)^3}$

65. $k(k - 1)(k - 2)(k - 3)(k - 4)x^{k-5}$

67. $f'(x) = \dfrac{3}{(x + 2)^2}, f''(x) = \dfrac{-6}{(x + 2)^3}, f'''(x) = \dfrac{18}{(x + 2)^4},$

$f^4(x) = \dfrac{-72}{(x + 2)^5}$ **69.** $s''(t) = 9.81$ m/sec^2; the value of the gravitational constant for Earth **71.** ✏ **73.** (a) Graph I; (b) Graph IV; (c) Graph II; (d) Graph III **75.** 5 **77.** $\dfrac{5}{2}$

79. -6 **81.** $\dfrac{17}{8}$ **83.** 2

85.

$v(t)$ switches at $t = -1.29$ and $t = 1.29$.

87.

$v(t)$ switches at $t = 0.604$ and $t = -1.104$.

Chapter 1 Review Exercises, p. 181

1. False **2.** False **3.** True **4.** False **5.** True **6.** True **7.** False **8.** True **9.** (e) **10.** (c) **11.** (a) **12.** (f) **13.** (b) **14.** (d)
15. (a)

$x \to -7^-$	$f(x)$	$x \to -7^+$	$f(x)$
-7.1	-10.1	-6.9	-9.9
-7.01	-10.01	-6.99	-9.99
-7.001	-10.001	-6.999	-9.999

(b) $\lim\limits_{x \to -7^-} f(x) = -10$; $\lim\limits_{x \to -7^+} f(x) = -10$; $\lim\limits_{x \to -7} f(x) = -10$

16.

17. $\lim\limits_{x \to -7} \dfrac{x^2 + 4x - 21}{x + 7} = \lim\limits_{x \to -7} \dfrac{(x + 7)(x - 3)}{x + 7} =$
$\lim\limits_{x \to -7} (x - 3) = -10$ **18.** -4 **19.** 10 **20.** -12 **21.** 3
22. -4 **23.** -4 **24.** Continuous at $x = 1$, since $\lim\limits_{x \to 1} g(x) = g(1)$
25. Does not exist **26.** -2 **27.** Not continuous, since
$\lim\limits_{x \to -2} g(x)$ does not exist **28.** $-\dfrac{2}{3}$ **29.** 0 **30.** Not defined
at $x = -2$, since g is discontinuous at $x = -2$ **31.** Not defined
at $x = -2$, since there is a corner there **32.** -2 **33.** -3
34. Yes, since $\lim\limits_{x \to -2} f(x) = f(-2)$ **35.** 2
36. $-6x + 3h, h \ne 0$ **37.** $6x^2 + 6xh + 2h^2, h \ne 0$
38. $y = x - 1$ **39.** $(4, 5)$ **40.** $(5, -108)$ **41.** $45x^4$

42. $\dfrac{8}{3}x^{-2/3}$ **43.** $\dfrac{24}{x^9}$ **44.** $6x^{-3/5}$ **45.** $0.7x^6 - 12x^3 - 3x^2$

46. $\frac{5}{2}x^5 + 32x^3 - 2$ **47.** $(x^3 - 5)\left(\dfrac{1}{2\sqrt{x}} + 4\right) +$

$(\sqrt{x} + 4x)(3x^2)$ **48.** $\dfrac{-x^2 + 16x + 8}{(8 - x)^2}$

49. $2(5 - x)(2x - 1)^4(-7x + 26)$ **50.** $35x^4(x^5 - 3)^6$

51. $\dfrac{x(11x + 4)}{(4x + 2)^{1/4}}$ **52.** $-48x^{-5}$ **53.** $3x^5 - 60x + 26$

54. (a) $P'(t) = 100t$; (b) 30,000 people; (c) 2000 people/yr

55. $(3, 5), (7, 8), (9, 13), (15, 18)$ **56.** $(7, 8), (15, 18)$
57. $(0, 3), (8, 9)$ **58.** $(5, 7), (13, 15)$ **59. (a)** $v(t) = 1 + 4t^3$;
(b) $a(t) = 12t^2$; **(c)** $v(2) = 33$ ft/sec, $a(2) = 48$ ft/sec^2
60. (a) $A_C(x) = 5x^{-1/2} + 100x^{-1}, A_R(x) = 40$,
$A_P(x) = 40 - 5x^{-1/2} - 100x^{-1}$;
(b) average cost is dropping at approximately $1.33 per lamp.

61. $\dfrac{d}{dx}(f \circ g)(x) = -4(1 - 2x), \dfrac{d}{dx}(g \circ f) = -4x$

62. $\dfrac{-9x^4 - 4x^3 + 9x + 2}{2\sqrt{1 + 3x}(1 + x^3)^2}$ **63.** $\dfrac{1}{243}x^{-242/243}$ **64.** -0.25

65. $\frac{1}{6}$ **66.**

$(-1.7137, 37.445), (0, 0), (1.7137, -37.445)$

Chapter 1 Test, p. 183

1. [1.1] **(a)**

$x \rightarrow 6^-$	$f(x)$
5.9	11.9
5.99	11.99
5.999	11.999

$x \rightarrow 6^+$	$f(x)$
6.1	12.1
6.01	12.01
6.001	12.001

(b) $\lim\limits_{x \to 6^-} f(x) = 12$; $\lim\limits_{x \to 6^+} f(x) = 12$; $\lim\limits_{x \to 6} f(x) = 12$
2. [1.1]

$f(x) = \dfrac{x^2 - 36}{x - 6}$

3. [1.2]

$\lim\limits_{x \to 6} \dfrac{x^2 - 36}{x - 6} = \lim\limits_{x \to 6} \dfrac{(x + 6)(x - 6)}{x - 6} = \lim\limits_{x \to 6} (x + 6) = 12$

4. [1.1] Does not exist **5.** [1.1] 0 **6.** [1.1] Does not exist
7. [1.1] 2 **8.** [1.1] 4 **9.** [1.1] 1 **10.** [1.1] 1
11. [1.1] 2 **12.** [1.4] 0 **13.** [1.4] 0
14. [1.2] $-5, -3, -2, 1, 4$ **15.** [1.4] $-5, -3, -2, -1, 1, 3, 4$
16. [1.2] Continuous **17.** [1.2] Not continuous,
since $\lim\limits_{x \to 3} f(x)$ does not exist **18.** [1.1, 1.2] **(a)** Does not exist;
(b) 1; **(c)** no **19.** [1.1, 1.2] 3 **20.** [1.1, 1.2] 6
21. [1.1, 1.2] $\frac{1}{8}$ **22.** [1.1, 1.2] Does not exist, since

$\lim\limits_{x \to 0^-} \dfrac{1}{x} \neq \lim\limits_{x \to 0^+} \dfrac{1}{x}$ **23.** [1.3] $4x + 3 + 2h$

24. [1.4] $y = \frac{3}{4}x + 2$ **25.** [1.5] $(0, 0), (2, -4)$
26. [1.5] $23x^{22}$ **27.** [1.5] $\frac{4}{3}x^{-2/3} + \frac{5}{2}x^{-1/2}$ **28.** [1.5] $\dfrac{10}{x^2}$
29. [1.5] $\frac{5}{4}x^{1/4}$ **30.** [1.5] $-1.0x + 0.61$ **31.** [1.5]

$x^2 - 2x + 2$ **32.** $(3\sqrt{x} + 1)(2x - 1) + (x^2 - x)\dfrac{1}{3\sqrt[3]{x^2}}$

33. [1.6] $\dfrac{5}{(5 - x)^2}$ **34.** [1.7] $(x + 3)^3(7 - x)^4(-9x + 13)$

35. [1.7] $-5(x^5 - 4x^3 + x)^{-6}(5x^4 - 12x^2 + 1)$

36. [1.6, 1.7] $\dfrac{2x^2 + 5}{\sqrt{x^2 + 5}}$ **37.** [1.8] $24x$

38. [1.5] **(a)** $M'(t) = -0.003t^2 + 0.2t$; **(b)** 9; **(c)** 1.7 words/min
39. [1.6] **(a)** $A_R = 50, A_C = x^{-1/3} + 750x^{-1}$,
$A_P = 50 - x^{-1/3} - 750x^{-1}$; **(b)** average cost is dropping at
approximately $11.74 per speaker. **40.** [1.7] $24x^5 - 1$
41. [1.7] $6(x^2 - x)^2(2x - 1)$ **42.** [1.8] **(a)**
43. [1.6, 1.7] $\dfrac{-1 - 9x}{2(1 - 3x)^{2/3}(1 + 3x)^{5/6}}$ **44.** [1.2] 27

45. [1.5]

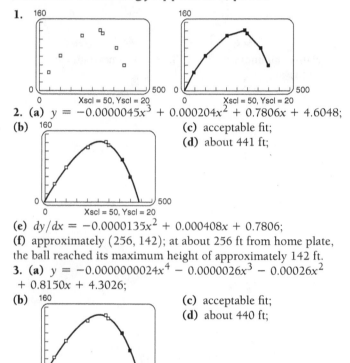

$(1.0836, 25.1029)$ and
$(2.9503, 8.6247)$

46. [1.5] 0.5

Extended Technology Application, p. 185

1.

2. (a) $y = -0.0000045x^3 + 0.000204x^2 + 0.7806x + 4.6048$;
(b) **(c)** acceptable fit;
(d) about 441 ft;

(e) $dy/dx = -0.0000135x^2 + 0.000408x + 0.7806$;
(f) approximately $(256, 142)$; at about 256 ft from home plate,
the ball reached its maximum height of approximately 142 ft.
3. (a) $y = -0.0000000024x^4 - 0.0000026x^3 - 0.00026x^2$
$+ 0.8150x + 4.3026$;
(b) **(c)** acceptable fit;
(d) about 440 ft;

(e) $dy/dx = -0.0000000096x^3 - 0.0000078x^2 -$
$0.00053x + 0.815$; **(f)** approximately $(257, 142)$; at about 257 ft
from home plate, the ball reached its maximum height of
approximately 142 ft.
4. (a) **(b)** 450 ft;
(c) $\dfrac{dy}{dx} = \dfrac{303.75 - 0.003x^2}{\sqrt{202,500 - x^2}}$;
(d) approximately $(318, 152)$;
at about 318 ft from home plate,
the ball reached its maximum
height of approximately 152 ft.

5. The two models are very similar. The main difference seems
to be that the maximum height is reached further from home
plate with the model in Exercise 4. **6.** 466 ft, 442 ft, 430 ft
7. The estimate of the reporters is way off. Even with a low
trajectory, the ball would at best have traveled a horizontal
distance of about 526 ft. **8. (a)** 523 ft; **(b)** 490 ft, 450 ft;
(c) 464 ft (rounded)

CHAPTER 2

Technology Connection, p. 198

1. $f(x) = 2 - (x - 1)^{2/3}$

2. $f'(x) = -\frac{2}{3}(x-1)^{-1/3}$

The derivative is not defined at $(1, 2)$.

Technology Connection, p. 200

1. Relative maximum at $(-1, 42)$; relative minimum at $\left(\frac{5}{2}, -\frac{175}{4}\right)$

Exercise Set 2.1, p. 201

1. Relative minimum at $(-3, -12)$
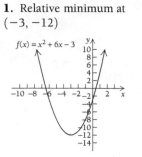
$f(x) = x^2 + 6x - 3$

3. Relative maximum at $\left(-\frac{3}{4}, \frac{25}{8}\right)$

$f(x) = 2 - 3x - 2x^2$

5. Relative minimum at $(-2, -13)$
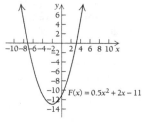
$F(x) = 0.5x^2 + 2x - 11$

7. Relative minimum at $\left(\frac{2}{3}, \frac{113}{27}\right)$; relative maximum at $\left(-1, \frac{13}{2}\right)$

$g(x) = x^3 + \frac{1}{2}x^2 - 2x + 5$

9. Relative minimum at $(2, -4)$; relative maximum at $(0, 0)$

$f(x) = x^3 - 3x^2$

11. No relative extrema exist.

$f(x) = x^3 + 3x$

13. No relative extrema exist.

$F(x) = 1 - x^3$

15. Relative minimum at $(4, -22)$; relative maximum at $(0, 10)$

$G(x) = x^3 - 6x^2 + 10$

17. Relative maximum at $\left(\frac{3}{4}, \frac{27}{256}\right)$

$g(x) = x^3 - x^4$

19. No relative extrema exist.

$f(x) = \frac{1}{3}x^3 - 2x^2 + 4x - 1$

21. Relative minima at $\left(-\frac{\sqrt{10}}{2}, -\frac{27}{4}\right)$ and $\left(\frac{\sqrt{10}}{2}, -\frac{27}{4}\right)$; relative maximum at $(0, 12)$

$f(x) = 3x^4 - 15x^2 + 12$

23. No relative extrema exist.

$G(x) = \sqrt[3]{x+2}$

25. Relative maximum at $(0, 1)$
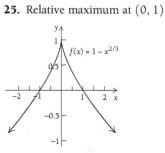
$f(x) = 1 - x^{2/3}$

27. Relative minimum at $(0, -8)$

$G(x) = \frac{-8}{x^2 + 1}$

29. Relative minimum at $(-1, -2)$; relative maximum at $(1, 2)$

$g(x) = \frac{4x}{x^2 + 1}$

31. No relative extrema exist.
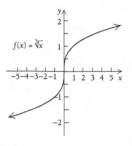
$f(x) = \sqrt[3]{x}$

33. Relative minimum at $(-1, 2)$

$g(x) = \sqrt{x^2 + 2x + 5}$

35–83. Left to the student.

85. ✎

87. Relative maximum at $(2.108, 52{,}644.383)$; relative minimum at $(3.897, 52{,}335.73)$

$E(t) = 107.833t^3 - 971.369t^2 + 2657.917t + 50347.833$

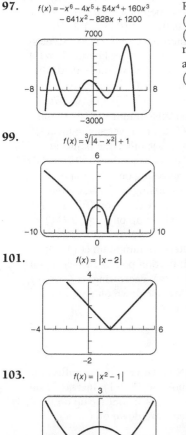

89. $16.08°S$

91. Increasing on $(-1, \infty)$, decreasing on $(-\infty, -1)$; relative minimum at $x = -1$. Graph left to the student.

93. Increasing on $(-\infty, 1)$, decreasing on $(1, \infty)$; relative maximum at $x = 1$. Graph left to the student.

95. Increasing on $(-4, 2)$, decreasing on $(-\infty, -4)$ and $(2, \infty)$; relative minimum at $x = -4$, relative maximum at $x = 2$. Graph left to the student.

97.

$f(x) = -x^6 - 4x^5 + 54x^4 + 160x^3 - 641x^2 - 828x + 1200$

Relative minima at $(-3.683, -2288.03)$ and $(2.116, -1083.08)$; relative maxima at $(-6.262, 3213.8)$ and $(-0.559, 1440.06)$ and $(5.054, 6674.12)$

99.

$f(x) = \sqrt[3]{|4 - x^2|} + 1$

Relative minima at $(-2, 1)$ and $(2, 1)$; relative maximum at $(0, 2.587)$

101.

$f(x) = |x - 2|$

Relative minimum at $(2, 0)$; increasing on $(2, \infty)$; decreasing on $(-\infty, 2)$; f' does not exist at $x = 2$

103.

$f(x) = |x^2 - 1|$

Relative maximum at $(0, 1)$; relative minima at $(-1, 0)$ and $(1, 0)$; increasing on $(-1, 0)$ and $(1, \infty)$; decreasing on $(-\infty, -1)$ and $(0, 1)$; f' does not exist at $x = -1$ and $x = 1$

105.

$f(x) = |9 - x^2|$

Relative maximum at $(0, 9)$; relative minima at $(-3, 0)$ and $(3, 0)$; increasing on $(-3, 0)$ and $(3, \infty)$; decreasing on $(-\infty, -3)$ and $(0, 3)$; f' does not exist at $x = -3$ and $x = 3$

107.

$f(x) = |x^3 - 1|$

Relative minimum at $(1, 0)$; increasing on $(1, \infty)$; decreasing on $(-\infty, 1)$; f' does not exist at $x = 1$

109. ✎ **111.** ✎

Technology Connection, p. 211

Left to the student

Technology Connection, p. 212

1. Relative minimum at $(1, -1)$; inflection points at $(0, 0)$, $(0.553, -0.512)$, $(1.447, -0.512)$, and $(2, 0)$

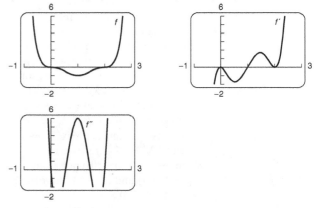

Technology Connection, p. 217

1–9. Left to the student

Exercise Set 2.2, p. 217

1. Relative maximum is $f(0) = 4$. **3.** Relative minimum is $f\left(-\frac{1}{2}\right) = -\frac{5}{4}$. **5.** Relative maximum is $f\left(\frac{3}{8}\right) = -\frac{7}{16}$.
7. Relative minimum is $f(2) = -17$; relative maximum is $f(-2) = 15$.

9.

$f(x) = x^3 - 27x$

Relative minimum at $(3, -54)$, relative maximum at $(-3, 54)$; inflection point at $(0, 0)$; increasing on $(-\infty, -3)$ and $(3, \infty)$, decreasing on $(-3, 3)$; concave down on $(-\infty, 0)$, concave up on $(0, \infty)$

11.

$f(x) = 2x^3 - 3x^2 - 36x + 28$

Relative minimum at $(3, -53)$, relative maximum at $(-2, 72)$; inflection point at $\left(\frac{1}{2}, \frac{19}{2}\right)$; increasing on $(-\infty, -2)$ and $(3, \infty)$, decreasing on $(-2, 3)$; concave down on $\left(-\infty, \frac{1}{2}\right)$, concave up on $\left(\frac{1}{2}, \infty\right)$

13.

$f(x) = 80 - 9x^2 - x^3$

Relative minimum at $(-6, -28)$, relative maximum at $(0, 80)$; inflection point at $(-3, 26)$; increasing on $(-6, 0)$, decreasing on $(-\infty, -6)$ and $(0, \infty)$; concave up on $(-\infty, -3)$, concave down on $(-3, \infty)$

15.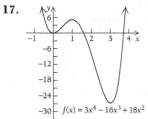

$f(x) = -x^3 + 3x - 2$

Relative minimum at $(-1, -4)$, relative maximum at $(1, 0)$; inflection point at $(0, -2)$; increasing on $(-1, 1)$, decreasing on $(-\infty, -1)$ and $(1, \infty)$; concave up on $(-\infty, 0)$, concave down on $(0, \infty)$

17.

$f(x) = 3x^4 - 16x^3 + 18x^2$

Relative minima at $(0, 0)$ and $(3, -27)$, relative maximum at $(1, 5)$; inflection points at $(0.451, 2.321)$ and $(2.215, -13.358)$; increasing on $(0, 1)$ and $(3, \infty)$, decreasing on $(-\infty, 0)$ and $(1, 3)$; concave up on $(-\infty, 0.451)$ and $(2.215, \infty)$, concave down on $(0.451, 2.215)$

19.

$f(x) = x^4 - 6x^2$

Relative minima at $\left(-\sqrt{3}, -9\right)$ and $\left(\sqrt{3}, -9\right)$, relative maximum at $(0, 0)$; inflection points at $(-1, -5)$ and $(1, -5)$; increasing on $\left(-\sqrt{3}, 0\right)$ and $\left(\sqrt{3}, \infty\right)$, decreasing on $(-\infty, -\sqrt{3})$ and $\left(0, \sqrt{3}\right)$; concave up on $(-\infty, -1)$ and $(1, \infty)$, concave down on $(-1, 1)$

21.

$f(x) = x^3 - 6x^2 + 9x + 1$

Relative minimum at $(3, 1)$, relative maximum at $(1, 5)$; inflection point at $(2, 3)$; increasing on $(-\infty, 1)$ and $(3, \infty)$, decreasing on $(1, 3)$; concave down on $(-\infty, 2)$, concave up on $(2, \infty)$

23.

$f(x) = x^4 - 2x^3$

Relative minimum at $\left(\frac{3}{2}, -\frac{27}{16}\right)$; inflection points at $(0, 0)$ and $(1, -1)$; increasing on $\left(\frac{3}{2}, \infty\right)$, decreasing on $\left(-\infty, \frac{3}{2}\right)$; concave down on $(0, 1)$, concave up on $(-\infty, 0)$ and $(1, \infty)$

25.

$f(x) = x^3 - 6x^2 - 135x$

Relative minimum at $(9, -972)$, relative maximum at $(-5, 400)$; inflection point at $(2, -286)$; increasing on $(-\infty, -5)$ and $(9, \infty)$, decreasing on $(-5, 9)$; concave down on $(-\infty, 2)$, concave up on $(2, \infty)$

27.

$f(x) = x^4 - 4x^3 + 10$

Relative minimum at $(3, -17)$; inflection points at $(0, 10)$ and $(2, -6)$; increasing on $(3, \infty)$, decreasing on $(-\infty, 3)$; concave down on $(0, 2)$, concave up on $(-\infty, 0)$ and $(2, \infty)$

29.

$f(x) = x^3 - 6x^2 + 12x - 6$

No relative extrema; inflection point at $(2, 2)$; increasing on $(-\infty, \infty)$; concave down on $(-\infty, 2)$, concave up on $(2, \infty)$

31.

$f(x) = 5x^3 - 3x^5$

Relative minimum at $(-1, -2)$, relative maximum at $(1, 2)$; inflection points at $(-0.707, -1.237)$, $(0, 0)$, and $(0.707, 1.237)$; increasing on $(-1, 1)$, decreasing on $(-\infty, -1)$ and $(1, \infty)$; concave down on $(-0.707, 0)$ and $(0.707, \infty)$, concave up on $(-\infty, -0.707)$ and $(0, 0.707)$

33.

$f(x) = x^2(1 - x)^2$

Relative minima at $(0, 0)$ and $(1, 0)$, relative maximum at $\left(\frac{1}{2}, \frac{1}{16}\right)$; inflection points at $(0.211, 0.028)$ and $(0.789, 0.028)$; increasing on $\left(0, \frac{1}{2}\right)$ and $(1, \infty)$, decreasing on $(-\infty, 0)$ and $\left(\frac{1}{2}, 1\right)$; concave down on $(0.211, 0.789)$, concave up on $(-\infty, 0.211)$ and $(0.789, \infty)$

35.

$f(x) = (x - 1)^{2/3}$

Relative minimum at $(1, 0)$; no inflection points; increasing on $(1, \infty)$, decreasing on $(-\infty, 1)$; concave down on $(-\infty, 1)$ and $(1, \infty)$

37.

$f(x) = (x - 3)^{1/3} - 1$

No relative extrema; inflection point at $(3, -1)$; increasing on $(-\infty, \infty)$; concave up on $(-\infty, 3)$, concave down on $(3, \infty)$

39.

Relative maximum at $(4, 5)$; no inflection points; increasing on $(-\infty, 4)$, decreasing on $(4, \infty)$; concave up on $(-\infty, 4)$ and $(4, \infty)$

41.

Relative minimum at $\left(\sqrt{\frac{1}{2}}, -\frac{1}{2}\right)$, relative maximum at $\left(-\sqrt{\frac{1}{2}}, \frac{1}{2}\right)$; inflection point at $(0, 0)$; increasing on $\left(-1, -\sqrt{\frac{1}{2}}\right)$ and $\left(\sqrt{\frac{1}{2}}, 1\right)$, decreasing on $\left(-\sqrt{\frac{1}{2}}, \sqrt{\frac{1}{2}}\right)$; concave up on $(0, 1)$, concave down on $(-1, 0)$

43.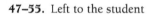

Relative minimum at $(-1, -4)$, relative maximum at $(1, 4)$; inflection points at $\left(-\sqrt{3}, -2\sqrt{3}\right)$ and $(0, 0)$ and $\left(\sqrt{3}, 2\sqrt{3}\right)$; increasing on $(-1, 1)$, decreasing on $(-\infty, -1)$ and $(1, \infty)$; concave up on $\left(-\sqrt{3}, 0\right)$ and $\left(\sqrt{3}, \infty\right)$, concave down on $\left(-\infty, -\sqrt{3}\right)$ and $\left(0, \sqrt{3}\right)$

45.

Relative minimum at $(0, -4)$; inflection points at $\left(-\sqrt{\frac{1}{3}}, -3\right)$ and $\left(\sqrt{\frac{1}{3}}, -3\right)$; decreasing on $(-\infty, 0)$, increasing on $(0, \infty)$; concave down on $\left(-\infty, -\sqrt{\frac{1}{3}}\right)$ and $\left(\sqrt{\frac{1}{3}}, \infty\right)$, concave up on $\left(-\sqrt{\frac{1}{3}}, \sqrt{\frac{1}{3}}\right)$

47–55. Left to the student

57.   **59.**

61. $(3.26, 18.36)$; the rate of change of the amount of rainfall is decreasing the fastest at this point   **63.**   **65.** Left to the student   **67.** False   **69.** True   **71.** True   **73.** True

75.

Relative maximum at $(0, 0)$; relative minimum at $(1, -2)$

77.

Relative minimum at $(0, 0)$; relative maximum at $(0.4, 0.035)$

79.

Relative maximum at $(-1, 1.587)$; relative minimum at $(1, -1.587)$

Technology Connection, p. 221

1. Vertical asymptotes: $x = -7$ and $x = 4$
2. Vertical asymptote: $x = 0$

Technology Connection, p. 224

1. Horizontal asymptote: $y = 3$ **2.** Horizontal asymptote: $y = 0$

Exercise Set 2.3, p. 230

1. $x = 2$ **3.** $x = -5$ and $x = 5$ **5.** $x = -1, x = 0$, and $x = 1$ **7.** $x = -4$ **9.** No vertical asymptotes   **11.** $y = \frac{3}{4}$ **13.** $y = 0$ **15.** $y = 4$ **17.** No horizontal asymptote   **19.** $y = 4$ **21.** $y = \frac{1}{2}$

23.

Decreasing on $(-\infty, 0)$ and $(0, \infty)$
No relative extrema
Asymptotes: $x = 0$ and $y = 0$
Concave down on $(-\infty, 0)$; concave up on $(0, \infty)$
No intercepts

25.

Increasing on $(-\infty, 5)$ and $(5, \infty)$
No relative extrema
Asymptotes: $x = 5$ and $y = 0$
Concave up on $(-\infty, 5)$; concave down on $(5, \infty)$
y-intercept: $\left(0, \frac{2}{5}\right)$

27.

Decreasing on $(-\infty, 3)$ and $(3, \infty)$
No relative extrema
Asymptotes: $x = 3$ and $y = 0$
Concave down on $(-\infty, 3)$; concave up on $(3, \infty)$
y-intercept: $\left(0, -\frac{1}{3}\right)$

29

Increasing on $(-\infty, -5)$ and $(-5, \infty)$
No relative extrema
Asymptotes: $x = -5$ and $y = 0$
Concave up on $(-\infty, -5)$; concave down on $(-5, \infty)$
y-intercept: $\left(0, -\frac{2}{5}\right)$

31.
Decreasing on $(-\infty, 0)$ and $(0, \infty)$
No relative extrema
Asymptotes: $x = 0$ and $y = 2$
Concave down on $(-\infty, 0)$; concave up on $(0, \infty)$
x-intercept: $\left(-\frac{1}{2}, 0\right)$

$f(x) = \frac{2x+1}{x}$

33.
$f(x) = x + \frac{2}{x}$
Increasing on $\left(-\infty, -\sqrt{2}\right)$ and $\left(\sqrt{2}, \infty\right)$; decreasing on $\left(-\sqrt{2}, 0\right)$ and $\left(0, \sqrt{2}\right)$
Relative minimum at $\left(\sqrt{2}, 2\sqrt{2}\right)$; relative maximum at $\left(-\sqrt{2}, -2\sqrt{2}\right)$;
Asymptotes: $x = 0$ and $y = x$
Concave down on $(-\infty, 0)$; concave up on $(0, \infty)$
No intercepts

35.
$f(x) = \frac{-1}{x^2}$
Decreasing on $(-\infty, 0)$; increasing on $(0, \infty)$
No relative extrema
Asymptotes: $x = 0$ and $y = 0$
Concave down on $(-\infty, 0)$ and $(0, \infty)$
No intercepts

37.
$f(x) = \frac{x}{x-3}$
Decreasing on $(-\infty, 3)$ and $(3, \infty)$
No relative extrema
Asymptotes: $x = 3$ and $y = 1$
Concave down on $(-\infty, 3)$; concave up on $(3, \infty)$
Intercept: $(0, 0)$

39.
$\left(0, \frac{1}{3}\right)$ $f(x) = \frac{1}{x^2+3}$
Increasing on $(-\infty, 0)$; decreasing on $(0, \infty)$
Relative maximum at $\left(0, \frac{1}{3}\right)$
Asymptote: $y = 0$
Concave down on $(-1, 1)$; concave up on $(-\infty, -1)$ and $(1, \infty)$
Inflection points: $\left(-1, \frac{1}{4}\right)$ and $\left(1, \frac{1}{4}\right)$
y-intercept: $\left(0, \frac{1}{3}\right)$

41.
$f(x) = \frac{x+3}{x^2-9}$
Decreasing on $(-\infty, -3)$, $(-3, 3)$, and $(3, \infty)$
No relative extrema
Asymptotes: $x = 3$ and $y = 0$
Concave down on $(-\infty, -3)$ and $(-3, 3)$; concave up on $(3, \infty)$
y-intercept: $\left(0, -\frac{1}{3}\right)$

43.
$f(x) = \frac{x-1}{x+2}$
Increasing on $(-\infty, -2)$ and $(-2, \infty)$
No relative extrema
Asymptotes: $x = -2$ and $y = 1$
Concave up on $(-\infty, -2)$; concave down on $(-2, \infty)$
x-intercept: $(1, 0)$;
y-intercept: $\left(0, -\frac{1}{2}\right)$

45.
$f(x) = \frac{x^2-9}{x+1}$
Increasing on $(-\infty, -1)$ and $(-1, \infty)$
No relative extrema
Asymptotes: $x = -1$ and $y = x - 1$
Concave up on $(-\infty, -1)$; concave down on $(-1, \infty)$
x-intercepts: $(-3, 0)$ and $(3, 0)$; y-intercept: $(0, -9)$

47.
Decreasing on $(-\infty, -5)$, $(-5, 3)$, and $(3, \infty)$
No relative extrema
Asymptotes: $x = -5$ and $y = 0$
Concave down on $(-\infty, -5)$; concave up on $(-5, 3)$ and $(3, \infty)$
y-intercept: $\left(0, \frac{1}{5}\right)$

$f(x) = \frac{x-3}{x^2+2x-15}$

49.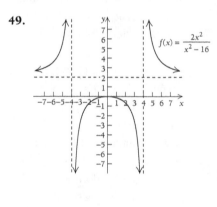
$f(x) = \frac{2x^2}{x^2-16}$
Increasing on $(-\infty, -4)$ and $(-4, 0)$; decreasing on $(0, 4)$ and $(4, \infty)$
Relative maximum at $(0, 0)$
Asymptotes: $x = -4$, $x = 4$, and $y = 2$
Concave up on $(-\infty, -4)$ and $(4, \infty)$; concave down on $(-4, 4)$
x- and y-intercept: $(0, 0)$

51.
$f(x) = \frac{10}{x^2+4}$
Increasing on $(-\infty, 0)$; decreasing on $(0, \infty)$
Relative maximum at $(0, 2.5)$
Asymptote: $y = 0$
Concave up on $\left(-\infty, -\frac{2}{\sqrt{3}}\right)$ and $\left(\frac{2}{\sqrt{3}}, \infty\right)$, or approximately $(-\infty, -1.1547)$ and $(1.1547, \infty)$; concave down on $\left(-\frac{2}{\sqrt{3}}, \frac{2}{\sqrt{3}}\right)$, or approximately $(-1.1547, 1.1547)$
Inflection points: $\left(-\frac{2}{\sqrt{3}}, \frac{15}{8}\right)$ and $\left(\frac{2}{\sqrt{3}}, \frac{15}{8}\right)$, or approximately $(-1.1547, 1.875)$ and $(1.1547, 1.875)$
y-intercept: $(0, 2.5)$

53.

$f(x) = \dfrac{x^2+1}{x}$

Increasing on $(-\infty, -1)$ and $(1, \infty)$; decreasing on $(-1, 0)$ and $(0, 1)$
Relative maximum at $(-1, -2)$; relative minimum at $(1, 2)$
Asymptotes: $x = 0$ and $y = x$
Concave down on $(-\infty, 0)$; concave up on $(0, \infty)$
No intercepts

55.

$f(x) = \dfrac{x^2 - 16}{x+4}$

Increasing on $(-\infty, -4)$ and $(-4, \infty)$
No relative extrema
No asymptotes
No concavity
x-intercept: $(4, 0)$; y-intercept: $(0, -4)$

57. (a) $A(x) = 3x + \dfrac{80}{x}$;
(c) Slant asymptote: $y = 3x$. As x, the number of units produced, increases, average cost approaches $3x$.

(b)

$A(x) = 3x + \dfrac{80}{x}$

59. (d)

$A(x) = -\tfrac{1}{2}x + 400 - \dfrac{5000}{x}$

61. (a) $0.85, $0.73, $0.52;
(b) 27.6 yr after 1990;
(c) 0

63. (a)

n	9	6	3	1	2/3	1/3
E	4.00	6.00	12.00	36.00	54.00	108.00

(b) $\lim\limits_{n \to 0} E(n) = \infty$. The pitcher gives up one or more runs but gets no one out (0 innings pitched).

65. ✎   **67.** Does not exist   **69.** ∞

71.

$f(x) = x^2 + \dfrac{1}{x^2}$

73.

$f(x) = \dfrac{x^3 + 4x^2 + x - 6}{x^2 - x - 2}$

75.

$f(x) = \dfrac{x^3 + 2x^2 - 3x}{x^2 - 25}$

77.

$f(x) = \dfrac{x^2 - 3}{2x - 4}$

(a) $(-1.732, 0)$ and $(1.732, 0)$;
(b) $(0, 0.75)$; **(c)** vertical: $x = 2$; slant: $y = 0.5x + 1$

79. Asymptote: $y = x^2 - 6$

$f(x) = \dfrac{x^5 + x - 9}{x^3 + 6x}$ and $y = x^2 - 6$

81. $f(x) = \dfrac{-2x}{x - 2}$

83. $g(x) = \dfrac{x^2 - 2}{x^2 - 1}$

85. $h(x) = \dfrac{x - 9}{x^2 + x - 6}$

Technology Connection, p. 236

1. On $[-2, 1]$, absolute minimum is -8 at $x = -2$, and absolute maximum is 2.185 at $x = -0.333$; on $[-1, 2]$, absolute minimum is 1 at $x = -1$ and $x = 1$, and absolute maximum is 4 at $x = 2$

Technology Connection, p. 237

1. Absolute minimum: -4 at $x = 2$; no absolute maximum

Technology Connection, p. 239

1. No absolute maximum; absolute minimum: 6.325 at $x = 0.316$

Exercise Set 2.4, p. 240

1. (a) 55 mph   **(b)** 5 mph   **(c)** 25 mpg
3. Absolute maximum: $5\frac{1}{4}$ at $x = \frac{1}{2}$; absolute minimum: 3 at $x = 2$ **5.** Absolute maximum: $6\frac{1}{2}$ at $x = -1$; absolute minimum: 3 at $x = -2$ **7.** Absolute maximum: $5\frac{1}{2}$ at $x = -1$; absolute minimum: 2 at $x = -2$ **9.** Absolute maximum: 6 at $x = 1$; absolute minimum: 2 at $x = -1$ **11.** Absolute maximum: 15 at $x = -2$; absolute minimum: -13 at $x = 5$
13. Absolute maximum: -5 for $-1 \le x \le 1$; absolute minimum: -5 for $-1 \le x \le 1$ **15.** Absolute maximum: 24 for $4 \le x \le 13$; absolute minimum: 24 for $4 \le x \le 13$ **17.** Absolute maximum: 10 at $x = -1$; absolute minimum: 1 at $x = 2$ **19.** Absolute maximum: 4 at $x = 1$; absolute minimum: -23 at $x = 4$ **21.** Absolute maximum: 2 at $x = -1$; absolute minimum: -110 at $x = -5$ **23.** Absolute maximum: 513 at $x = -8$; absolute minimum: -511 at $x = 8$ **25.** Absolute maximum: 10 at $x = 0$; absolute minimum: -22 at $x = 4$ **27.** Absolute maximum: $\frac{27}{256}$ at $x = \frac{3}{4}$; absolute minimum: -2 at $x = -1$
29. Absolute maximum: 13 at $x = -2$ and $x = 2$; absolute minimum: 4 at $x = -1$ and $x = 1$ **31.** Absolute maximum: 1 at $x = 0$; absolute minimum: -3 at $x = -8$ and $x = 8$ **33.** Absolute maximum: -4 at $x = -2$; absolute minimum: $-\frac{17}{2}$ at $x = -8$ **35.** Absolute maximum: $\frac{4}{5}$ at $x = -2$ and $x = 2$; absolute minimum: 0 at $x = 0$ **37.** Absolute maximum: 3 at $x = 26$; absolute minimum: -1 at $x = -2$ **39–47.** Left to the student
49. Absolute maximum: 225 at $x = 15$ **51.** Absolute minimum: 70 at $x = 10$ **53.** Absolute maximum: $21\frac{1}{3}$ at $x = 2$ **55.** Absolute maximum: 900 at $x = 30$
57. Absolute maximum: $\frac{10\sqrt{5}}{3}$ at $x = -\sqrt{5}$; absolute minimum: $-\frac{10\sqrt{5}}{3}$ at $x = \sqrt{5}$ **59.** Absolute maximum: 5700 at $x = 2400$
61. Absolute maximum: $5\frac{13}{27}$ at $x = \frac{5}{3}$ **63.** Absolute maximum: 2000 at $x = 20$; absolute minimum: 0 at $x = 0$ and $x = 30$ **65.** Absolute minimum: 24 at $x = 6$ **67.** Absolute

minimum: 108 at $x = 6$ **69.** Absolute maximum: 3 at $x = 1$; absolute minimum: $-\frac{3}{8}$ at $x = -\frac{1}{2}$ **71.** Absolute maximum: $2\sqrt[3]{3}$ at $x = 8$; absolute minimum: 0 at $x = 0$ **73.** No absolute maximum or minimum   **75.** Absolute maximum: -1 at $x = 1$; absolute minimum: -5 at $x = -1$ **77.** No absolute maximum; absolute minimum: -5 at $x = -1$ **79.** Absolute maximum; 19 at $x = -2$; no absolute minimum   **81.** No absolute maximum; absolute minimum: 0 at $x = 0$ **83.** No absolute maximum or minimum   **85.** No absolute maximum; absolute minimum: -1 at $x = -1$ and $x = 1$ **87–95.** Left to the student   **97.** 1430 units; after 25 yr of employment   **99.** 2011   **101.** 2001; about 23,858,000 barrels
103. (a) $P(x) = -\frac{1}{2}x^2 + 400x - 5000$;   **(b)** 400 items
105. About 1.26 at $x = \frac{1}{9}$ cc, or about 0.11 cc

107. Absolute maximum: 3 at $x = 1$; absolute minimum: -5 at $x = -3$ **109.** Absolute maxima: 1 at $x = 0$ and 1 at $x = 2$; absolute minimum: -15 at $x = -4$

111. (a)   **(b)** Absolute maximum: 6 at $x = -2$; **(c)** $f(x) = 2$ over $[0, 4]$
113. Absolute maximum: $3\sqrt{6}$ at $x = 3$; absolute minimum: -2 at $x = -2$
115. Minimum: $20,000 at $x = 7$ "quality units"

117. 2003–2004; at about 640,000 barrels/yr
119. (a) 2.755 billion barrels in 1981; **(b)** 0.1014 billion barrels/yr; 0.1234 billion barrels/yr   **121.** No absolute maximum; absolute minimum: 0 at $x = 1$
123. (a) $P(t) = t + 8.857$; $P(7) = 15.857$ mm Hg;
(b) $P(t) = 0.117t^4 - 1.520t^3 + 6.193t^2 - 7.018t + 10.009$; $P(7) = 24.86$ mm Hg; $P(0.765) = 7.62$ mm Hg is the smallest contraction

Technology Connection, p. 253

1–4. Left to the student

Exercise Set 2.5, p. 254

1. Maximum $Q = 1225$; $x = 35, y = 35$ **3.** Minimum product $= -9$; $x = 3, y = -3$ **5.** Maximum $Q = 4$; $x = 2, y = \sqrt{2}$, or approximately 1.414   **7.** Minimum $Q = 6$; $x = 2, y = 1$ **9.** Maximum $Q = \frac{1}{3}$; $x = \frac{2}{3}, y = \frac{1}{2}$
11. Maximum area $= 4800 \text{ yd}^2$ $(x = 40 \text{ yd}, y = 120 \text{ yd})$
13. Maximum area $= 45,000 \text{ yd}^2$ (150 yd by 300 yd)
15. Maximum area $= 110.25 \text{ ft}^2$; $x = 10.5$ ft; $y = 10.5$ ft
17. Dimensions: $13\frac{1}{3}$ in. by $13\frac{1}{3}$ in. by $3\frac{1}{3}$ in.; maximum volume: $592\frac{16}{27} \text{ in}^3$ **19.** Dimensions: 4 ft by 4 ft by 2 ft; minimum surface area $= 48 \text{ ft}^2$ **21.** 2.08 yd by 4.16 yd by 1.387 yd
23. $1048; 46 units   **25.** $19; 70 units   **27.** $5481; 1667 units   **29. (a)** $R(x) = x(280 - 0.4x)$;
(b) $P(x) = -x^2 + 280x - 5000$; **(c)** 140 refrigerators;

(d) $14,600; **(e)** $224/refrigerator   **31.** $201 per day
33. 1 fewer officer   **35. (a)** $q(x) = -\frac{12}{41}x + \frac{53}{41}$; **(b)** 221% of the January 2001 price   **37.** $11.50   **39.** 62.55 ft by 79.93 ft; $1439   **41.** 6.98 in. by 10.47 in.   **43.** Order 20 times/yr; lot size is 10.   **45.** Order 12 times/yr; lot size is 30.
47. Order 12 times/yr; lot size is 30.   **49.** $r \approx 5.03$ cm, $h \approx 5.03$ cm   **51.** $r \approx 4.08$ cm, $h \approx 7.65$ cm   **53.** 6 yd by 8 yd (8-yd side is opposite the side shared with neighbor)
55. $x \approx 2.76$ ft, $y \approx 4.92$ ft   **57–109.** Left to the student
111. $\sqrt[3]{0.1}$, or approximately 0.4642   **113.** 9%   **115.** S is 3.25 mi downshore from A.   **117.** Left to the student

119. (a) $A(x) = 8 + \dfrac{20}{x} + \dfrac{x^2}{100}$ **(b)** $C'(x) = \dfrac{3x^2}{100} + 8$ and $A'(x) = \dfrac{x}{50} - \dfrac{20}{x^2}$;   **(c)** minimum $= 11/unit$ at $x_0 = 10$ units; $C'(10) = 11/unit$;   **(d)** they are equal.
121. Minimum: $6 - 4\sqrt{2}$, or approximately 0.343, at $x = 2 - \sqrt{2} \approx 0.586$ and $y = -1 + \sqrt{2} \approx 0.414$

123. Order $\sqrt{\dfrac{aQ}{2b}}$ times; lot size: $\sqrt{\dfrac{2bQ}{a}}$
125. $x = 25, y = 16.67$; $Q = 416.67$
127. $x \approx 2.24, y \approx 2.74$; $Q \approx 45.93$

Technology Connection, p. 261

1. $P'(50) = 140/unit$; $P(51) - P(50) = 217/unit$

Exercise Set 2.6, p. 265

1. (a) $P(x) = -0.5x^2 + 46x - 10$;
(b) $R(20) = 800, C(20) = 90, P(20) = 710$;
(c) $R'(x) = 50 - x$; $C'(x) = 4$; $P'(x) = 46 - x$;
(d) $R'(20) = 30, C'(20) = 4, P'(20) = 26$
3. (a) $226,800; **(b)** $5994; **(c)** $5960; **(d)** $238,720
5. (a) $1799; **(b)** $235.88; **(c)** $75.40;
(d) $R(71) = 1874.40, R(72) = 1949.80$, $R(73) = 2025.20$ **7. (a)** $3685.03; **(b)** $276.63;
(c) $138.20; **(d)** $3823.23   **9.** If the price increases from $1000 to $1001, sales will decrease by 100 units.
11. $3.21; $3.20   **13.** $2; $2
15. (a) $P(x) = -0.01x^2 + 1.4x - 100$; **(b)** $-$0.21; $-$0.20
17. (a) $dS/dp = 0.021p^2 - p + 150$; **(b)** 3547 units; **(c)** ✎
(d) ✎   **19. (a)** 630 units, 980 units, 1430 units, 630 units; **(b)** $M'(t) = -4t + 100$; **(c)** ✎ **(d)** ✎
21. $526.75 billion   **23.** ✎   **25.** About $0.28 paid in taxes per dollar earned   **27.** 0.1206; 0.12   **29.** 0.2816; 0.28
31. -0.1667; -0.2 **33.** 6; 6   **35.** 5.100   **37.** 10.100
39. 10.017   **41.** $\dfrac{3}{2\sqrt{3x - 2}}\,dx$ **43.** $9x^2\sqrt{2x^3 + 1}\,dx$
45. $\dfrac{x^4 + 8x^2 - 4x + 3}{(x^2 + 3)^2}\,dx$ **47.** $(4x^3 - 6x^2 + 10x + 3)\,dx$
49. $-22,394.88   **51.** 7.2   **53.** 657.00   **55.** -0.01345 m^2
57. Ticket price will increase more between 2014 and 2016.
59. $A'(x) = \dfrac{x \cdot C'(x) - C(x)}{x^2}$ **61.** $dV = 4,019,200 \text{ ft}^3$
63. $R'(x) = 400 - 2x$ **65.** $R'(x) = 3$ **67.** ✎

Exercise Set 2.7, p. 273

1. (a) $E(x) = \dfrac{x}{400 - x}$; **(b)** $\dfrac{5}{11}$, inelastic; **(c)** $200

3. (a) $E(x) = \dfrac{x}{50 - x}$; **(b)** 11.5, elastic; **(c)** $25

5. (a) $E(x) = 1$; **(b)** 1, unit elasticity; **(c)** total revenue is independent of x.   **7. (a)** $E(x) = \dfrac{x}{2(600 - x)}$; **(b)** 0.10, inelastic; **(c)** $400   **9. (a)** $E(x) = \dfrac{2x}{x + 3}$; **(b)** 0.5, inelastic; **(c)** $3   **11. (a)** $E(x) = \dfrac{6x^2 - 300x}{50{,}000 + 300x - 3x^2}$;   **(b)** 0.2, inelastic; **(c)** 0.6, inelastic; **(d)** 1.38, elastic; **(e)** $114.98 per barrel; **(f)** about 51.55 billion barrels;   **(g)** increase   **13. (a)** $E(x) = \dfrac{3x^3}{2(200 - x^3)}$; **(b)** $\dfrac{81}{346}$;   **(c)** increase   **15. (a)** $E(x) = \dfrac{10x}{180 - 10x}$; **(b)** 0.8; **(c)** $9   **(d)** ✎   **17.** ✎

Exercise Set 2.8, p. 279

1. $\dfrac{9x^2}{2y}$; 4.5   **3.** $\dfrac{-3x^2}{4y}$; 3   **5.** $\dfrac{-x}{y}$, $\dfrac{-1}{\sqrt{3}}$ **7.** $\dfrac{-3y}{2x}$; 4.5

9. $\dfrac{4x^2 - 2y^3}{3xy^2}$; $-\dfrac{7}{3}$ **11.** $\dfrac{2 - y}{x + 2y}$; $-\dfrac{4}{3}$ **13.** $\dfrac{12x^2 + 5}{4y^3 + 3}$; $-\dfrac{17}{29}$

15. $\dfrac{y + x}{3y - x}$ **17.** $\dfrac{x}{y}$ **19.** $\dfrac{5x^4}{3y^2}$ **21.** $\dfrac{-3xy^2 - 2y}{4x^2y + 3x}$

23. $\dfrac{-2}{2p + 1}$ **25.** $\dfrac{-p}{3x}$ **27.** $\dfrac{2 - 2xp - p}{x^2 + x - 1}$ **29.** $\dfrac{-p - 4}{x + 3}$

31. 0; $-\dfrac{3}{2\sqrt{6}}$; $-\dfrac{9}{4}$ **33.** $200/day, $50/day, $150/day

35. $36,000/day, $72,000/day, $-36,000/day
37. -1.18 sales/day   **39.** $-23{,}389$ mi^2/yr
41. Decreasing by 0.0256 m^2/month

43. (a) $\dfrac{dV}{dt} = 952.38R\,\dfrac{dR}{dt}$; **(b)** 0.0143 mm/sec^2

45. $-2\frac{1}{12}$ ft/sec   **47.** About 494.8 cm^3/week   **49.** $\dfrac{-y^3}{x^3}$

51. $\dfrac{2x}{y(x^2 + 1)^2}$, or $\dfrac{x(1 - y^2)}{y(1 + x^2)}$

53. $\dfrac{5x^4 - 3(x - y)^2 - 3(x + y)^2}{3(x + y)^2 - 3(x - y)^2 - 5y^4}$, or $\dfrac{6y^2 - 5x^4 + 6x^2}{y(5y^3 - 12x)}$

55. $\dfrac{-6(y^2 - xy + x^2)}{(2y - x)^3}$ **57.** $\dfrac{2x(y^3 - x^3)}{y^5}$ **59.** ✎

61.   **63.**

Chapter 2 Review Exercises, p. 288

1. (g)   **2.** (e)   **3.** (f)   **4.** (a)   **5.** (b)   **6.** (d)   **7.** (c)
8. False   **9.** False   **10.** True   **11.** False   **12.** True
13. False   **14.** False   **15.** True   **16.** True

17. Relative maximum: $\dfrac{25}{4}$ at $x = -\dfrac{3}{2}$

18. Relative minima: 2 at $x = -1$ and 2 at $x = 1$; relative maximum: 3 at $x = 0$

19. Relative minimum: -4 at $x = 1$; relative maximum: 4 at $x = -1$

20. No relative extrema

21. Relative minimum: $\dfrac{76}{27}$ at $x = \dfrac{1}{3}$; relative maximum: 4 at $x = -1$

22. Relative minimum: 0 at $x = 0$

23. Relative maximum: 17 at $x = -1$; relative minimum: -10 at $x = 2$

$f(x) = 2x^3 - 3x^2 - 12x + 10$

24. Relative maximum: 4 at $x = -1$; relative minimum: 0 at $x = 1$

$f(x) = x^3 - 3x + 2$

25.

$f(x) = \frac{1}{3}x^3 + 3x^2 + 9x + 2$

No relative extrema
Inflection point at $(-3, -7)$
Increasing on $(-\infty, \infty)$
Concave down on $(-\infty, -3)$;
concave up on $(-3, \infty)$

26.

$f(x) = x^2 - 10x + 8$

Relative minimum: -17 at $x = 5$
Decreasing on $(-\infty, 5)$; increasing on $(5, \infty)$
Concave up on $(-\infty, \infty)$

27.

$f(x) = 4x^3 - 6x^2 - 24x + 5$

Relative minimum: -35 at $x = 2$;
relative maximum: 19 at $x = -1$
Inflection point at $\left(\frac{1}{2}, -8\right)$
Increasing on $(-\infty, -1)$ and $(2, \infty)$; decreasing on $(-1, 2)$
Concave down on $\left(-\infty, \frac{1}{2}\right)$;
concave up on $\left(\frac{1}{2}, \infty\right)$

28.

$f(x) = x^4 - 2x^2$

Relative minima: -1 at $x = -1$ and -1 at $x = 1$;
relative maximum: 0 at $x = 0$
Inflection points at $\left(-\sqrt{\frac{1}{3}}, -\frac{5}{9}\right)$ and $\left(\sqrt{\frac{1}{3}}, -\frac{5}{9}\right)$
Increasing on $(-1, 0)$ and $(1, \infty)$;
decreasing on $(-\infty, -1)$ and $(0, 1)$
Concave up on $\left(-\infty, -\sqrt{\frac{1}{3}}\right)$ and $\left(\sqrt{\frac{1}{3}}, \infty\right)$;
concave down on $\left(-\sqrt{\frac{1}{3}}, \sqrt{\frac{1}{3}}\right)$

29.

$f(x) = 3x^4 + 2x^3 - 3x^2 + 1$

Relative minima: -1 at $x = -1$ and $\frac{11}{16}$ at $x = \frac{1}{2}$;
relative maximum: 1 at $x = 0$
Inflection points at $(-0.608, -0.147)$ and $(0.274, 0.833)$
Increasing on $(-1, 0)$ and $\left(\frac{1}{2}, \infty\right)$;
decreasing on $(-\infty, -1)$ and $\left(0, \frac{1}{2}\right)$
Concave down on $(-0.608, 0.274)$; concave up on $(-\infty, -0.608)$ and $(0.274, \infty)$

30.

$f(x) = \frac{1}{5}x^5 + \frac{3}{4}x^4 - \frac{4}{3}x^3 + 8$

Relative minimum: $\frac{457}{60}$ at $x = 1$;
relative maximum: $\frac{1208}{15}$ at $x = -4$
Inflection points at $(-2.932, 53.701)$, $(0, 8)$, and $(0.682, 7.769)$
Increasing on $(-\infty, -4)$ and $(1, \infty)$; decreasing on $(-4, 1)$
Concave down on $(-\infty, -2.932)$ and $(0, 0.682)$; concave up on $(-2.932, 0)$ and $(0.682, \infty)$

31.

$f(x) = \frac{2x + 5}{x + 1}$

No relative extrema
Decreasing on $(-\infty, -1)$ and $(-1, \infty)$
Concave down on $(-\infty, -1)$; concave up on $(-1, \infty)$
Asymptotes: $x = -1$ and $y = 2$
x-intercept: $\left(-\frac{5}{2}, 0\right)$; y-intercept: $(0, 5)$

32.

$f(x) = \frac{x}{x - 2}$

No relative extrema
Decreasing on $(-\infty, 2)$ and $(2, \infty)$
Concave down on $(-\infty, 2)$; concave up on $(2, \infty)$
Asymptotes: $x = 2$ and $y = 1$
x-intercept: $(0, 0)$; y-intercept: $(0, 0)$

33.

$$f(x) = \frac{5}{x^2 - 16}$$

Relative maximum at $\left(0, -\frac{5}{16}\right)$

Decreasing on $(0, 4)$ and $(4, \infty)$; increasing on $(-\infty, -4)$ and $(-4, 0)$

Concave down on $(-4, 4)$; concave up on $(-\infty, -4)$ and $(4, \infty)$

Asymptotes: $x = -4$, $x = 4$, and $y = 0$

y-intercept: $\left(0, -\frac{5}{16}\right)$

34.

$$f(x) = -\frac{x + 1}{x^2 - x - 2}$$

No relative extrema

Increasing on $(-\infty, -1)$, $(-1, 2)$, and $(2, \infty)$

Concave up on $(-\infty, -1)$ and $(-1, 2)$; concave down on $(2, \infty)$

Asymptotes: $x = 2$ and $y = 0$

y-intercept: $\left(0, \frac{1}{2}\right)$

35.

$$f(x) = \frac{x^2 - 2x + 2}{x - 1}$$

Relative minimum at $(2, 2)$; relative maximum at $(0, -2)$

Decreasing on $(0, 1)$ and $(1, 2)$; increasing on $(-\infty, 0)$ and $(2, \infty)$

Concave down on $(-\infty, 1)$; concave up on $(1, \infty)$

Asymptotes: $x = 1$ and $y = x - 1$

y-intercept: $(0, -2)$

36.

$$f(x) = \frac{x^2 + 3}{x}$$

Relative minimum at $\left(\sqrt{3}, 2\sqrt{3}\right)$; relative maximum at $\left(-\sqrt{3}, -2\sqrt{3}\right)$

Decreasing on $\left(-\sqrt{3}, 0\right)$ and $\left(0, \sqrt{3}\right)$; increasing on $\left(-\infty, -\sqrt{3}\right)$ and $\left(\sqrt{3}, \infty\right)$

Concave down on $(-\infty, 0)$; concave up on $(0, \infty)$

Asymptotes: $x = 0$ and $y = x$

No intercepts

37. Absolute maximum: 66 at $x = 3$; absolute minimum: 2 at $x = 1$ **38.** Absolute maximum: $75\frac{23}{27}$ at $x = \frac{16}{3}$; absolute minima: 0 at $x = 0$ and $x = 8$ **39.** No absolute maxima; absolute minimum: $10\sqrt{2}$ at $x = 5\sqrt{2}$ **40.** No absolute maxima; absolute minima: 0 at $x = -1$ and $x = 1$ **41.** $Q = 12$ when $x = 4$ and $y = 3$ **42.** $Q = -1$ when $x = -1$ and $y = -1$ **43.** Maximum profit is \$451 when 30 units are produced and sold.   **44.** 10 ft by 10 ft by 25 ft   **45.** Order 12 times per year with a lot size of 30   **46. (a)** \$108; **(b)** \$1/dinner; **(c)** \$109   **47.** $\Delta y = -0.335$, $dy = -0.35$
48. (a) $(6x^2 + 1)\,dx$; **(b)** 0.25   **49.** 9.111

50. $dV = \pm 240{,}000$ ft^3 **51. (a)** $E(x) = \dfrac{5x}{400 - 5x}$, or $\dfrac{x}{80 - x}$

(b) 0.14, inelastic; **(c)** 1.67, elastic; **(d)** increase; **(e)** \$40

52. $\dfrac{-3y - 2x^2}{2y^2 + 3x}$; $\dfrac{4}{5}$ **53.** -1.75 ft/sec

54. \$600/day, \$450/day, \$150/day   **55.** No maximum; absolute minimum: 0 at $x = 3$ **56.** Absolute maxima: 4 at $x = 2$ and $x = 6$; absolute minimum: -2 at $x = -2$

57. $\dfrac{3x^5 - 2(x - y)^3 - 2(x + y)^3}{2(x + y)^3 - 2(x - y)^3 - 3y^5}$ **58.** Relative maximum at $(0, 0)$; relative minima at $(-9, -9477)$ and $(15, -37{,}125)$

59. $f(x) = \dfrac{3x + 3}{x + 2}$ (answers may vary)   **60.** Relative maxima at $(-1.714, 37.445)$; relative minimum at $(1.714, -37.445)$

61. Relative maximum at $(0, 1.08)$; relative minima at $(-3, -1)$ and $(3, -1)$

62. (a) Linear: $y = 6.998187602x - 124.6183581$

Quadratic: $y = 0.0439274846x^2 + 2.881202838x - 53.51475166$

Cubic: $y = -0.0033441547x^3 + 0.4795643605x^2 - 11.35931622x + 5.276985809$

Quartic: $y = -0.00005539834x^4 + 0.0067192294x^3 - 0.0996735857x^2 - 0.8409991942x - 0.246072967$

(b) The quartic function best fits the data. **(c)** The domain is $[26, 102]$. Very few women outside of the age range from 26 to 102 years old develop breast cancer. **(d)** Maximum: 466 per 100,000 women at $x = 79.0$ years old

Chapter 2 Test, p. 290

1. [2.1, 2.2] Relative minimum: -9 at $x = 2$
Decreasing on $(-\infty, 2)$ increasing on $(2, \infty)$

$$f(x) = x^2 - 4x - 5$$

2. [2.1, 2.2] Relative minimum: 2 at $x = -1$; relative maximum: 6 at $x = 1$
Decreasing on $(-\infty, -1)$ and $(1, \infty)$; increasing on $(-1, 1)$

3. [2.1, 2.2] Relative minimum: -4 at $x = 2$
Decreasing on $(-\infty, 2)$; increasing on $(2, \infty)$

4. [2.1, 2.2] Relative maximum: 4 at $x = 0$
Increasing on $(-\infty, 0)$; decreasing on $(0, \infty)$

5. [2.3]

Relative maximum: 2 at $x = -1$; relative minimum: $\frac{22}{27}$ at $x = \frac{1}{3}$
Inflection point: $\left(-\frac{1}{3}, \frac{38}{27}\right)$

6. [2.3]

Relative maximum: 1 at $x = 0$;
relative minima: -1 at $x = -1$ and $x = 1$
Inflection points: $\left(-\sqrt{\frac{1}{3}}, -\frac{1}{9}\right)$ and $\left(\sqrt{\frac{1}{3}}, -\frac{1}{9}\right)$

7. [2.3]

No relative extrema
Inflection point: $(2, 3)$

8. [2.3]

Relative maximum: $\frac{9}{2}$ at $x = \sqrt{\frac{9}{2}}$;
relative minimum: $-\frac{9}{2}$ at $x = -\sqrt{\frac{9}{2}}$
Inflection point: $(0, 0)$

9. [2.3]

No relative extrema
Asymptotes: $x = 1$ and $y = 0$

10. [2.3]

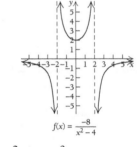

Relative minimum: 2 at $x = 0$
Asymptotes: $x = -2$, $x = 2$, and $y = 0$

11. [2.3]

No relative extrema
Asymptotes: $x = 0$ and $y = x$

12. [2.3]

No relative extrema
Asymptotes: $x = -2$ and $y = 1$
13. [2.4] Absolute maximum: 9 at $x = 3$; no absolute minimum
14. [2.4] Absolute maximum: 2 at $x = -1$; absolute minimum: -1 at $x = -2$ **15.** [2.4] Absolute maximum: 28.49 at $x = 4.3$; no absolute minimum   **16.** [2.4] Absolute maximum: 7 at $x = -1$; absolute minimum: 3 at $x = 1$ **17.** [2.4] There

are no absolute extrema.   **18.** [2.4] Absolute minimum: $-\frac{13}{12}$ at $x = \frac{1}{6}$ **19.** [2.4] Absolute minimum: 48 at $x = 4$

20. [2.5] $Q = \dfrac{125,000}{27}$ when $x = \dfrac{50}{3}$ and $y = \dfrac{50}{3}$

21. [2.5] $Q = 50$ for $x = 5$ and $y = -5$

22. [2.5] Maximum profit: \$24,980; 500 units

23. [2.5] Dimensions: 40 in. by 40 in. by 10 in; maximum volume: 16,000 in^3 **24.** [2.5] Order 35 times per year; lot size, 35

25. [2.6] $\Delta y = 1.01; f'(x)\,\Delta x = 1$ **26.** [2.6] 7.0714

27. [2.6] **(a)** $\dfrac{x}{\sqrt{x^2 + 3}}\,dx$; **(b)** 0.00756

28. [2.7] **(a)** $E(x) = \dfrac{2x}{x + 4}$; **(b)** 0.4, inelastic; **(c)** 1.5, elastic; **(d)** decrease; **(e)** \$4   **29.** [2.8] $\dfrac{-x^2}{y^2}; -\dfrac{1}{4}$

30. [2.6] $dV = \pm 1413$ cm^3 **31.** [2.8] -0.96 ft/sec

32. [2.4] Absolute maximum: $\dfrac{2^{2/3}}{3} \approx 0.529$ at $x = \sqrt[3]{2}$; absolute minimum: 0 at $x = 0$ **33.** [2.5] 10,000 units

34. [2.4] Absolute minimum: 0 at $x = 0$; relative maximum: 25.103 at $x = 1.084$; relative minimum: 8.625 at $x = 2.95$

35. [2.4] Relative minimum: -0.186 at $x = 0.775$; relative maximum: 0.186 at $x = -0.775$ **36.** [2.5] $Q = 1185.19$ when $x = 2.58$ and $y = 13.33$

37. [2.1, 2.2] **(a)** Linear: $y = -0.7707142857x + 12691.60714$
Quadratic: $y = -0.9998904762x^2 + 299.1964286x + 192.9761905$
Cubic: $y = 0.000084x^3 - 1.037690476x^2 + 303.3964286x + 129.9761905$
Quartic: $y = -0.000001966061x^4 + 0.0012636364x^3 - 1.256063636x^2 + 315.8247403x + 66.78138528$
(b) Since the number of bowling balls sold cannot be negative, the domain is $[0, 300]$. This is supported by both the quadratic model and the raw data. The cubic and quartic models can also be used but are more complicated. **(c)** Based on the quadratic function, the maximum value is 22,575 bowling balls. The company should spend \$150,000 on advertising.

Extended Technology Application, p. 293

1. (a)

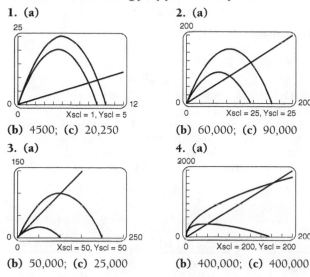

(b) 4500; **(c)** 20,250

2. (a)

(b) 60,000; **(c)** 90,000

3. (a)

(b) 50,000; **(c)** 25,000

4. (a)

(b) 400,000; **(c)** 400,000

5. (a)

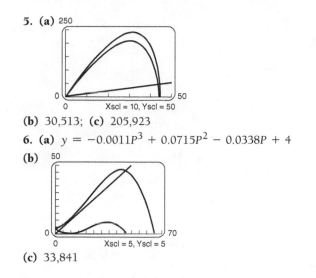

(b) 30,513; **(c)** 205,923

6. (a) $y = -0.0011P^3 + 0.0715P^2 - 0.0338P + 4$

(b)

(c) 33,841

CHAPTER 3

Technology Connection, p. 298

Left to the student

Exercise Set 3.1, p. 304

1.

3.

5.

7.

9.

11. e^x **13.** $2e^{2x}$ **15.** $6e^x$ **17.** $-7e^{-7x}$ **19.** $15e^{5x}$

21. $7e^{-x}$ **23.** $-\frac{5}{2}e^{-5x}$ **25.** $-\dfrac{4x}{3}\cdot e^{x^2}$ **27.** $-2e^{2x}$

29. $3x^2 - 10e^{2x}$ **31.** $5x^4 \cdot e^{2x} + 2x^5 \cdot e^{2x}$ **33.** $\dfrac{2e^{2x}(x - 2)}{x^5}$

35. $x^2 \cdot e^x$ **37.** $\dfrac{e^x(x - 4)}{x^5}$ **39.** $(-2x + 8)e^{-x^2 + 8x}$

41. $xe^{x^2/2}$ **43.** $\dfrac{e^{\sqrt{x-7}}}{2\sqrt{x - 7}}$ **45.** $\dfrac{e^x}{2\sqrt{e^x - 1}}$ **47.** $3x^2 - xe^x$

49. $3e^{-3x}$ **51.** ke^{-kx} **53.** $(4x^2 + 3x)e^{x^2 - 7x}(2x - 7) + (8x + 3)e^{x^2 - 7x}$, or $(8x^3 - 22x^2 - 13x + 3)e^{x^2 - 7x}$

55.

$g(x) = e^{-2x}$

57.

$f(x) = e^{(1/3)x}$

59.

$f(x) = \frac{1}{2}e^{-x}$

No critical values
No inflection points
Decreasing on $(-\infty, \infty)$
Concave up on $(-\infty, \infty)$

61.

$F(x) = -e^{(1/3)x}$

No critical values
No inflection points
Decreasing on $(-\infty, \infty)$
Concave down on $(-\infty, \infty)$

63.

$f(x) = 3 - e^{-x}$
$x \geq 0$

65–73. Left to the student
75. -6 **77.** $y = 2x + 1$
79. Left to the student
81. **(a)** \$184.5 billion, \$222.7 billion;   **(b)** \$17.3 billion/yr, \$20.9 billion/yr

83. **(a)** $C'(t) = 50e^{-t}$; **(b)** \$50 million/yr; **(c)** \$916,000/yr; **(d)** 100, 0   **85.** **(a)** 113,000; **(b)**

$q = 240e^{-0.003x}$

(c) $q'(x) = -0.72e^{-0.003x}$; **(d)** ✎   **87.** **(a)** \$29,287.17;
(b) \$1595.80/yr; **(c)** in about 12.7 yr   **89.** **(a)** $V(t) = 14,450(0.85)^t$; **(b)** $-\$2348.40/\text{yr}$ **(c)** \$20,000; **(d)** 4.27 yr
91. **(a)** 0 ppm, 3.7 ppm, 5.4 ppm, 4.5 ppm, 0.05 ppm;
(b)

$C(t) = 10t^2e^{-t}$

(c) $C'(t) = 10te^{-t}(2 - t)$;
(d) 5.4 ppm at $t = 2$ hr;
(e) ✎

93. $15e^{3x}(e^{3x} + 1)^4$ **95.** $\dfrac{(x^2 - 2x + 1)e^x}{(x^2 + 1)^2}$

97. $e^{x/2}\left(\dfrac{x}{2\sqrt{x - 1}}\right)$ **99.** $\dfrac{4}{(e^x + e^{-x})^2}$

101. Equilibrium point: (166.16, 145,787); supply is increasing at a rate of about 583 units per dollar, and demand is decreasing at a rate of about 437 units per dollar.   **103.** 4; 2.86797; 2.73200; 2.71964; 2.71855   **105.** ✎

107.

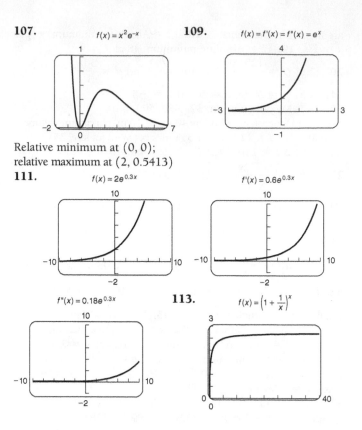

$f(x) = x^2 e^{-x}$

Relative minimum at $(0, 0)$;
relative maximum at $(2, 0.5413)$

109.

$f(x) = f'(x) = f''(x) = e^x$

111.

$f(x) = 2e^{0.3x}$

$f'(x) = 0.6e^{0.3x}$

$f''(x) = 0.18e^{0.3x}$

113.

$f(x) = \left(1 + \dfrac{1}{x}\right)^x$

Technology Connection, p. 309

Left to the student

Technology Connection, p. 311

1. Graph is left to the student; function values are 1000, 5, 0.699, 3.
2. Left to the student; graph is obtained by entering $y = \log x / \log 2$.

Technology Connection, p. 312

1. $t = 6.907755$ **2.** $x = -4.094345$ **3.** $t = 74.893307$
4. $x = 46.219585$ **5.** $x = 38.744475$

Technology Connection, p. 313

Left to the student

Exercise Set 3.2, p. 319

1. $3^4 = 81$ **3.** $27^{1/3} = 3$ **5.** $a^K = J$ **7.** $b^{-w} = V$
9. 2   **11.** 2   **13.** 243   **15.** $\frac{1}{2}$ **17.** $\ln p = t$
19. $\log_{10} 1000 = 3$ **21.** $\log_{10} 0.01 = -2$ **23.** $\log_Q T = n$
25. -1.609 **27.** $\frac{3}{2}$ **29.** 4.317   **31.** 4.382   **33.** -1.6094
35. 2.3863   **37.** 4   **39.** -0.2231 **41.** 0.3863
43. 11.512915   **45.** -4.006334 **47.** -4.509860
49. $t \approx 4.382$ **51.** $t \approx 2.267$ **53.** $t \approx 4.605$
55. $t \approx 140.671$ **57.** $-\dfrac{9}{x}$ **59.** $\dfrac{7}{x}$ **61.** $x^5 + 6(\ln x)x^5 - x^3$
63. $\dfrac{1}{x}$ **65.** $\dfrac{1}{x}$ **67.** $x^4 + 5x^4 \ln (3x)$ **69.** $x^3 + 4x^3 \ln |6x|$
71. $\dfrac{1 - 5\ln x}{x^6}$ **73.** $\dfrac{1 - 2\ln |3x|}{x^3}$ **75.** $\dfrac{2}{x}$ **77.** $\dfrac{2(3x + 1)}{3x^2 + 2x - 1}$
79. $\dfrac{x^2 + 7}{x(x^2 - 7)}$ **81.** $\dfrac{2e^x}{x} + 2e^x \ln x$ **83.** $\dfrac{e^x}{e^x + 1}$

85. $\dfrac{4(\ln x)^3}{x}$ **87.** $\dfrac{1}{x\ln(8x)}$ **89.** $\dfrac{\ln(5x)+\ln(3x)}{x}$

91. $y=8.455x-11.94$ **93.** $y=0.732x-0.990$

95. (a) 2000 units; **(b)** $N'(a)=\dfrac{500}{a}$, $N'(10)=50$ units per

\$1000 spent on advertising; **(c)** minimum is 2000 units;
(d)   **97.** 86 days   **99. (a)** $R(x)=x(53.5-8\ln x)$;
(b) $R'(x)=45.5-8\ln x$; **(c)**   **101. (a)** $P'(x)=$
$1.7-0.3\ln x$; **(b)**   **(c)** 289.069   **103. (a)** 78%;

(b) 45.8%; **(c)** 13.6%; **(d)** 17.4%; **(e)** $S'(t)=\dfrac{-20}{t+1}$;

(f) maximum $=78\%$; **(g)**   **105. (a)** 2.44 ft/s;

(b) 3.39 ft/s; **(c)** $v'(p)=\dfrac{0.37}{p}$; **(d)**   **107.** $t=\dfrac{\ln(P/P_0)}{k}$

109. $\dfrac{4[\ln(x+5)]^3}{x+5}$ **111.** $\dfrac{-1}{1-t}-\dfrac{1}{1+t}$, or $\dfrac{-2}{(1-t)(1+t)}$

113. $\dfrac{1}{x\ln 5}$ **115.** $\dfrac{x}{x^2+5}$ **117.** $x^n\ln x$ **119.** Definition
of logarithm; Product Rule for exponents; definition of logarithm;
substitution   **121.** Definition of logarithm; if $u=v$, then
$u^c=v^c$; Power Rule for exponents; definition of logarithm; substitution and the commutative law for multiplication   **123.** 1
125. e^π **127.** Minimum: $-e^{-1}\approx-0.368$

129. (a)

[graph of $y=\ln|x|$]

(b) $-\tfrac{1}{3},-\tfrac{1}{2},-1$
(c) They are the opposites
of those slopes. **(d)**

Technology Connection, p. 326

1. 312 billion   **2.** 179 trillion   **3.** 1.97 quadrillion
4. 7.91×10^{22} **5.** Left to the student
6. $y=12{,}767.750(1.0320889)^x$ **7.** \$18,651.75; \$19,250.27;
\$21,163.53

Exercise Set 3.3, p. 331

1. $f(x)=ce^{4x}$ **3.** $A(t)=ce^{-9t}$ **5.** $Q(t)=ce^{kt}$
7. (a) $N(t)=483{,}000e^{0.058t}$; **(b)** $N(11)=914{,}170$; **(c)** 12 yr
9. (a) $P(t)=P_0e^{0.059t}$; **(b)** \$1060.78, \$1125.24; **(c)** 11.7 yr
11. (a) $G(t)=4.7e^{0.093t}$; **(b)** 48.07 billion gallons; **(c)** 7.5 yr
13. 4.62%   **15.** 6.9 yr after 2012   **17.** 11.2 yr; \$102,256.88
19. \$7,500; 8.3 yr   **21. (a)** $k=0.151$, or 15.1%,
$V(t)=30{,}000e^{0.151t}$; **(b)** \$549,188,702; **(c)** 4.6 yr; **(d)** 69 yr
23. (a) $F(t)=2.3e^{0.092969t}$; **(b)** \$3.34 trillion; **(c)** after about
15.8 yr, or in 2026   **25. (a)** $y=1.60680697(1.60414481)^x$,
$y=1.60680697e^{0.4725068483x}$; **(b)** 47.3%; **(c)** 43.9 EB;
(d) about 7.3 yr; **(e)** about 1.47 yr   **27.** Approximately \$8.6 billion
29. (a) $S(t)=4e^{0.0482t}$; **(b)** 4.82%/yr; **(c)** 54¢, 59¢, 65¢;
(d) \$11,000; **(e)**   **31. (a)** 2%; **(b)** 3.8%, 7%, 21.6%, 50.2%,
93.1%, 98%; **(c)** $P'(x)=\dfrac{637e^{-0.13x}}{(1+49e^{-0.13x})^2}$

(d)

[graph: $P(x)=\dfrac{100}{1+49e^{-0.13x}}$]

33. (a) $V(t)=0.10e^{0.227t}$;
(b) \$12,132,700; **(c)** 3.05 yr;
(d) after about 86 yr, or in 2024
35. 2019   **37.** 1%/yr
39. 4%/yr   **41. (a)** 2.23%;
(b)

43. (a) 20, 46, 119, 146; **(b)** $P'(t)=\dfrac{83{,}460e^{-0.214t}}{(20+130e^{-0.214t})^2}$

(c) 3.71 tortoises/yr, 6.86 tortoises/yr, 5.28 tortoises/yr,
0.93 tortoise/yr; **(d)** 150   **45.** $N(t)=48{,}869e^{0.0367t}$, where
$t_0=1930$; exponential growth rate $=3.67\%$ **47. (a)** 11.8,
221.4, 547.2; **(b)** 4.4 new cases per week; **(c)**

49. (a) $N(t)=\dfrac{29.47232081}{1+79.56767122e^{-0.809743969t}}$; **(b)** 29 students;

(c) $N(t)=\dfrac{29.47232081}{1+79.56767122e^{-0.809743969t}}$

[graph, axes 0 to 30 and 0 to 15]

(d) $N'(t)=\dfrac{1898.885181e^{-0.809743969t}}{(1+79.56767122e^{-0.809743969t})^2}$; **(e)**

51–59.   **61.** $\ln 4=kT_4$ **63.** 2 yr   **65.**   **67.** 10 yr
69. 9.9 yr, 19.8 yr   **71. (a)** $R(0)=\$2$ million; this represents the initial revenue of the corporation at its inception.
(b) $\lim\limits_{t\to\infty}R(t)=\$4000$ million $=R_{max}$; this represents the
upper limit of the revenue of the company over all time. It is
never actually attained. **(c)** $t=24$

Exercise Set 3.4, p. 343

1. 5.78 yr   **3.** 86.64 months   **5.** 23.1 yr   **7.** 36.48 wk
9. (a) $N(t)=N_0e^{-0.096t}$; **(b)** 341 g; **(c)** 7.2 days
11. (a) $A(t)=A_0e^{-kt}$; **(b)** 11 hr   **13.** 23.1%/min   **15.** 22 yr
17. 42.9 g   **19.** 4223 yr   **21.** 25 days   **23.** 3965 yr
25. \$13,858.23   **27.** \$6,788,463   **29.** \$42,863.76
31. (a) \$40,000; **(b)** \$5413.41; **(c)**   **33. (a)** 0.022,
0.031, 0.069; **(b)**

[graph: $Q(t)=(Q_0-0.00055)e^{0.163t}+0.00055$, axes 0.01 to 0.10 and 1 to 10]

35. (a) $N(t)=5{,}650{,}000e^{-0.015t}$; **(b)** 2,099,000; 1,977,000
(c) about 2065   **37. (a)** $B(t)=64.6e^{-0.0068t}$; **(b)** 58.3 lb;
(c) 2172   **39. (a)** $k=-0.00855$, $P(t)=51.9e^{-0.00855t}$;
(b) 42.63 million; **(c)** 2025   **41. (a)** 27; **(b)** 0.05878;
(c) 83°; **(d)** 28.7 min; **(e)**   **43.** The murder was committed
at 7 P.M.   **45. (a)** 145 lb; **(b)** -1.2 lb/day   **47. (a)** 11.2 W;
(b) 173 days; **(c)** 402 days; **(d)** 50 W; **(e)**   **49. (c)**
51. (e)   **53. (f)**   **55. (d)**   **57. (a)**   **59. (a)** 12.05 wk;
(b) about 24.1 wk   **61. (a)** $x=\$166.16$, $q=292$ printers;
(b) 0.3   **63. and 65.**

Exercise Set 3.5, p. 352

1. $(\ln 6)6^x$ **3.** $(\ln 8)8^x$ **5.** $x^5\cdot\ln 3.7\cdot(3.7)^x+5x^4(3.7)^x$
7. $(\ln 7)\cdot 7^{x^4+2}\cdot 4x^3$ **9.** $2xe^{x^2}$ **11.** $(\ln 3)\cdot 3^{x^4+1}\cdot(4x^3)$
13. $\dfrac{1}{x\cdot\ln 8}$ **15.** $\dfrac{1}{x\cdot\ln 17}$ **17.** $\dfrac{9}{(9x-2)\ln 32}$
19. $\dfrac{6}{(6x-7)\ln 10}$ **21.** $\dfrac{4x^3-1}{(x^4-x)\ln 9}$ **23.** $\dfrac{2}{(x-2\sqrt{x})\ln 7}$

25. $\dfrac{5^x}{x \cdot \ln 2} + 5^x \cdot \ln 5 \cdot \log_2 x$ **27.** $5(\log_{12} x)^4 \left(\dfrac{1}{x \ln 12} \right)$

29. $\dfrac{(5x - 1)6^x \cdot \ln 6 - 5 \cdot 6^x}{(5x - 1)^2}$

31. $\dfrac{6 \cdot 5^{2x^3 - 1}}{(6x + 5)(\ln 10)} + (\ln 5)5^{2x^3 - 1} \cdot 6x^2 \cdot \log (6x + 5)$

33. $6 \cdot \log_9 x \cdot 4^{6x} \cdot \ln 4 + \dfrac{4^{6x}}{\ln 9 \cdot x}$

35. $5(3x^5 + x)^4(15x^4 + 1) \cdot (\log_3 x) + \dfrac{(3x^5 + x)^5}{\ln 3 \cdot x}$

37. (a) $V'(t) = 5200(\ln 0.80)(0.80)^t$; (b) ✏
39. (a) $N'(t) = 400{,}000(\ln 0.341)(0.341)^t$; (b) ✏
41. (a) 22.4 million; (b) 187,000/yr; (c) ✏
43. (a) $A(t) = 78{,}947.36842[(1.012666667)^{3t} - 1]$
(b) \$45,255.66;   (c) \$4690.07/yr   **45.** 7.0
47. (a) 63 times more intense; (b) 398 times more intense
49. (a) $I = I_0 10^7$; (b) $I = I_0 10^8$; (c) $I_0 10^8$ is 10 times
greater than $I_0 10^7$; (d) $dI/dR = I_0 10^R(\ln 10)$
51. (a) $\dfrac{dR}{dI} = \dfrac{1}{(\ln 10)I}$; (b) ✏   **53.** (a) $\dfrac{dy}{dx} = \dfrac{m}{(\ln 10)x}$;

(b) ✏   **55.** $\ln 5 \approx 1.6094$ **57.** $\frac{1}{2}$ **59.** $(\ln 2)2^{x^4} \cdot 4x^3$

61. $\dfrac{1}{\ln 3 \cdot \log x \cdot \ln 10 \cdot x}$ **63.** $\ln a \cdot a^{f(x)} \cdot f'(x)$

65. $\left(\dfrac{g(x) \cdot f'(x)}{f(x)} + g'(x) \cdot \ln (f(x)) \right) \cdot [f(x)]^{g(x)}$ **67.** ✏

Technology Connection, p. 358

1. 5 months, about \$243.27   **2.** 14 months, about \$644.14

Exercise Set 3.6, p. 359

1. \$135.33   **3.** \$593.88   **5.** \$42.60   **7.** \$4936.26
9. \$8762.22   **11.** (a) \$355.13; (b) \$21,307.80; (c) \$3157.80
13. (a) \$803.07; (b) \$289,105.20; (c) \$142,855.20
15. (a) \$10.59; (b) \$1270.80; (c) \$770.80
17.

Balance	Payment	Portion to interest	Portion to principal	New balance
\$18,150.00	\$355.13	\$98.31	\$256.82	\$17,893.18
\$17,893.18	\$355.13	\$96.92	\$258.21	\$17,634.97

19.

Balance	Payment	Portion to interest	Portion to principal	New balance
\$146,250.00	\$803.07	\$633.75	\$169.32	\$146,080.68
\$146,080.68	\$803.07	\$633.02	\$170.05	\$145,910.63

21.

Balance	Payment	Portion to interest	Portion to principal	New balance
\$500.00	\$10.59	\$9.48	\$1.11	\$498.89
\$498.89	\$10.59	\$9.46	\$1.13	\$497.76

23. \$18,205.38   **25.** \$370,291.65   **27.** (a) \$227.56, \$193.26;
(b) \$13,653.60, \$13,914.72; (c) option 1, \$261.12
29. (a) \$1073.64; (b) \$1199.10; (c) \$45,165.60
31. (a) \$89,955.16; (b) \$88.39   **33.** \$151,212.94
35. (a) \$1073.64; (b) \$186,510.40; (c) about 22.5 yr;
(d) about \$133,366; (e) about \$53,144

37. Start with $P \left(1 + \dfrac{r}{n} \right)^{nt} = \dfrac{p\left[\left(1 + \dfrac{r}{n} \right)^{nt} - 1 \right]}{\dfrac{r}{n}}$. Multiply both

sides by $\dfrac{r}{n}$, distribute p to clear the parentheses, and rearrange
terms so that the two terms containing $\left(1 + \dfrac{r}{n} \right)^{nt}$ are on one
side of the equation. Isolate the expression $\left(1 + \dfrac{r}{n} \right)^{nt}$, and take
the natural logarithm of both sides of the equation.

39.

Balance	Payment	Portion to interest	Portion to principal	New balance
\$18,150.00	\$355.13	\$98.31	\$256.82	\$17,893.18
\$17,893.18	\$355.13	\$96.92	\$258.21	\$17,634.97
\$17,634.97	\$355.13	\$95.52	\$259.61	\$17,375.37
\$17,375.37	\$355.13	\$94.12	\$261.01	\$17,114.35
\$17,114.35	\$355.13	\$92.70	\$262.43	\$16,851.93
\$16,851.93	\$355.13	\$91.28	\$263.85	\$16,588.08
\$16,588.08	\$355.13	\$89.85	\$265.28	\$16,322.80
\$16,322.80	\$355.13	\$88.42	\$266.71	\$16,056.08
\$16,056.08	\$355.13	\$86.97	\$268.16	\$15,787.92
\$15,787.92	\$355.13	\$85.52	\$269.61	\$15,518.31
\$15,518.31	\$355.13	\$84.06	\$271.07	\$15,247.24
\$15,247.24	\$355.13	\$82.59	\$272.54	\$14,974.70

41.

Balance	Payment	Portion to interest	Portion to principal	New balance
\$146,250.00	\$803.07	\$633.75	\$169.32	\$146,080.68
\$146,080.68	\$803.07	\$633.02	\$170.05	\$145,910.63
\$145,910.63	\$803.07	\$632.28	\$170.79	\$145,739.84
\$145,739.84	\$803.07	\$631.54	\$171.53	\$145,568.30
\$145,568.30	\$803.07	\$630.80	\$172.27	\$145,396.03
\$145,396.03	\$803.07	\$630.05	\$173.02	\$145,223.01
\$145,223.01	\$803.07	\$629.30	\$173.77	\$145,049.24
\$145,049.24	\$803.07	\$628.55	\$174.52	\$144,874.72
\$144,874.72	\$803.07	\$627.79	\$175.28	\$144,699.44
\$144,699.44	\$803.07	\$627.03	\$176.04	\$144,523.40
\$144,523.40	\$803.07	\$626.27	\$176.80	\$144,346.60
\$144,346.60	\$803.07	\$625.50	\$177.57	\$144,169.03

43.

Balance	Payment	Portion to interest	Portion to principal	New balance
$500.00	$10.59	$9.48	$1.11	$498.89
$498.89	$10.59	$9.46	$1.13	$497.76
$497.76	$10.59	$9.44	$1.15	$496.60
$496.60	$10.59	$9.41	$1.18	$495.43
$495.43	$10.59	$9.39	$1.20	$494.23
$494.23	$10.59	$9.37	$1.22	$493.01
$493.01	$10.59	$9.35	$1.24	$491.77
$491.77	$10.59	$9.32	$1.27	$490.50
$490.50	$10.59	$9.30	$1.29	$489.21
$489.21	$10.59	$9.27	$1.32	$487.89
$487.89	$10.59	$9.25	$1.34	$486.55
$486.55	$10.59	$9.22	$1.37	$485.19

Chapter 3 Review Exercises, p. 366

1. (b) **2.** (e) **3.** (f) **4.** (c) **5.** (a) **6.** (d) **7.** False
8. True **9.** True **10.** False **11.** True **12.** False
13. True **14.** False **15.** True **16.** (a) -3; (b) 81;
(c) 1024 **17.** $\dfrac{1}{x}$ **18.** e^x **19.** $\dfrac{4x^3}{x^4 + 5}$ **20.** $\dfrac{e^{2\sqrt{x}}}{\sqrt{x}}$

21. $\dfrac{1}{2x}$ **22.** $3x^4 e^{3x} + 4x^3 e^{3x}$ **23.** $\dfrac{1 - 3\ln x}{x^4}$

24. $2xe^{x^2}(\ln 4x) + \dfrac{e^{x^2}}{x}$ **25.** $4e^{4x} - \dfrac{1}{x}$ **26.** $\dfrac{1 - x}{e^x}$

27. $(\ln 9)9^x$ **28.** $\dfrac{1}{(\ln 2)x}$

29. $3^x(\ln 3)(\log_4(2x + 1)) + \dfrac{(3^x)2}{(2x + 1)(\ln 4)}$

30.

31.

32. 6.93 **33.** -3.2698 **34.** 8.7601 **35.** 3.2698
36. 2.54995 **37.** -3.6602 **38.** $Q(t) = 25e^{7t}$ **39.** 4.3%
40. 18.24 yr **41.** (a) $C(t) = 15.81e^{0.023t}$; (b) $30.27, $34.19
42. (a) $C(t) = 2.69e^{0.0282t}$; (b) $6.26, $8.31
43. (a) $N(t) = 60e^{0.12t}$; (b) 97 franchises; (c) 13.4 yr after 2014
44. (a) $N(t) = 24e^{0.07t}$; (b) about 39; (c) in about 9.9 yr
45. 5.3 yr **46.** 18.2% **47.** (a) $A(t) = 800e^{-0.07t}$;
(b) 197 g; (c) 9.9 days **48.** (a) 0.50, 0.75, 0.97, 0.999, 0.9999;
(b) $p'(t) = 0.7e^{-0.7t}$; (c) ✏ (d)

49. $186,373.98 **50.** (a) $5813.33; (b) $871.52/yr
51. (a) $190.77; (b) $1696.20 **52.** $508,192.17
53. (a) $23.79; (b) $20.75 in interest; $3.04 to principal
54. $\dfrac{-8}{(e^{2x} - e^{-2x})^2}$ **55.** $-\dfrac{1}{1024e} \approx 0$
56.

$$f(x) = \dfrac{e^{1/x}}{(1 + e^{1/x})^2}$$

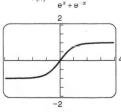

57. 0 **58.** (a) $y = 169.3145859(1.151556523^x)$,
$y = 169.3145859e^{0.1411145255x}$, 14.1%; (b) $395 billion,
$694 billion; (c) 12.6 yr after 2010; (d) 4.9 yr

Chapter 3 Test, p. 368

1. [3.1] $6e^{3x}$ **2.** [3.2] $\dfrac{4(\ln x)^3}{x}$ **3.** [3.1] $-2xe^{-x^2}$

4. [3.2] $\dfrac{1}{x}$ **5.** [3.1] $e^x - 15x^2$ **6.** [3.1, 3.2] $\dfrac{3e^x}{x} + 3e^x \cdot \ln x$

7. [3.5] $(\ln 7)7^x + (\ln 3)3^x$ **8.** [3.5] $\dfrac{1}{(\ln 14)x}$ **9.** [3.2] (a) 5;

(b) 2 **10.** [3.2] 1.0674 **11.** [3.2] 0.5554 **12.** [3.2] 0.4057
13. [3.3] $M(t) = 2e^{6t}$ **14.** [3.3] 23.1%/hr **15.** [3.3] 10.0 yr
16. [3.3] (a) $C(t) = 3.22e^{0.012t}$; (b) $3.63, $3.81
17. [3.4] (a) $A(t) = 3e^{-0.1t}$; (b) 1.1 cc; (c) 6.9 hr
18. [3.4] About 16.47 centuries, or 1647 yr
19. [3.4] 4.0773%/sec **20.** [3.3] (a) 4%; (b) 5.2%, 14.5%,
40.7%, 73.5%, 91.8%, 99.5%, 99.9%;

(c) $P'(t) = \dfrac{672e^{-0.28t}}{(1 + 24e^{-0.28t})^2}$; **(d)** ✏;

(e)

$$P(t) = \dfrac{100}{1 + 24e^{-0.28t}}$$

21. [3.5] (a) $1057.01; (b) $1093.81/yr **22.** [3.6] (a) $1667.22;
(b) $600,199.20; (c) 240,199.20 **23.** [3.6] $20,815.15

24. [3.2] $(\ln x)^2$ **25.** [3.1] Maximum is $\dfrac{256}{e^4} \approx 4.689$;

minimum is 0. **26.** [3.1]

$$f(x) = \dfrac{e^x - e^{-x}}{e^x + e^{-x}}$$

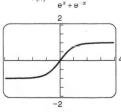

27. [3.1] 0 **28.** [3.3] (a) $y = 726522.8277(1.076351493)^x$,
$y = 726522.8277e^{0.073577t}$; (b) $5.3 million, $6.6 million;
(c) 98 yr; (d) 9.4 yr; (e) ✏

Extended Technology Application, p. 370

Graphs left to the student.

1. Linear: $G(t) = -14.745t + 98.91$; quadratic: $G(t) = 3.694t^2 - 47.994t + 154.324$; cubic: $G(t) = -0.544t^3 + 11.039t^2 - 76.012t + 181.254$; exponential: $G(t) = 240.282(0.527)^t$. The dramatic decrease in revenue and its "flattening" suggests that an exponential model is most appropriate. Note that the linear model will eventually give negative revenue values, as will the quadratic and cubic models. **2.** $0.75, $0.40, $0.21, $0.11, $0.06 (millions)

3. $261.21, $261.61, $261.82, $261.93, $261.99 (millions)

4. $R(t) = 260.36/(1 + 3.187e^{-0.982t})$; about $260 to $262 million

5. $R'(t) = \dfrac{814.832e^{-0.982t}}{(1 + 3.187e^{-0.982t})^2}$; $\lim\limits_{t \to \infty} R'(t) = 0$

6. The release date may have been delayed to coincide with the holiday shopping season. The date is close to Halloween, a natural "tie-in" with the movie's theme.

7. Linear: $G(t) = 0.053t + 1.693$; quadratic: $G(t) = -0.24t^2 + 2.216t - 1.912$; cubic: $G(t) = 0.007t^3 - 0.332t^2 + 2.565t - 2.248$; exponential: $G(t) = 1.022(1.088)^t$. None are satisfactory. The limited early release resulted in small revenue figures for weeks 1–3.

8. Linear: $G(t) = -0.827t + 7.314$; quadratic: $G(t) = 0.009t^2 - 0.938t + 7.63$; cubic: $G(t) = -0.009t^3 - 0.174t^2 - 1.897t + 9.423$; exponential: $G(t) = 25.302(0.655)^t$. The exponential model fits the data best.

9. About $17 million

Index of Applications

Index

Summary of Important Formulas for Differentiation

1. **Power Rule.**   For any real number k, $\dfrac{d}{dx} x^k = kx^{k-1}$.

2. **Derivative of a Constant Function.**   If $F(x) = c$, then $F'(x) = 0$.

3. **Derivative of a Constant Times a Function.**   If $F(x) = cf(x)$, then $F'(x) = cf'(x)$.

4. **Derivative of a Sum.**   If $F(x) = f(x) + g(x)$, then $F'(x) = f'(x) + g'(x)$.

5. **Derivative of a Difference.**   If $F(x) = f(x) - g(x)$, then $F'(x) = f'(x) - g'(x)$.

6. **Derivative of a Product.**   If $F(x) = f(x)g(x)$, then $F'(x) = f(x)g'(x) + g(x)f'(x)$.

7. **Derivative of a Quotient.**   If $F(x) = \dfrac{f(x)}{g(x)}$, then $F'(x) = \dfrac{g(x)f'(x) - f(x)g'(x)}{[g(x)]^2}$.

8. **Extended Power Rule.**   If $F(x) = [g(x)]^k$, then $F'(x) = k[g(x)]^{k-1}g'(x)$.

9. **Chain Rule.**   If $F(x) = f[g(x)]$, then $F'(x) = f'[g(x)]g'(x)$.

   Or, if $y = f(u)$ and $u = g(x)$, then $\dfrac{dy}{dx} = \dfrac{dy}{du} \cdot \dfrac{du}{dx}$.

10. $\dfrac{d}{dx} e^x = e^x$

11. $\dfrac{d}{dx} e^{f(x)} = e^{f(x)} \cdot f'(x)$

12. $\dfrac{d}{dx} \ln x = \dfrac{1}{x}, \quad x > 0$

13. $\dfrac{d}{dx} \ln f(x) = \dfrac{f'(x)}{f(x)}, \quad f(x) > 0$

14. $\dfrac{d}{dx} \ln |x| = \dfrac{1}{x}, \quad x \neq 0$

15. $\dfrac{d}{dx} \ln |f(x)| = \dfrac{f'(x)}{f(x)}, \quad f(x) \neq 0$

16. $\dfrac{d}{dx} a^x = (\ln a)a^x, \quad a > 0$

17. $\dfrac{d}{dx} \log_a |x| = \dfrac{1}{\ln a} \cdot \dfrac{1}{x}, \quad a > 0 \text{ and } x \neq 0$

Table of Integrals

- **Antiderivative of a constant:** $\int k\,dx = kx + C$
- **Antiderivative of a constant times a function:** $\int k \cdot f(x)\,dx = k\int f(x)\,dx$
- **Sum/difference property of antidifferentiation:**
$$\int f(x) \pm g(x)\,dx = \int f(x)\,dx \pm \int g(x)\,dx$$

1. $\displaystyle\int x^n\,dx = \frac{x^{n+1}}{n+1} + C, \quad n \neq -1$

2. $\displaystyle\int \frac{1}{x}\,dx = \ln|x| + C, \quad \text{or} \quad \int \frac{1}{x}\,dx = \ln x + C, \quad x > 0$

3. $\displaystyle\int u\,dv = uv - \int v\,du$

4. $\displaystyle\int e^x\,dx = e^x + C$

5. $\displaystyle\int e^{ax}\,dx = \frac{1}{a} \cdot e^{ax} + C$

6. $\displaystyle\int xe^{ax}\,dx = \frac{1}{a^2} \cdot e^{ax}(ax - 1) + C$

7. $\displaystyle\int x^n e^{ax}\,dx = \frac{x^n e^{ax}}{a} - \frac{n}{a}\int x^{n-1}e^{ax}\,dx + C$

8. $\displaystyle\int \ln x\,dx = x\ln x - x + C$

9. $\displaystyle\int (\ln x)^n\,dx = x(\ln x)^n - n\int (\ln x)^{n-1}\,dx + C, \quad n \neq -1$

10. $\displaystyle\int x^n \ln x\,dx = x^{n+1}\left[\frac{\ln x}{n+1} - \frac{1}{(n+1)^2}\right] + C, \quad n \neq -1$

11. $\displaystyle\int a^x\,dx = \frac{a^x}{\ln a} + C, \quad a > 0, a \neq 1$

12. $\displaystyle\int \frac{1}{\sqrt{x^2 + a^2}}\,dx = \ln|x + \sqrt{x^2 + a^2}| + C$

13. $\displaystyle\int \frac{1}{\sqrt{x^2 - a^2}}\,dx = \ln|x + \sqrt{x^2 - a^2}| + C$

14. $\displaystyle\int \frac{1}{x^2 - a^2}\,dx = \frac{1}{2a}\ln\left|\frac{x-a}{x+a}\right| + C$

15. $\displaystyle\int \frac{1}{a^2 - x^2}\,dx = \frac{1}{2a}\ln\left|\frac{a+x}{a-x}\right| + C$

16. $\displaystyle\int \frac{1}{x\sqrt{a^2 + x^2}}\,dx = -\frac{1}{a}\ln\left|\frac{a + \sqrt{a^2 + x^2}}{x}\right| + C$

17. $\displaystyle\int \frac{1}{x\sqrt{a^2 - x^2}}\,dx = -\frac{1}{a}\ln\left|\frac{a + \sqrt{a^2 - x^2}}{x}\right| + C$

18. $\displaystyle\int \frac{x}{a + bx}\,dx = \frac{a}{b^2} + \frac{x}{b} - \frac{a}{b^2}\ln|a + bx| + C$

19. $\displaystyle\int \frac{x}{(a + bx)^2}\,dx = \frac{a}{b^2(a + bx)} + \frac{1}{b^2}\ln|a + bx| + C$

20. $\displaystyle\int \frac{1}{x(a + bx)}\,dx = \frac{1}{a}\ln\left|\frac{x}{a + bx}\right| + C$

21. $\displaystyle\int \frac{1}{x(a + bx)^2}\,dx = \frac{1}{a(a + bx)} + \frac{1}{a^2}\ln\left|\frac{x}{a + bx}\right| + C$

22. $\displaystyle\int \sqrt{x^2 \pm a^2}\,dx$
$$= \tfrac{1}{2}\left[x\sqrt{x^2 \pm a^2} \pm a^2\ln|x + \sqrt{x^2 \pm a^2}|\right] + C$$

23. $\displaystyle\int x\sqrt{a + bx}\,dx = \frac{2}{15b^2}(3bx - 2a)(a + bx)^{3/2} + C$

24. $\displaystyle\int x^2\sqrt{a + bx}\,dx$
$$= \frac{2}{105b^3}(15b^2x^2 - 12abx + 8a^2)(a + bx)^{3/2} + C$$

25. $\displaystyle\int \frac{x\,dx}{\sqrt{a + bx}} = \frac{2}{3b^2}(bx - 2a)\sqrt{a + bx} + C$

26. $\displaystyle\int \frac{x^2\,dx}{\sqrt{a + bx}}$
$$= \frac{2}{15b^3}(3b^2x^2 - 4abx + 8a^2)\sqrt{a + bx} + C$$

MA 1613   - Business Calculus

TEXTBOOK: CALCULUS and Its Applications, Bittinger and Ellenbogen, 4th Custom Edition for Mississippi State University and MYLABS PLUS registration code

Website to register for MY MATH LAB: www.msstate.mylabsplus.com

     Login Name: Net ID (e.g. abc123)

     Password : This will be sent to you in an email from MYLABSPLUS. This initial password is generated by the software and I recommend that you change this after you sign in for the first time. If you used the software last semester or in the past it is the same password as before. If you do not receive the email you will need to go to the website and click on forgot username/password and it will give you the option to reset your password.

All of your grades will be kept in the gradebook on MYLABSPLUS.

This course will consist of 800 points.

TESTS: There will be **four** major in-class tests given this semester before the final exam. Each test will count 100 points. The test questions will be similar to the examples done in class and the homework and quiz problems from My Labs Plus and your textbook. You cannot use graphing calculators or any scientific calculator with calculus functions on the test. Check with your instructor at the beginning of the semester and have your calculator approved.   The final exam will count 200 points. It is a comprehensive, departmental exam and everyone must take it. You should bring #2 pencils, your calculator and your MSU ID to the final exam.

NO Make- Up tests will be given. Arrangements should be made ahead of time if you must miss a scheduled test. If you are absent on a test day and have a valid, written excuse, then the final exam will count in place of the missed test.   If you do not have an excuse, you will receive a 0. The final exam will count for only 1 missed test. A 0 will be assigned for any other missed test. It is usually not a good idea to substitute the final exam for a missed test, except in case of an emergency. Everyone must take the final exam. There are no exemptions.

HOMEWORK: There will be a homework grade valued at 100 points. These problems will be on MYLABSPLUS, the software program included with your textbook. You may complete the homework from anywhere you like and you may work the problems multiple times. You should check the calendar on MY LABSPLUS for due dates. Homework assignments will not be accepted after the due date. You will have a total of 13 homework assignments. The best 10 will be counted. There will also be homework problems assigned from your textbook. These textbook problems will not have any point value, but they are vital to your success in this course. Homework assignments are due at 11:59 p.m.

QUIZZES: There will be a quiz grade valued at 100 points. The quiz grade will consist of 13 quizzes from MYLABSPLUS. The best 10 scores will be counted. The quizzes must be taken in the MATH DOMAIN, located on the first floor of ALLEN HALL (Allen 111). You will have 1 chance per quiz. It is the student's responsibility to check the calendar on MYLABSPLUS and submit each quiz on time. We will not accept quizzes after the due date. You may use your book, notes and non-graphing calculators on the quizzes.

BONUS POINTS: If you miss 0 -2 days of class (**excused or unexcused**) , you will receive 15 bonus points that will be added to test 4. If you miss 3 or more days (**excused or unexcused**), you will not receive the bonus points. Also, if you miss 5 or fewer days of class (**excused or unexcused**), you may substitute the final exam for your lowest test score if the final exam is higher than your lowest test score. These are both ways to reward students for good class attendance.

GRADING: The grading scale is based on the following points. There are 800 total points for the entire semester.

Points:		Grading Scale	
4 tests	400 points	720 - 815 points	A
Final Exam	200 points	640 – 719 points	B
Quizzes	100 point	560 – 639 points	C
Homework	100 points	480 – 559 points	D
		0 – 479 points	F

The prerequisites for this course are MA 1313, College Algebra, with a C or better, or an ACT math subscore of 24 or higher. If the student does not meet the prerequisite for this course, then they must drop. If the student does not drop, then the math department will force-drop the student through the Registrar's office. The student will be held responsible if this drops them below the required number of hours to be considered a full-time student.

Electronic Devices: All pagers, cell phones, and other electronic equipment should be turned off and stored out of sight during class. **No text messaging is allowed during class**. Only **scientific calculators** will be allowed on tests. Graphing calculators or calclulators with calculus functions may not be used on tests.

If anyone has a cell phone out during a test, your test paper will be collected and you will receive a 0 for the test grade. There are **no** cell phones allowed in the Math Domain during quizzes.

The Learning Center is located in Allen 267. It offers tutoring services provided by MSU students. It is free. The center is open from 2 p.m. – 7 p.m. Monday – Thursday. The phone number is 325-2957.

Math Domain Hours:
Monday – Thursday   8 a.m. – 8 p.m.
Friday   8 a.m. – 4 p.m.

Remember the quizzes must be taken in the Math Domain. Please start the quizzes at least 1 hour before the closing time so that you will have time to finish. Check the MYLABSPLUS calendar frequently for due dates. We will not accept any late assignments.

This syllabus may be amended as deemed necessary by the instructor.

Student Honor Code
Mississippi State has an approved Honor Code that applies to all students. The code is as follows: "As a Mississippi State University student, I will conduct myself with honor and integrity at all times. I will not lie, cheat, or steal, nor will I accept the actions of those who do." Upon accepting admission to Mississippi State University, a student immediately assumes a commitment to uphold the Honor Code, to accept responsibility for learning, and to follow the philosophy and rules of the Honor Code. Student will be required to state their commitment on examinations, research papers, and other academic work. Ignorance of the rules does not exclude any member of the MSU community from the requirements or the processes of the Honor Code. For additional information, please visit: http://honorcode.msstate.edu/policy.

Title IX
MSU is committed to complying with Title IX, a federal law that prohibits discrimination, including violence and harassment, based on sex. This means that MSU's educational programs and activities must be free from sex discrimination, sexual harassment, and other forms of sexual misconduct. If you or someone you know has experienced sex discrimination, sexual violence and/or harassment by any member of the University community, you are encouraged to report the conduct to MSU's Director of Title IX/EEO Programs at 325-8124 or by e-mail to titleix@msstate.edu. Additional resources are available at http://www.msstate.edu/web/security/title9-12.pdf, or at http://students.msstate.edu/sexualmisconduct/ .

Support Services

Students who need academic accommodations based on a disability should visit the Office of Student Support Services, 01 Montgomery Hall, call 662-325-3335, or visit the website at www.sss.msstate.edu.

MATH DOMAIN RULES:

1. No graphing calculators.
2. No other windows can be open and in use during quizzes.
3. Students can use their own class notes, books or homework during quizzes. They cannot share notes or help each other during quizzes. Students cannot receive help for lab workers during quizzes.
4. Food the drinks are not allowed in the lab.
5. Cell phones must be on silent at all times. Cell phones must be put away during quizzes. No texting is allowed during quizzes. The calculator on your cell phone cannot be used during quizzes.

TESTBOOK: Calculus and its Applications, 4th Custom Edition for Mississippi State University, Bittinger and Ellenbogen

TEST 1 : Sections R.1, R.2, R.3, R. 4, R.5 (ALGEBRA REVIEW) , 1.1, 1.2

Section R.1 : p. 10   1-13 odd, 19, 29, 31

Section R. 2 : p. 21   29, 31, 33, 39 – 50, 55 – 61, 63 – 69 odd

Section R. 3 : p. 31   1-19 odd, 25 – 29, 33 – 53 odd

Section R.4: p. 44   1, 3, 9, 13, 19 – 41 odd

Section R. 5: p. 64   55 – 85 odd

Section 1.1 : p. 102   1 – 49 odd, 53, 55, 56, 61 – 65, 67

Section 1.2: p. 113   9 – 35 odd, 37 – 41, 43 - 69 odd

Homework 1 – R. 1, R.2, R.3
Homework 2 - R. 4, R.5
Homework 3 -1.1, 1.2

TEST 2: Sections 1.3, 1.4, 1.5, 1.6, 1.7, 1.8

Section 1.3 : p. 122   1 – 13 odd, 27, 29, 41, 42

Section 1.4: p. 135   1, 7, 11, 17, 21

Section 1.5:   p. 145   1 – 59 odd, 63, 67, 69, 75, 79, 83

Section 1.6:   p. 154   3, 5, 9. 13, 15, 21, 22, 23, 24, 27, 29, 43 – 49 odd, 53 – 57 odd, 101, 103, 105

Section 1.7 : p. 163   1 – 13 odd, 17, 19, 21, 23, 25, 29, 31, 35, 58, 63, 65

Section 1.8 : p. 172   1 – 17 odd, 25 , 29, 31, 35, 37, 39, 43, 59, 61

Homework 4 – 1.3, 1.4
Homework 5 – 1.5
Homework 6 – 1.6
Homework 7 – 1.7, 1.8

TEST 3 : Sections 2.1, 2.2, 2.3

Section 2.1 : p. 201   1 – 25 odd, 69, 71

Section 2.2 : p. 217   1 – 15 odd, 19, 25, 27, 29, 35, 47, 49

Section 2.3:   p. 230   1 -22, 23, 25, 27, 35

Homework 8 – 2.1
Homework 9 – 2.2
Homework 10 – 2.3

TEST 4 : Sections 2.4, 2.5, 2.6, 3.1, 3.2

Section 2.4 : p. 240   3 – 6, 9, 11, 14, 15, 18, 19, 21, 29, 49, 53, 61, 63, 81

Section 2.5:   p. 254   1- 7, 13, 14, 15, 17, 23, 25, 27, 29, 30

Section 2.6 : p. 265   1, 3, 5, 7, 8, 18, 63, 64, 65

Section 3.1 ; p. 304   1-37 odd, 41, 43, 45, 53, 75, 77

Section 3.2 : p. 319   1-4, 11, 13, 17 , 19, 21, 25- 35 odd, 49 – 57 odd,
                          61, 63, 67, 71, 77 – 85 odd

Homework 11 – 2.4
Homework 12– 2.5, 2.6
Homework 13 – 3.1, 3.2

MA 1613 – Test 1 Study Sheet – Sections R1, R2, R3, R4, R5, 1.1 ,1.2

1. Graph:

   (a) $Y = \frac{2}{3}x - 4$ (b $y = 9 - x^2$ (c) $y = x^2 - 6$

2. Suppose $ 4000 is invested at 7% for 5 years. How much money is in the account at the end of 5 years if the interest is compounded:

   (a) Annually   (b) quarterly   (c) monthly

3. Vertical Line Test - p. 22 - 39 -50

4. A function is given by f(x) $= 3x^2 - 5$. Find:

   (a) F (7)   (b) f(0)   (c) f(-2)   (d) f(x + 1)

5. For f(x) $= -2x^2 - 3x - 1$, find $\frac{f(x+h)-f(x)}{h}$.

6. If f(x) = $\begin{cases} 2 - 5x & \text{if } x \le -2 \\ 3x & \text{if } -2 < x < 6 \\ 4x + 3 & \text{if } x \ge 6 \end{cases}$ find:

   (a) f (-3)   (b) f(0)   (c) f(3)   (d) f (7)

7. Graph:

   (a) F(x) = $\begin{cases} x^2 + 1 & for\ x \ge -1 \\ x - 2 & for\ x < -1 \end{cases}$

(b) $G(x) = \begin{cases} -4x - 2 & for\ x < -2 \\ 4 & for\ -2 \le x \le 5 \\ x & for\ x > 5 \end{cases}$

8. Write in interval notation.

(a)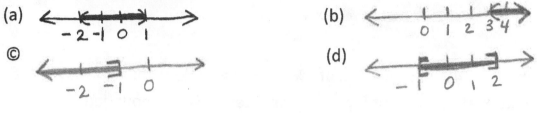

(b)

©

(d)

9. Graph: (a)   -5 ≤ x < 2   (b) x ≥ -3

10. Find the domain:

(a) $F(x) = \dfrac{6x}{x^2 - 36}$

(b) $f(x) = 3x^2 - 7x + 2$

© $f(x) = \dfrac{x}{x^2 + 7x + 6}$

(d) $f(x) = \sqrt{5x - 8}$

11. Find the slope and y-intercept of the line   -8x-7y = 21.

12. Write the equation of the line with slope of -6 and containing (-3 , -1).

13. Write the equation of the line with slope of   -3/2 and y –intercept of (0 , -2).

14. Find the slope of the line containing:
   (a) (4 , 1) and (-7 , 9)
   (b) (-2 , -3) and (-2 , 5)
   (c) (-6, -8) and (3, -8)

15. Rewrite with rational exponents.

(a) $\sqrt{x^3}$

(b) $\frac{5}{\sqrt[3]{x}}$

(c) $\sqrt{x^2+5}$

(d) $\frac{1}{\sqrt[4]{(2x+3)^3}}$

16. Rewrite with radical notation.

(a) $x^{\frac{2}{3}}$

(b) $(5x^2-2)^{\frac{-4}{5}}$

(c) $5x^{\frac{-1}{3}}$

17. Simplify:

(a) $25^{\frac{3}{2}}$

(b) $64^{\frac{2}{3}}$

(c) $49^{\frac{5}{2}}$

18. If f(x) = $\begin{cases} x+8 & \text{for } x \le 4 \\ 7x-19 & \text{for } x > 4 \end{cases}$ find:

(a) $\lim_{x\to 4-} f(x)$

(b) $\lim_{x\to 4+} f(x)$

(c) $\lim_{x\to 4} f(x)$

19. For the graph of f(x) , find the following:

(a) $\lim_{x\to -5} f(x)$

(b) $\lim_{x\to -2} f(x)$

(c) $\lim_{x\to 3} f(x)$

(d) $\lim_{x\to 1-} f(x)$

(e) $\lim_{x\to 1+} f(x)$

(f) $\lim_{x\to 4} f(x)$

(g) f(3)

(h) Is f (x) continuous at x = -2 ?

20. Find the limit:

(a) $\lim_{x\to 1} (-x^2 + 2x - 6)$

(e) $\lim_{x\to 4} \sqrt{7x - 2}$

(b) $\lim_{x\to -2}(4x - 7)$

(f) $\lim_{x\to 5} \frac{x-5}{x^2-x-20}$

(c) $\lim_{x\to -3} \frac{x^2-7}{3-x}$

(g) $\lim_{x\to 0} \frac{8}{x}$

(d) $\lim_{x\to 8} \frac{x^2-64}{x-8}$

(h) $\lim_{x\to 2} \frac{3x}{x-2}$

21. Find each of the following for the graph.

(a) $\lim_{x\to 4-} f(x)$

(d) $\lim_{x\to\infty} f(x)$

(b) $\lim_{x\to 4+} f(x)$

(e) $\lim_{x\to -\infty} f(x)$

(c) $\lim_{x\to 4} f(x)$

22. Is $g(x) = \begin{cases} \frac{1}{2}x+3 & \text{for } x < -2 \\ X-1 & \text{for } x \geq -2 \end{cases}$ continuous at x = -2?

23. Is $g(x) = \begin{cases} -x + 3 \text{ for } x \leq 2 \\ x^2 - 3 \text{ for } x > 2 \end{cases}$ continuous?

ANSWERS

2. a) $5610.21   b) $5659.11   c) $5670.50

4. a) 142   b) -5   c) 7   d) $3x^2 + 6x - 2$

5. -4x -2h -3

6. a) 17   b) 0   c) 9   d) 31

8. a) (-2 , 1)   b) (3, ∞)   c) (- ∞ , –1]   d) $[-1 , 2]$

9. a)

b)

10. a) x ≠ 6 , x≠ −6   b) All Reals
    c) x ≠ −6, x≠ −1 or   d) x ≥ $\frac{8}{5}$ or $[\frac{8}{5}, ∞)$
    (−∞ , -6) ∪ (-6, -1) ∪ (−1 ,∞)

11.   m = $\frac{-8}{7}$ b = -3

12.   y = -6x -19

13.   y = $\frac{-3}{2}$ x − 2

14. a) $\frac{-8}{11}$ b) undefined slope   c) 0

15. a) $x^{\frac{3}{2}}$ b) $5x^{\frac{-1}{3}}$ c) $(x^2 + 5)^{\frac{1}{2}}$ d) $(2x + 3)^{\frac{-3}{4}}$

16. a) $\sqrt[3]{x^2}$ b) $\dfrac{1}{\sqrt[5]{5\,x^2-2)^4}}$ c) $\dfrac{5}{\sqrt[3]{x}}$

17. a) 125 b) 16 c) 16807

18. a) 12 b) 9 c) DNE

19. a) DNE b) DNE c) -1
    d) 1 e) 2 f) DNE
    g) 2 h) no

20. a) -5 b) -15 c) $\dfrac{1}{3}$
    d) 16 e) $\sqrt{26}$ f) $\dfrac{1}{9}$
    g) DNE h) DNE

21. a) ∞ b) $-\infty$ c) DNE d) 1 e) 1

22. no
23. yes

1. Find the average rate of change for f(x) = $x^2 + 4x + 3$ from x = 2 to x = 5.

2. Which of the following represents the derivative of f(x) = $3x^2 + 4x + 2$?

(A) $\lim_{h \to 0} \dfrac{3(x+h)^2 + 4(x+h)+2-3x^2-4x-2}{h}$

(B) $\lim_{x \to 0} \dfrac{3(x+h)^2 + 4\,(x+h)+2-3x^2-4x-2}{x}$

(C) $\dfrac{3(x+h)^2+4(x+h)+2-3x^2-4x-2}{h}$

(D) $\lim_{h \to 0} \dfrac{3(x+h)^2+4(x+h)+2-3x^2+4x+2}{h}$

3. If $f(3) = -8$ and $f\,'(3) = 6$, write the equation of the tangent line to $f(x)$ when x = 3.

4. (a) If C(x) = $950 + 15x + 30x^2$, find the average cost.
   (b) Find the rate the average cost is changing when 50 items are produced.

5. Find the slope of the tangent line when x = 1 for :

(a) f (x) = $\dfrac{1}{2x} + \dfrac{x^2}{4}$

(b) y = $5x^3 - 6x$

© f(x) = $x^{\frac{3}{2}} - 4\sqrt{x}$

6. If $y = \frac{3}{2} x^4 + 6x^3 + \frac{1}{2} x^2 + 8$, find y' (1).

7. If $y = \frac{4}{5} x^5 - 2 x^3 + \frac{3}{2} x^2 - 7$, find y''' (1).

8. If $f(x) = \sqrt{4x + 4}$, find f' (0).

9. Write the equation of the tangent line to :
   (a) $y = 3x^2 - 4x + 7$ at x = 3
   (b) $y = \sqrt{x^2 + 3x}$ at the point (1,2)
   (c) $Y = \frac{x^2 + 3}{x - 1}$ at x = 2

10. Find the x – values of the points where the tangent line is **horizontal.**

   (a) $y = 20 - x^2$
   (b) $Y = -x^3 + x^2 + 5x - 1$
   (c) $Y = x^3 - 12x + 2$

11. Write the equation of the tangent line to $f(x) = x^3 - 2x + 1$ at x = 2.

12. If $f(x) = \sqrt{x}$ and g(x) $= x - 1$, find:

(a) $(f \circ g)(x)$

(b) $(f \circ g)(10)$

© $(g \circ f)(x)$

(d) $(g \circ f)(25)$

13. (a) If $f(x) = \dfrac{x-5}{x+6}$, find $f''(x)$.

(b) If $f(x) = \sqrt{2x + 5}$, find $f''(x)$.

14. If $(x) = \dfrac{5}{(2x-3)^4}$, find $f'(1)$.

Find the derivative of each function. (Questions 15 – 25)

15. $y = \dfrac{2}{3}x^3 + 4x^2 - \dfrac{1}{2}x + 3$

16. $f(x) = 2x^5 + \dfrac{3}{x} - 8\sqrt{x} + 6x - 9$

17. $y = -10(4 - 5x^2)^8$

18. $f(x) = \dfrac{7}{(8x-4)^3}$

19. $f(x) = (2x - 7) (3x^2 + 4x - 5)$

20. $y = \dfrac{x^2 - 2}{x^2 + 3x}$

21. $f(x) = x^3 (4 - 6x^2)^2$

22. $y = (x - 4)^8 (2x + 3)^6$

23. $f(x) = \dfrac{8x^2 + 4x}{4x^2}$

24. $f(x) = x^{\frac{5}{2}} + 6\sqrt{x}$

25. $y = \dfrac{1}{5} x^5 - \dfrac{1}{4} x^4 + \dfrac{2}{3} x^3 - \dfrac{1}{4}x^2 + 3x - 4$

ANSWERS

1. 11

2. A

3. $y = 6x - 26$

4. (a) $950\,x^{-1} + 15 + 30x$ (b) $ 29.62

5. (a) 0   (b) 9   (c) $\dfrac{-1}{2}$

6. 25

7. 36

8. 1

9. (a) $y = 14x - 20$ (b) $y = \dfrac{5}{4}x + \dfrac{3}{4}$ (c) $y = -3x + 13$

10. (a) $x = 0$ (b) $x = \dfrac{5}{3}$ and $x = -1$ (c) $x = 2$ and $x = -2$

11. $y = 10x - 15$

12. (a) $\sqrt{x - 1}$ (b) 3   (c) $\sqrt{x} - 1$ (d) 4

13. (a) $f''(x) = \dfrac{-22}{(x+6)^3}$ (b) $f''(x) = \dfrac{-1}{(2x+5)^{\frac{3}{2}}}$

14. 40

15. $y' = 2x^2 + 8x - \dfrac{1}{2}$

16. $f'(x) = 10x^4 - \dfrac{3}{x^2} - \dfrac{4}{x^{\frac{1}{2}}} + 6$

17. $y' = 800\,x\,(4 - 5x^2)^7$

18. $f'(x) = \dfrac{-168}{(8x-4)^4}$

19. $f'(x) = 18x^2 - 26\,x - 38$

20. $y' = \dfrac{3\,x^2 + 4x + 6}{(x^2 + 3x)^2}$

21. $f'(x) = 3x^2\,(4 - 6x^2)(-14x^2 + 4)$

22. $y' = 4\,(x - 4)^7\,(2x + 3)^5\,(7x - 6)$

23. $f'(x) = \dfrac{-1}{x^2}$

24. $f'(x) = \dfrac{5}{2}\,x^{\frac{3}{2}} + \dfrac{3}{x^{\frac{1}{2}}}$

25. $y' = x^4 - x^3 + 2x^2 - \dfrac{1}{2}x + 3$

Look at the graph for problems 1 – 4.

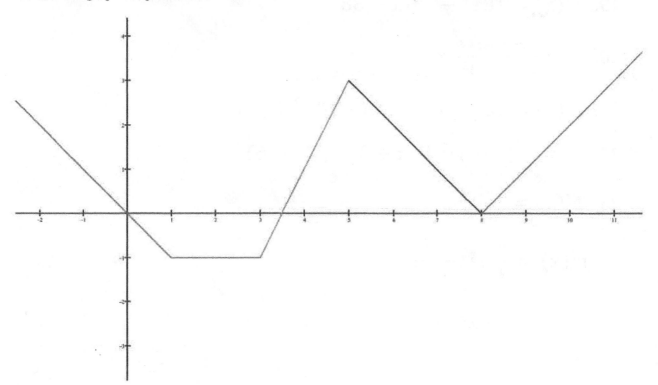

1. Find the intervals where $f(x)$ is decreasing.

2. Find the intervals where $f(x)$ is increasing.

3. Where is $f'(x) > 0$?

4. Where is $f'(x) < 0$?

For each of the following functions (problems 5 – 11), find: Critical Points, Relative Extrema, Increasing/Decreasing, Concavity, and Inflection Points.

5. $f(x) = 2 - 6x - 3x^2$

6. $f(x) = -1 - x + x^2$

7. $f(x) = x^3 - \frac{3}{2}x^2 - 6x - 1$

8. $f(x) = x^4 - 18x^2 - 4$

9. $f(x) = 3x^3 + 8$

10. $f(x) = (x - 7)^5$

11. $f(x) = (x - 2)^{\frac{2}{3}}$

12. Where is $f(x) = x^4 - 2x^2 + 4$ decreasing?

13. Find all the inflection points of $f(x) = 2x^3 - 3x^2 - 12x + 5$.

Use the Second Derivative Test to find the relative extrema of the following problem (14 – 16):

14. $f(x) = 4x^3 + 7x^2 - 10x + 8$

15. $f(x) = 2x^3 - 4x^2 + 2$

16. $f(x) = x^4 + 7$

17. Where is the graph of $f(x)$ concave up and concave down?

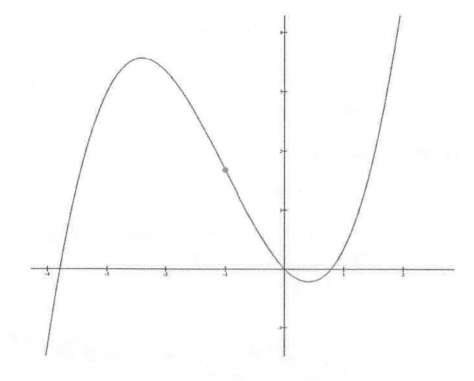

18. On each sketch, determine if the sketch has a positive or negative first and second derivative.

a.   b.   c.   d.

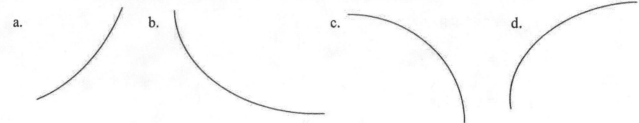

19. Let $f''(x) = 2x^2 - 1$ and $x = -4$, $x = 4$, and $x = 0$ be critical values for $f(x)$. Use the second derivative test to find the relative extrema of the function.

20. Determine the vertical asymptotes.

a. $f(x) = \frac{3x+7}{x-5}$

c. $f(x) = \frac{64x}{x^2+4}$

e. $f(x) = \frac{x+2}{x^2+6x+18}$

b. $f(x) = \frac{15x}{x^2-25}$

d. $f(x) = \frac{x+3}{x^3-x}$

f. $f(x) = \frac{x+6}{x^2+7x+6}$

21. Determine the horizontal asymptotes.

a. $f(x) = \frac{6x}{8x^2+3}$

c. $f(x) = \frac{3x^2}{6x^2+2}$

e. $f(x) = \frac{x^2-16}{x+4}$

b. $f(x) = \frac{x-3}{x^2+2x-15}$

d. $f(x) = \frac{8x^4-5x^2}{2x^3+x^2}$

f. $f(x) = \frac{5-3x^3}{2x^3+x-7}$

22. Sketch the graph of the function $f(x) = \frac{5}{x-3}$

23. Sketch the graph of the function $f(x) = \frac{5}{x+4}$

24. Sketch the graph of the function $f(x) = 9x^2 - 2x^3$

ANSWERS

1. $(-\infty, 1] \cup [5, 8]$

2. $[3, 5] \cup [8, \infty)$

3. $[3, 5] \cup [8, \infty)$

4. $(-\infty, 1] \cup [5, 8]$

	Critical Values	Relative Maximum	Relative Minimum	Increasing	Decreasing	Concave Up	Concave Down	Inflection Points
5.	$x = -1$	(-1, 5)	None	$(-\infty, -1]$	$[-1, \infty)$	None	$(-\infty, \infty)$	None
6.	$x = \frac{1}{2}$	None	(½, ⊖∕⊖)	$[\frac{1}{2}, \infty)$	$(-\infty, \frac{1}{2}]$	$(-\infty, \infty)$	None	None
7.	$x = -1,$ 2	(-1, 5/2)	(2, -11)	$(-\infty, -1] \cup$ $[2, \infty)$	$[-1, 2]$	(½, ∞)	$(-\infty, \frac{1}{2})$	(½, -17/4)
8.	$x = -3$ $x = 0$ $x = 3$	(0, -4)	(3, -85), (-3, -85)	$[-3, 0] \cup$ $[3, \infty)$	$(-\infty, -3] \cup$ $[0, 3]$	$(-\infty, -\sqrt{3})$ $\cup (\sqrt{3}, \infty)$	$(-\sqrt{3}, \sqrt{3})$	$x = \sqrt{3}$ $x = -\sqrt{3}$
9.	$x = 0$	None	None	$(-\infty, \infty)$	None	$(0, \infty)$	$(-\infty, 0)$	(0, 8)
10.	$x = 7$	None	None	$(-\infty, \infty)$	None	$(7, \infty)$	$(-\infty, 7)$	(7, 0)
11.	$x = 2$	None	(2, 0)	$[2, \infty)$	$(-\infty, 2]$	None	$(\infty, 2) \cup$ $(2, \infty)$	None

12. $(-\infty, -1] \cup [0, 1]$

13. $\left(\frac{1}{2}, -\frac{3}{2}\right)$

14. Relative min @ $x = \frac{1}{2}$
    Relative max @ $x = -\frac{5}{3}$

15. Relative min @ $x = \frac{4}{3}$
    Relative max @ $x = 0$

16. Relative min @ $x = 0$
    No Relative max

17. Concave Up: $(-1, \infty)$
    Concave Down: $(-\infty, -1)$

18. a. $f'(x) > 0$ (Increasing)
   $f''(x) > 0$ (Concave Up)

   b. $f'(x) < 0$ (Decreasing)
   $f''(x) > 0$ (Concave Up)

   c. $f'(x) < 0$ (Decreasing)
   $f''(x) < 0$ (Concave Down)

   d. $f'(x) > 0$ (Increasing)
   $f''(x) < 0$ (Concave Down)

19. $x = 4$ and $x = -4$ are Relative minimums
   $x = 0$ is a Relative maximum

20.
   a. $x = 5$ d. $x = -1$, $x = 0$, and $x = 1$
   b. $x = -5$ and $x = 5$ e. none
   c. None   f. $x = -1$

21.
   a. $y = 0$ d. None
   b. $y = 0$ e. None
   c. $y = \frac{1}{2}$ f. $y = -3/2$

22. a.

b.

c.

MA 1613 TEST 4 STUDY SHEET - Sections 2.4, 2.5, 2.6, 3.1, 3.2

1. Find the absolute maximum and absolute minimum of $f(x)$ on $[-4, 3]$.

2. Find the location of the absolute max and absolute min of $f(x) = x^3 - x^2 - x + 2$ on $[-1, 0]$.

3. Find the absolute max and absolute min of $f(x) = x^3 - 3x + 2$ on $\left[-2, \frac{3}{2}\right]$.

4. Find the absolute max and absolute min of $f(x) = 12x - x^2$ on $(-\infty, \infty)$.

5. Of all the numbers whose sum is 70, find the two that have the maximum product.

6. Maximize $Q = 6xy^2$ where x and y are positive numbers such that $x + y^2 = 6$.

7. A large rectangular garden is to be enclosed by a fence and divided into 5 regions as shown below. Find the overall dimensions of the garden if 1200 ft of fencing is available and the area is maximized.

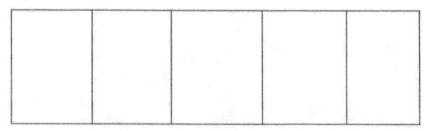

8. A rectangular field is to be fenced using 300 ft of fencing. The field is bordered on one side by a barn and needs no fencing on that side. Find the dimensions that will produce a field with maximum area.

9. If $p = 900 - 3x^2$, find the marginal revenue when $x = 6$.

10. If $C(x) = \frac{2}{3}x^3 - 2x^2 - 5x + 4$, find the marginal cost when $x = 5$.

11. If $R(x) = 1600x - x^2$ and $C(x) = 500 + 1500x$, find the number of units that will maximize the profit.

12. If $p = 200 - x$ and $C(x) = 100x + 1000$, find the maximum profit.

13. Find the number of units that will minimize average cost if $C(x) = 3x^2 + 12x + 75$.

14. Graph $y = 3^x$

15. Graph $y = \left(\frac{1}{4}\right)^x$

   For 16 – 20, find the derivative.

16. $f(x) = e^x$

17. $f(x) = e^{\frac{2x}{3}}$

18. $f(x) = e^{2x^2-1} + 5x$

19. $y = 6e^{4x} - 2e^{-3x}$

20. $y = 3x^2 e^{5x}$

21. Find the equation of the tangent line to the graph of $f(x) = 2e^{-3x}$ at the point $(0, 2)$.

22. Write an equivalent exponential equation.
   a. $\log_3 81 = 4$
   b. $\log_8 2 = \frac{1}{3}$

23. Write an equivalent logarithmic equation.
   a. $10^3 = 1000$
   b. $3^2 = 9$

24. Given $\ln 2 = 0.6931$ and $\ln 5 = 1.6094$, find:
   a. $\ln \frac{5}{4}$
   b. $\ln 40$

25. Solve the exponential equation for t.
   a. $e^{3t} = 900$
   b. $e^{-t} = 0.1$

For 26 – 31, find the derivative.

26. $f(x) = \ln 2x$

27. $f(x) = \ln(8x^3 - x^2)$

28. $y = x^2 \ln x + 5x$

29. $y = e^x \ln x$

30. $y = e^{2x} \ln x^2$

31. $y = e^{x^2} \ln x$

Test 4 Review Sheet Answers

1. Absolute max of 3 at $x = -2$
   Absolute min of -2 at $x = -4$

2. Absolute max at $x = -\frac{1}{3}$
   Absolute min at $x = -1$

3. Absolute max of 4 at $x = -1$
   Absolute min of 0 at $x = -2$ and $x = 1$

4. Absolute max of 36 at $x = 6$
   No Absolute min

5. $x = 35, y = 35$
   Product is 1225

6. $x = 3, y = \sqrt{3}$

7. 100 ft × 300 ft

8. 75 ft × 150 ft

9. $576.00

10. $25.00

11. 50

12. $1500.00

13. 5

14.

15.

16. $f'(x) = e^x$

17. $f'(x) = \frac{2}{3}e^{\frac{2}{3}x}$

18. $f'(x) = 4xe^{2x^2-1} + 5$

19. $y' = 24e^{4x} + 6e^{-3x}$

20. $y' = 3xe^{5x}(5x + 2)$

21. $y = -6x + 2$

22. a. $3^4 = 81$
    b. $8^{\frac{1}{3}} = 2$

23. a. $\log 1000 = 3$
    b. $\log_3 9 = 2$

24. a. 0.2232
    b. 3.6887

25. a. $t \approx 2.267$
    b. $t \approx 2.303$

26. $f'(x) = \frac{1}{x}$

27. $f'(x) = \frac{24x-2}{8x^2-x}$

28. $y' = x + 2x \ln x + 5$

29. $y' = e^x \left(\frac{1}{x} + \ln x\right)$

30. $y' = 2e^{2x} \left(\frac{1}{x} + \ln x^2\right)$

31. $y' = e^{x^2} \left(\frac{1}{x} + 2x \ln x\right)$

MA 1613 – Business Calculus   SAMPLE

FINAL EXAM

INSTRUCTIONS

- Give the following information on the top of your answer sheet. YOUR NAME AND I.D. NUMBER, THE NAME OF YOUR INSTRUCTOR, THE COURSE AND SECTION NUMBER AND THE DATE.
- Make no marks on the exam. Use the scratch paper provided.
- Use a #2 pencil to mark your answer sheet. Keep your answer sheet neat – no stray marks, no smudges, and no wrinkles.
- Be careful to mark your answer in the proper space. If you must change your answer, erase the old answer completely.
- Return your answer sheet, the exam questions and all the scratch paper to your instructor when finished.
- Graphing Calculators may NOT be used during the exam. You may use a scientific calculator. Because of the wide variety of the scientific calculators that students may be using when taking the exam, some of the answers may be left in a form students may not expect. Please check your answers to make sure you have marked the answer you believe is correct.

1) Find the domain of the function

$$f(x) = \frac{1}{\sqrt{4x - 2}}$$

A) $\left(\frac{1}{2}, \infty\right)$ B) $[2, \infty)$ C) $[\frac{1}{2}, \infty)$ D) $\left(-\infty, \frac{1}{2}\right)$

2) Find the slope of the line through (2,- 5) and (-3,1).

A) $-\frac{5}{6}$ B) $\frac{6}{5}$ C) 4   D) $-\frac{6}{5}$

3) Graph $y = \frac{1}{2}x - 1$

A)

B)

C)

D)

4) Find $f(-4)$ and $f(0)$ if

$$f(x) = \begin{cases} x^2 + 4 & if & x < -2 \\ x^2 + 2x - 8 & if -2 \le x \le 0 \\ -3x - 4 & if & x > 0 \end{cases}$$

A) -12, -4   B) 8, 4   C) 20, -8   D) -8, 4

5) Find

$$\frac{f(x+h) - f(x)}{h} \quad if \quad f(x) = 9x^2 - 5$$

A) $18xh + 9h^2$ B) $18x + 9h$

C) $9h^2 - 5$ D) none of these

6) Rewrite using radical notation.

$$(x^4 + 16)^{\frac{-1}{4}}$$

A) $\sqrt{x^4 + 16}$

B) $\sqrt[4]{x^4 + 16}$

C) $\dfrac{1}{\sqrt[4]{x^4+16}}$

D) $\dfrac{1}{x+4}$

7) Evaluate:

$$\lim_{x \to 1} \frac{x^2 + 3x - 4}{x - 1}$$

A) 5   B) -3   C) 0   D) Does not exist

8) Evaluate :

$$\lim_{x \to 3} \frac{x + 3}{x^2 - 9}$$

A) 0   B) $\dfrac{1}{6}$ C) $-\dfrac{1}{6}$ D) Does not exist

9) Evaluate :

$$\lim_{x \to -4} \frac{x^2 + 6x + 8}{x^2 + 16}$$

A) 1   B) $-\dfrac{3}{4}$ C) 0   D) Does not exist

10) Evaluate:

$$\lim_{x \to 5} f(x)$$

Where $f(x) = \begin{cases} 3-x & if \ x \le 5 \\ x+4 & if \ x > 5 \end{cases}$

A) 9   B) 2   C) 8   D) Does not exist

11) Given the graph of $f(x)$, which of the following is false?

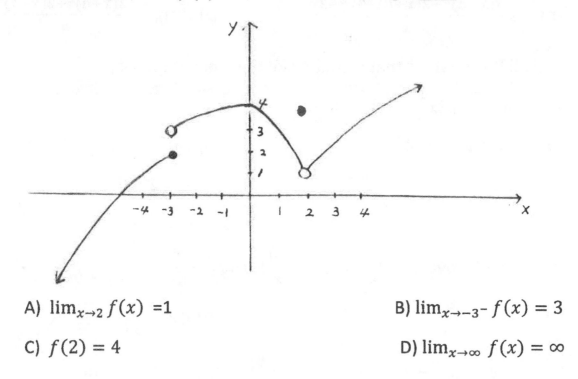

A) $\lim_{x \to 2} f(x) = 1$ B) $\lim_{x \to -3^-} f(x) = 3$

C) $f(2) = 4$ D) $\lim_{x \to \infty} f(x) = \infty$

12) Which of the following is not continuous at $= 6$?

A) $f(x) = 3x^3 + 2x - 7$ B) $f(x) = \dfrac{10x}{x^2 + 36}$

C) $f(x) = \begin{cases} x^2 - 6 & if \quad x < 6 \\ 30 & if \quad x = 6 \\ 4x+6 & if \quad x > 6 \end{cases}$ D) $f(x) = \dfrac{x^2 - 6x}{x^2 - 36}$

13) Find the average rate of change for $f(x) = 4x^2 - 3x + 1$ between

$x = 1$ and $x = 3$.

A) 15   B) 26   C) 13   D) 2

14) Which of the following represents the derivative of $f(x) = 3x^2 + 2x$?

A) $\lim_{h \to 0} \dfrac{3(x+h)^2 + 2(x+h) - 3x^2 - 2x}{h}$

B) $\dfrac{3(x+h)^2 + 2(x+h) - (3x^2 + 2x)}{h}$

C) $\lim_{x \to 0} \dfrac{3(x+h)^2 + 2(x+h) - 3x^2 - 2x}{x}$

D) $\lim_{h \to 0} \dfrac{3(x+h)^2 + 2(x+h)}{h}$

15) Find all the x-values that would make the tangent line of

$f(x) = 4x^3 - 12x^2 + 1$ horizontal.

A) $x = -2$ and $x = 2$ B) $x = 0$ only

C) $x = 0$ and $x = 2$ D) $x = 2$ only

16) Find the derivative of $f(x) = 2x^2 + \dfrac{8}{x} + 16\sqrt{x} + 9$.

A) $4x + \dfrac{8}{x^2} + \dfrac{8}{\sqrt{x}}$ B) $4x - \dfrac{8}{x^2} + \dfrac{8}{\sqrt{x}}$

C) $4x - \dfrac{8}{x^2} + 8\sqrt{x}$ D) $4x + 8 + \dfrac{16}{\sqrt{x}}$

17) Find the $\dfrac{dy}{dx}$ for the function $(3x + 1)(5x^2 - 6x + 3)$.

A) $45x^2 - 26x + 3$ B) $30x - 18$

C) $45x^2 + 21x - 6$ D) $45x^2 + 10x - 4$

18) Find y' for the function $y = \dfrac{6x+1}{3x-7}$.

A) $-\dfrac{39}{(3x-7)^2}$

B) 3

C) $\dfrac{-36x-45}{(3x-7)^2}$

D) $-\dfrac{45}{(3x-7)^2}$

19) Find derivative of $f(x) = -6(x^2 + 3)^5$.

A) $-30(x^2 + 3)^4$

B) $-60x(x^2 + 3)^4$

C) $-30(2x)^4$

D) $-6(2x + 3)^4$

20) Find the derivative of $f(x) = \dfrac{1}{(6x^2-7)^5}$.

A) $-\dfrac{5x}{(6x^2-7)^6}$

B) $-\dfrac{60x}{(6x^2-7)^6}$

C) $-\dfrac{60x}{(6x^2-7)^4}$

D) $\dfrac{5}{(6x^2-7)^6}$

21) Find the equation of the tangent line to the function
$f(x) = \sqrt{3x^2 + 1}$ through the point (1,2).

A) $y = \dfrac{3}{2}x + \dfrac{1}{2}$

B) $y = \dfrac{3}{2}x + 2$

C) $y = \dfrac{1}{2}x + \dfrac{1}{2}$

D) $y = -\dfrac{3}{2}x - \dfrac{1}{2}$

22) Find $f'(x)$ if $f(x) = x^2(2x^3 - 3)^8$.

A) $2x(2x^3 - 3)^7(26x^3 - 3)$

B) $16x(2x^3 - 3)^7$

C) $8x^2(2x^3 - 3)^7$

D) $2x(2x^3 - 3)^7(50x^3 - 6)$

23) Find $g^4(2)$ if $g(x) = x^6 + 7x^4 + 3x^2 - 8x + 4$.

A) 822

B) 1296

C) 1608

D) 420

24) Find $f''(x)$ if $f(x) = \frac{x+2}{x-3}$.

A) 0

B) $\frac{10}{(x-3)^3}$

C) $\frac{-5}{(x-3)}$

D) $-\frac{10}{(x-3)^3}$

25) Find $(f \circ g)(x)$ if $f(x) = 3x^2 - 8x$ and $g(x) = 2x$.

A) $12x^2 - 8x$

B) $6x^2 - 16x$

C) $3x^2 - 6x$

D) $12x^2 - 16x$

26) Find the interval(s) where $f(x)$ is <u>decreasing</u>.

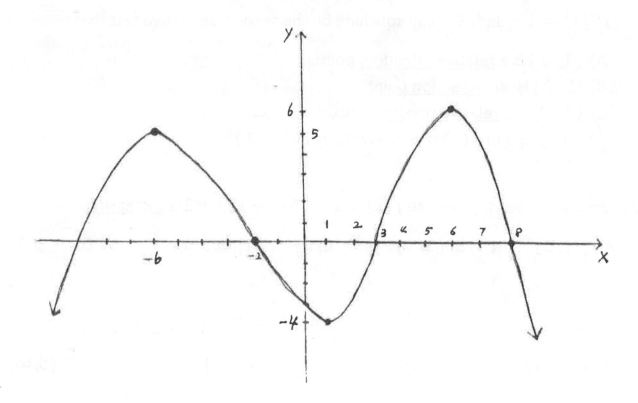

A) $(-\infty, -6]$ and $[1,6]$

B) $(-\infty, -2]$ and $[3, \infty)$

C) $[-6, 1]$ and $[6, \infty)$

D) $[-6, 6]$

27) Find the relative maxima and relative minima for $f(x) = \frac{1}{3}x^3 - \frac{7}{2}x^2 + 12x$.

A) Rel max : (4,13.3)   Rel min : (3,0)

B) Rel max : (-4,-125.3)   Rel min : (3,13.5)

C) Rel max : (3, 13.5)   Rel min : (4, 13.3)

D) Rel max : (-3,-76.5)   Rel min : (-4,-125.3)

28) For a continuous function $f(x)$, $f(1) = -2$, $f'(1) = 0$ and

$f''(x) = 4 - 3x^2$. We can conclude be the second derivative test that :

A) (1, -2) is a <u>relative minimum</u> point.
B) (1, -2) is an <u>inflection point</u>.
C) (1, -2) is a <u>relative maximum</u> point.
D) The graph of $f(x)$ is concave down at (1, -2).

29) Find the interval(s) where $f(x) = x^3 - 6x^2 - 15x + 2$ is <u>increasing</u> .

A) [-1, 5]   B) [3, 5]   C) $(-\infty, -1]$ and $[5, \infty)$ D) $(-\infty, 2]$

30) Find the interval(s) where $f(x) = x^3 - 6x^2 - 15x + 2$ is <u>concave up</u> .

A) $(-\infty, 2)$ B) $(2, \infty)$ C) $(-1, 5)$ D) $(5, \infty)$

31) Find the relative extrema of the function $y = 6(x - 1)^5$.

A) Rel Max : (1, 0)   B) Rel Min : (1, 0)

C) Rel Max : (1, 6)   D) no relative extrema

32) The x- value for the point(s) of inflection for $f(x) = 4x^3 - x^4$ are

A) $x = 0$ and $x = 2$ B) $x = 0$ only

C) $x = 0$ and $x = 3$ D) $x = 0$, $x = 2$ and $x = 3$

33) Find the interval(s) where $f(x)$ is <u>concave up</u>.

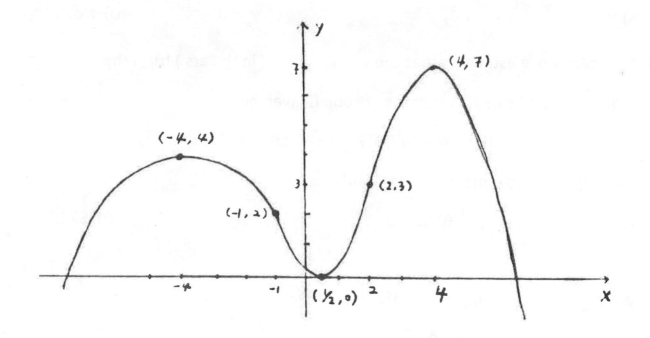

A) $(-1,2)$

B) $(-4,4)$

C) $(-\infty, -1)\, and\, (2, \infty)$

D) $(-\infty, -4)\, and\, (4, \infty)$

34) The vertical asymptote(s) of $f(x) = \dfrac{x^2+5x+4}{x^2-3x+2}$ are :

A) $x = -1\, and\, x = -4$

B) $x = 1\, and\, x = 2$

C) $x = -1\, and\, x = -2$

D) $x = 2\, only$

35) The horizontal asymptote(s) of $f(x) = \dfrac{x^2+4}{x-2}$ are :

A) $y = 1$

B) $y = 0$

C) $y = 2$

D) None

36) The horizontal asymptote(s) of $f(x) = \dfrac{6x^3 - 2x + 6}{7 - x^2 + 2x^3}$ are :

A) $y = 0$ B) $y = \dfrac{6}{7}$ C) $y = 3$ D) None

37) A grocery store estimates that the weekly profit (in dollars) from the

production and sale of x cases of soup is given by

$$P(x) = -5600 + 9.5x - 0.0017x^2$$

Find the marginal profit at $x = 1300$

A) $ 4.42   B) $5.08   C) $3877   D) $7.29

38) Which of the following is <u>true</u> about the following sketch

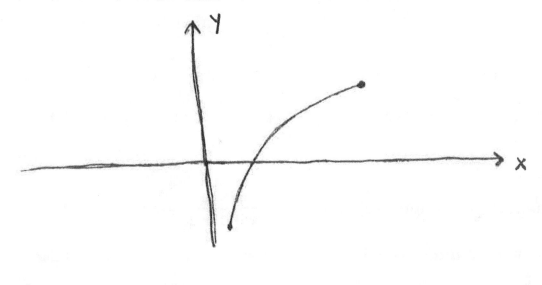

A) $f'(x) > 0, f''(x) > 0$ B) $f'(x) > 0, f''(x) < 0$

C) $f'(x) < 0, f''(x) > 0$ D) $f'(x) < 0, f''(x) < 0$

39) The absolute maximum of $f(x) = x^3 - 6x^2 + 40$ on $[-2, 5]$ is

A) 40   B) 15   C) 11   D) 50

40) For a company, the total cost is $C(x) = 0.0025x^2 + 80x + 10000$.

How many items should it manufacture so that its <u>average cost</u> of production

is a minimum ?

A)200   B) 20,000   C) 2,000   D) 0

41) The cost function for a product is $C(x) = 1600 + 8x$ and its revenue
function is $R(x) = 160x - \frac{1}{4}x^2$. How many units should be produced in
order to maximize the profit?

A) 152   B) 304   C) 608   D) 1600

42) A carpenter building a rectangular room with a fixed perimeter of 420ft.
What are the dimensions of the largest room that can built? What is the
area?

A) 105 ft by 105 ft; $11,025\ ft^2$ B) 210 ft by 210 ft; $44,100 ft^2$

C) 42 ft by 378 ft; $15,876\ ft^2$ D) 105 ft by 315 ft; $33,075\ ft^2$

43) A company has 400ft of fencing available to build a rectangular storage area and cross-fences as shown (not to scale). What is the largest area that can be enclosed?

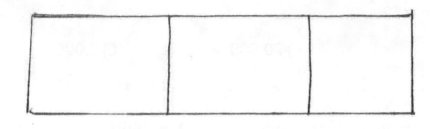

A) 4,000 ft^2 B) 50,000 ft^2 C) 5,000 ft^2 D) 40,000 ft^2

44) Graph $y = \left(\frac{1}{3}\right)^x$

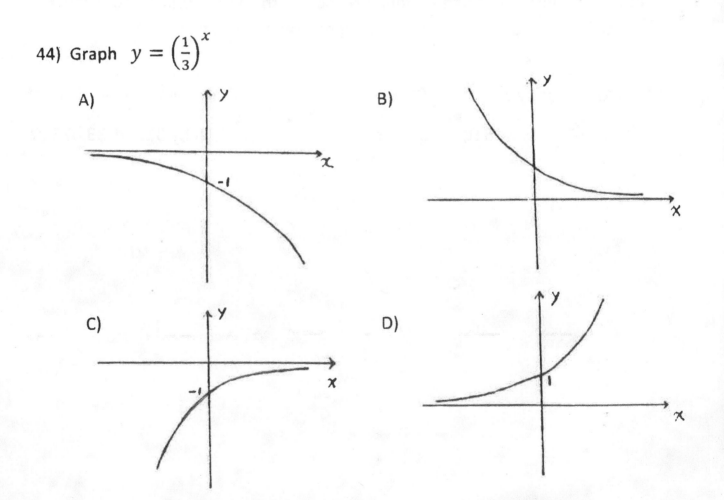

A)

B)

C)

D)

45) Solve the exponential equation $e^t = 1000$ for t.

 A) 3   B) 367.879   C) 6.908   D) 2718.282

46) Find the derivative of $y = e^{9x^2} + x$.

 A) $18xe + 1$ B) $18xe^{2x} + 1$

 C) $18xe^{9x^2} + 1$ D) $18xe^{x^2} + 1$

47) Find the equation of the tangent line to the graph of $f(x) = e^{2x}$ at the point $(0, 1)$.

 A) $y = 2e + 1$ B) $y = 2x + 1$

 C) $y = 2x + 2$ D) $y = x + 1$

48) Find the derivative of $y = 5x^2 e^{3x}$

 A) $5xe^{3x}(2x + 3)$ B) $10xe^{3x}(3x + 2)$

 C) $5xe^{3x}(3x + 2)$ D) $10xe^{3x}(2x + 3)$

49) Find the derivative of $y = \ln(4x)$.

 A) $-\dfrac{1}{x}$ B) $-\dfrac{1}{4x}$ C) $\dfrac{1}{4x}$ D) $\dfrac{1}{x}$

50) Find the derivative of $y = e^{2x} \ln x^3$.

 A) $\dfrac{3e^{2x}}{x}$ B) $e^{2x}\left(\dfrac{3}{x} + 2\ln x^3\right)$

 C) $3e^{2x}\left(\dfrac{1}{x} + \ln x^3\right)$ D) $e^{2x}\left(\dfrac{3}{x} + \ln x^3\right)$

Solutions for Sample Final Exam

1.	A		45.	C
2.	D		46.	C
3.	A		47.	B
4.	C		48.	C
5.	B		49.	D
6.	C		50.	B
7.	A			
8.	D			
9.	C			
10.	D			
11.	B			
12.	D			
13.	C			
14.	A			
15.	C			
16.	B			
17.	A			
18.	D			
19.	B			
20.	B			
21.	A			
22.	A			
23.	C			
24.	B			
25.	D			
26.	C			
27.	C			
28.	A			
29.	C			
30.	B			
31.	D			
32.	A			
33.	A			
34.	B			
35.	D			
36.	C			
37.	B			
38.	B			
39.	A			
40.	C			
41.	B			
42.	A			
43.	C			
44.	B			

MA 1613 – Business Calculus

FINAL EXAM   Sample 2

INSTRUCTIONS

- Give the following information on the top of your answer sheet. YOUR NAME AND I.D. NUMBER, THE NAME OF YOUR INSTRUCTOR, THE COURSE AND SECTION NUBER AND THE DATE.
- Make no marks on the exam. Use the scratch paper provided.
- Use a #2 pencil to mark your answer sheet. Keep your answer sheet neat – no stray marks, no smudges, and no wrinkles.
- Be careful to mark your answer in the proper space. If you must change your answer, erase the old answer completely.
- Return your answer sheet, the exam questions and all the scratch paper to your instructor when finished.
- Graphing Calculators may NOT be used during the exam. You may use a scientific calculator. Because of the wide variety of the scientific calculators that students may be using when taking the exam, some of the answers may be left in a form students may not expect. Please check your answers to make sure you have marked the answer you believe is correct.

1) Find the domain of the function.

$$f(x) = \frac{x^2 - 25}{x^2 + 3x - 10}$$

A) $(-\infty, 2) \cup (2, \infty)$

B) $(-\infty, -2) \cup (-2,5) \cup (5, \infty)$

C) $(-\infty, -5) \cup (-5,5) \cup (5, \infty)$

D) $(-\infty, -5) \cup (-5,2) \cup (2, \infty)$

2) Find the slope of the line containing (5, - 3) and (-7, -5).

A) $-\frac{1}{6}$ B) $\frac{3}{2}$ C) 4   D) $\frac{1}{6}$

3) Graph $f(x) = \begin{cases} -1 & \text{if } x < 1 \\ x+1 & \text{if } x \geq 1 \end{cases}$

A)

B)

C)

D)

4) Find

$$\frac{f(x+h) - f(x)}{h} \qquad \text{if } f(x) = 2x^2 + 3.$$

A) $4x + 2h$

B) $2h^2 + 3$

C) $2h + \frac{3}{h}$

D) $4xh + 2h^2$

5) Find $f(-1)$ and $f(4)$ if

$$f(x) = \begin{cases} x^2 + 3 & \text{if } x \leq -1 \\ x^2 & \text{if } -1 < x \leq 4 \\ 2x + 1 & \text{if } x > 4 \end{cases}$$

A) 4, 16   B) 1, 9   C) -1, 1   D) 2, 19

6) Rewrite using radical notation.

$$(x^2 + 36)^{\frac{-2}{3}}$$

A) $\dfrac{1}{\sqrt[3]{x+6}}$

B) $\dfrac{1}{\sqrt[3]{(x^2+36)^2}}$

C) $\sqrt[3]{(x^2 + 36)^2}$

D) $\dfrac{1}{\sqrt{(x^2+36)^3}}$

7) Evaluate:

$$\lim_{x \to -9} \frac{x^2 + 6x - 27}{x + 9}$$

A) 0 B) -3 C) -12 D) Does not exist

8) Evaluate:

$$\lim_{x \to -1} \frac{x^2 + 3x + 2}{x^2 + 2}$$

A) 0 B) -1 C) 3 D) Does not exist

9) Evaluate:

$$\lim_{x \to 5} \frac{x + 5}{x^2 - 25}$$

A) $-\dfrac{1}{10}$ B) $\dfrac{1}{10}$ C) 0 D) Does not exist

10) Evaluate:

$$\lim_{x \to 1^-} f(x)$$

Where $f(x) = \begin{cases} x + 3 & if \ x < 1 \\ 2 & if \ \ \ x = 1 \\ x^2 - 4 & if \ \ x > 1 \end{cases}$

A) 2   B) 4   C) -3   D) Does not exist

11) Given the graph of $f(x)$, which of the following is <u>false</u>?

A) $\lim_{x \to 1^+} f(x) = 4$ B) $\lim_{x \to 5^-} f(x) = 4$

C) $\lim_{x \to -\infty} f(x) = -\infty$ D) $f(5) = 6$

12) Which of the following is <u>not</u> continuous at $= 6$?

A) $f(x) = \frac{2x-12}{x^2+36}$ B) $f(x) = \begin{cases} 2x + 10 & if \ \ \ x < 6 \\ x^2 - 14 & if \ \ \ x \geq 6 \end{cases}$

C) $f(x) = 2x^4 + 6x^2 - 1$ D) $f(x) = \frac{2x^2+7x-1}{x-6}$

13) Find the average rate of change for $f(x) = 2x^2 - 3x$ between $x = 1$ and $x = 4$.

A) 7   B) $\frac{19}{3}$ C) 1   D) 13

14) Which of the following represents the derivative of $f(x) = 2x^2 + 4$?

A) $\dfrac{2(x+h)^2 + 4 - (2x^2 + 4)}{h}$ B) $\lim_{x \to 0} \dfrac{2(x+h)^2 + 4 - 2x^2 - 4}{x}$

C) $\lim_{h \to 0} \dfrac{2(x+h)^2 + 4 - 2x^2 - 4}{h}$ D) $\lim_{h \to 0} \dfrac{2(x+h)^2 + 4 - 2x^2 + 4}{h}$

15) Find all the x-values that would make the tangent line of $f(x) = x^3 - 12x + 2$ horizontal.

A) $0, 2$ only   B) 2 only

C) $-2, 2$ only   D) $-2, 0, 2$

16) Find the derivative of $f(x) = \dfrac{8}{\sqrt{x}} - \dfrac{3}{x} + \dfrac{6}{x^4}$.

A) $\dfrac{-4}{x^{3/2}} - \dfrac{3}{x^2} - \dfrac{24}{x^3}$ B) $\dfrac{-4}{x^{3/2}} + \dfrac{3}{x^2} - \dfrac{24}{x^5}$

C) $4\sqrt{x} + \dfrac{3}{x^2} - \dfrac{24}{x^3}$ D) $\dfrac{4}{x^{1/2}} - \dfrac{3}{x^2} - \dfrac{24}{x^5}$

17) Find the equation of the tangent line to the function $f(x) = \frac{2}{3}x^3 - x^2 + 4x - 5$ at $x = 0$.

A) $y = -4x - 5$ B) $y = 4x - 5$

C) $y = -x + 5$ D) $y = -x - 1$

18) Find derivative of $y = (2x - 4)(2x^3 - x^2 + 1)$.

A) $16x^3 - 30x^2 + 8x + 2$

B) $4x^3 + 10x^2 - 30x + 2$

C) $12x^3 + 30x^2 - 10x + 2$

D) $16x^3 - 10x^2 + 30x + 2$

19) Find $\frac{dy}{dx}$ for the function $y = \frac{3x^2 + 5}{x - 7}$.

A) $\frac{3x^2 - 42x - 5}{(x-7)^2}$

B) $\frac{-3x^2 + 42x + 5}{(x-7)^2}$

C) $\frac{-9x^2 - 42x + 5}{(x-7)^2}$

D) $\frac{6x}{(x-7)^2}$

20) Find y' for the function $y = \sqrt{x^2 + 3x + 7}$.

A) $\frac{2x+3}{2\sqrt{x^2+3x+7}}$

B) $\frac{2x+3}{\sqrt{2(x^2+3x+7)}}$

C) $\frac{2(2x+3)}{\sqrt{x^2+3x+7}}$

D) $\frac{1}{2}\sqrt{x^2 + 3x + 7}$

21) Find the <u>slope</u> of the tangent line to the curve of $f(x) = \frac{-1}{(3-2x^2)^3}$ at the point $x = 1$.

A) -12   B) -1   C) -4   D) 0

22) Find $f'(x)$ if $f(x) = x^2(3 - 2x^2)^3$.

A) $-36x^3(3 - 2x^3)$

B) $3x^2(3 - 2x^2)^2$

C) $2x(3 - 4x^2)$

D) $2x(3 - 2x^2)^2(3 - 8x^2)$

23) Find $f''(x)$ if $f(x) = \frac{x+3}{x-4}$.

A) $-\dfrac{14}{(x-4)^3}$

B) $-\dfrac{7}{(x-4)^2}$

C) $\dfrac{14}{(x-4)^3}$

D) none of these

24) Find $f'''(x)$ if $f(x) = 2x^4 - 3x^{-2} + 5$.

A) $48 + \dfrac{72}{x^5}$

B) $48x$

C) $48x + \dfrac{72}{x^5}$

D) $\dfrac{1}{72x^5}$

25) Find $(g \circ f)(x)$ if $f(x) = x^2 + 5$ and $g(x) = \sqrt{x-1}$.

A) $x + 4$

B) $x + 2$

C) $\sqrt{x-1}(x^2 + 5)$

D) $\sqrt{x^2 + 4}$

26) Find the interval(s) where $f'(x) > 0$.

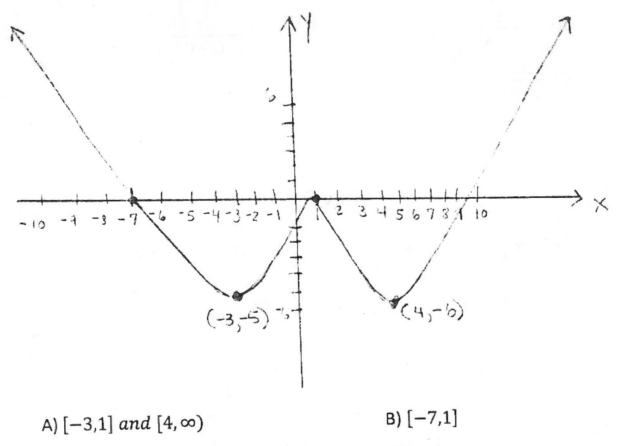

A) $[-3,1]$ and $[4, \infty)$

B) $[-7,1]$

C) $(-\infty, -3]$ and $[1,4]$

D) $[-3, \ 4]$

27) Find the location of the relative extrema of the function

$$f(x) = x^3 - \frac{3}{2}x^2 - 6x - 1.$$

A) Relative max. at $x = -1$ and relative min. at $x = 2$

B) Relative max at $x = -\frac{1}{2}$ and no relative minimum

C) Relative max at $x = 2$ and relative min at $x = -1$

D) Relative min at $x = -\frac{1}{2}$ and no relative maximum

28) Which of the following statements is _true_ of $f(x) = x^4 - 2x^2 + 4$?

A) f is increasing on $(0,1)$

B) f is decreasing on $(1, \infty)$

C) f is decreasing on $(0,1)$

D) f is increasing on $(-\infty, \infty)$

29) For a continuous function $f(x)$, $f''(x) = 2x^2 - 1$ and $x = -4$, $x = 0$ and $x = 4$ are critical numbers. Use the second derivative to find the location of the relative minimum.

A) $x = 0$ only

B) $x = 4$ only

C) $x = 4$ and $x = -4$

D) no relative minimum

30) Find the relative extrema of the function $= 5(x - 2)^3$.

A) Rel Max : (2, 0)

B) Rel Min : (2, 0)

C) Rel Max : (0, 2)

D) no relative extrema

31) Find the interval(s) where $f(x) = 2x^3 - 3x^2 - 12x + 5$ is _concave down_ .

A) $\left(\frac{1}{2}, \infty\right)$

B) $(1,2)$ only

C) $(-\infty, -1)$ and $(2, \infty)$

D) $\left(-\infty, \frac{1}{2}\right)$

32) The x- value for the point(s) of inflection for $f(x) = 2x^3 - 3x^2 - 12x + 5$ are

A) $x = -1$ and $x = 2$.

B) $x = 4$ and $x = -3$.

C) $x = -3$ only.

D) $x = \frac{1}{2}$ only.

33) Find the interval(s) where $f(x)$ is <u>concave up</u>.

A) $(-\infty, 0)$ only

B) $(0, \infty)$ only

C) $(-\infty, 0) \cup (0, \infty)$

D) none

34) The <u>vertical</u> asymptote(s) of $f(x) = \dfrac{x^2+3x-10}{2x^2-4x}$ are:

A) $x = 0 \; only$

B) $x = 0 \; and \; x = 2$

C) $x = 2 \; only$

D) $x = \dfrac{1}{2} \; only$

35) The <u>horizontal</u> asymptote(s) of $f(x) = \dfrac{-x^2+3x+2}{6x^3-6}$ are:

A) $y = -\dfrac{1}{6}$

B) $y = 0$

C) $y = 1$

D) None

36) The <u>horizontal</u> asymptote(s) of $f(x) = \dfrac{6x^3 - 2x + 6}{7 - x^2 + 2x^3}$ are:

A) $y = \dfrac{6}{7}$ 　　　　　 B) $y = 3$ 　　　　　 C) $y = 0$ 　　　　　 D) None

37) Which of the following is <u>true</u> about the following sketch?

A) $f'(x) > 0 , f''(x) > 0$ 　　　　　　　　　 B) $f'(x) > 0 , f''(x) < 0$

C) $f'(x) < 0 , f''(x) > 0$ 　　　　　　　　　 D) $f'(x) < 0 , f''(x) < 0$

38) Suppose the demand function for a certain product is $p(x) = 600 - 3x$. Find the marginal revenue when $x = 30$.

A) $ 420 　　　　　 B) $510 　　　　　 C) $3 　　　　　 D) $15,300

39) The <u>absolute maximum</u> of $f(x) = 2x^2 - 7x - 10$ on [-1, 3] is

A) $\dfrac{7}{4}$ 　　　　　 B) -1 　　　　　 C) -16.13 　　　　　 D) -13

40) For a company, the total cost is $C(x) = 10,000 + 5x + \frac{1}{9}x^2$. How many items should it manufacture so that its <u>average cost</u> of production is a minimum?

A) 30   B) 300   C) 3,000   D) 30,000

41) The total profit from the production and sale of a particular product is given by the function $P(x) = \overset{600,000x}{\cancel{60,000}}x - 800 - 150x^2 - x^3$, where x is the number of items produced and sold. Determine the level of production which will maximize profit.

A) 200   B) 600   C) 400   D) 100

42) Maximize $Q = x^2 y$ where x and y are positive numbers, such that $x + y = 540$.

A) $x = 360$; $y = 180$ B) $x = 180$; $y = 360$

C) $x = 405$; $y = 135$ D) $x = 135$; $y = 405$

43) A storage area is to be fenced and cross-fenced as shown using 1200 ft. of fencing. Find the dimensions which will maximize the total area fenced.

A) 50 ft. x 60 ft.   B) 100 ft. x 300 ft.

C) 150 ft. x 300 ft.   D) 200 ft. x 300 ft.

44) Graph $y = 4^x$.

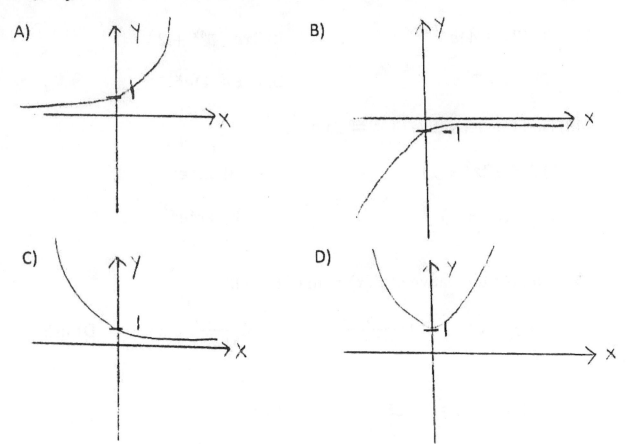

A)

B)

C)

D)

45) Solve the exponential equation $e^t = 2000$ for t.

   A) 7.6   B) 735.76   C) 2000   D) none of these

46) Find the equation of the tangent line to the graph of $f(x) = e^{3x}$ at the point (0, 1).

   A) $y = 3x - 1$ B) $y = 2e - 1$

   C) $y = 3x + 3$ D) $y = 3x + 1$

47) Find the derivative of $y = e^{x^2+4x} + 2x$.

A) $(2x + 4)e^{x^2+4x} + 2$

B) $2xe^{x^2+4x} + 2$

C) $2xe^{x^2+4x}$

D) $(2x + 4)e^{x^2+4x}$

48) Find the derivative of $y = 2xe^{x^2}$.

A) $2e^{x^2}(2x^2 + 1)$

B) $2x^3e^{2x}$

C) $e^{x^2}(2x + 2)$

D) $4x^2e^{x^2}$

49) Find the derivative of $f(x) = \ln(5x + 1)$.

A) $\dfrac{5}{5x+1}$

B) $\dfrac{5}{\ln(5x+1)}$

C) $\dfrac{1}{5x+1}$

D) $\ln 5$

50) Find the derivative of $f(x) = e^x \ln x$.

A) $e^x + \dfrac{1}{x}$

B) $e^x\left(\dfrac{1}{x} + \ln x\right)$

C) $\dfrac{e^x + \ln x}{x}$

D) $\dfrac{e^x}{x}$

Solutions for Sample Final Exam # 2

1.	D		45.	A
2..	D		46.	D
3.	D		47.	A
4.	A		48.	A
5.	A		49.	A
6.	B		50.	B
7.	C			
8.	A			
9.	D			
10.	B			
11.	A			
12.	D			
13.	A			
14.	C			
15.	C			
16.	B			
17.	B			
18.	A			
19.	A			
20.	A			
21.	A			
22.	D			
23.	C			
24.	C			
25.	D			
26.	A			
27.	A			
28.	C			
29.	C			
30.	D			
31.	D			
32.	D			
33.	B			
34.	A			
35.	B			
36.	B			
37.	D			
38.	A			
39.	B			
40.	B			
41.	C			
42.	A			
43.	C			
44.	A			